Biology:
Concepts and Applications
Volume I
Houston Community College

Cecie Starr

THOMSON

BROOKS/COLE

Australia · Canada · Mexico · Singapore · Spain · United Kingdom · United States

Biology: Concepts and Applications Volume I
Cecie Starr

Executive Editors:
Michele Baird, Maureen Staudt &
Michael Stranz

Project Development Manager:
Linda deStefano

Sr. Marketing Coordinators:
Lindsay Annett and Sara Mercurio

Production/Manufacturing Manager:
Donna M. Brown

Production Editorial Manager:
Dan Plofchan

Pre-Media Services Supervisor:
Becki Walker

Rights and Permissions Specialist:
Kalina Ingham Hintz

Cover Image
Getty Images*

The Adaptable Courseware Program consists of products and additions to existing Brooks/Cole products that are produced from camera-ready copy. Peer review, class testing, and accuracy are primarily the responsibility of the author(s).

For more information, please contact Thomson Custom Solutions, 5191 Natorp Boulevard, Mason, OH 45040. Or you can visit our Internet site at www.thomsoncustom.com

For permission to use material from this text or product, contact us by:
Tel (800) 730-2214
Fax (800) 730 2215
www.thomsonrights.com

ISBN-13: 978-0-495-49514-7
ISBN-10: 0-495-49514-X

International Divisions List

Asia (Including India):
Thomson Learning
(a division of Thomson Asia Pte Ltd)
5 Shenton Way #01-01
UIC Building
Singapore 068808
Tel: (65) 6410-1200
Fax: (65) 6410-1208

Australia/New Zealand:
Thomson Learning Australia
102 Dodds Street
Southbank, Victoria 3006
Australia

Latin America:
Thomson Learning
Seneca 53
Colonia Polano
11560 Mexico, D.F., Mexico
Tel (525) 281-2906
Fax (525) 281-2656

Canada:
Thomson Nelson
1120 Birchmount Road
Toronto, Ontario
Canada M1K 5G4
Tel (416) 752-9100
Fax (416) 752-8102

UK/Europe/Middle East/Africa:
Thomson Learning
High Holborn House
50-51 Bedford Row
London, WC1R 4LS
United Kingdom
Tel 44 (020) 7067-2500
Fax 44 (020) 7067-2600

Spain (Includes Portugal):
Thomson Paraninfo
Calle Magallanes 25
28015 Madrid
España
Tel 34 (0)91 446-3350
Fax 34 (0)91 445-6218

Brief Contents

Introduction

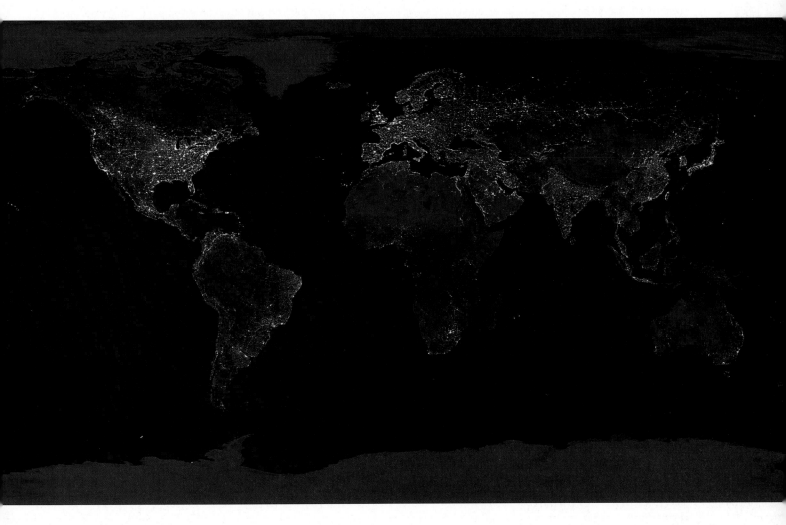

Current configurations of the Earth's oceans and land masses—the geologic stage upon which life's drama continues to unfold. This composite satellite image reveals global energy use at night by the human population. Just as biological science does, it invites you to think more deeply about the world of life—and about our impact upon it.

IMPACTS, ISSUES   *What Am I Doing Here?*

Leaf through a newspaper on any given Sunday and you may get an uneasy feeling that the world is spinning out of control. There's a lot about the Middle East, where

World Trade Center

great civilizations have come and gone. You won't find much on the amazing coral reefs in the surrounding seas, especially at the northern end of the Red Sea. Now the news is about oil and politics, terrorists, and war.

Think back on the 1991 Persian Gulf conflict, when thick smoke from oil fires blocked out sunlight, and black rain fell. Iraqis deliberately released about 460 million gallons of crude oil into the Gulf. Uncounted numbers of reef organisms died. So did thousands of birds.

Today Kuwaitis wonder if the oil fires caused their higher cancer rates. They join New Yorkers who are worried about developing lung problems from breathing dense, noxious dust that filled the air after the horrific terrorist attack on the World Trade Center.

Nature, too, seems to have it in for us. Cholera, the flu, and SARS pose global threats. An AIDS pandemic is unraveling the very fabric of African societies. Forests burn fiercely. Storms, droughts, and heat waves are often monstrous. Polar ice caps and once-vast glaciers are melting too rapidly, and the whole atmosphere is warming up.

It's enough to make you throw down the paper and long for the good old days, when things were so much simpler.

Of course, read up on the good old days and you'll find they weren't so good. Bioterrorists were around in 1346, when soldiers catapulted the corpses of bubonic

the big picture

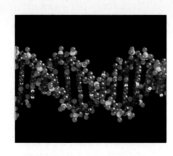

Life's Underlying Unity   Life shows a hierarchy of organization, extending from the molecular level through the biosphere. Shared features at the molecular level are the basis of life's unity.

Life's Diversity   Life also shows spectacular diversity. Several million kinds of organisms already have been named, past and present, each with some traits that make it unique from all the others.

plague victims into a walled city under siege. Infected people and rats fled the city and helped fuel the Black Death, a plague that left 25 million dead in Europe. In 1918, the Spanish flu raced around the world and left somewhere between 30 and 40 million people dead. Between 1945 and 1949, about 100,000 people in the United States contracted polio, a disease that left many permanently paralyzed. In those times, too, many felt helpless in a world that seemed out of control.

What it boils down to is this: For a couple of million years, we humans and our immediate ancestors have been trying to make sense of the natural world and what we're doing in it. We observe it, come up with ideas, then test the ideas. But the more pieces of the puzzle we fit together, the bigger the puzzle gets. We now know that it is almost overwhelmingly big.

You could walk away from the challenge and simply not think. You could let others tell you what to think. Or you could choose to develop your own understanding of the puzzle.

Maybe you're interested in the pieces that affect your health, the food you eat, or your children, should you choose to reproduce. Maybe you just find life fascinating. No matter what your focus might be, you can deepen your perspective. You can learn ways to sharpen how you interpret the natural world, including human nature. This is the gift of biology, the scientific study of life.

 *How Would You Vote?*

The warm seas of the Middle East support some of the world's most spectacular coral reef ecosystems. Should the United States provide funding to help preserve the reefs? See the Media Menu for details, then vote online.

Explaining Unity in Diversity Evolutionary theories, especially the theory of evolution by natural selection, help us see a profound connection between life's underlying unity and its diversity.

How We Know Biologists find out about life by observing, asking questions, and formulating and testing hypotheses in nature or the laboratory. They report results in ways that others can test.

1.1 Life's Levels of Organization

The world of life shows levels of organization, from the simple to the complex. Take time to see how these levels connect to get a sense of how the topics of this book are organized and where they will take you.

FROM SMALL TO SMALLER

Imagine yourself on the deck of a sailing ship, about to journey around the world. The distant horizon of a vast ocean beckons, and suddenly you sense that you are just one tiny part of the great scheme of things.

Now imagine one of your red blood cells can think. It realizes it's only a tiny part of the great scheme of your body. A string of 375 cells like itself would fit across a straightpin's head—and you have trillions of cells. One of the fat molecules at the red blood cell's surface is thinking about how small it is. A string of 1,200,000 molecules like itself would stretch across that pinhead. Now a hydrogen atom in the molecule is pondering the great scheme of a fat molecule. Figure 1.1a depicts one. It would take 53,908,355 side-by-side hydrogen atoms to stretch across the head of a pin!

FROM SMALLER TO VAST

With that single atom, you have reached the entry level of nature's great pattern of organization. Like nonliving things, all organisms are made of building blocks called atoms. At the next level are molecules. Life's unique properties emerge when certain kinds of molecules are organized into cells. These "molecules of life" are complex carbohydrates, complex fats and other lipids, proteins, DNA, and RNA (Figure 1.1b). The **cell** is the smallest unit of organization with the

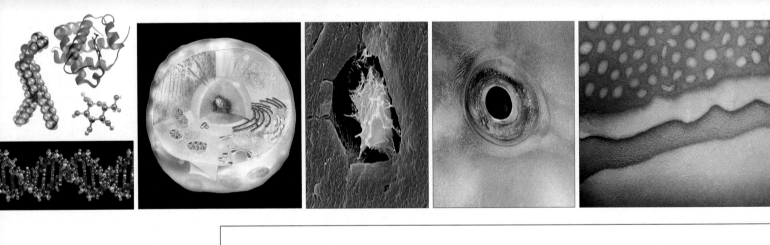

b molecule — Two or more joined atoms of the same or different elements. "Molecules of life" are complex carbohydrates, lipids, proteins, DNA, and RNA. Only living cells now make them.

c cell — Smallest unit that can live and reproduce on its own or as part of a multicelled organism. It has an outer membrane, DNA, and other components.

d tissue — Organized aggregation of cells and substances interacting in a specialized activity. Many cells (*white*) made this bone tissue from their own secretions.

e organ — Structural unit made of two or more tissues interacting in some task. A parrotfish eye is a sensory organ used in vision.

f organ system — Organs interacting physically, chemically, or both in some task. Parrotfish skin is an integumentary system with tissue layers, organs such as glands, and other parts.

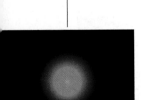

a atom — Smallest unit of an element that still retains the element's properties. Electrons, protons, and neutrons are its building blocks. This hydrogen atom's electron zips around a proton in a spherical volume of space.

Figure 1.1 Increasingly complex levels of organization in nature, extending from subatomic particles to the biosphere.

capacity to survive and reproduce on its own, given raw materials, energy inputs, information encoded in its DNA, and suitable conditions in its environment.

At the next level of organization are multicelled organisms made of specialized, interdependent cells, often organized as tissues, organs, and organ systems. A higher level of organization is the **population**, a group of single-celled or multicelled individuals of the same species occupying a specified area. A school of fish is a population (Figure 1.1*h*), as are all of the single-celled amoebas in an isolated lake.

Next comes the **community**, all populations of all species occupying one area. Its extent depends on the area specified. It might be the Red Sea, an underwater cave, or a forest in South America. It might even be a community of tiny organisms that live, reproduce, and die quickly inside the cupped petals of a flower.

The next level of organization is the **ecosystem**, or a community together with its physical and chemical environment. Finally, the **biosphere** is the highest level of life. It encompasses all regions of the Earth's crust, waters, and atmosphere in which organisms live.

This book is a journey through the globe-spanning organization of life. So take a moment to study Figure 1.1. You can use it as a road map of where each part fits in the great scheme of things.

> Nature shows levels of organization, from the simple to the increasingly complex.
>
> Life's unique characteristics originate at the atomic and molecular level. They extend through cells, populations, communities, ecosystems, and the biosphere.

Read Me First!
and watch the narrated animation on life's levels of organization

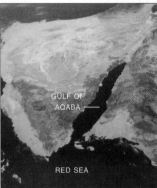

GULF OF AQABA

RED SEA

g multicelled organism
Individual made of different types of cells. Cells of most multicelled organisms, including this Red Sea parrotfish, are organized as tissues, organs, and organ systems.

h population
Group of single-celled or multicelled individuals of the same species occupying a specified area. This is a fish population in the Red Sea.

i community
All populations of all species occupying a specified area. This is part of a coral reef in the Gulf of Aqaba at the northern end of the Red Sea.

j ecosystem
A community that is interacting with its physical environment. It has inputs and outputs of energy and materials. Reef ecosystems flourish in warm, clear seawater throughout the Middle East.

k the biosphere
All regions of the Earth's waters, crust, and atmosphere that hold organisms. In the vast universe, Earth is a rare planet. Without its abundance of free-flowing water, there would be no life.

1.2 Overview of Life's Unity

"Life" isn't easy to define. It's just too big, and it's been changing for 3.9 billion years! Even so, you can frame a definition in terms of its unity and diversity. Here's the unity part: All living things grow and reproduce with the help of DNA, energy, and raw materials. They sense and respond to what is going on. But details of their traits differ among many millions of kinds of organisms. That's the diversity part—variation in traits.

DNA, THE BASIS OF INHERITANCE

You will never, ever find a rock made of nucleic acids, proteins, and complex carbohydrates and lipids. In the natural world, only living cells make these molecules. And the signature molecule of life is the nucleic acid called DNA. No chunk of granite or quartz has it.

DNA holds information for building proteins from smaller molecules, the amino acids. By analogy, if you follow suitable instructions and invest enough energy in the task, you might organize a pile of a few kinds of ceramic tiles (representing amino acids) into diverse patterns (representing proteins), as in Figure 1.2.

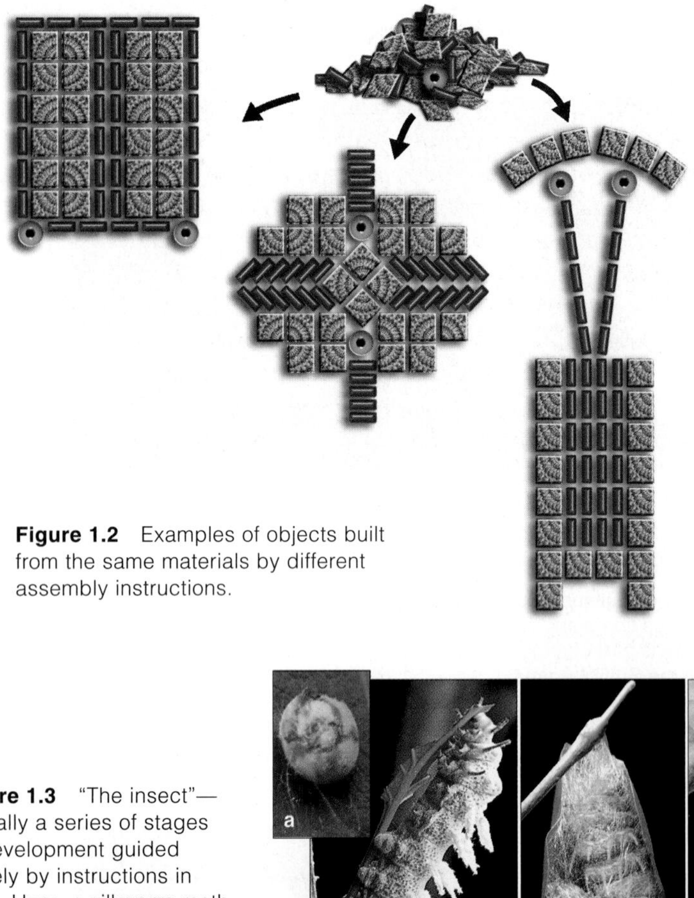

Why are proteins so important? Many are structural materials, regulators of cell activities, and enzymes. Enzymes are the cell's main worker molecules. They build, split, and rearrange the molecules of life in ways that keep cells alive. Without enzymes, nothing much could be done with DNA's information. There would be no new organisms.

In nature, each organism inherits its DNA—and its traits—from parents. *Inheritance* means an acquisition of traits after parents transmit their DNA to offspring. Think about it. Baby storks look like storks and not like pelicans because they inherited stork DNA, which isn't exactly the same as pelican DNA.

Reproduction refers to actual mechanisms by which parents transmit DNA to offspring. For frogs, humans, trees, and other organisms, the information in DNA guides *development*—the transformation of the first cell of a new individual into a multicelled adult, typically with many different tissues and organs (Figure 1.3).

ENERGY, THE BASIS OF METABOLISM

Becoming alive and maintaining life processes requires energy—the capacity to do work. Each normal living cell has ways to obtain and convert energy from its surroundings. By a process called **metabolism**, every cell acquires and uses energy to maintain itself, grow, and make more cells.

Where does the energy come from? Nearly all of it flows from the sun into the world of life, starting with **producers**. Producers are plants and other organisms that make their own food molecules from simple raw materials. Animals and decomposers are **consumers**. They cannot make their own food; they survive by feeding on tissues of producers and other organisms.

Figure 1.2 Examples of objects built from the same materials by different assembly instructions.

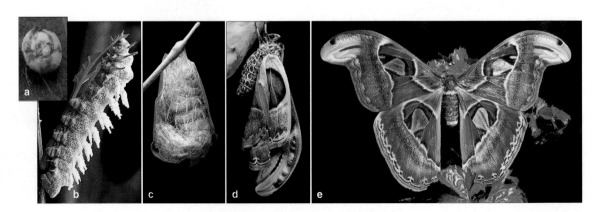

Figure 1.3 "The insect"— actually a series of stages of development guided largely by instructions in DNA. Here, a silkworm moth, from a fertilized egg (**a**), to a larval stage called a caterpillar (**b**), to a pupal stage (**c**), to the winged form of the adult (**d,e**).

When, say, zebras browse on plants, some energy stored in plant tissues is transferred to them. Later on, energy is transferred to a lion as it devours the zebra. And it gets transferred again as decomposers go to work, acquiring energy from the remains of zebras, lions, and other organisms.

Decomposers are mostly the kinds of bacteria and fungi that break down sugars and other molecules to simpler materials. Some of the breakdown products are cycled back to producers as raw materials. Over time, energy that plants originally captured from the sun returns to the environment.

Energy happens to flow in one direction, from the environment, through producers, then consumers, and then back to the environment (Figure 1.4). These are the energy exchanges that maintain life's organization. Later on, you will see how life's interconnectedness relates to modern-day problems, including major food shortages, AIDS, cholera, acid rain, global warming, and rapid losses in biodiversity.

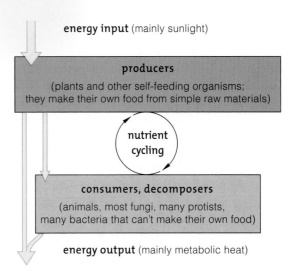

Figure 1.4 The one-way flow of energy and cycling of materials in the world of life.

LIFE'S RESPONSIVENESS TO CHANGE

It's often said that only living things respond to the environment. Yet even a rock shows responsiveness, as when it yields to gravity's force and tumbles down a hill or changes its shape slowly under the repeated batterings of wind, rain, or tides.

The difference is this: Living things sense changes in their surroundings, and they make compensatory, controlled responses to them. How? With receptors. Receptors are molecules and structures that detect stimuli, which are specific kinds of energy. Different receptors respond to different stimuli. A stimulus may be sunlight energy, chemical potential energy (as when a substance is more concentrated outside a cell than inside), or the mechanical energy of a bite (Figure 1.5).

Switched-on receptors can trigger changes in cell activities. As a simple example, after you finish eating a piece of fruit, sugars leave your gut and enter your bloodstream. Think of blood and the fluid around cells as an *internal* environment, which must be kept within tolerable limits. Too much or too little sugar in blood changes that internal environment. This can cause diabetes and other medical problems. Normally, when there is too much sugar in blood, your pancreas starts secreting more insulin. Most living cells in your body have receptors for this hormone, which stimulates them to take up more sugar. When enough cells do so, the blood sugar level returns to normal.

In such ways, organisms keep the internal environment within a range that cells can tolerate. This state is called **homeostasis**, and it is one of the key defining characteristics of life.

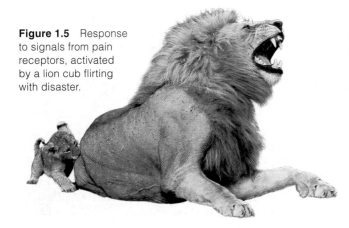

Figure 1.5 Response to signals from pain receptors, activated by a lion cub flirting with disaster.

Organisms build proteins based on instructions in DNA, which they inherit from their parents. Organisms reproduce, grow, and stay alive by way of metabolism—ongoing energy conversions and energy transfers at the cellular level.

Organisms interact through a one-way flow of energy and a cycling of materials. Collectively, their interdependencies have global impact.

Organisms sense and respond to changing conditions in controlled ways. The responses help them maintain tolerable conditions in their internal environment.

1.3 If So Much Unity, Why So Many Species?

Although unity pervades the world of life, so does diversity. Organisms differ enormously in body form, in the functions of their body parts, and in behavior.

Superimposed on life's unity is tremendous diversity. Millions of kinds of organisms, or **species**, live on Earth. Many more lived during the past 3.9 billion years, but their lineages vanished; about 99.9 percent of all species have become extinct.

For centuries, scholars have tried to make sense of diversity. In 1735, a physician named Carolus Linnaeus devised a scheme for classifying organisms by assigning a two-part name to each species. The first part designates the *genus* (plural, genera). Each genus is one or more species grouped together on the basis of a number of traits that are unique to that group alone. The second part of the name refers to a particular species within the genus. Today, biologists attempt to sort out the relationships among species not only on the basis of observable traits, but also using evidence of descent from a common ancestor.

For instance, *Scarus gibbus* is the scientific name for the humphead parrotfish (Figure 1.1*g*). Another species in the same genus is *S. coelestinus*, the midnight parrotfish. We abbreviate a genus name once it's been spelled out in a document.

Biologists are still working out how to group the organisms. Most now favor a classification system with three domains: Bacteria, Archaea, and Eukarya (Figure 1.6). As shown in Figure 1.7, the third domain includes protists, plants, fungi, and animals.

The **archaea** and **bacteria** are single-celled. They are *prokaryotic*, meaning they do not have a nucleus (a membrane-bound sac that keeps DNA separated from the rest of the cell's interior). Prokaryotes include diverse producers or consumers. Of all groups, theirs shows the greatest metabolic diversity.

Archaea live in boiling ocean water, freezing desert rocks, sulfur-rich lakes, and other habitats as harsh as those thought to have prevailed when life originated.

protists Diverse single-celled and multicelled eukaryotic species that range from microscopic single cells to giant seaweeds. Even this tiny sampling conveys why many biologists now believe the "protists" are many separate lineages.

archaea These prokaryotes are evolutionarily closer to the eukaryotes than to bacteria. This is a colony of methane-producing cells.

Figure 1.7 A few representatives of life's diversity.

Bacteria are sometimes called eubacteria, which means "true bacteria," to distinguish them from archaea. They are far more common than archaeans, and they live throughout the world in diverse habitats.

Plants, fungi, animals, and protists are members of the group **eukarya**, which means they have nuclei. Eukaryotes are generally larger and far more complex than the prokaryotes. The differences among protistan lineages are so great that they could be divided into several separate groups, which would result in a major reorganization of the domain.

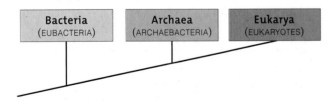

| Bacteria (EUBACTERIA) | Archaea (ARCHAEBACTERIA) | Eukarya (EUKARYOTES) |

Figure 1.6 Three domains of life.

Read Me First!
and watch
the narrated
animation on
life's diversity

plants   Generally, photosynthetic, multicelled eukaryotes, many with roots, stems, and leaves. Plants are the primary producers for ecosystems on land. Redwoods and flowering plants are examples.

fungi   Single-celled and multicelled eukaryotes; mostly decomposers, also many parasites and pathogens. Without the fungal and bacterial decomposers, communities would become buried in their own wastes.

animals   Multicelled eukaryotes that ingest tissues or juices of other organisms. Like this basilisk lizard, most actively move about during at least part of their life.

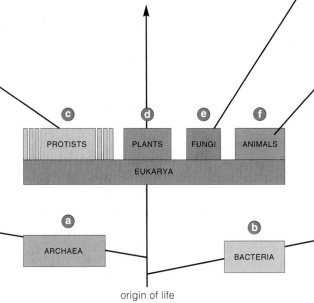

bacteria   By far the most common prokaryotes; collectively, these single-celled species are the most metabolically diverse organisms on Earth.

[diagram labels: PROTISTS (c), PLANTS (d), FUNGI (e), ANIMALS (f), EUKARYA, ARCHAEA (a), BACTERIA (b), origin of life]

Plants are multicelled, photosynthetic producers. They can make their own food by using simple raw materials and sunlight as an energy source.

Most **fungi**, such as the mushrooms sold in grocery stores, are multicelled decomposers and consumers with a distinct way of feeding. They secrete enzymes that digest food outside the fungal body, then their individual cells absorb the digested nutrients. **Animals** are multicelled consumers that ingest tissues of other organisms. Different kinds are herbivores (grazers), carnivores (meat eaters), scavengers, and parasites.

All develop by a series of embryonic stages, and they actively move about during their life.

Pulling this information together, are you getting a sense of what it means when someone says that life shows unity *and* diversity?

To make the study of life's diversity more manageable, we group organisms related by descent from a shared ancestor. We recognize three domains—archaea, bacteria, and eukarya (protists, fungi, plants, and animals).

1.4 An Evolutionary View of Diversity

How can organisms be so much alike and still show staggering diversity? A theory of evolution by natural selection explains this. For now, simply think about how it starts with a simple observation: Individuals of a population show variation in the details of their shared traits.

Your traits make you and 6.3 billion other individuals members of the human population. Traits are different aspects of an organism's form, function, or behavior. For example, humans show a range of height and hair color. All natural populations have differences among their individuals.

What causes variation in traits? **Mutations**. These are heritable changes in DNA. Some mutations lead to novel traits that make an individual better able to secure food, a mate, hiding places, and so on. We call these *adaptive* traits.

An adaptive form of a trait tends to become more common over generations, because it gives individuals a better chance to live and bear more offspring than

WILD ROCK DOVE

individuals who don't have it. When different forms of a trait are becoming more or less common, evolution is under way. To biologists, **evolution** simply means heritable change in a line of descent. Mutations, the source of new traits, provide the variation that serves as the raw material for evolution.

"Diversity" refers to variations in traits that have accumulated in lines of descent. Later chapters show the actual mechanisms that bring it about. For now, start thinking about what a great naturalist, Charles Darwin, discovered about evolution:

First, populations tend to increase in size, past the capacity of their environment to sustain them, so their members must compete for resources (food, shelter).

Second, individuals of natural populations differ from one another in the details of their shared traits. Most variation has a heritable basis.

Third, when individuals differ in their ability to survive and reproduce, the traits that help them do so tend to become more common in the population over time. This outcome is called **natural selection**.

Take a look at the pigeons in Figure 1.8. They differ in feather color, size, and other traits. Suppose pigeon breeders are looking for, say, pigeons with black, curly-tipped feathers. They allow only the pigeons with the darkest and curliest-tipped feathers to mate. In time, only pigeons with black, curly-tipped feathers make up the breeders' captive population. Lighter, less curly feathers will become less common.

Pigeon breeding is a case of *artificial* selection. One form of a trait is favored over others in an artificial environment under contrived, manipulated conditions. Darwin saw that breeding practices could be an easily understood model for *natural* selection, a favoring of some forms of a given trait over others in nature.

Just as breeders are "selective agents" promoting reproduction of particular captive pigeons, different agents operate across the range of variation in the wild. Pigeon-eating peregrine falcons are among them (Figure 1.8). Swifter or better camouflaged pigeons are more likely to avoid peregrine falcons and live long enough to reproduce, compared with not-so-swift or too-conspicuous pigeons.

Figure 1.8 Outcome of artificial selection. Just a few of the more than 300 varieties of domesticated pigeons, all descended from captive populations of wild rock doves. By contrast, peregrine falcons are one of the agents of natural selection in the wild.

Traits are variations in form, function, or behavior that arise as a result of mutations in DNA. Some traits are more adaptive than others to prevailing conditions.

Natural selection is an outcome of differences in survival and reproduction among individuals of a population that vary in one or more heritable traits. The process of evolution, or change in lines of descent, gives rise to life's diversity.

1.5 The Nature of Biological Inquiry

The preceding sections introduced some big concepts. Consider approaching this or any other collection of "facts" with a critical attitude. "Why should I accept that they have merit?" The answer requires a look at how biologists make inferences about observations, then test their inferences against actual experience.

OBSERVATIONS, HYPOTHESES, AND TESTS

To get a sense of "how to do science," you might start with practices that are common in scientific research:

1. Observe some aspect of nature, carefully check what others have found out about it, then frame a question or identify a problem related to your observation.

2. Formulate **hypotheses**, or educated guesses, about possible answers to questions or solutions to problems.

3. Using hypotheses as your guide, make a **prediction** —a statement of what you should find in the natural world if you were to go looking for it. This is often called the "if–then" process. *If* gravity does not pull objects toward the Earth, *then* it should be possible to observe apples falling up, not down, from a tree.

4. Devise ways to **test** the accuracy of predictions, as by making systematic observations, building models, and conducting experiments. **Models** are theoretical, detailed descriptions or analogies that might help us visualize something that hasn't been directly observed.

5. If your tests do not confirm a prediction, check to see what might have gone wrong. It may be that you overlooked a factor that had an impact on the results. Or maybe a hypothesis is not a good one.

6. Repeat the tests or devise new ones—the more the better, because hypotheses that withstand many tests are likely to have a higher probability of being useful.

7. Objectively analyze and report the test results as well as the conclusions you drew from them.

You might hear someone refer to these practices as "the scientific method," as if all scientists march to the drumbeat of an absolute, fixed procedure. They do not. Many observe, describe, and report on some aspect of nature, then leave the hypothesizing to others. Some scientists are lucky; they stumble onto information that they are not even looking for. Of course, it isn't always a matter of luck. Chance seems to favor a mind that has already been prepared, by education, experience, or both, to recognize what the information might mean. So it is not a single method that scientists have in common. It is a critical attitude about being shown rather than being told—that is, by accepting ideas supported by tests, and by taking a logical approach to problem solving.

ABOUT THE WORD "THEORY"

Suppose no one has disproved a hypothesis after years of rigorous tests. Suppose scientists use it to interpret more data or observations, which could involve more hypotheses. When a hypothesis meets these criteria, it may become accepted as a **scientific theory**.

You may hear people apply the word "theory" to a speculative idea, as in the expression "It's just a theory." But a scientific theory differs from speculation for this reason: *After testing the predictive power of a scientific theory many times and in many ways in the natural world, researchers have yet to find evidence that disproves it.* This is why the theory of natural selection is respected. It successfully explains diverse issues, such as how life originated, how river dams can alter ecosystems, and why antibiotics aren't working.

Maybe a well-tested theory is as close to the truth as scientists can get with known evidence. For instance, after more than a century of many thousands of tests, Darwin's theory holds, with only minor modification. We can't prove it holds under all possible conditions; that would take an infinite number of tests. As for any theory, we can only say *it has a high probability of being a good one*. Biologists do keep looking for information and devising tests that might disprove its premises.

A scientific approach to studying nature is based on asking questions, formulating hypotheses, making predictions, testing the predictions, and objectively reporting the results.

A scientific theory is a time-tested intellectual framework that is used to interpret a broad range of observations and data. Scientific theories remain open to rigorous tests, revision, and tentative acceptance or rejection.

1.6 The Power of Experimental Tests

Experiments are tests that simplify observation in nature, because conditions under which observations are made can be controlled. Well-designed experiments help you predict what you'll find in nature when a hypothesis is a good one—or won't find if it is wrong.

AN ASSUMPTION OF CAUSE AND EFFECT

A scientific experiment starts with a key premise: *Any aspect of nature has an underlying cause that can be tested by observation.* This premise is what sets science apart from faith in the supernatural ("beyond nature"). It means a scientific hypothesis must be testable in the natural world in ways that might well disprove it.

Most aspects of nature are complex, an outcome of many interacting variables. A **variable** is a specific aspect of an object or event that can differ among individuals or changes over time. Scientists simplify their observation of complex phenomena by designing experiments to test one variable at a time. They define a **control group**—a standard for comparison with one or more **experimental groups**. There are two kinds of control groups. A control group can be identical to an experimental group; except for *one variable event*, it is tested the same way as the experimental group. A control group may also differ from an experimental group in *one variable aspect*; in this case, it is tested exactly the same way as the experimental group.

EXAMPLE OF AN EXPERIMENTAL DESIGN

In 1996, the FDA approved Olestra®, a type of synthetic fat replacement made from sugar and vegetable oil, for use as a food additive. The first Olestra-containing product to reach consumers in the United States was a potato chip. Soon controversy raged. Some people complained of severe gastrointestinal distress after eating the chips. In 1998, medical researchers at Johns Hopkins University performed an experiment to test whether the new chips were indeed causing problems. Their prediction was this: *If Olestra causes intestinal problems, then people who eat products that contain Olestra will end up with gastrointestinal cramps.*

A suburban Chicago multiplex theater was chosen as the "laboratory" for this experiment. More than 1,100 people were invited to watch a movie and eat their fill of potato chips while they were there. They ranged between 13 and 88 years old. Unmarked bags each contained a family-size portion of potato chips. Some of the bags held Olestra potato chips, and the others held regular potato chips.

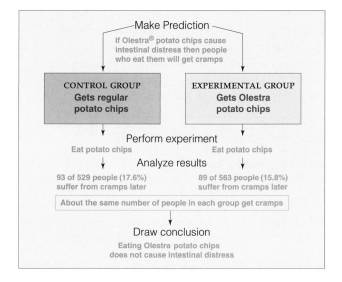

Figure 1.9 Example of a typical sequence of steps taken in a scientific experiment.

In this experiment, both control and experimental groups consisted of a random sample of moviegoers; each group got different chips (the variable event).

Later, the researchers telephoned the moviegoers at home and tabulated reports of gastrointestinal distress. They found that 89 of 563 people (15.8 percent) who ate Olestra chips complained of stomach cramps. Of 529 people, 93 (17.6 percent) who ate the regular chips did as well. They concluded that eating Olestra potato chips—at least during one sitting—does not cause gastrointestinal distress (Figure 1.9).

EXAMPLE OF A FIELD EXPERIMENT

Consider that many toxic or unpalatable species are vividly colored, often with distinctive patterning. Predators learn to avoid individuals that display particular visual cues after eating a few of them and suffering ill consequences.

In 1879, a naturalist named Fritz Müller formulated a hypothesis about unrelated species of distasteful butterflies that show striking resemblance to one another. A visual similarity between different species that may confuse potential predators (or prey) is called **mimicry**. Müller thought such a resemblance benefits individuals of both butterfly species because they share the burden of educating predatory birds.

Durrell Kapan, an evolutionary biologist, tested the hypothesis in 2001 with a field experiment in the rain forests of Ecuador. There are two forms of *Heliconius cydno*, an unpalatable species of butterfly. One has yellow markings on its wings; the other does not.

Figure 1.10 *Heliconius* butterflies. (**a**) Two forms of *H. cydno* and (**b**) *H. eleuchia.*

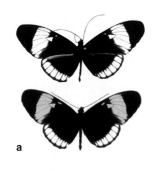

a

b

(**c**) Kapan's experiment with *Heliconius* butterflies in an Ecuadoran rain forest. *H. cydno* butterflies with or without yellow markings on their wings were captured and transferred to a habitat of *H. eleuchia*, a species that also has yellow wing markings. Local predatory birds, familiar with untasty yellow *H. eleuchia*, avoided the *H. cydno* butterflies with yellow markings but ate the white ones.

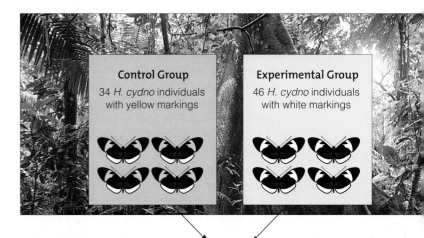

Control Group
34 *H. cydno* individuals with yellow markings

Experimental Group
46 *H. cydno* individuals with white markings

one of the agents of selection

Experiment

Both yellow and white forms of *H. cydno* butterflies are introduced into isolated rain forest habitat of yellow *H. eleuchia* butterflies. Numbers of individuals resighted recorded on a daily basis for two weeks.

Results

Experimental group (*H. cydno* individuals without yellow wing markings) is selected against. 37 of the original group of 46 white butterflies disappear (80%), compared with 20 of the 34 yellow controls (58%).

c

Both resemble another unpalatable species that lives nearby, *H. eleuchia*, which also has yellow in its wings (Figure 1.10). Kapan made a prediction: Birds that had already learned not to prey on *H. eleuchia* would also avoid *H. cydno* butterflies with yellow markings.

He captured both forms of *H. cydno*. The form with no yellow markings was the experimental group, and the form with the yellow markings was the control. He released both groups into parts of the forest that held isolated populations of *H. eleuchia* butterflies. He made daily counts of how many of the transplanted butterflies survived during the next two weeks, the approximate life span of the butterflies.

Kapan found that individuals of the experimental group were less likely to survive in the new habitat (Figure 1.10*c*). Resident birds familiar with *H. eleuchia* butterflies most likely ate them because they did not bear the familiar visual cue—yellow markings—that signaled bad taste. The control group did better, as you can see from the test results listed in Figure 1.10*c*. Local birds probably had an idea of how the new butterflies would taste, and avoided them.

Kapan's test results confirmed his prediction, and it also turned out to be evidence of natural selection.

BIAS IN REPORTING RESULTS

Experimenters run a risk of interpreting data in terms of what they wish to prove or dismiss. That is why scientists prefer *quantitative* reports of experiments, with numbers or some other precise measurement. Such data give other experimenters an opportunity to confirm tests, and, perhaps more importantly, allow others to check their conclusions.

This last point gets us back to the value of thinking critically. Scientists must keep asking themselves: *Will observations or experiments show that a hypothesis is false?* They expect one another to put aside pride or bias by testing ideas in ways that may prove them wrong. Even if someone won't, others will—because science is a cooperative yet competitive community. Ideally, individuals share ideas, knowing it's as useful to expose errors as to applaud insights. They can and often do change their mind when evidence contradicts their ideas. And therein lies the strength of science.

Experiments simplify observations in nature by restricting a researcher's focus to one variable at a time.

Tests are based on the premise that any aspect of nature has one or more underlying causes. Scientific hypotheses can be tested in ways that might disprove them.

1.7 The Limits of Science

Beyond the realm of scientific inquiry, some events are unexplained. Why do we exist, for what purpose? Why do we have to die at a particular moment? Such questions lead to *subjective* answers, which come from within as an integrated outcome of all the experiences and mental connections that shape our consciousness. People differ enormously in this regard. That is why subjective answers do not readily lend themselves to scientific analysis and experiments.

This is not to say subjective answers are without value. No human society can function for long unless its individuals share a commitment to standards for making judgments, even if they are subjective. Moral, aesthetic, philosophical, and economic standards vary from one society to the next. But they all guide people in deciding what is important and good, and what is not. All attempt to give meaning to what we do.

Every so often, scientists stir up controversy when they explain something that was thought to be beyond natural explanation, or belonging to the supernatural. This is often the case when a society's moral codes are interwoven with religious interpretations of the past. Exploring a long-standing view of the natural world from a scientific perspective might be misinterpreted as questioning morality, even though the two are not the same thing.

As one example, centuries ago in Europe, Nikolaus Copernicus studied the planets and concluded that the Earth circles the sun. Today this seems obvious. Back then, it was heresy. The prevailing belief was that the Creator made the Earth—and, by extension, humans—the immovable center of the universe. One respected scholar, Galileo Galilei, studied the Copernican model of the solar system, thought it was a good one, and said so. He was forced to retract his statement, on his knees, and put the Earth back as the fixed center of things. (Word has it that he also muttered, "Even so, it *does* move.") Later, Darwin's theory of evolution also ran up against prevailing belief.

Today, as then, society has sets of standards. Those standards might be questioned when a new, natural explanation runs counter to supernatural beliefs. This doesn't mean scientists who raise questions are less moral, less lawful, less sensitive, or less caring than anyone else. It only means one more standard guides their work. Their ideas about nature must be tested in the external world, in ways that can be repeated.

The external world, not internal conviction, is the testing ground for the theories generated in science.

Summary

Section 1.1 Life shows many levels of organization. All things, living and nonliving, are made of atoms. The properties of life emerge in cells. An organism may be a single cell or multicelled. In most multicelled species, cells are organized as tissues, organs, and organ systems.

A population consists of individuals of the same species in a specified area. A community consists of all populations occupying the same area. An ecosystem is a community and its environment. The biosphere includes all regions of Earth's atmosphere, waters, and land where we find living organisms.

Section 1.2 Life shows unity. All organisms have DNA, which holds instructions for building proteins. They inherit the instructions from their parents and pass them on to offspring. All require energy and raw materials from the environment to grow and reproduce. All sense changes in the surroundings and respond to them in controlled ways (Table 1.1).

Section 1.3 Life shows tremendous diversity. Many millions of species exist; many more lived in the past. Each is unique in some aspects of its body plan, function, and behavior. We group species that are related by descent from a common ancestor. A current classification system puts species in three domains: archaea, bacteria, and eukarya. Protists, plants, fungi, and animals are eukaryotes.

Table 1.1 Summary of Life's Characteristics

Shared characteristics that reflect life's unity

1. All life forms contain "molecules of life" (complex carbohydrates, lipids, proteins, and nucleic acids).
2. Organisms consist of one or more cells.
3. Cells are constructed of the same kinds of atoms and molecules according to the same laws of energy.
4. Organisms acquire and use energy and materials to survive and reproduce.
5. Organisms sense and make controlled responses to conditions in their internal and external environments.
6. Heritable information is encoded in DNA.
7. Characteristics of individuals in a population can change over generations; the population can evolve.

Foundations for life's diversity

1. Mutations in DNA give rise to variations in traits, or details of body form, function, and behavior.
2. Traits enhancing survival and reproduction become more common in a population over generations. This process is called natural selection.
3. Diversity is the sum total of variations that accumulated in different lines of descent over the past 3.9 billion years.

Section 1.4 Mutations change DNA and give rise to new variations of heritable traits. Natural selection occurs if a variation affects survival and reproduction. A population is evolving by natural selection when an adaptive form of a trait is becoming more common.

Section 1.5 Scientific methods are varied, but all are based on a logical approach to explaining nature. Scientists observe some aspect of nature, then develop a hypothesis about what might have caused it. They use the hypothesis to make predictions that can be tested by making more observations, building models, or doing experiments.

Scientists analyze test results, draw conclusions from them, and share this information with other scientists. A hypothesis that does not hold up under repeated testing is modified or discarded. A scientific theory is a long-standing hypothesis that explains a broad range of related phenomena and has been supported by many different tests.

Section 1.6 Science cannot answer all questions. It deals only with aspects of nature that lend themselves to systematic observation, hypotheses, predictions, and experiments.

Most aspects of nature are complex, an outcome of many interacting variables. A scientific experiment allows a scientist to change one variable at a time and observe what happens. Experiments are designed so experimental groups can be compared with a control group. Scientists share their results so others can check their conclusions.

Self-Quiz
Answers in Appendix III

1. The smallest unit of life is the _____ .

2. _____ is the capacity of cells to extract energy from sources in the environment, and use it to live, grow, and reproduce.

3. _____ is a state in which the internal environment is being maintained within a tolerable range.

4. A trait is _____ if it improves an organism's ability to survive and reproduce in a given environment.

5. Differences in heritable traits arise through _____ .

6. Researchers assign all species to one of three _____ .

7. _____ secure energy from their surroundings.
   a. Producers   c. Decomposers
   b. Consumers   d. All of the above

8. DNA _____ .
   a. contains instructions for building proteins
   b. undergoes mutation
   c. is transmitted from parents to offspring
   d. all of the above

9. _____ is the acquisition of traits after parents transmit their DNA to offspring.
   a. Metabolism   c. Homeostasis
   b. Reproduction   d. Inheritance

10. A control group is _____ .
    a. a standard against which experimental groups can be compared
    b. an experiment that gives conclusive results

11. Match the terms with the most suitable descriptions.
    ____ adaptive trait
    ____ natural selection
    ____ scientific theory
    ____ hypothesis
    ____ prediction

    a. statement of what you can expect to observe in nature
    b. proposed explanation; an educated guess
    c. improves chances of surviving and reproducing
    d. related set of hypotheses that form a broadly useful, testable explanation
    e. outcome of differences in survival, reproduction among individuals of a population that differ in the details of one or more traits

Critical Thinking

1. A scientific theory about some aspect of nature rests upon inductive logic—inference of a generalized conclusion from particular instances. The assumption is that, because an outcome of some event has been observed to happen with great regularity, it will happen again. However, we can't know this for certain, because there is no way to account for all possible variables that may affect the outcome. To illustrate this point, Garvin McCain and Erwin Segal offer a parable:

Once there was a highly intelligent turkey. The turkey lived in a pen, attended by a kind, thoughtful master, and it had nothing to do but reflect upon the world's wonders and regularities. Morning always began with the sky getting light, followed by the clop, clop, clop of its master's friendly footsteps, which was followed by the appearance of delicious food. Other things varied—sometimes the morning was warm and sometimes cold—but food always followed footsteps. The sequence of events was so predictable that it eventually became the basis of the turkey's theory about the goodness of the world.

One morning, after more than a hundred confirmations of the goodness theory, the turkey listened for the clop, clop, clop, heard it, and had its head chopped off.

The turkey learned the hard way that explanations about the world only have a high or low probability of being correct. Today, some people take this uncertainty to mean that "facts are irrelevant—facts change." If that is so, should we just stop doing scientific research? Why or why not?

2. Witnesses in a court of law are asked to "swear to tell the truth, the whole truth, and nothing but the truth." What are some of the problems inherent in the question? Can you think of a better alternative?

3. Many popular magazines publish an astounding array of articles on diet, exercise, and other health-related topics. Some authors recommend a diet or dietary supplement. What kinds of evidence do you think the articles should include so that you can decide whether to accept their recommendations?

b The jar is hidden before she removes her blindfold. She observes a single green jelly bean in her hand and assumes the jar holds only green jelly beans.

a Natalie, blindfolded, randomly plucks a jelly bean from a jar of 120 green and 280 black jelly beans. That's a ratio of 30 to 70 percent.

c Still blindfolded, Natalie randomly picks 50 jelly beans from the jar and ends up with 10 green and 40 black ones.

d The larger sample leads her to assume one-fifth of the jar's jelly beans are green and four-fifths are black (a ratio of 20 to 80). Her larger sample more closely approximates the jar's green-to-black ratio. The more times Natalie repeats the sampling, the greater the chance she will come close to knowing the actual ratio.

Figure 1.11 A simple demonstration of sampling error.

4. Rarely can experimenters observe all individuals of a group. They select subsets or samples of populations, events, and other aspects of nature. They must avoid *sampling error*, which means obtaining misleading results by using subsets that aren't really representative of the whole (Figure 1.11). Test results are less likely to be distorted when a sampling is large and the test is repeated. Explain how sampling error might have affected the results of the butterfly experiment described in Section 1.6.

5. The Olestra® potato chip experiment in Section 1.6 was a *double-blind* study: Neither the subjects of the experiment nor the researchers knew which potato chips were in which bag until after all the subjects had reported. What do you think are some of the challenges for researchers performing a double-blind study?

6. In 1988 Dr. Randolph Byrd and his colleagues undertook a study of 393 patients admitted to the San Francisco General Hospital Coronary Care Unit. In the experiment, "born-again" Christian volunteers were asked to pray daily for a patient's rapid recovery and for prevention of complications and death. None of the patients knew if he or she was being prayed for or not, and none of the volunteers or patients knew each other. How each patient fared in the hospital was classified by Byrd as "good," "intermediate," or "bad." Byrd determined that the patients who had been prayed for fared a little better than those who had not. His was the first experiment to document, in a scientific fashion, statistically significant results in support of the prediction that prayer has beneficial effects on the outcome of seriously ill patients. Publication of these results engendered a storm of criticism, mostly from scientists who cited bias in Byrd's experimental design. For instance, Byrd classified the patients after the experiment had been finished. Think about how bias might play a role in interpreting medical data. Why do you think this experiment generated a dramatic response from the rest of the scientific community?

I Principles of Cellular Life

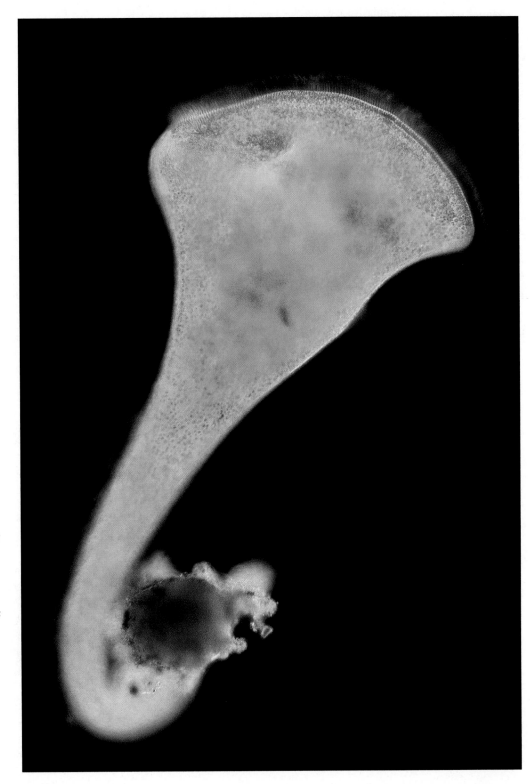

Staying alive means securing energy and raw materials from the environment. Shown here, a living cell of genus Stentor. This single-celled protist has hairlike projections around the opening to a cavity in its body, which is about two millimeters long. Its "hairs" are fused-together cilia, which beat the surrounding water. They create a current that wafts food into the cavity.

2 LIFE'S CHEMICAL BASIS

IMPACTS, ISSUES   *What Are You Worth?*

Hollywood thinks Leonardo DiCaprio is worth $20 million a picture, the Yankees think shortstop Alex Rodriguez is worth $217 million per decade, and the United States thinks the average teacher is worth $44,367 per year. Chemically, though, how much is a human body really worth (Figure 2.1a)?

Think about it. The human body is a collection of **elements**, or types of atoms. **Atoms** are fundamental substances that have mass and take up space, and cannot be broken apart by everyday means. Keep grinding up a chunk of copper, and the smallest bit you will end up with will be a lone atom of copper. Atoms are the smallest units of an element that still retain the element's properties.

Oxygen, hydrogen, carbon, and nitrogen are the most abundant elements in organisms. Next are phosphorus, potassium, sulfur, calcium, and sodium. *Trace* elements make up less than 0.01 percent of body weight. Selenium is an example.

Wait a minute! Selenium, mercury, arsenic, lead, and many other elements in the body are toxic, right? Maybe, or maybe not. As researchers

Figure 2.1 **(a)** What are you worth, chemically speaking? **(b)** Proportions of the most common elements in a human body, Earth's crust, and seawater. How are they similar? How do they differ?   **a**

Element	Amount	Value
Oxygen (O)	43.00 kg	$0.021739
Carbon (C)	16.00 kg	6.400000
Hydrogen (H)	7.00 kg	0.028315
Nitrogen (N)	1.80 kg	9.706929
Calcium (Ca)	1.00 kg	15.500000
Phosphorus (P)	780.00 g	68.198594
Potassium (K)	140.00 g	4.098737
Sulfur (S)	140.00 g	0.011623
Sodium (Na)	100.00 g	2.287748
Chlorine (Cl)	95.00 g	1.409496
Magnesium (Mg)	19.00 g	0.444909
Iron (Fe)	4.20 g	0.054600
Fluorine (F)	2.60 g	7.917263
Zinc (Zn)	2.30 g	0.088090
Silicon (Si)	1.00 g	0.370000
Rubidium (Rb)	0.68 g	1.087153
Strontium (Sr)	0.32 g	0.177237
Bromine (Br)	0.26 g	0.012858
Lead (Pb)	0.12 g	0.003960
Copper (Cu)	72.00 mg	0.012961
Aluminum (Al)	60.00 mg	0.246804
Cadmium (Cd)	50.00 mg	0.010136
Cerium (Ce)	40.00 mg	0.043120
Barium (Ba)	22.00 mg	0.028776
Iodine (I)	20.00 mg	0.094184
Tin (Sn)	20.00 mg	0.005387
Titanium (Ti)	20.00 mg	0.010920
Boron (B)	18.00 mg	0.002172
Nickel (Ni)	15.00 mg	0.031320
Selenium (Se)	15.00 mg	0.037949

Element	Amount	Value
Chromium (Cr)	14.00 mg	0.003402
Manganese (Mn)	12.00 mg	0.001526
Arsenic (As)	7.00 mg	0.023576
Lithium (Li)	7.00 mg	0.024233
Cesium (Cs)	6.00 mg	0.000016
Mercury (Hg)	6.00 mg	0.004718
Germanium (Ge)	5.00 mg	0.130435
Molybdenum (Mo)	5.00 mg	0.001260
Cobalt (Co)	3.00 mg	0.001509
Antimony (Sb)	2.00 mg	0.000243
Silver (Ag)	2.00 mg	0.013600
Niobium (Nb)	1.50 mg	0.000624
Zirconium (Zr)	1.00 mg	0.000830
Lanthanum (La)	0.80 mg	0.000566
Gallium (Ga)	0.70 mg	0.003367
Tellurium (Te)	0.70 mg	0.000722
Yttrium (Y)	0.60 mg	0.005232
Bismuth (Bi)	0.50 mg	0.000119
Thallium (Tl)	0.50 mg	0.000894
Indium (In)	0.40 mg	0.000600
Gold (Au)	0.20 mg	0.001975
Scandium (Sc)	0.20 mg	0.058160
Tantalum (Ta)	0.20 mg	0.001631
Vanadium (V)	0.11 mg	0.000322
Thorium (Th)	0.10 mg	0.004948
Uranium (U)	0.10 mg	0.000103
Samarium (Sm)	50.00 µg	0.000118
Beryllium (Be)	36.00 µg	0.000218
Tungsten (W)	20.00 µg	0.000007

Grand Total: $118.63

the big picture

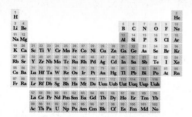

Atoms and Elements

All substances are made of one or more elements. Atoms are the smallest units of matter that still retain the element's properties. They are composed of protons, neutrons, and electrons.

Why Electrons Matter

Whether an atom will interact with other atoms depends on how many electrons it has and how they are arranged. Chemical bonds unite two or more atoms.

Human		Earth's Crust		Ocean	
Oxygen	61.0%	Oxygen	46.0%	Oxygen	85.7%
Carbon	23.0	Silicon	27.0	Hydrogen	10.8
Hydrogen	10.0	Aluminum	8.2	Chlorine	2.0
Nitrogen	2.6	Iron	6.3	Sodium	1.1
Calcium	1.4	Calcium	5.0	Magnesium	0.1
Phosphorus	1.1	Magnesium	2.9	Sulfur	0.1
Potassium	0.2	Sodium	2.3	Calcium	0.04
Sulfur	0.2	Potassium	1.5	Potassium	0.03

b

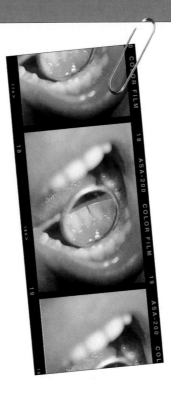

decipher chemical processes peculiar to life, they are finding that many trace elements considered to be poisons actually perform essential biological functions. For instance, large doses of chromium damage nerves and cause cancer, but one form works with insulin, a hormone that helps control the glucose level in blood. A little selenium is toxic, but too little causes heart and thyroid problems. An intricate balance of the right kinds of elements keeps the body functioning properly.

One more point: Earth's crust contains the same elements as the human body, but we're not just dirt. Like all living things, the proportions and organization of our elements are unique (Figure 2.1*b*). And building and maintaining that organization takes tremendous input of energy (just ask any pregnant woman).

You could buy all of the elements in a 150-pound human body for about $118.63. But constructing any living thing requires a remarkably complex interplay of energy and biological molecules that is far beyond the scope of any laboratory to duplicate, at least for now.

 How Would You Vote?

Fluoride has been proven to help prevent tooth decay. But too much wrecks bones and teeth, and causes birth defects. A lot can kill you. Many communities in the United States add fluoride to their drinking water. Do you want it in yours? See the Media Menu for details, then vote online.

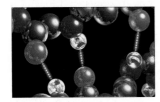

Atoms Bond

The molecular organization and the activities of every living thing arise from ionic, covalent, and hydrogen bonds between atoms.

No Water, No Life

Water's unique characteristics, including temperature-stabilizing effects, cohesion, and solvent properties, make life possible on Earth.

Hydrogen Ions Rule

Life is adapted to the properties of water and to changing concentrations of hydrogen ions and other substances dissolved in water.

2.1 Start With Atoms

Life's chemical properties start with protons, neutrons, and electrons. The unique character of each element actually begins with the number of protons, which is the same in all of its atoms.

Atoms, again, are the smallest units that retain the properties of an element. All atoms are made of three kinds of subatomic particles: protons, neutrons, and electrons (Figure 2.2). Each **proton** carries a positive *charge*, or a defined amount of electricity. Protons are symbolized as p+. An atom's nucleus (core) holds one or more protons. It also holds **neutrons**, which have no charge. Zipping about the nucleus are one or more **electrons**, which carry a negative charge (e−).

The positive charge of a proton and the negative charge of an electron balance each other. So an atom that has the same number of electrons and protons has no net electrical charge.

Each element has a unique **atomic number**, or the number of protons in the nucleus of its atoms. For example, the atomic number for hydrogen, which has one proton, is 1. For carbon, with six protons, it is 6.

Each element also has a **mass number**, equal to the total number of protons and neutrons in the atomic nucleus. For example, carbon, with six protons and six neutrons, has a mass number of 12.

Why bother with atomic and mass numbers? If you know how many electrons, protons, and neutrons the atoms of an element contain, you can predict what the

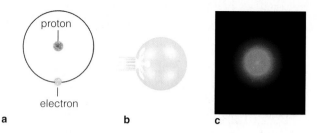

a   b   c

Figure 2.2 Different ways of representing atoms, using hydrogen (H) as the example. (**a**) A shell model shows the number of electrons and their relative distances from the nucleus. (**b**) Balls show relative sizes of atoms. (**c**) Electron density clouds show electron distribution around the nucleus.

chemical behavior of that element will probably be under different conditions.

Elements were being classified in terms of chemical similarities long before their subatomic particles were discovered. In 1869, Dmitry Mendeleev, known more for his extravagant hair than his discoveries (he cut it only once per year), arranged the known elements into a repeating pattern based on their chemical properties. Using gaps in this **periodic table**, Mendeleev was able to predict correctly the existence of other elements that had yet to be discovered.

The elements fall into order in the periodic table according to their atomic number (Figure 2.3). Those in the same column of the table have the same number of electrons available for interaction with other atoms. As a result, they behave in a remarkably similar way. For instance, helium, neon, radon, and other gases in the vertical column farthest to the right are called *inert* elements because none of their electrons is available for chemical interaction. Consequently, they rarely do much; they exist mostly as solitary atoms.

Not all of the elements in the periodic table occur in nature. The elements after atomic number 92 are so highly unstable that they have been produced only in very small quantities in the laboratory—sometimes no more than a single atom. They wink out of existence fast. Some elements still haven't been made.

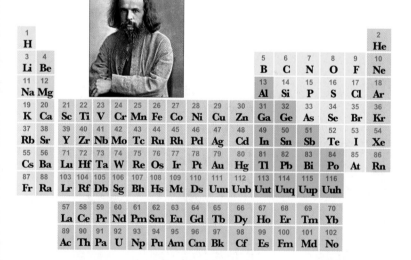

Figure 2.3 Periodic table of the elements and Dmitry Mendeleev, who created it. Some of the symbols for elements are abbreviations for their Latin names. For instance, Pb (lead) is short for *plumbum;* the word "plumbing" is related, because ancient Romans used lead to make their water pipes.

Atoms are the smallest units of an element, or fundamental substance, that still retain the properties of that element. Ninety-two elements occur naturally on Earth.

One or more positively charged protons, negatively charged electrons, and (except for hydrogen) neutrons make up atoms.

An element's chemical properties are a direct consequence of the number of electrons it has available for interacting with other atoms.

2.2 Radioisotopes

*All elements are defined by the number of protons in their atoms—but an element's atoms can differ in their number of neutrons. We call such atoms **isotopes** of the same element. And some are radioactive.*

Henri Becquerel discovered radioactivity by accident in 1896. He put some crystals of phosphorescent uranium salts on top of an unexposed photographic plate inside a desk drawer. Between the uranium and the plate were several sheets of opaque black paper, a coin, and a metal screen. A day later, he used the film and developed it. Surprisingly, a negative image of the coin and screen appeared on it. Energy emitted by the uranium had exposed the film all around the metal. Becquerel concluded that uranium salts emit some form of "radiation" capable of going through things that light cannot penetrate. What was it?

As we now know, most elements in nature have two or more kinds of isotopes. Carbon has three, nitrogen has two, and so on. A superscript number to the left of an element's symbol is the isotope's mass number (combined number of protons and neutrons). For instance, carbon's three natural isotopes are ^{12}C (or carbon 12, the most common form, with six protons, six neutrons), ^{13}C (six protons, seven neutrons), and ^{14}C (six protons, eight neutrons).

Too many or too few neutrons in the nucleus of an atom can cause it to be unstable, or radioactive. A radioactive atom spontaneously emits energy as subatomic particles and x-rays when its nucleus disintegrates. This process, called **radioactive decay**, transforms one element into another. ^{13}C and ^{14}C are radioactive isotopes, or **radioisotopes**, of carbon. Each radioisotope decays with a particular amount of energy into a predictable, more stable product. For example, after 5,700 years, about half of the atoms in a sample of ^{14}C will have turned into ^{14}N (nitrogen) atoms. As you'll see in Chapter 17, researchers use radioactive decay to estimate the age of fossils.

Different isotopes of an element are still the same element. For the most part, carbon is carbon, regardless of how many neutrons it has. Living systems use ^{12}C the same way as ^{14}C. Knowing this, researchers or clinicians studying a certain type of molecule make **tracers**, in which a radioisotope gets substituted for a stable element in that molecule. They deliver tracers into a cell, a multicelled body, or an ecosystem. Energy from radioactive decay is like a shipping label; it helps us track the molecule of interest with instruments that detect radioactivity.

Melvin Calvin and his colleagues used a tracer, carbon dioxide gas made with ^{14}C, to discover the specific steps of photosynthesis. By steeping plants in the radioactive gas, they were able to follow the path of the radioactive carbon atoms through each reaction step in the formation of sugars and starches.

Radioisotopes also are used in medicine. *PET* (short for *Positron-Emission Tomography*) uses radioisotopes to form images of body tissues. Clinicians attach a radioisotope to glucose or another sugar. They inject this tracer into a patient, who is moved into a PET scanner (Figure 2.4*a*). Cells throughout the body absorb the tracer at different rates. The scanner then detects radiation caused by energy from the decay of the radioisotope, and that radiation is used to form an image. Such images can reveal variations and abnormalities in metabolic activity (Figure 2.4*d*).

detector ring inside PET scanner   body section inside ring

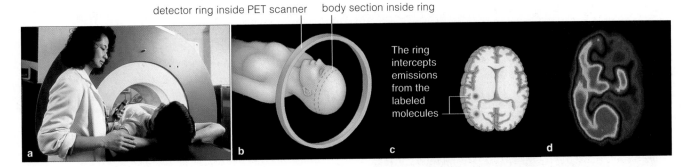

The ring intercepts emissions from the labeled molecules

Figure 2.4 (**a**) Patient moving into a PET scanner. (**b,c**) Inside, a ring of detectors intercepts radioactive emissions from labeled molecules that were injected into the patient. Computers analyze and color-code the number of emissions from each location in the scanned body region.

(**d**) Different colors in a brain scan signify differences in metabolic activity. Cells of this brain's left half absorbed and used the labeled molecules at expected rates. However, cells in the right half showed little activity. The patient was diagnosed as having a neurological disorder.

2.3 What Happens When Atom Bonds With Atom?

Atoms acquire, share, and donate electrons. Atoms of some elements do this easily; others do not. Why is this so? To come up with an answer, look to the number and arrangement of electrons in atoms.

ELECTRONS AND ENERGY LEVELS

In our world, simple physics explains the motion of an apple falling from a tree. Tiny electrons belong to a strange world where everyday physics doesn't apply. (If electrons were as big as apples, you'd be about 3.5 times taller than our solar system is wide.) Different forces bring about the motion of electrons, which can get from here to there without going in between!

We can calculate where an electron is, although not exactly. The best we can do is say that it's somewhere in a fuzzy cloud of probability density. Where it can go depends on how many other electrons are buzzing about an atom's nucleus. As it turns out, electrons can occupy orbitals, which are volumes of space around the nucleus. There are many orbitals, with different three-dimensional shapes.

An atom has about same number of electrons as protons. For most atoms, that's a lot of electrons. How are these electrons arranged, given that they repel each other? Think of an atom as a multilevel apartment building with lots of vacant rooms to rent to electrons, and a nucleus in the basement. Each "room" is one orbital, and it rents out to two electrons at most. An orbital holding one electron only has a vacancy; another electron can move in.

Each floor in that atomic apartment building corresponds to an energy level. There is only one room on the first floor (one orbital at the lowest energy level, closest to the nucleus), and it fills first. For hydrogen, the simplest atom, that room has a single electron (Figure 2.5). For helium, it has two. In other words, helium has no vacancies at the first (lowest) energy level. In larger atoms, more electrons rent second-floor rooms. If the second floor is filled, additional electrons rent third-floor rooms, and so on. *They fill orbitals at successively higher energy levels.*

The farther an electron is from the basement (the nucleus), the greater its energy. An electron in a first-floor room can't move to the second or third floor, let alone the penthouse, unless a boost of energy gets it there. Suppose it absorbs the right amount of energy from, say, sunlight, to get excited about moving up. Move it does. If nothing fills that lower room, though, the electron will quickly go back to it, emitting extra energy as it does. Later, you'll see how cells in plants and in your eyes can harness and use that energy.

FROM ATOMS TO MOLECULES

In shell models, nested "shells" correspond to energy levels. They offer us an easy way to check for electron vacancies in various atoms (Figure 2.6). Bear in mind, atoms do not look like these flat diagrams. The shells are not three-dimensional volumes of space, and they certainly don't show the electron orbitals.

Atoms that have vacancies in the outermost "shell" tend to give up, acquire, or share electrons with other atoms. This kind of electron-swapping between atoms is known as **chemical bonding** (Section 2.4). Atoms with zero vacancies rarely bond with other atoms. By contrast, the most common atoms in organisms—such as oxygen, carbon, hydrogen, nitrogen, and calcium—have vacancies in orbitals at their outermost energy level. And they do bond with other atoms.

third energy level (second floor)

second energy level (first floor)

first energy level (closest to the basement)

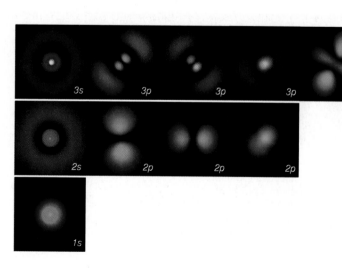

Figure 2.5 First, second, and third levels of the atomic apartment building. Each picture is a three-dimensional approximation of an electron orbital. Colors are most intense in locations where electrons are most likely to be. Orbitals farthest from the nucleus have greater energy and are more complex.

c **Third shell** shows the third set of orbitals: one *s* orbital, three *p* orbitals, and five *d* orbitals, a total of nine orbitals with room for 18 electrons. Sodium has one electron in the third shell of orbitals, and chlorine has seven. Both have vacancies, so they form chemical bonds.

b **Second shell** shows the second energy level, which combines a set of one *s* orbital plus three *p* orbitals. The second shell of orbitals has room for a total of eight electrons. Carbon has six electrons, two in the first shell and four in the second shell. It has four vacancies. Oxygen has two vacancies. Both carbon and oxygen form chemical bonds.

a **First shell** shows the first energy level, containing a single orbital (*1s*). Hydrogen has only one electron in this orbital that can hold two. Hydrogen gives up its electron easily, becoming a chemically reactive free proton. A helium atom has two electrons in the *1s* orbital. Having no vacancies, helium does not usually form chemical bonds.

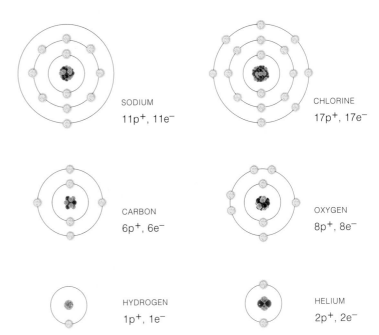

SODIUM
$11p^+$, $11e^-$

CHLORINE
$17p^+$, $17e^-$

CARBON
$6p^+$, $6e^-$

OXYGEN
$8p^+$, $8e^-$

HYDROGEN
$1p^+$, $1e^-$

HELIUM
$2p^+$, $2e^-$

Figure 2.6 Shell model. Using this model, it is easy to see the vacancies in each atom's outer orbitals. Each circle represents all of the orbitals on one energy level. Larger circles correspond to higher energy levels. This model is highly simplified; a more realistic rendering would show the electrons as fuzzy clouds of probability density about ten thousand times bigger than the nucleus.

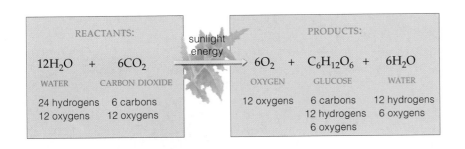

REACTANTS:

$$12H_2O \ + \ 6CO_2$$

WATER   CARBON DIOXIDE

24 hydrogens   6 carbons
12 oxygens   12 oxygens

sunlight energy

PRODUCTS:

$$6O_2 \ + \ C_6H_{12}O_6 \ + \ 6H_2O$$

OXYGEN   GLUCOSE   WATER

12 oxygens   6 carbons   12 hydrogens
            12 hydrogens   6 oxygens
            6 oxygens

Figure 2.7 Chemical bookkeeping. Chemical equations are representations of reactions, or interactions between atoms and molecules. Substances entering a reaction are to the left of a reaction arrow (reactants), and products are to the right, as shown by this chemical equation for photosynthesis.

A **molecule** is simply two or more atoms of the same or different elements joined in a chemical bond. You can write a molecule's chemical composition as a formula that uses symbols for elements. A formula shows the number of each kind of atom in a molecule (Figure 2.7). Water has the chemical formula H_2O. The subscript number tells you that two hydrogen (H) atoms are present for each oxygen (O) atom.

Compounds are molecules that consist of two or more different elements in proportions that never do vary. Water is an example. All water molecules have one oxygen atom bonded to two hydrogen atoms. The ones in rain clouds, the seas, a Siberian lake, a flower's petals, your bathtub, or anywhere else always have twice as many hydrogen as oxygen atoms.

In a **mixture**, two or more molecules intermingle without chemically bonding. For instance, you can make a mixture by swirling water and sugar together. The proportions of elements in a mixture can vary.

Electrons occupy orbitals, or defined volumes of space around an atom's nucleus. Successive orbitals correspond to levels of energy, which become higher with distance from the nucleus.

One or at most two electrons can occupy any orbital. Atoms with vacancies in their highest level orbitals can interact with other atoms.

A molecule is two or more atoms joined in a chemical bond. Atoms of two or more elements are bonded together in compounds. A mixture consists of intermingled molecules.

2.4 Bonds in Biological Molecules

The distinctive properties of biological molecules start with atoms interacting at the level of electrons.

ION FORMATION AND IONIC BONDING

An electron, recall, has a negative charge equal to a proton's positive charge. When an atom has as many electrons as protons, these charges balance each other, so the atom will have a net charge of zero.

Atoms with more electrons than protons carry a net negative charge, and those with more protons than electrons carry a net positive charge. An atom that has either a positive or negative charge is known as an **ion**. Ions form when atoms gain or lose electrons.

Example: An uncharged chlorine atom has seven electrons, hence one vacancy, in the third orbital level. Chlorine tends to grab an electron from other places. That extra electron will make it a chloride ion (Cl^-), with a net negative charge. A sodium atom has a lone electron in the same orbital level, but it is easier to give that one up than to acquire seven more. If it does, it will only have second-level orbitals, and they will be full of electrons—so no vacancy. It becomes a sodium ion with a net positive charge (Na^+).

What happens when one atom gives up an electron that another accepts? The two resulting ions may stay close together, because they have opposite charges that attract each other. A close association of ions is an **ionic bond**. Figure 2.8*a* shows a crystal of table salt, or NaCl. In such crystals, ionic bonds hold the ions in an orderly arrangement.

COVALENT BONDING

In an ionic bond, one atom donates an extra electron that the other accepts. What if both atoms want an extra electron? They can *share* one of their electrons in a hybrid orbital that spans both nuclei. Each atom's vacancy becomes partly filled with a shared electron. When atoms share one or more electrons, they are joined in a **covalent bond** (Figure 2.8*b*). Such bonds are stable and are much stronger than ionic bonds.

Unlike chemical formulas, structural formulas show how atoms are physically arranged in a molecule—they reveal the bonding pattern. A single line that connects two atoms in a structural formula represents two shared electrons in one covalent bond. Molecular hydrogen, with one covalent bond, is written H—H.

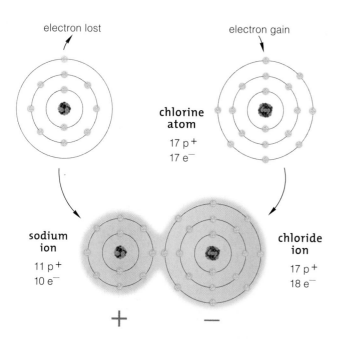

a Ionic bonding. A sodium atom donates its extra electron to a chlorine atom.

In each crystal of table salt, or NaCl, many sodium and chloride ions stay close together because of the mutual attraction of opposite charges. Their ongoing interaction is a case of ionic bonding.

Figure 2.8 Important bonds in biological molecules.

Two atoms can share two electron pairs in a *double* covalent bond. Molecular oxygen (O=O) is like this. In a *triple* covalent bond, two atoms share three pairs, as they do in molecular nitrogen (N≡N). Each time you breathe in, a stupendous number of gaseous O_2 and N_2 molecules flows into your lungs.

In a *nonpolar* covalent bond, two identical atoms share electrons equally, and the molecule shows no difference in charge between its two ends. Molecular hydrogen (H_2) has such symmetry, as do O_2 and N_2.

A *polar* covalent bond forms between atoms of different elements. One of the atoms pulls the shared electrons a little toward one end of the bond. Because the electrons spend extra time there, that part of the molecule bears a slight negative charge. The opposite end bears a slight positive charge. A water molecule (H—O—H) has two polar covalent bonds; the oxygen is negatively charged, and the hydrogens are positive.

HYDROGEN BONDING

A hydrogen atom taking part in a polar covalent bond bears a slight positive charge, so it attracts negatively charged atoms. When the negatively charged atom is bound to a different molecule or to a different part of the same molecule, the interaction between it and the hydrogen atom is called a **hydrogen bond**.

Because they are weak, hydrogen bonds form and break easily. They play crucial roles in the structure and function of biological molecules, especially with water (Section 2.5). They often form between different parts of very large molecules that have folded over on themselves, and hold them in a particular shape. They are also what holds the two nucleotide strands of large DNA molecules together. You can get a sense of these interactions from Figure 2.8c.

Ions form when atoms acquire a net charge by gaining or losing electrons. Two ions of opposite charge attract each other. They can associate in an ionic bond.

In a covalent bond, atoms share a pair of electrons. When atoms share the electrons equally, the bond is nonpolar. When the sharing is not equal, the bond is polar—slightly positive at one end, slightly negative at the other.

In a hydrogen bond, a covalently bound hydrogen atom attracts a negatively charged atom taking part in a different covalent bond.

Read Me First!
and watch the narrated animation on how atoms bond

Two hydrogen atoms, each with one proton, share two electrons in a single nonpolar covalent bond.

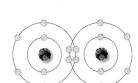

molecular hydrogen (H_2)
H—H

Two oxygen atoms, each with eight protons, share four electrons in a nonpolar double covalent bond.

molecular oxygen (O_2)
O=O

Oxygen has vacancies for two electrons in its highest energy level orbitals. Two hydrogen atoms can each share an electron with oxygen. The resulting two polar covalent bonds form a water molecule.

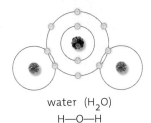

water (H_2O)
H—O—H

b Covalent bonding. Each atom becomes more stable by sharing electron pairs in hybrid orbitals.

Two molecules interacting weakly in one H bond, which can form and break easily.

H bonds helping to hold part of two large molecules together.

Many H bonds hold DNA's two strands together along their length. Individually they are weak, but collectively stabilize DNA's large structure.

hydrogen bond

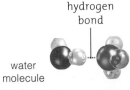

water molecule   ammonia molecule

c Hydrogen bonds. Such bonds can form at a hydrogen atom that is already covalently bonded in a molecule. The atom's slight positive charge weakly attracts an atom with a slight negative charge that is already covalently bonded to something else. As shown, this can happen between one of the hydrogen atoms of a water molecule and the nitrogen atom of an ammonia molecule.

2.5 Water's Life-Giving Properties

No sprint through basic chemistry is complete unless it leads to the collection of molecules called water. Life originated in water. Organisms still live in it or they cart water around with them inside cells and tissue spaces. Many metabolic reactions use water. Cell shape and cell structure absolutely depend on it.

POLARITY OF THE WATER MOLECULE

Figure 2.9*a* shows the structure of a water molecule. Two hydrogen atoms have formed polar covalent bonds with an oxygen atom. The molecule has no net charge. Even so, the oxygen pulls the shared electrons more than the hydrogen atoms do. Thus, the molecule of water has a slightly negative "end" that's balanced out by its slightly positive "end."

A water molecule's polarity attracts other water molecules. Also, it is so attractive to sugars and other polar molecules that hydrogen bonds readily form between them. That is why polar molecules are known as **hydrophilic** (water-loving) substances.

That same polarity repels oils and other nonpolar molecules, which are **hydrophobic** (water-dreading) substances. Shake a bottle filled with water and salad oil, then set it on a table. Soon, new hydrogen bonds replace the ones that the shaking broke. The reunited water molecules push out oil molecules, which cluster as oil droplets or as an oily film at the water's surface.

The same kinds of interactions occur at the thin, oily membrane between the water inside and outside cells. Membrane organization, and life itself, starts with hydrophilic and hydrophobic interactions. You'll be reading about membrane structure in Chapter 4.

WATER'S TEMPERATURE-STABILIZING EFFECTS

Cells are mostly water, and they also release a lot of metabolic heat. Without water's hydrogen bonds, cells would cook in their own juices. How? All molecules vibrate nonstop, and they move more as they absorb heat. **Temperature** is a measure of molecular motion. Compared to most other fluids, water absorbs more heat energy before it gets measurably hotter. So water acts as a heat reservoir, and its temperature remains relatively stable. In time, increases in heat step up the motion within water molecules. Before that happens, however, much of the heat will go into disrupting hydrogen bonds between molecules.

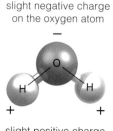

slight negative charge on the oxygen atom

The + and − ends balance each other; the whole molecule carries no net charge, overall.

slight positive charge on the hydrogen atoms

a

Figure 2.9 Water, a substance essential for life.

(**a**) Polarity of an individual water molecule.

(**b**) Hydrogen bonding pattern among water molecules in liquid water. Dashed lines signify hydrogen bonds, which break and reform rapidly.

(**c**) Hydrogen bonding in ice. Below 0°C, every water molecule hydrogen-bonds to four others, in a rigid three-dimensional lattice. The molecules are farther apart, or less dense, than they are in liquid water. As a result, ice floats on water.

Thanks partly to rising levels of methane and other greenhouse gases that are contributing to global warming, the Arctic ice cap is melting. At current rates, it will be gone in fifty years. So will the polar bears. Already their season for hunting seals is shorter, bears are thinner, and they are giving birth to fewer cubs.

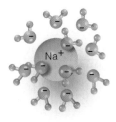

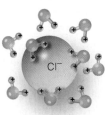

Figure 2.10 Two spheres of hydration.

Figure 2.11 Examples of water's cohesion. (**a**) When a pebble hits liquid water and forces molecules away from the surface, the individual water molecules don't fly off every which way. They stay together in droplets. Why? Countless hydrogen bonds exert a continuous inward pull on individual molecules at the surface.

(**b**) And just how does water rise to the very top of trees? Cohesion, and evaporation from leaves, pulls it upward.

a

b

With a fairly stable water temperature, hydrogen bonds form as fast as they break. Energy inputs can increase the molecular motion so much that the bonds stay broken, and individual molecules at the water's surface escape into air. By this process, **evaporation**, heat energy converts liquid water to a gas. An energy input has overcome the attraction between molecules of water, which break free. The surface temperature of water decreases during evaporation.

Evaporative water loss helps you and some other mammals cool off when you sweat on hot, dry days. Sweat, about 99 percent water, evaporates from skin.

Below 0°C, water molecules don't move enough to break their hydrogen bonds, and they become locked in the latticelike bonding pattern of ice (Figure 2.9c). Ice is less dense than water. During winter freezes, ice sheets may form near the surface of ponds, lakes, and streams. The ice blanket "insulates" the liquid water beneath it and helps protect many fishes, frogs, and other aquatic organisms against freezing.

WATER'S SOLVENT PROPERTIES

Water is an excellent *solvent*, meaning ions and polar molecules easily dissolve in it. A dissolved substance is known as a **solute**. In general, a substance is said to be *dissolved* after water molecules cluster around ions or molecules of it and keep them dispersed in fluid.

Water molecules cluster around a solute, thereby forming a *sphere of hydration*. Spheres form around any solute in cellular fluids, tree sap, blood, the fluid in your gut, and every other fluid associated with life. Watch it happen after you pour table salt (NaCl) into a cup of water. In time, the crystals of salt separate into ions of sodium (Na^+) and chloride (Cl^-). Each Na^+ attracts the negative end of some water molecules even as Cl^- attracts the positive end of others (Figure 2.10). Spheres of hydration formed this way keep the ions dispersed in fluid.

WATER'S COHESION

Still another life-sustaining property of water is its cohesion. **Cohesion** means something is showing a capacity to resist rupturing when it is stretched, or placed under tension. You see its effect when a tossed pebble breaks the surface of a lake, a pond, or some other body of liquid water (Figure 2.11a). At or near the surface, uncountable numbers of hydrogen bonds are exerting a continuous, inward pull on individual molecules. Bonding creates a high surface tension.

Cohesion is in play inside organisms, too. Plants, for example, absorb nutrient-laden water while they grow. Very narrow columns of liquid water rise inside pipelines of vascular tissues, which extend from roots to leaves and other plant parts. On sunny days, water evaporates from leaves as molecules break free and diffuse into the air (Figure 2.11b). The cohesive force of hydrogen bonds pulls replacements into the leaf cells, in ways you'll read about in Section 26.3.

> *Being slightly polar, water molecules hydrogen bond to one another and to other polar (hydrophilic) substances. They tend to repel nonpolar (hydrophobic) substances.*
>
> *The unique properties of liquid water make life possible. Water has cohesion, temperature-stabilizing effects, and a capacity to dissolve many substances.*

2.6 Acids and Bases

Ions are dissolved in fluids inside and outside a cell, and they affect its structure and function. Among the most influential are hydrogen ions. They have far-reaching effects largely because they are chemically active and there are so many of them.

THE PH SCALE

At any instant in liquid water, some water molecules split into ions of hydrogen (H^+) and hydroxide (OH^-). These ions are the basis of the **pH scale**. The scale is a way to measure the relative amount of hydrogen ions in solutions such as seawater, blood, or sap. The greater the H^+ concentration, the lower the pH. Pure water (not rainwater or tap water) always has as many H^+ as OH^- ions. This state is neutrality, or pH 7.0 (Figure 2.12).

A one unit decrease from neutrality corresponds to a tenfold increase in H^+ concentration, and an increase by one unit corresponds to a tenfold decrease in H^+ concentration. One way to get a sense of the range is to taste baking soda (pH 9), water (pH 7), and lemon juice (pH 2).

HOW DO ACIDS AND BASES DIFFER?

Substances called **acids** *donate* hydrogen ions and **bases** *accept* hydrogen ions when dissolved in water. *Acidic* solutions, such as lemon juice, gastric fluid, and coffee, release H^+; their pH is below 7. *Basic* solutions, such as seawater, baking soda, and egg white, combine with H^+. Basic solutions (also known as alkaline solutions) have a pH above 7.

Nearly all of life's chemistry occurs near pH 7. Most of your body's internal environment (tissue fluids and blood) is between pH 7.3 and 7.5. Seawater is more basic than body fluids of the organisms living in it.

Acids and bases can be weak or strong. The weak acids, such as carbonic acid (H_2CO_3), are stingy H^+ donors. Strong acids readily give up H^+ in water. An example is the hydrochloric acid that dissociates into H^+ and Cl^- inside your stomach. The H^+ makes your gastric fluid far more acidic, which in turn activates protein-digesting enzymes.

Too much HCl can cause an *acid stomach*. Antacids taken for this condition, including milk of magnesia, release OH^- ions that combine with H^+ to reduce the pH of stomach contents.

High concentrations of strong acids or bases can disrupt ecosystems and make it impossible for cells

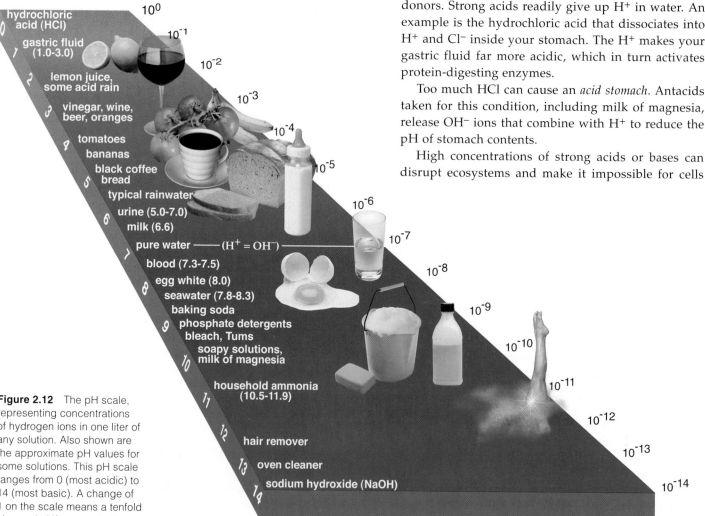

Figure 2.12 The pH scale, representing concentrations of hydrogen ions in one liter of any solution. Also shown are the approximate pH values for some solutions. This pH scale ranges from 0 (most acidic) to 14 (most basic). A change of 1 on the scale means a tenfold change in H^+ concentration.

Figure 2.13 Emissions of sulfur dioxide from a coal-burning power plant. Airborne pollutants such as sulfur dioxide dissolve in water vapor to form acidic solutions. They are a component of acid rain.

to survive. Read the labels on containers of ammonia, drain cleaner, and other products commonly stored in households. Many cause severe *chemical burns*. So does sulfuric acid in car batteries. Fossil fuel burning and nitrogen fertilizers release strong acids that lower the pH of rainwater (Figure 2.13). Some regions are quite sensitive to this *acid rain*. Alterations in the chemical composition of soil and water can harm organisms. We return to this topic in Section 42.2.

SALTS AND WATER

A **salt** is any compound that dissolves easily in water and releases ions *other than* H^+ and OH^-. It commonly forms when an acid interacts with a base. For example:

$$HCl \text{ (acid)} + NaOH \text{ (base)} \rightleftharpoons NaCl \text{ (salt)} + H_2O$$

HYDROCHLORIC ACID SODIUM HYDROXIDE SODIUM CHLORIDE

$$Na^+ \quad Cl^- \text{ (ionization)}$$

Bidirectional arrows indicate that the reaction goes in both directions. Many of the ions released when salts dissolve in fluid are important components of cellular processes. For example, ions of sodium, potassium, and calcium help nerve and muscle cells function and help plant cells take up water from soil.

BUFFERS AGAINST SHIFTS IN PH

Cells must respond fast to even slight shifts in pH, because excess H^+ or OH^- can alter the functions of biological molecules. Responses are rapid with **buffer systems**. Think of such a system as a dynamic chemical partnership between a weak acid or base and its salt. These two related chemicals work in equilibrium to counter slight shifts in pH. For example, if a small amount of a strong base enters a buffered fluid, the weak acid partner can neutralize the excess OH^- ions by donating some H^+ ions to the solution.

Most body fluids are buffered. Why? Enzymes, receptors, and all other essential biological molecules function properly only within a narrow range of pH. Deviation from the range halts cellular processes.

Carbon dioxide, a by-product of many reactions, combines with water in the blood to compose a buffer system of carbonic acid and bicarbonate ions. When blood pH rises a bit, the carbonic acid neutralizes the excess OH^- by releasing some hydrogen ions, which combine with the OH^- to form water:

$$OH^- + H_2CO_3 \longrightarrow HCO_3^- + H_2O$$

CARBONIC ACID BICARBONATE (SALT) WATER

When blood becomes more acidic, this salt mops up the excess H^+ and so shifts the balance of the buffer system toward the acid:

$$HCO_3^- + H^+ \longrightarrow H_2CO_3$$

BICARBONATE CARBONIC ACID

Buffer systems can neutralize only so many excess ions. With even a slight excess above that point, the pH swings widely. When the blood pH (7.3–7.5) falls even to 7, the individual may fall into a *coma*, an often irreversible state of unconsciousness. This happens in *respiratory acidosis*. Carbon dioxide accumulates, too much carbonic acid forms, and blood pH plummets. By contrast, when the blood pH increases even to 7.8, *tetany* may occur; skeletal muscles cannot be released from contraction. In *alkalosis*, a rise in blood pH can't be reversed. Such conditions can be lethal.

Ions dissolved in fluids on the inside and outside of cells have key roles in cell function. Acidic substances release hydrogen ions, and basic substances accept them. Salts are compounds that release ions other than H^+ and OH^-.

Acid–base interactions help maintain pH, which is the H^+ concentration in a fluid. Buffer systems help control the body's acid–base balance at levels suitable for life.

Summary

Introduction   Chemistry helps us understand the nature of all substances that make up cells, organisms, and the Earth, its waters, and the atmosphere. Table 2.1 summarizes some key chemical terms that you will encounter throughout this book.

Table 2.1	Summary of Important Players in the Chemical Basis of Life
ATOM	Fundamental form of matter that occupies space, has mass, and cannot be broken apart by ordinary physical or chemical means.
Proton (p^+)	Positively charged particle of the atomic nucleus.
Electron (e^-)	Negatively charged particle that can occupy a volume of space (orbital) around the nucleus.
Neutron	Uncharged particle of the atomic nucleus. For a given element, the mass number is the sum of the number of protons and neutrons in the nucleus.
ELEMENT	Type of atom defined by the number of protons, which is its atomic number. Each element has unique chemical properties.
MOLECULE	Unit of matter in which two or more atoms of the same element, or different ones, are bonded together by shared electrons.
Compound	Molecule composed of two or more different elements in unvarying proportions. Water is an example.
Mixture	Intermingling of two or more elements or compounds in proportions that vary.
ISOTOPE	One of two or more forms of an element that differ in the number of neutrons in their nuclei.
Radioisotope	Unstable isotope, having an unbalanced number of protons and neutrons, that emits particles and energy.
Tracer	Molecule of a substance to which a radioisotope is attached. Together with tracking devices, it is used to identify movement or destination of the substance in a metabolic pathway, the body, or some other system.
ION	Atom in which the number of electrons differs from the number of protons; negatively or positively charged. A proton without an electron zipping around it is a hydrogen ion (H^+).
SOLUTE	Any molecule or ion dissolved in some solvent.
Hydrophilic substance	Polar molecule or molecular region that can readily dissolve in water.
Hydrophobic substance	Nonpolar molecule or molecular region that strongly resists dissolving in water.
ACID	Substance that donates H^+ when dissolved in water.
BASE	Substance that accepts H^+ when dissolved in water.
SALT	Compound that releases ions other than H^+ or OH^- when dissolved in water.

Section 2.1   All substances consist of one or more elements. Ninety-two elements are naturally occurring. An atom consists of one or more positively charged protons, negatively charged electrons, and (except for hydrogen atoms) one or more uncharged neutrons. Protons and neutrons occupy the core region, or nucleus. In elements, all of the atoms have the same number of protons.

Section 2.2   Most elements have isotopes, which are two or more forms of atoms that have the same number of protons but different numbers of neutrons. An atom is radioactive when its nucleus is unstable. All elements have one or more radioactive isotopes.

Section 2.3   Whether an atom interacts with others depends on the number and arrangement of its electrons, which occupy orbitals (volumes of space) around the atomic nucleus. When an atom has one or more vacancies in orbitals at its highest energy level, it can interact with other atoms by donating, accepting, or sharing electrons.

Section 2.4   An atom may lose or gain one or more electrons and thus become an ion, which has a positive or negative charge.
Generally, a chemical bond is a union between the electron structures of atoms.
a. In an ionic bond, a positive ion and negative ion stay together by mutual attraction of opposite charges.
b. Atoms often share one or more pairs of electrons in covalent bonds. Electron sharing is equal in nonpolar covalent bonds, and it is unequal in polar covalent bonds. Interacting atoms have no net charge overall, even though the bond can be slightly negative at one end and slightly positive at the other.
c. In a hydrogen bond, one covalently bonded atom (e.g., oxygen) that has a slight negative charge is weakly attracted to the slight positive charge of a hydrogen atom taking part in a different polar covalent bond.

Section 2.5   Polar covalent bonds join together three atoms in a water molecule (two hydrogens and one oxygen). The water molecule's polarity invites extensive hydrogen bonding between molecules in bodies of water. Such bonding is the basis of liquid water's ability to resist temperature changes (more than other fluids do), display internal cohesion, and easily dissolve polar or ionic substances. These properties make life possible.

Section 2.6   The pH of a solution indicates its hydrogen ion concentration. A typical pH range is from 0 (highest H^+ concentration, most acidic) to 14 (lowest H^+ concentration, most basic). At pH 7, or neutrality, H^+ and OH^- concentrations are equal. Acids release H^+ ions in water; bases combine with them. Buffer systems help maintain a favorable pH in internal environments. This is important because most biological processes operate only within a narrow range of pH.

Self-Quiz

Answers in Appendix III

1. Is this statement true or false: Every type of atom consists of protons, neutrons, and electrons.

2. Electrons carry a _____ charge.
   a. positive   b. negative   c. zero

3. A(n) _____ is any molecule to which a radioisotope has been attached for research or diagnostic purposes.
   a. ion   c. element
   b. isotope   d. tracer

4. Atoms share electrons unequally in a(n) _____ bond.
   a. ionic   c. polar covalent
   b. hydrogen   d. nonpolar covalent

5. In a hydrogen bond, a hydrogen atom covalently bonded to one molecule weakly interacts with a _____ part of a neighboring molecule.
   a. polar   b. nonpolar   c. hydrophobic

6. Liquid water shows _____ .
   a. polarity   d. cohesion
   b. hydrogen-bonding capacity   e. b through d
   c. notable heat resistance   f. all of the above

7. Hydrogen ions (H^+) are _____ .
   a. the basis of pH values   d. dissolved in blood
   b. unbound protons   e. both a and b
   c. targets of certain buffers f. a through d

8. When dissolved in water, a(n) _____ donates H^+; however, a(n) _____ accepts H^+.

9. A(n) _____ is a dynamic chemical partnership between a weak acid and a weak base.
   a. ionic bond   c. buffer system
   b. solute   d. solvent

10. Match the terms with their most suitable description.
    ___ trace element   a. atomic nucleus components
    ___ salt   b. two atoms sharing electrons
    ___ covalent   c. any polar molecule that readily
    bond   dissolves in water
    ___ hydrophilic   d. releases ions other than H^+ and
    substance OH^- when dissolved in water
    ___ protons,   e. makes up less than 0.001
    neutrons   percent of body weight

Critical Thinking

1. By weight, oxygen is the most abundant element in organisms, ocean water, and Earth's crust. Predict which element is the most abundant in the whole universe.

2. *Ozone* is a chemically active form of oxygen gas. High in Earth's atmosphere, a vast layer of it absorbs about 98 percent of the sun's harmful rays. Normal oxygen gas consists of two oxygen atoms joined in a double nonpolar covalent bond: O=O. Ozone has three covalent bonds in this arrangement: O=O—O. It is highly reactive with a variety of substances, and it gives up an oxygen atom and releases gaseous oxygen (O=O). Using what you know about chemistry, explain why you think it is so reactive.

3. Some undiluted acids are less corrosive than when diluted with a little water. In fact, lab workers are told to wipe off splashes with a towel before washing. Explain.

4. Medieval scientists and philosophers called alchemists were the predecessors of modern-day chemists. Many of them tried to transform lead (atomic number 82) into gold (atomic number 79). Explain why they never succeeded.

5. David, an inquisitive three-year-old, poked his fingers into warm water in a metal pan on the stove and didn't sense anything hot. Then he touched the pan itself and got a nasty burn. Explain why water in a metal pan heats up far more slowly than the pan itself.

6. How do many insects, and the basilisk lizard shown in Figure 1.7, walk on water?

7. Why do you think H^+ is often written as H_3O^+?

Media Menu

Student CD-ROM

Impacts, Issues Video
   What Are You Worth?
Big Picture Animation
   Elements, bonding patterns, and pH
Read-Me-First Animation
   How atoms bond
Other Animations and Interactions
   The shell model of electron distribution
   Structure of water
   How salt dissolves
   The pH scale

InfoTrac
   • One-Molecule Chemistry Gets Big Reaction. *Science News*, September 2000.
   • What's Water Got to Do with It? *Astronomy*, August 2001.
   • Walking on Water. *Natural History*, April 2000.

Web Sites
   • Web Elements: www.webelements.com/
   • Chemistry Review: web.mit.edu/esgbio/www/chem/review.html
   • Water Science for Schools: ga.water.usgs.gov/edu/

How Would You Vote?
Fluoride has been proven to prevent tooth decay. However, a high intake of fluoride can discolor teeth, weaken bones, and cause birth defects. Really large amounts can kill you. Many communities in the United States add fluoride to their water supply. Do you want it added to yours?

IMPACTS, ISSUES *Science or the Supernatural?*

About 2,000 years ago, in the mountains of Greece, the oracle of Delphi delivered prophecies from Apollo after inhaling sweet-smelling fumes that had collected in the sunken floor of her temple. Her prophecies tended to be rambling and cryptic. Why? She was babbling in a hydrocarbon-induced trance. Geologists recently found intersecting, earthquake-prone faults under the temple. When the faults slipped, methane, ethane, and ethylene

methane

ethane

ethylene

Figure 3.1 *Left:* In Greece, ruins of the Temple of Apollo, where hydrocarbon gases seep from the earth. *Above:* The oracle at Delphi, believed to dispense cryptic advice direct from Apollo to people who, like her, had no knowledge of chemistry. The invisible, hallucinogenic fumes that induced her babblings are fancifully depicted in this painting.

the big picture

No Carbon, No Life Living cells build carbohydrates, lipids, proteins, and nucleic acids from simpler organic compounds. These large molecules of life have a backbone of carbon atoms with attached functional groups that help dictate their structure and function.

Carbohydrates Carbohydrates are the most abundant biological molecules. Simple types function as quick energy sources or transportable forms of energy. Complex types function as structural materials or energy reservoirs.

seeped out from the depths. All three gases are mild narcotics. The sweet-smelling ethylene can bring on hallucinations (Figure 3.1).

Ancient Greeks thought that Apollo spoke to them through the oracle; they believed in the supernatural. Scientists looked for a natural explanation, and they found carbon compounds behind her words. Why is their explanation more compelling? It started with tested information about the structure and effects of the world's substances, and it was based on analysis of three gaseous substances drawn from the site.

All three gases are nothing more than a few carbon and hydrogen atoms; hence the name, hydrocarbons. Thanks to scientific inquiry, we now know a lot about them. For example, we know that methane was present when Earth first formed. We know it is released when volcanoes erupt, when we burn wood or peat or fossil fuels, and when termites and cattle pass gas. Methane collects in the atmosphere and in ocean depths along the continental shelves. We also know methane is one of the greenhouse gases, which you will read about in Chapter 41, and that it is a contributing factor in global warming.

In short, knowledge about lifeless substances can tell you a lot about life. It will serve you well when you turn your mind to almost any topic concerning the past, present, and future—from Greek myths, to health and disease, to forests, and to physical and chemical conditions that span the globe and affect life everywhere.

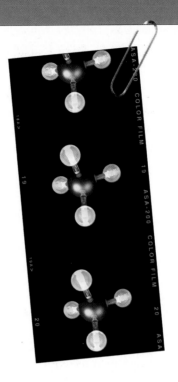

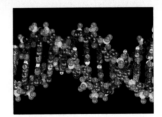 *How Would You Vote?*

Undersea methane deposits might be developed as a vast supply of energy, but the environmental costs are unknown. Should we continue to move toward exploiting this resource? See the Media Menu for details, then vote online.

Lipids

Certain lipids function as energy reservoirs, others as structural components of cell membranes, as waterproofing or lubricating substances, and as signaling molecules.

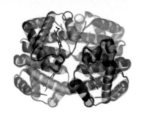

Proteins

Structurally and functionally, proteins are the most diverse molecules of life. They include enzymes, structural materials, signaling molecules, and transporters.

Nucleotides and Nucleic Acids

The nucleic acids DNA and RNA are made of a few kinds of nucleotide subunits. They store, retrieve, and translate genetic information that provides instructions for building proteins.

3.1 Molecules of Life—From Structure to Function

Under present-day conditions on Earth, only living cells can make complex carbohydrates and lipids, proteins, and nucleic acids. These are the molecules of life, and their structure holds clues to how each kind functions.

The molecules of life are **organic compounds**, which contain carbon and at least one hydrogen atom. They have a precise number of atoms arranged in specific ways. **Functional groups** are lone atoms or clusters of atoms that are covalently bonded to carbon atoms of organic compounds.

CARBON'S BONDING BEHAVIOR

Living things consist mainly of oxygen, hydrogen, and carbon. Most of the oxygen and hydrogen are in the form of water. Put water aside, and carbon makes up more than half of what's left.

Carbon's importance in life arises from its versatile bonding behavior. *Each carbon atom can covalently bond with as many as four other atoms.* Such bonds, in which two atoms share one, two, or three pairs of electrons, are relatively stable. They often join carbon atoms into "backbones" to which hydrogen, oxygen, and other elements are attached. The three-dimensional shapes of large organic compounds start with these bonds.

Methane, mentioned in the chapter introduction, is the simplest organic compound. It has four hydrogen atoms bonded covalently to a carbon atom (CH_4).

Figure 3.2*a* is a ball-and-stick model for glucose, an organic compound with hydrogen and oxygen bonded covalently to a backbone of six carbon atoms. Usually this backbone coils back on itself, with two carbons joined to form a ring structure (Figure 3.2*b*).

You can represent a carbon ring in different ways. A flat structural model may show the carbons but not the atoms bonded to it (Figure 3.2*c*).

We use insights into the structure of molecules to explore how cells and multicelled organisms function. For instance, virus particles can infect a cell if they dock at specific protein molecules of a cell membrane. Like Lego® blocks, membrane proteins have ridges, clefts, and charged regions that can match up with ridges, clefts, and charged regions of a protein at the surface of a virus particle.

a

b

c

Figure 3.2 Some ways of representing organic compounds. (**a**) Ball-and-stick model for glucose, linear structure. (**b**) Glucose ring structure. (**c**) Two kinds of simplified six-carbon rings.

FUNCTIONAL GROUPS

Functional groups, again, are either atoms or clusters of atoms that impart distinct properties to a molecule. The number, kind, and arrangement of functional groups influences structural and chemical properties of carbohydrates, lipids, proteins, and nucleic acids (Figure 3.3).

For example, hydrocarbons (organic molecules of only carbon and hydrogen atoms) are hydrophobic, or nonpolar. Fatty acids have chains of them, which is why lipids with fatty acid tails resist dissolving. Sugars, a class of compounds called alcohols, contain one or more polar *hydroxyl* (—OH) groups. Molecules of water quickly form hydrogen bonds with these groups; that is why sugars dissolve fast in water.

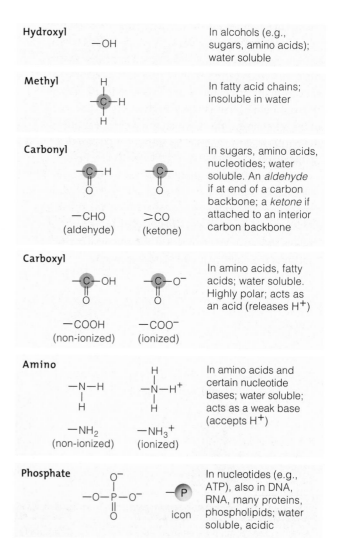

Figure 3.3 Common functional groups in the molecules of life, with examples of their chemical characteristics.

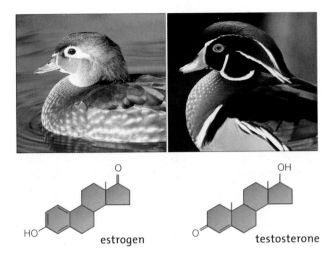

estrogen   testosterone

Figure 3.4 Observable differences in traits between female and male wood ducks (*Aix sponsa*), influenced by estrogen and testosterone. These two sex hormones have the same carbon ring structure. They differ only in the position of functional groups attached to the rings.

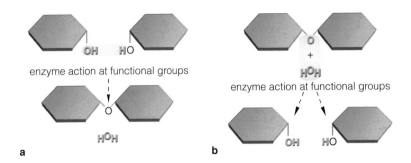

a   b

Figure 3.5 Two metabolic reactions with frequent roles in building organic compounds. (**a**) A condensation reaction, with two molecules being joined into a larger one. (**b**) Hydrolysis, a water-requiring cleavage reaction.

As another example, testosterone and estrogen are sex hormones. Both are remodeled versions of a type of lipid called cholesterol, and they differ slightly in their functional groups (Figure 3.4). That seemingly tiny difference has big consequences. Consider: Early on, a vertebrate embryo is neither male nor female; it just has a set of tubes that will slowly develop into a reproductive system. In the presence of testosterone, the tubes will become male sex organs, and male traits will develop. In the absence of testosterone, however, the tubes will become female sex organs that secrete estrogens. Those estrogens will guide the formation of distinctly female traits.

HOW DO CELLS ACTUALLY BUILD ORGANIC COMPOUNDS?

Cells build big molecules mainly from four families of small organic compounds: simple sugars, fatty acids, amino acids, and nucleotides. These compounds have two to thirty-six carbon atoms, at most. We refer to them as *monomers* when they are structural units of larger molecules. Molecules that contain repeating monomers are also known as polymers (*mono–*, one; *poly–*, many). As you will see shortly, starch can be considered a polymer of many glucose units.

How do cells actually do the construction work? At this point, just be aware that reactions by which a cell builds, rearranges, and splits apart all organic compounds require more than inputs of energy. They also require **enzymes**: proteins that make substances react faster than they would on their own. Different enzymes mediate the following classes of reactions:

1. *Functional-group transfer.* A functional group split away from one molecule is transferred to another.

2. *Electron transfer.* An electron split away from one molecule is donated to another.

3. *Rearrangement.* One type of organic compound is converted to another by a juggling of internal bonds.

4. *Condensation.* Covalent bonding between two small molecules results in a larger molecule.

5. *Cleavage.* A molecule splits into two smaller ones.

To get a sense of these cell activities, think of what happens in a **condensation reaction**. Enzymes split an —OH group from one molecule and an H atom from another. A covalent bond between the discarded parts forms H_2O (Figure 3.5a). Polymers such as starch form by repeated condensation reactions.

Another example: **Hydrolysis**, a type of cleavage reaction, is like condensation in reverse (Figure 3.5b). Enzymes split molecules at specific groups, then attach one —OH group and a hydrogen atom derived from water to the exposed sites.

Complex carbohydrates, complex lipids, proteins, and nucleic acids are the molecules of life.

Organic compounds have diverse, three-dimensional shapes and functions that arise from their carbon backbone and with functional groups covalently bonded to it.

Enzyme-mediated reactions build the molecules of life mainly from smaller organic compounds—simple sugars, fatty acids, amino acids, and nucleotides.

3.2 Bubble, Bubble, Toil and Trouble

Why include methane, a "lifeless" hydrocarbon, in a chapter on the molecules of life? Consider: Vast methane hydrate deposits beneath the ocean floor could explode at any time, as a colossal methane belch that could actually end life as we know it.

This story started long ago, when organic remains and wastes of countless marine organisms sank to the bottom of the ocean. Over time, more and more sediments accumulated above them. Today, a few kilometers under the seafloor, this organic collection nourishes methane-producing archaea. A tremendous amount of methane, the product of metabolic activity, bubbles upward and emerges into ocean water in places called *methane seeps* (Figures 3.6 and 3.7).

In the mud near seeps, methane pressure is high. There, unrelated microorganisms associate in tight clusters. Archaea inside the clusters use methane as

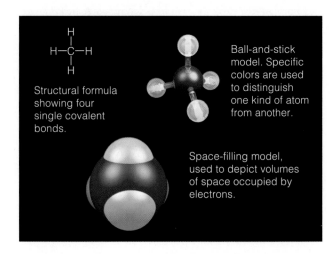

Structural formula showing four single covalent bonds.

Ball-and-stick model. Specific colors are used to distinguish one kind of atom from another.

Space-filling model, used to depict volumes of space occupied by electrons.

Figure 3.6 Molecular models for methane (CH_4). The ball-and-stick model is good for conveying bond angles and the distribution of a molecule's mass. The space-filling model is better for showing a molecule's surfaces.

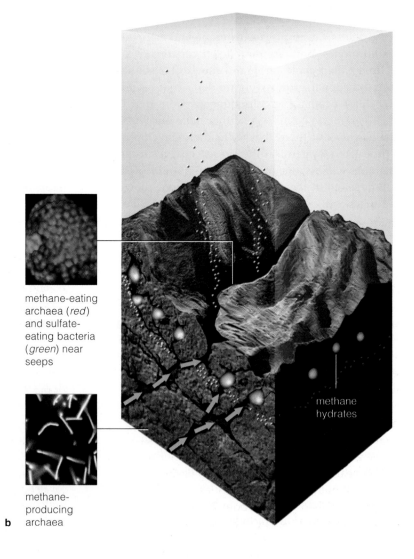

methane-eating archaea (*red*) and sulfate-eating bacteria (*green*) near seeps

methane-producing archaea

methane hydrates

Figure 3.7 (**a**) "Chimneys" of microorganisms and bubbles of methane gas almost 230 meters (750 feet) below sea level in the Black Sea.

(**b**) The seafloor methane cycle. Methane, formed by archaea far beneath the seafloor, seeps out through vents. Some is captured by clusters of microorganisms that release carbon dioxide and hydrogen sulfide as metabolic products. Other microbes use those products and become the basis of deep-sea food webs.

Figure 3.8 A blob of methane hydrate on the seafloor. Notice the methane bubbles above it.

Figure 3.9 *Lystrosaurus*, about a meter long. This animal is now extinct but made it through the Permian mass extinction.

an energy source, and carbon dioxide and hydrogen are released as wastes. In a remarkable metabolic handoff, bacteria that surround them immediately use the hydrogen. During the process they convert sulfate dissolved in seawater to hydrogen sulfide.

The allied organisms accomplish a chemical feat that neither would be capable of on its own. But this doesn't account for all of the methane produced by the underground archaea. What happens to the rest? At methane seeps, high water pressure and low temperature "freezes" the bubbling methane into an icy material called *methane hydrate* (Figure 3.8).

Recently, scientists discovered vast deposits of methane hydrate around the world. They estimate that a thousand billion tons of methane are frozen on the seafloor. The deposits actually are the world's largest reserve of natural gas, but we don't have a safe, efficient way to retrieve it.

Here's the problem. The icy crystals are unstable. Methane hydrate instantly falls apart into methane gas and liquid water as soon as the temperature goes up or the pressure goes down. It doesn't take much, only a few degrees. Methane hydrate disintegration can be explosive. It can cause an irreversible chain reaction that can vaporize neighboring deposits. We have physical evidence of ancient methane hydrate explosions. Small ones pockmarked the ocean floor; immense ones caused underwater landslides that stretched from one continent to another.

The greatest of all mass extinctions occurred 250 million years ago; it marked the end of the Permian period. All but about five percent of marine species abruptly vanished. So did about 70 percent of the known plants, insects, and other species on land.

Chemical clues locked in fossils point to a huge spike in the atmospheric concentration of carbon dioxide—not just any carbon dioxide, but rather carbon dioxide that had been assembled by living things. Something caused lots of methane hydrate to disintegrate at once. In an abrupt, gargantuan burp, millions of tons of methane exploded from the seafloor. Methane-eating bacteria quickly converted most of it to carbon dioxide, which displaced most of the oxygen in the atmosphere and ocean.

Too much carbon dioxide, too little oxygen. Just imagine being instantaneously transported to the top of Mount Everest and trying to jog in the "thin air," with its lower oxygen concentration. You would pass out and die. Before the Permian's Great Dying, oxygen made up about 35 percent of the atmosphere. After the burp, its concentration plummeted to 12 percent. Nearly all of the animals on land and in the seas probably suffocated.

For a long time, scientists couldn't figure out why *Lystrosaurus* didn't become extinct along with nearly everything else. Lucky *Lystrosaurus*. Someone finally figured out that this mammal-like reptile did not suffocate because it was already adapted to the stale, oxygen-poor air of its underground burrows. As Figure 3.9 indicates, *Lystrosaurus* had a big chest cavity, big lungs, stout ribs, and a short route for gas flow inside its stubby nostrils.

The methane problem is closer than you might think. Not long ago, huge methane hydrate deposits were discovered about 96 kilometers (60 miles) off the coast of Newport, Oregon, and off the Atlantic seaboard. What is to become of small-lunged, thin-ribbed people after another methane burp?

3.3 The Truly Abundant Carbohydrates

Which biological molecules are most plentiful in nature? Carbohydrates. Most consist of carbon, hydrogen, and oxygen in a 1:2:1 ratio. Cells use different carbohydrates as structural materials and transportable or storable forms of energy. Monosaccharides, oligosaccharides, and polysaccharides are the main classes.

THE SIMPLE SUGARS

"Saccharide" is from a Greek word that means sugar. The *mono*saccharides (one sugar unit) are the simplest carbohydrates. They have at least two —OH groups bonded to their carbon backbone and one aldehyde or ketone group. Most dissolve easily in water. Common types have a backbone of five or six carbon atoms that tends to form a ring structure when dissolved.

Ribose and deoxyribose are the sugar monomers of RNA and DNA, respectively; each has five carbon atoms. Glucose has six (Figure 3.10*a*). Cells use glucose as an energy source, a structural unit, or a precursor

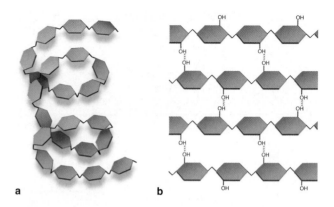

Figure 3.11 Bonding patterns for glucose units in (**a**) starch, and (**b**) cellulose. In amylose, a form of starch, a series of covalently bonded glucose units form a chain that coils. In cellulose, bonds form between glucose chains. The pattern stabilizes the chains, which can become tightly bundled.

(parent molecule) for other organic compounds, such as vitamin C (a sugar acid) and glycerol, an alcohol with three —OH groups.

SHORT-CHAIN CARBOHYDRATES

Unlike the simple sugars, an *oligo*saccharide is a short chain of covalently bonded sugar monomers. (*Oligo*– means a few.) The *di*saccharides consist of two sugar monomers. Sucrose, the most plentiful sugar in nature, contains a glucose and a fructose unit (Figure 3.10*b*). Lactose, a disaccharide in milk, has one glucose and one galactose unit. Table sugar is sucrose extracted from sugarcane and sugar beets. Many proteins and lipids have oligosaccharide side chains. Later in the book, you will come across chains with essential roles in self-recognition and immunity. You also will see how such chains are part of receptors that function in cell-to-cell communication.

COMPLEX CARBOHYDRATES

The "complex" carbohydrates, or *poly*saccharides, are straight or branched chains of many sugar monomers —often hundreds or thousands. Different kinds have one or more types of monomers. The most common polysaccharides are cellulose, starch, and glycogen. Even though all three are made of glucose, they differ a lot in their properties. Why? The answer starts with differences in covalent bonding patterns between their glucose units, which are joined together in chains.

In starch, the pattern of covalent bonding puts each glucose unit at an angle relative to the next unit in line. The chain ends up coiling like a spiral staircase

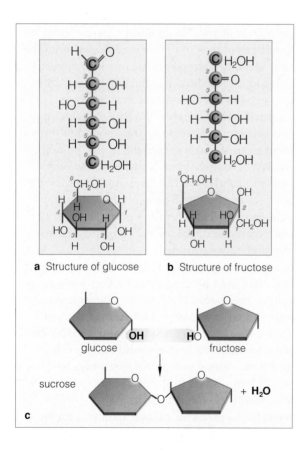

a Structure of glucose   **b** Structure of fructose

glucose   fructose

sucrose   + H₂O

c

Figure 3.10 (**a,b**) Straight-chain and ring forms of glucose and fructose. For reference purposes, carbon atoms of these simple sugars are numbered in sequence, starting at the end closest to the molecule's aldehyde or ketone group. (**c**) Condensation of two monosaccharides into a disaccharide.

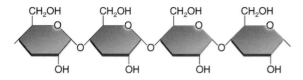

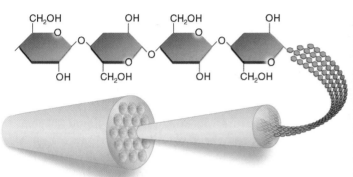

a Structure of amylose, a soluble form of starch. Cells inside tree leaves briefly store excess glucose monomers as starch grains in their chloroplasts, which are tiny, membrane-bound sacs that specialize in photosynthesis.

b Structure of cellulose. In cellulose fibers, chains of glucose units stretch side by side and hydrogen-bond at –OH groups. The many hydrogen bonds stabilize the chains in tight bundles that form long fibers. Few organisms produce enzymes that can digest this insoluble material. Cellulose is a structural component of plants and plant products, such as wood and cotton dresses.

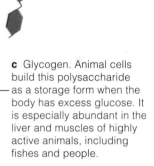

c Glycogen. Animal cells build this polysaccharide as a storage form when the body has excess glucose. It is especially abundant in the liver and muscles of highly active animals, including fishes and people.

Figure 3.12 Molecular structure of starch (**a**), cellulose (**b**), and glycogen (**c**), and their typical locations in a few organisms. All three carbohydrates consist only of glucose units.

(Figure 3.11*a*). Many —OH groups project outward from the coiled chains and make the chains accessible to certain enzymes. This is important. For example, plants briefly store their photosynthetically produced glucose in the form of starch. When free glucose is scarce, enzymes quickly hydrolyze the starch.

In cellulose, glucose chains stretch side by side and hydrogen-bond to one another, as in Figure 3.11*b*. This bonding arrangement stabilizes the chains in a tightly bundled pattern that can resist hydrolysis by most enzymes. Long fibers of cellulose are a structural part of plant cell walls (Figure 3.12*b*). Like steel rods in reinforced concrete, these fibers are tough, insoluble, and resistant to weight loads and mechanical stress, such as strong winds against stems.

In animals, glycogen is the sugar-storage equivalent of starch in plants (Figure 3.12*c*). Muscle and liver cells store a lot of it. When the sugar level in blood falls, liver cells degrade glycogen, and the released glucose enters blood. Exercise strenuously but briefly, and muscle cells tap glycogen for a burst of energy.

Figure 3.13 (*Right*) A tick's body covering is a protective cuticle reinforced with a polysaccharide called chitin (*below*). You may "hear" chitin when big spider legs clack across an aluminum oil pan on a garage floor.

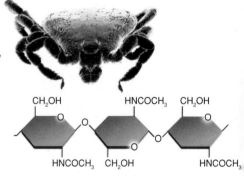

Chitin has nitrogen-containing groups attached to its glucose units. This polysaccharide derivative strengthens the external skeletons and other hard body parts of many animals, including crabs, earthworms, insects, spiders, and ticks of the sort shown in Figure 3.13. It also strengthens the cell walls of fungi.

The simple sugars (such as glucose), oligosaccharides, and polysaccharides (such as starch) are carbohydrates. Each cell requires carbohydrates as structural materials, and as storable or transportable packets of energy.

3.4 Greasy, Oily—Must Be Lipids

If something is greasy or oily to the touch, you can bet it's a lipid or has lipid parts. Cells use different lipids as energy packages, structural materials, and signaling molecules. Fats, phospholipids, and waxes have fatty acid tails. Sterols have a backbone of four carbon rings.

FATS AND FATTY ACIDS

Lipids are nonpolar hydrocarbons. Although they do not dissolve in water, they mix with other nonpolar substances, as butter does in warm cream sauce.

The lipids called **fats** have one, two, or three fatty acids attached to a glycerol molecule. A **fatty acid** has a backbone of as many as thirty-six carbon atoms, a carboxyl group at one end, and hydrogen atoms at most or all of the remaining carbons (Figure 3.14). They stretch out like flexible tails from the glycerol. *Unsaturated* fatty acids have one or more double bonds. *Saturated* types have single bonds only.

Weak interactions keep many saturated fatty acids tightly packed in animal fats. These fats are solid at room temperature. Most plant fats stay liquid at room temperature, as "vegetable oils." Their packing isn't as stable because of rigid kinks in their fatty acid tails. That's why vegetable oils flow freely.

Neutral fats such as butter, lard, and vegetable oils, are mostly **triglycerides**. Each has three fatty acid tails linked to a glycerol (Figure 3.15). Triglycerides are the most abundant lipids inside your body and its richest reservoir of energy. Gram for gram, they yield more than twice as much energy as complex carbohydrates such as starches. All vertebrates store triglycerides as droplets in fat cells that make up adipose tissue.

Layers or patches of adipose tissue insulate the body and cushion some of its parts. Like many other kinds of

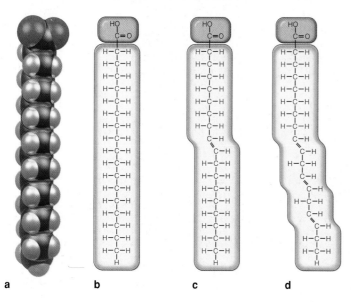

Figure 3.14 Three fatty acids. (**a**,**b**) Space-filling model and structural formula for stearic acid. The carbon backbone is fully saturated with hydrogen atoms. (**c**) Oleic acid, with a double bond in its backbone, is an unsaturated fatty acid. (**d**) Linolenic acid, also unsaturated, has three double bonds.

Figure 3.15 Condensation of (**a**) three fatty acids and one glycerol molecule into (**b**) a triglyceride. The photograph shows triglyceride-protected emperor penguins during an Antarctic blizzard.

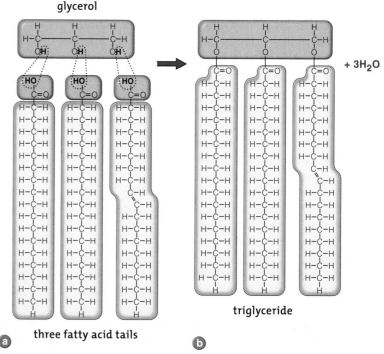

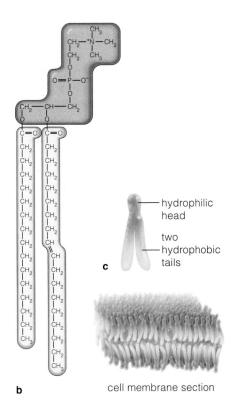

hydrophilic head

two hydrophobic tails

c

Figure 3.16 (**a**) Space-filling model, (**b**) structural formula, and (**c**) an icon for a phospholipid. This is the most common type in animal and plant cell membranes. Are its two tails saturated or unsaturated?

b

cell membrane section

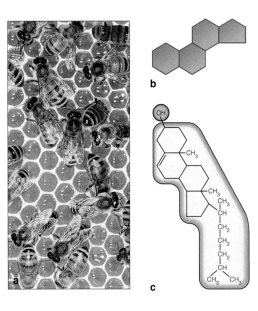

Figure 3.17 (**a**) Honeycomb: food warehouses and bee nurseries. Bees construct the compartments from their own water-repellent, waxy secretions. (**b**) Sterol backbone. (**c**) Structural formula for cholesterol, the main sterol of animal tissues. Your liver makes enough cholesterol for your body. A fat-rich diet may lead to clogged arteries.

animals, penguins of the Antarctic can keep warm in extremely cold winter months thanks to a thick layer of triglycerides beneath their skin (Figure 3.15).

PHOSPHOLIPIDS

Phospholipids have a glycerol backbone, two nonpolar fatty acid tails, and a polar head (Figure 3.16). They are a main component of cell membranes, which have two layers of lipids. The heads of one layer are dissolved in the cell's fluid interior; heads of the other layer are dissolved in the surroundings. Sandwiched between the two are the tails. You will read about membranes in Chapter 4.

WAXES

Waxes have long-chain fatty acids tightly packed and linked to long-chain alcohols or carbon rings. All have a firm consistency; all repel water. Surfaces of plants have a cuticle that contains waxes and another lipid, cutin. A plant cuticle restricts water loss and thwarts some parasites. Waxes also protect, lubricate, and lend pliability to skin and to hair. Birds secrete waxes, fats, and fatty acids that waterproof feathers. Bees use beeswax for honeycomb, which houses each new bee generation as well as honey (Figure 3.17a).

CHOLESTEROL AND OTHER STEROLS

Sterols are among the many lipids with no fatty acids. The sterols differ in the number, position, and type of their functional groups, but all have a rigid backbone of four fused-together carbon rings (Figure 3.17b).

Sterols are components of every eukaryotic cell membrane. The most common type in animal tissues is cholesterol (Figure 3.17c). Cholesterol also becomes remodeled into compounds as diverse as bile salts, steroids, and the vitamin D required for good bones and teeth. Bile salts assist in fat digestion in the small intestine. Sex hormones are vital for the formation of gametes and the development of secondary sexual traits. Such traits include the amount and distribution of hair in mammals, and feather color in birds.

Being largely hydrocarbon, lipids can intermingle with other nonpolar substances, but they resist dissolving in water.

Triglycerides, or neutral fats, have a glycerol head and three fatty acid tails. They are the major energy reservoirs. Phospholipids are a main component of cell membranes.

Sterols such as cholesterol serve as membrane components and precursors of steroid hormones and other compounds. Waxes are firm, yet pliable, components of water-repellent and lubricating substances.

3.5 Proteins—Diversity in Structure and Function

Of all large biological molecules, proteins are the most diverse. Some kinds speed reactions; others are the stuff of spider webs or feathers, bones, hair, and other body parts. Nutritious types abound in seeds and eggs. Many proteins move substances, help cells communicate, or defend against pathogens. Amazingly, cells assemble thousands of different proteins from only twenty kinds of amino acids!

An **amino acid** is a small organic compound with an amino group ($-NH_3^+$), a carboxyl group ($-COO^-$, the acid part), a hydrogen atom, and one or more atoms called its R group. In most cases, these components are attached to the same carbon atom (Figure 3.18a). Biological amino acids are shown in Appendix VI.

When a cell constructs a protein, it strings amino acids together, one after the other. Instructions coded

Read Me First!
and watch the narrated animation on peptide bond formation

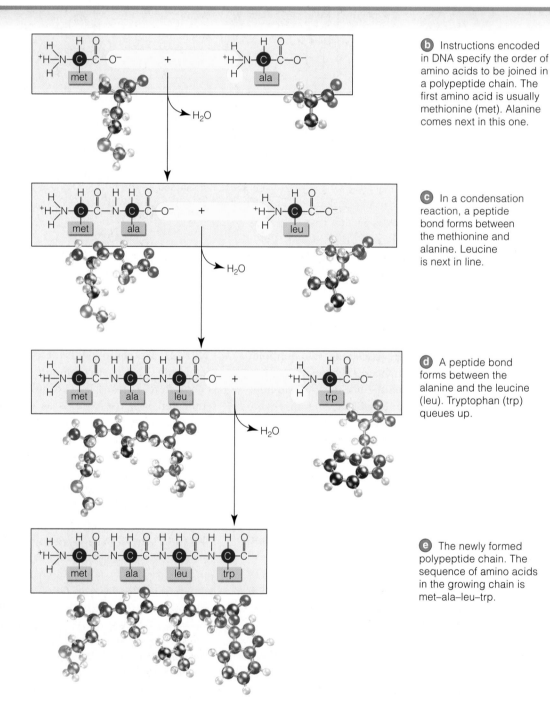

b Instructions encoded in DNA specify the order of amino acids to be joined in a polypeptide chain. The first amino acid is usually methionine (met). Alanine comes next in this one.

c In a condensation reaction, a peptide bond forms between the methionine and alanine. Leucine is next in line.

d A peptide bond forms between the alanine and the leucine (leu). Tryptophan (trp) queues up.

e The newly formed polypeptide chain. The sequence of amino acids in the growing chain is met–ala–leu–trp.

amino group   carboxyl group

R group (20 kinds, each with distinct properties)

a

Figure 3.18 (**a**) Generalized formula for amino acids. The green box highlights the R group, one of the side chains that include functional groups. (**b–e**) Peptide bond formation during protein synthesis. Chapter 13 provides a closer look at protein synthesis.

Figure 3.19 Three levels of protein structure. (**a**) Primary structure is a linear sequence of amino acids. (**b**) Many hydrogen bonds (dotted lines) along a polypeptide chain result in a helically coiled or sheetlike secondary structure. (**c**) Coils and sheets packed into stable domains represent a third structural level.

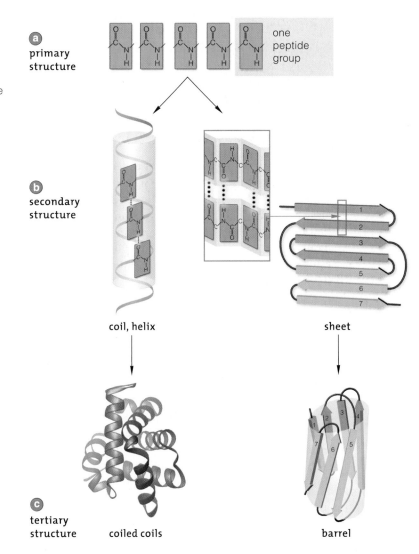

in DNA specify the order in which any of the twenty kinds of amino acids will occur in a given protein. A *peptide* bond forms as a condensation reaction joins the amino group of one amino acid and the carboxyl group of the next in line. Each **polypeptide chain** consists of three or more amino acids. The carbon backbone of this chain incorporates nitrogen atoms in this regular pattern: —N—C—C—N—C—C—.

The sequence of amino acids in a polypeptide chain is its *primary* structure. A new polypeptide chain twists, bends, loops, and folds, which is its *secondary* structure. Hydrogen bonds between R groups make some stretches of amino acids coil into a helical shape, a bit like a spiral staircase; they might make other regions form sheets or loops (Figure 3.19*b*). Bear in mind, the primary structure for each type of protein is unique in some respects, but similar patterns of coils, sheets, and loops do recur among them.

Much as an overly twisted rubber band coils back on itself, the coils, sheets, and loops of a protein fold up even more, into compact domains. A "domain" is a polypeptide chain or part of it that has become organized as a structurally stable unit. This third level of organization, a protein's *tertiary* structure, is what makes the protein a functional molecule. For instance, barrel-shaped domains of some proteins function as subway tunnels through membranes (Figure 3.19*c*).

Many proteins are two or more polypeptide chains that are bonded together or closely associated with one another. This is the fourth level of organization, or *quaternary* protein structure. Many enzymes and other proteins are globular, with multiple polypeptide chains folded into rounded shapes. Hemoglobin, described shortly, is a classic example of such a protein.

Protein structure doesn't stop here. Enzymes often attach short, linear, or branched oligosaccharides to a new polypeptide chain, making a *glyco*protein. Many glycoproteins occur at the cell surface or are secreted from cells. Lipids also get attached to many proteins. The cholesterol, triglycerides, and phospholipids that your body absorbs after a meal are transported about as components of *lipo*proteins.

Many proteins are fibrous, with polypeptide chains organized as strands or sheets. They contribute to cell shape and organization, and help cells and cell parts move about. Other proteins make up cartilage, hair, skin, and parts of muscles and brain cells.

A protein has primary structure, a sequence of amino acids covalently bonded as a polypeptide chain.

Local regions of a polypeptide chain become twisted and folded into helical coils, sheetlike arrays, and loops. These arrangements are the protein's secondary structure.

A polypeptide chain or parts of it become organized as structurally stable, compact, functional domains. Such domains are a protein's tertiary structure.

Many proteins show quaternary structure; they consist of two or more polypeptide chains.

3.6 Why Is Protein Structure So Important?

Cells are good at making proteins that are just what their DNA specifies. But sometimes a protein just turns out wrong. A different amino acid may lead to a misfolded shape that has far-reaching consequences.

JUST ONE WRONG AMINO ACID . . .

Four tightly packed polypeptides called globins make up each hemoglobin molecule. Each globin chain is folded into a pocket that cradles a **heme** group, a large organic molecule with an iron atom at its center (Figure 3.20a). Heme is an oxygen transporter. During its life span, each of the red blood cells in your body transports billions of oxygen molecules, all bound to the heme in globin molecules.

Globin comes in two slightly different forms, alpha and beta. Two of each form make up one hemoglobin molecule in adult humans. Glutamate is normally the sixth amino acid in the beta globin chain, but a DNA mutation sometimes puts a different amino acid—valine—in the sixth position instead (Figure 3.21b). Unlike glutamate, which carries an overall negative charge, valine has no net charge. As a result of that one substitution, a tiny patch of the protein changes from polar to nonpolar, which in turn causes the globin's behavior to change slightly. Hemoglobin with this mutation in its beta chain is designated HbS.

. . . AND YOU GET SICKLE-SHAPED CELLS!

Every human inherits two genes for beta globin, one from each of two parents. (Genes are units of DNA that encode heritable traits.) Cells use both genes when they make beta globin. If one is normal and the other has the valine mutation, a person makes enough normal hemoglobin and can lead a relatively normal life. But someone who inherits two mutant genes can only make the mutant hemoglobin HbS. The outcome is sickle-cell anemia, a severe genetic disorder.

As blood moves through lungs, the hemoglobin in red blood cells binds oxygen, then gives it up in body regions where oxygen levels are low. After oxygen is released, red blood cells quickly return to the lungs and pick up more. In the few moments when they have no bound oxygen, the hemoglobin molecules clump together just a bit. But HbS molecules do not form such clusters in places where oxygen levels are low. They form large, stable, rod-shaped aggregates.

Red blood cells containing these aggregates become distorted into a sickle shape (Figure 3.21c). The sickle cells clog tiny blood vessels called capillaries, which disrupts blood circulation. Tissues become oxygen-starved. Figure 3.21d lists the far-reaching effects of sickle-cell anemia on tissues and organs.

DENATURATION

The shape of a protein defines its biological activity. A globin molecule cradles heme, an enzyme speeds some reaction, a receptor transduces an energy signal. These proteins and others cannot function unless they stay coiled, folded, and packed in a precise way. Their shape depends on many hydrogen bonds and other interactions—which heat, shifts in pH, or detergents can disrupt. At such times, polypeptide chains unwind and change shape in an event called **denaturation**.

Consider albumin, a protein in the white of an egg. When you cook eggs, the heat does not disrupt the covalent bonds of albumin's primary structure. But it destroys albumin's weaker hydrogen bonds, and so the protein unfolds. When the translucent egg white turns opaque, we know albumin has been altered. For a few proteins, denaturation might be reversed if and when normal conditions return, but albumin isn't one of them. There is no way to uncook an egg.

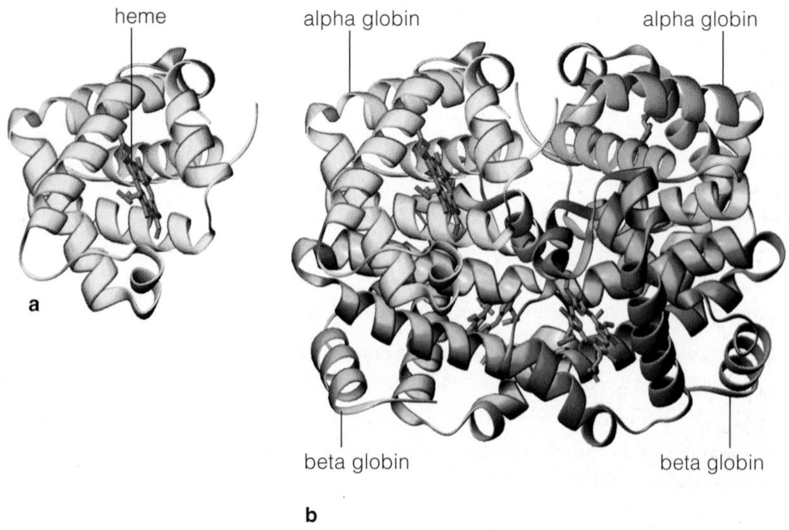

heme   alpha globin   alpha globin
beta globin   beta globin

a
b

Figure 3.20 (**a**) Globin. This coiled polypeptide chain cradles heme, a functional group that contains an iron atom. (**b**) Hemoglobin, an oxygen-transport protein in red blood cells. This is one of the proteins with quaternary structure. It consists of four globin molecules (two alphas and two betas) held together by hydrogen bonds.

Read Me First!
*and watch the narrated
animation on sickle-cell anemia*

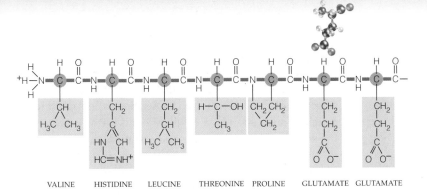

VALINE   HISTIDINE   LEUCINE   THREONINE   PROLINE   GLUTAMATE   GLUTAMATE

a Normal amino acid sequence at the start of a beta chain for hemoglobin.

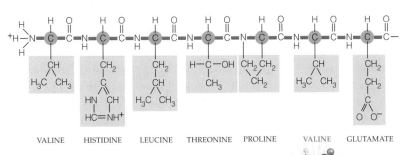

VALINE   HISTIDINE   LEUCINE   THREONINE   PROLINE   VALINE   GLUTAMATE

b One amino acid substitution results in the abnormal beta chain in HbS molecules. During protein synthesis, valine was added instead of glutamate at the sixth position of the growing polypeptide chain.

c Glutamate has an overall negative charge; valine has no net charge. This difference gives rise to a water-repellent, sticky patch on HbS molecules. They stick together because of that patch, forming rod-shaped clumps that distort normally rounded red blood cells into sickle shapes. (A sickle is a farm tool that has a crescent-shaped blade.)

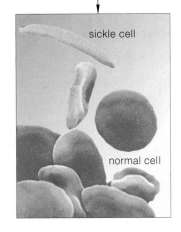

sickle cell

normal cell

Clumping of cells in bloodstream

↓

Circulatory problems, damage to brain, lungs, heart, skeletal muscles, gut, and kidneys

↓

Heart failure, paralysis, pneumonia, rheumatism, gut pain, kidney failure

Spleen concentrates sickle cells

↓

Spleen enlargement

↓

Immune system compromised

Rapid destruction of sickle cells

↓

Anemia, causing weakness, fatigue, impaired development, heart chamber dilation

↓

Impaired brain function, heart failure

d *Above left:* Melba Moore, celebrity spokesperson for sickle-cell anemia organizations. *Above right:* Range of symptoms for a person with two mutated genes (Hb^S) for hemoglobin's beta chain.

Figure 3.21 Sickle-cell anemia's molecular basis and its main symptoms. Sections 16.9 and 33.3 touch upon the evolutionary and ecological aspects of this genetic disorder.

So what is the big take-home lesson? Hemoglobin, hormones, enzymes, transporters—these are the kinds of proteins that help us survive. Twists and folds in their polypeptide chains form anchors, or membrane-spanning barrels, or jaws that can grip enemy agents in the body. Mutation can alter the chains enough to block or enhance an anchoring, transport, or defensive function. Sometimes the consequences are awful. Yet changes in the sequences and functional domains also give rise to variation in traits—the raw material of evolution. *Learn about the structure and function of proteins, and you are on your way to comprehending life in its richly normal and abnormal expressions.*

The structure of proteins dictates function. Mutations that alter a protein's structure can have drastic consequences on its function, and the health of organisms harboring them.

3.7 Nucleotides and the Nucleic Acids

Certain small organic compounds called nucleotides are energy carriers, enzyme helpers, and messengers. Some are the building blocks for DNA and RNA. They are, in short, central to metabolism, survival, and reproduction.

Nucleotides have one sugar, at least one phosphate group, and one nitrogen-containing base. Deoxyribose or ribose is the sugar. Both sugars have a five-carbon ring structure; ribose has an oxygen atom attached to carbon 2 of the ring and deoxyribose does not. The bases have a single or double carbon ring structure.

The nucleotide **ATP** (adenosine triphosphate) has a row of three phosphate groups attached to its sugar (Figure 3.22). ATP can readily transfer the outermost phosphate group to many other molecules and make them reactive. Such transfers are vital for metabolism.

Other nucleotides have different metabolic roles. Some are **coenzymes**, necessary for enzyme function. They move electrons and hydrogen from one reaction site to another. NAD⁺ and FAD are major kinds.

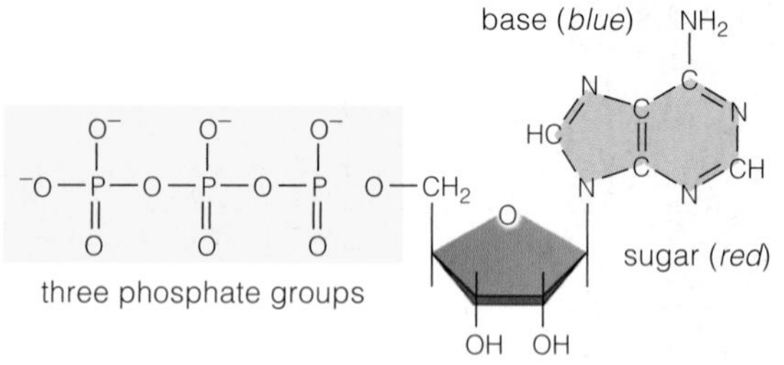

Still other nucleotides act as chemical messengers within and between cells. Later in the book, you will read about one of these messengers, which is known as cAMP (cyclic adenosine monophosphate).

Certain nucleotides also function as monomers for single- and double-stranded molecules called **nucleic acids**. In such strands, a covalent bond forms between the sugar of one nucleotide and the phosphate group of the next (Figure 3.23). The nucleic acids DNA and RNA store and retrieve heritable information.

All cells start out life and maintain themselves with instructions in their double-stranded molecules of deoxyribonucleic acid, or **DNA**. This nucleic acid is made of four kinds of deoxyribonucleotides. Figure 3.23*a* shows their structural formulas. As you can see, the four differ only in their component base, which is adenine, guanine, thymine, or cytosine.

Figure 3.24 shows how hydrogen bonds between bases join the two strands along the length of a DNA molecule. Think of every "base pairing" as one rung of a ladder, and the two sugar–phosphate backbones as the ladder's two posts. The ladder twists and turns in a regular pattern, forming a double helical coil.

The sequence of bases in DNA encodes heritable information about all the proteins that give each new cell the potential to grow, maintain itself, and even to reproduce. Part of that sequence is unique for each species. Some parts are identical, or nearly so, among many species. We return to DNA's structure and its function in Chapter 12.

base (*blue*)   NH₂

three phosphate groups

sugar (*red*)

Figure 3.22
Structural formula for an ATP molecule.

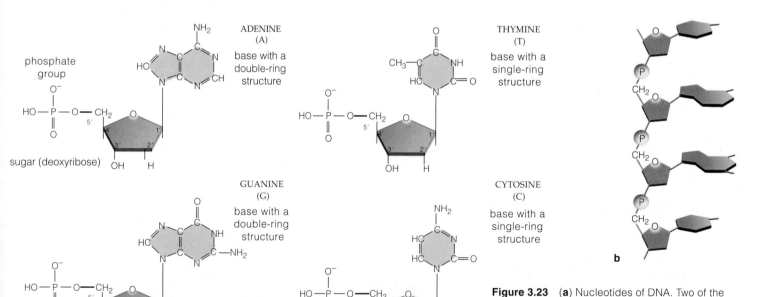

a

phosphate group

sugar (deoxyribose)

ADENINE (A)
base with a double-ring structure

GUANINE (G)
base with a double-ring structure

THYMINE (T)
base with a single-ring structure

CYTOSINE (C)
base with a single-ring structure

b

Figure 3.23 **(a)** Nucleotides of DNA. Two of the nucleotide bases, adenine and guanine, have a double-ring structure. The two others, thymine and cytosine, have a single-ring structure. **(b)** Bonding pattern between successive bases in nucleic acids.

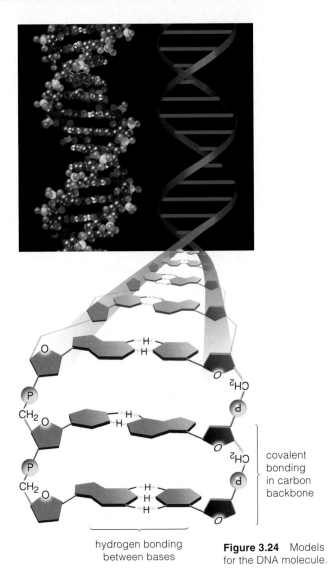

covalent bonding in carbon backbone

hydrogen bonding between bases

Figure 3.24 Models for the DNA molecule.

The **RNAs** (ribonucleic acids) have four kinds of ribonucleotide monomers. Unlike DNA, most RNAs are single strands, and one base is uracil instead of thymine. One type of RNA is a messenger that carries eukaryotic DNA's protein-building instructions out of the nucleus and into the cytoplasm, where they are translated by other RNAs. Chapter 13 returns to RNA and its role in protein synthesis.

Different nucleotides serve as coenzymes, subunits of nucleic acids, energy carriers, and chemical messengers.

The nucleic acid DNA consists of two nucleotide strands joined by hydrogen bonds and twisted as a double helix. Its nucleotide sequence contains heritable instructions about how to build all of a cell's proteins.

RNA is a single-stranded nucleic acid. Different RNAs have roles in the processes by which a cell retrieves and uses genetic information in DNA to build proteins.

Summary

Section 3.1 Organic compounds consist of carbon and at least one hydrogen atom. Carbon atoms bond covalently with up to four other atoms, often forming long chains or rings. Functional groups attached to a carbon backbone contribute to an organic compound's properties. Enzyme-driven reactions synthesize carbohydrates, proteins, lipids, and nucleic acids from smaller organic subunits. Table 3.1 on the next page summarizes these compounds.

Section 3.2 Methane gas produced by archaea far below the seafloor is partially metabolized by diverse microorganisms. Millions of tons of the remaining methane has become frozen into unstable, potentially explosive methane hydrate deposits on the seafloor.

Section 3.3 Carbohydrates include simple sugars, oligosaccharides, and polysaccharides. Living cells use carbohydrates as energy sources, transportable or storage forms of energy, and structural materials.

Section 3.4 Lipids are greasy or oily compounds that tend not to dissolve in water but mix easily with nonpolar compounds, such as other lipids. Neutral fats (triglycerides), phospholipids, waxes, and sterols are lipids. Cells use lipids as major sources of energy and as structural materials.

Section 3.5 Structurally and functionally, proteins are the most diverse molecules of life. Their primary structure is a sequence of amino acids—a polypeptide chain. Such chains twist, coil, and bend into functional domains. Many proteins, including hemoglobin and most enzymes, consist of two or more chains. Certain protein aggregates form hair, muscle, connective tissue, cytoskeleton, and other materials.

Section 3.6 A protein's overall structure determines its function. Sometimes a mutation in DNA results in an amino acid substitution that can drastically alter a protein. Such changes can cause genetic diseases, including sickle-cell anemia. Weak bonds that hold a protein's shape are disrupted by temperature, pH shifts, or exposure to detergent, and usually result in the protein unfolding permanently.

Section 3.7 Nucleotides consist of sugar, phosphate, and a nitrogen-containing base. They have essential roles in metabolism, survival, and reproduction. ATP energizes many kinds of molecules by phosphate-group transfers. Other nucleotides are coenzymes or chemical messengers. DNA and RNA are nucleic acids, each composed of four kinds of nucleotide subunits.

The sequence of nucleotide bases in DNA encodes instructions for how to construct all of a cell's proteins. Different kinds of RNA molecules interact in the translation of DNA's genetic information.

Table 3.1 Summary of the Main Organic Compounds in Living Things

Category	Main Subcategories	Some Examples and Their Functions	
CARBOHYDRATES . . . contain an aldehyde or a ketone group, and one or more hydroxyl groups	**Monosaccharides** (simple sugars) **Oligosaccharides** (short-chain carbohydrates) **Polysaccharides** (complex carbohydrates)	Glucose Sucrose (a disaccharide) Starch, glycogen Cellulose	Energy source Most common form of sugar; the form transported through plants Energy storage Structural roles
LIPIDS . . . are mainly hydrocarbon; generally do not dissolve in water but do dissolve in nonpolar substances, such as other lipids	**Lipids with fatty acids** *Glycerides:* Glycerol backbone with one, two, or three fatty acid tails *Phospholipids:* Glycerol backbone, phosphate group, one other polar group, and (often) two fatty acids *Waxes:* Alcohol with long-chain fatty acid tails **Lipids with no fatty acids** *Sterols:* Four carbon rings; the number, position, and type of functional groups differ among sterols	Fats (e.g., butter), oils (e.g., corn oil) Phosphatidylcholine Waxes in cutin Cholesterol	Energy storage Key component of cell membranes Conservation of water in plants Component of animal cell membranes; precursor of many steroids and vitamin D
PROTEINS . . . are one or more polypeptide chains, each with as many as several thousand covalently linked amino acids	**Fibrous proteins** Long strands or sheets of polypeptide chains; often tough, water-insoluble **Globular proteins** One or more polypeptide chains folded into globular shapes; many roles in cell activities	Keratin Collagen Enzymes Hemoglobin Insulin Antibodies	Structural component of hair, nails Structural component of bone Great increase in rates of reactions Oxygen transport Control of glucose metabolism Tissue defense
NUCLEIC ACIDS (AND NUCLEOTIDES) . . . are chains of units (or individual units) that each consist of a five-carbon sugar, phosphate, and a nitrogen-containing base	**Adenosine phosphates** **Nucleotide coenzymes** **Nucleic acids** Chains of thousands to millions of nucleotides	ATP cAMP (Section 20.8) NAD^+, $NADP^+$, FAD DNA, RNAs	Energy carrier Messenger in hormone regulation Transfer of electrons, protons (H^+) from one reaction site to another Storage, transmission, translation of genetic information

Self-Quiz

Answers in Appendix III

1. Name the molecules of life and the families of small organic compounds from which they are built.

2. Each carbon atom can share pairs of electrons with as many as _____ other atoms.
   a. one   b. two   c. three   d. four

3. Sugars are a class of _____ , which have one or more _____ groups.
   a. proteins; amino   c. alcohols; hydroxyl
   b. acids; phosphate   d. carbohydrates; carboxyl

4. _____ is a simple sugar (a monosaccharide).
   a. Glucose   c. Ribose   e. both a and b
   b. Sucrose   d. Chitin   f. both a and c

5. The fatty acid tails of unsaturated fats incorporate one or more _____ .
   a. single covalent bonds   b. double covalent bonds

6. Sterols are among the many lipids with no _____ .
   a. saturation   c. phosphates
   b. fatty acids   d. carbons

7. Which of the following is a class of molecules that encompasses all of the other molecules listed?
   a. triglycerides   c. waxes   e. lipids
   b. fatty acids   d. sterols   f. phospholipids

8. _____ are to proteins as _____ are to nucleic acids.
   a. Sugars; lipids   c. Amino acids; hydrogen bonds
   b. Sugars; proteins   d. Amino acids; nucleotides

9. A denatured protein has lost its _____ .
   a. hydrogen bonds   c. function
   b. shape   d. all of the above

10. Nucleotides occur in _____ .
   a. ATP   b. DNA   c. RNA   d. all are correct

11. Which of the following nucleotides is *not* found in DNA?
   a. adenine   b. uracil   c. thymine   d. guanine

12. Match the molecule with the most suitable description.
   _____ long sequence of amino acids   a. carbohydrate
   _____ a rechargeable battery in cells   b. phospholipid
   _____ glycerol, fatty acids, phosphate   c. polypeptide
   _____ two strands of nucleotides   d. DNA
   _____ one or more sugar monomers   e. ATP

Critical Thinking

1. In the following list, identify which is the carbohydrate, the fatty acid, the amino acid, and the polypeptide:

   a. $^+NH_3—CHR—COO^-$
   c. (glycine)$_{20}$

   b. $C_6H_{12}O_6$
   d. $CH_3(CH_2)_{16}COOH$

2. A clerk in a health-food store tells you that "natural" vitamin C extracts from rose hips are better than synthetic tablets of this vitamin. Given what you know about the structure of organic compounds, what would be your response? How would you design an experiment to test whether a natural and synthetic version of a vitamin differ?

3. It seems there are "good" and "bad" unsaturated fats. The double bonds of both put a bend in their fatty acid tails. But the bend in *trans* fatty acid tails keeps them aligned in the same direction along their whole length. The bend in *cis* fatty acid tails makes them zigzag (Figure 3.25).

   Some *trans* fatty acids occur naturally in beef. But most form by industrial processes that solidify vegetable oils for margarine, shortening, and the like. These substances are widely used in prepared foods (such as cookies) and in french fries and other fast-food products. *Trans* fatty acids are linked to heart attacks. Speculate on why your body might have an easier time dealing with *cis* fatty acids than *trans* fatty acids.

4. The shapes of protein domains often are clues to functions. For example, shown at left is an HLA, a type of recognition protein at the surface of vertebrate body cells. Certain cells of the immune system use HLAs to distinguish self (the body's own cells) from nonself. Each HLA has a jawlike region (*arrow*) that can bind and display nonself fragments, thus alerting the immune system to the presence of an invader or some other threat. Speculate on what may happen if a mutation caused the jawlike region to misfold.

5. Cholesterol from food or synthesized in the liver is too hydrophobic to circulate in blood; complexes of protein and lipids ferry it around. Low density lipoprotein, or *LDL*, transports cholesterol out of the liver and into cells. High density lipoprotein, or *HDL*, ferries the cholesterol that is released from dead cells back to the liver.

   High LDL levels are implicated in atherosclerosis, heart disease, and stroke. The main protein in LDL is called ApoA1, and a mutant form of it has the wrong amino acid (cysteine instead of arginine) at one location in its primary sequence. Carriers of this LDL mutation have very low levels of HDL, which is typically predictive of heart disease, but paradoxically they have no heart problems.

   Some heart patients received injections of the mutant LDL, which acted like a drain cleaner; it quickly reduced the size of cholesterol deposits in the patients' arteries.

   A few years from now, it might be possible to reverse years of damage with such treatment. However, many caution that a low-fat, low-cholesterol diet is still the best preventive measure for long-term health. Would you opt for artery-rooting treatments over a healthy diet?

cis fatty acid   *trans* fatty acid

Figure 3.25 Maybe rethink the french fries?

Media Menu

Student CD-ROM

Impacts, Issues Video
 Science or the Supernatural?
Big Picture Animation
 The chemistry of organic compounds
Read-Me-First Animation
 Peptide bond formation
 Sickle-cell anemia
Other Animations and Interactions
 Condensation and hydrolysis
 Triglyceride formation
 Structure of hemoglobin
 DNA structure

InfoTrac

- Sweet Medicines. *Scientific American*, July 2002.
- The Form Counts: Proteins, Fats, and Carbohydrates. *Consumers' Research Magazine*, August 2001.
- Sorting Fat from Fiction. *Prepared Foods*, October 2002.
- Proteins Rule. *Scientific American*, April 2002.

Web Sites

- General Chemistry Online: antoine.frostburg.edu/chem/senese/101/index.shtml
- The Molecules of Life: biop.ox.ac.uk/www/mol_of_life/index.html
- The Protein Data Bank: www.rcsb.org/pdb

How Would You Vote?

Huge methane reservoirs lie off the east coast of the United States and in arctic regions of North America. The environmental impact of disturbing the reserves is not known but might be significant. Yet using them could lessen our dependence on foreign oil. Should the government encourage use of these reserves for research and development?

IMPACTS, ISSUES   *Where Did Cells Come From?*

Do you ever think of yourself as being close to 1/1,000 of a kilometer tall? Probably not. Yet that's how we think of cells. We measure them in micrometers—in millionths of a millimeter, which is a thousandth of a meter, which is a thousandth of a kilometer. The bacteria in Figure 4.1 are a few micrometers "tall."

Somewhere in the distant past, between 3.9 billion and 2.5 billion years ago, cells no bigger than this first appeared on Earth. They were prokaryotic, meaning their DNA was exposed to the rest of their insides. They had no nucleus. At the time, the atmosphere had little free oxygen. The earliest cells probably extracted energy from their food by way of anaerobic reactions, which

don't use free oxygen. Plenty of food—simple organic compounds—had already accumulated in the environment through natural geologic processes.

By 2.1 billion years ago, in tidal flats and freshwater habitats, tiny cells were slowly changing the world. Vast populations were making food by a photosynthetic pathway that released oxygen as a by-product. At first, all of that oxygen combined with iron in rocks, forming rust. When oxygen saturated all of the exposed iron deposits on Earth, free oxygen became more and more concentrated in water, then in air.

Oxygen, a reactive gas, attacks organic compounds, including the ones making up cells. The oxygen-enriched

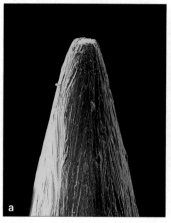

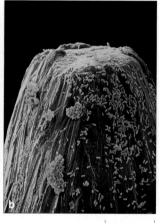
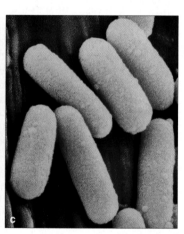

Figure 4.1 How small are cells? Shown here, bacterial cells peppering the tip of a household pin.

a   100 µm

b   20 µm

c   0.5 µm

the big picture

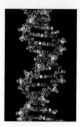

Basic Cell Features   Nearly all cells are microscopic in size. They all start out life with a plasma membrane, a semifluid interior called cytoplasm, and an inner region of DNA. The plasma membrane helps control the flow of specific substances into and out of cells.

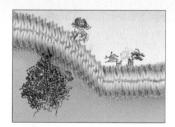

Cell Membrane Features   Two layers of phospholipid molecules are the structural basis of cell membranes. Proteins in this bilayer and those attached to its surfaces carry out many different membrane functions.

atmosphere became a selection pressure of global dimensions. Cell lineages that couldn't neutralize oxygen never left mud and other anaerobic habitats. In other lineages, though, mutations changed metabolic steps in ways that could neutralize oxygen, then *use* it. Aerobic respiration, an oxygen-requiring pathway, had emerged in most groups, and it proved handy in the growing competition for resources.

With so much oxygen around, the free organic compounds that were food for microorganisms became scarce. Compounds made by living cells became the sought-after sources of carbon and energy. Coinciding with this major change in available food sources, novel predators, parasites, and partners evolved. The first eukaryotic cells were among them.

The new cells ran reactions and stored things inside tiny sacs and other compartments made of membranes. One sac, the nucleus, controlled access to their DNA. Others, called mitochondria, yielded far more energy from metabolism than anaerobic reactions, enough to power more active life-styles and build larger, more complex bodies. Without such innovations in small cells, big plants and animals never would have evolved.

This chapter introduces the key defining features of prokaryotic and eukaryotic cells. It invites you to reflect on the earliest, simplest ancestors of you and all other eukaryotic forms of life. Why bother? Science is close to *creating* simple forms of life in test tubes. A bioethical line is about to be crossed.

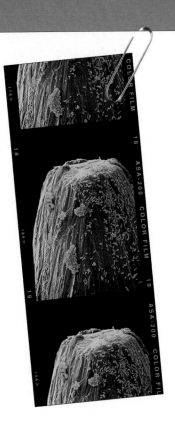

 How Would You Vote?

Researchers are modifying prokaryotes in efforts to make the simplest form of life possible. They are creating "new" organisms by removing genes one at a time. Should this research continue? See the Media Menu for details, then vote online.

Prokaryotic Cells Compared to eukaryotic cells, prokaryotes have little internal complexity, and no nucleus. However, when taken as a group, they are the most metabolically diverse organisms. All species have prokaryotic ancestors.

Eukaryotic Cells Eukaryotic cells contain organelles. These membrane-bound compartments divide the cell interior into functional regions for specialized tasks. A major organelle, the nucleus, keeps the DNA away from cytoplasmic machinery.

4.1 So What Is "A Cell"?

Inside your body and at all of its moist surfaces, many trillions of cells live in interdependency. In northern forests, four-celled structures called pollen grains drift down from pine trees. In scummy pond water, free-living single cells called bacteria and amoebas move about. How are these cells alike, and how do they differ?

COMPONENTS OF ALL CELLS

The **cell** is the smallest unit with the properties of life: a capacity for metabolism, controlled responses to the environment, growth, and reproduction. Cells differ in size, shape, and activities, yet are alike in three respects. They start out life with a plasma membrane, a region of DNA, and cytoplasm (Figure 4.2):

1. **Plasma membrane**. A thin, outermost membrane maintains a cell as a distinct entity. It lets metabolic events proceed in controllable ways, separated from the outside environment. Yet this plasma membrane does not isolate the cell interior. It's a bit like a house with many windows and doors that don't open for just anyone. Water, oxygen, and carbon dioxide cross in and out freely. Other substances, such as nutrients and ions, get escorted across.

2. **Nucleus** or **nucleoid**. DNA occupies a membrane-bound sac (nucleus) inside the cell or, in the simplest kinds of cells, a nucleoid (part of the cytoplasm).

3. **Cytoplasm**. Cytoplasm is everything between the plasma membrane and the region of DNA. It consists of a semifluid matrix and other components, such as **ribosomes**, the structures on which proteins are built.

In structural terms, prokaryotes are the simplest cells; nothing separates their DNA from the cytoplasm. Bacteria and archaea are the only prokaryotes. All other organisms—from amoebas and trees to puffball mushrooms and elephants—are eukaryotic. Internal membranes divide the cytoplasm of eukaryotic cells into functional compartments. One compartment, the nucleus, is the key defining feature of these cells.

WHY AREN'T CELLS BIGGER?

Can any cells be observed with the unaided eye? Just a few types can. They include "yolks" of bird eggs, cells in watermelon tissues, and fish eggs. These get big because they aren't doing much, metabolically speaking, at maturity. Most metabolically active cells are too tiny to be seen by the unaided eye (Figure 4.3).

So why aren't all cells big? A physical relationship called the **surface-to-volume ratio** constrains increases in cell size. By this relationship, an object's volume increases with the cube of its diameter, but the surface area increases only with the square.

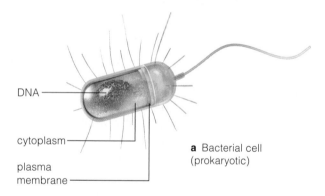

DNA

cytoplasm

plasma membrane

a Bacterial cell (prokaryotic)

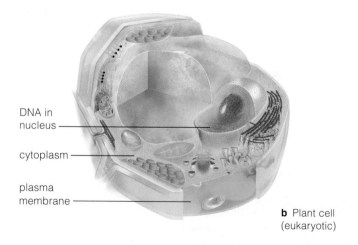

DNA in nucleus

cytoplasm

plasma membrane

b Plant cell (eukaryotic)

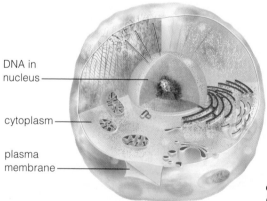

DNA in nucleus

cytoplasm

plasma membrane

c Animal cell (eukaryotic)

Figure 4.2 Overview of the general organization of prokaryotic cells and eukaryotic cells. The three cells are not drawn to the same scale.

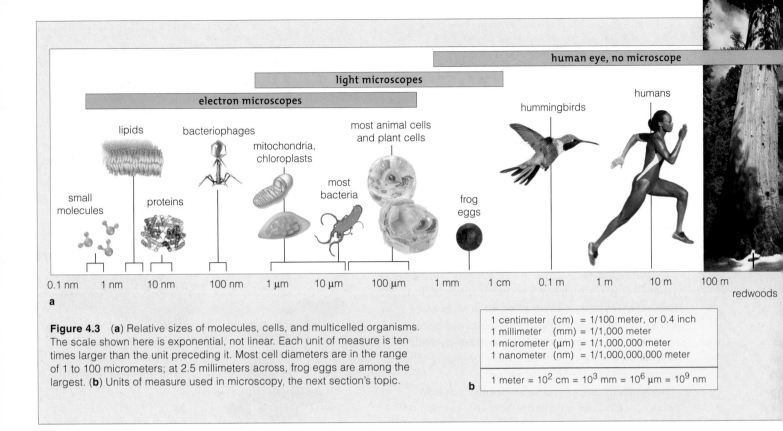

Figure 4.3 **(a)** Relative sizes of molecules, cells, and multicelled organisms. The scale shown here is exponential, not linear. Each unit of measure is ten times larger than the unit preceding it. Most cell diameters are in the range of 1 to 100 micrometers; at 2.5 millimeters across, frog eggs are among the largest. **(b)** Units of measure used in microscopy, the next section's topic.

1 centimeter (cm)	= 1/100 meter, or 0.4 inch
1 millimeter (mm)	= 1/1,000 meter
1 micrometer (µm)	= 1/1,000,000 meter
1 nanometer (nm)	= 1/1,000,000,000 meter

$1 \text{ meter} = 10^2 \text{ cm} = 10^3 \text{ mm} = 10^6 \text{ µm} = 10^9 \text{ nm}$

diameter (cm):	0.5	1.0	1.5
surface area (cm^2):	0.79	3.14	7.07
volume (cm^3):	0.06	0.52	1.77
surface-to-volume ratio:	13.17:1	6.04:1	3.99:1

Figure 4.4 One example of the surface-to-volume ratio. This physical relationship between increases in volume and surface area puts constraints on cell sizes and shapes.

Apply this constraint to a round cell. As Figure 4.4 shows, *if a cell expands in diameter during growth, then its volume will increase faster than its surface area does.* Suppose you induce a round cell to grow four times wider. Its volume increases 64 times (4^3). However, its surface area increases only 16 times (4^2). This means each unit of plasma membrane must service four times as much cytoplasm as before. A lot more substances have to get in and out!

If a cell's diameter is too great, the inward flow of nutrients and the outward flow of wastes just won't be fast enough to keep up with metabolic activity, and you'll end up with a dead cell.

A big, round cell also would have trouble moving materials throughout its cytoplasm. Random motions of molecules distribute materials through tiny cells. If a cell isn't tiny, you can expect it to be long or thin, or have outfoldings or infoldings that increase its surface relative to its volume. *The smaller or narrower or more frilly-surfaced the cell, the more efficiently materials cross its surface and become distributed through the interior.*

Surface-to-volume constraints also shape the body plans of multicelled species. For example, small cells attach end to end in strandlike algae, so each interacts directly with its surroundings. Cells in your muscles are as long as the muscle itself, but each one is thin enough to facilitate diffusion.

All living cells have an outermost plasma membrane, an internal region called cytoplasm, and an internal region where DNA is concentrated.

Bacteria and archaea are prokaryotic cells. Unlike eukaryotic cells, they do not have a nucleus.

As cells grow, their volume increases faster than their surface area. A surface-to-volume ratio is a physical relationship that affects metabolic activity, and thus constrains cell size. It also constrains cell shape and body plans of multicelled organisms.

4.2 How Do We "See" Cells?

Like their centuries-old forerunners, modern microscopes are our best windows on the cellular world.

THE CELL THEORY

Early in the seventeenth century, Galileo Galilei put two glass lenses inside a cylinder and peered at the patterns of an insect's eyes. He was one of the first to record a biological observation with a microscope. The study of the cellular basis of life was about to begin, first in Italy, then in France and England.

At midcentury, Robert Hooke focused a microscope on thinly sliced cork from a mature tree and saw tiny compartments (Figure 4.5). He gave them the Latin name *cellulae*, meaning small rooms—hence the origin of the biological term "cell." They actually were dead plant cell walls, which is what cork is made of, but Hooke didn't think of them as being dead because neither he nor anyone else knew cells could be alive.

Antony van Leeuwenhoek, a shopkeeper, made exceptional lenses. By the late 1600s, he was spying on sperm, protists, even a bacterium.

In the 1820s, improved lenses brought cells into sharper focus. Robert Brown, a botanist, saw an opaque spot in cells and called it a nucleus. Later, the botanist Matthias Schleiden wondered if a plant cell develops as an independent unit even though it's part of the plant. By 1839, after years of studying animal tissues, the zoologist Theodor Schwann reported that cells and cell products make up animals as well as plants—and that cells have an individual life of their own even when they are part of a multicelled species.

Rudolf Virchow, a physiologist, completed his own studies of a cell's growth and reproduction—that is, its division into daughter cells. Every cell, he decided, comes from a cell that already exists.

And so, microscopic analysis yielded three generalizations, which constitute the **cell theory**. *First*, every organism consists of one or more cells. *Second*, the cell is the smallest unit that still displays the properties of life. *Third*, the continuity of life arises directly

Figure 4.5 Robert Hooke's microscope and his drawing of cell walls from cork tissue.

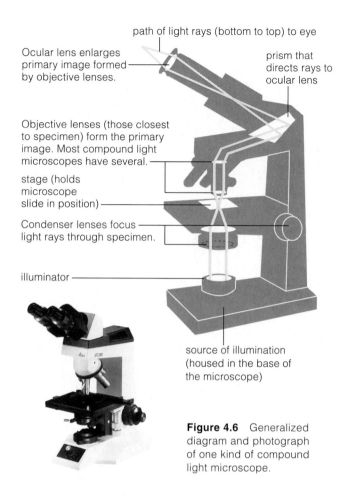

path of light rays (bottom to top) to eye

Ocular lens enlarges primary image formed by objective lenses.

prism that directs rays to ocular lens

Objective lenses (those closest to specimen) form the primary image. Most compound light microscopes have several.

stage (holds microscope slide in position)

Condenser lenses focus light rays through specimen.

illuminator

source of illumination (housed in the base of the microscope)

Figure 4.6 Generalized diagram and photograph of one kind of compound light microscope.

from the growth and division of single cells. Today, microscopy still supports all three insights.

SOME MODERN MICROSCOPES

Like the earlier instruments, many microscopes still use light rays to make images. Picture a series of waves moving across an ocean. Each **wavelength** is the distance from one wave's peak to the peak of the wave behind it. Light also travels in waves as it moves. In a *compound light microscope* (Figure 4.6), two or more sets of glass lenses bend light waves passing through a cell or some other specimen in ways that form an enlarged view of it.

Cells are visible under the microscope when they are thin enough for light to pass through them, but most are nearly colorless and look uniformly dense. Some colored dyes stain cells nonuniformly, and are used to make their components visible.

The best light microscopes can enlarge cells up to 2,000 times. Beyond that, cell parts appear larger but not clearer. Why? Parts that are smaller than one-half

Figure 4.7 Generalized diagram of an electron microscope.

You can get an idea of the diameter of the lenses from this photograph of a transmission electron microscope (TEM). A beam of electrons from an electron gun moves down the microscope column and is focused by magnets.

In transmission electron microscopy, electrons pass through a thin slice of specimen, then illuminate a fluorescent screen on the monitor. The shadows cast by the specimen's internal details appear, as in Figure 4.8c.

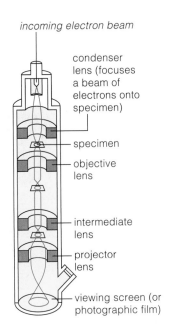

incoming electron beam

condenser lens (focuses a beam of electrons onto specimen)

specimen

objective lens

intermediate lens

projector lens

viewing screen (or photographic film)

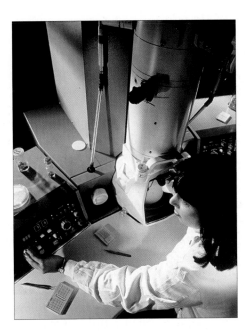

of a wavelength of light are too small to make light bend, so they don't show up.

Electron microscopes use magnetic lenses to bend and focus beams of electrons, which can't be focused through a glass lens (Figure 4.7). Electrons travel in wavelengths that are about 100,000 times shorter than those of visible light. That is why an electron microscope can bring into focus objects 100,000 times smaller than you can see with a light microscope.

In a *transmission* electron microscope, electrons pass through a sample and are focused into an image of the specimen's internal details (Figure 4.8c). In *scanning* electron microscopes, a beam of electrons moves back and forth across a specimen that has a thin coating of metal. The metal responds by emitting its own electrons and x-rays, which can be converted into an image of the surface. The images can have fantastic detail. Figure 4.8d shows an example.

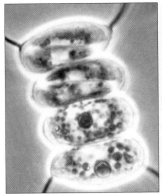  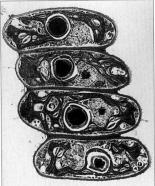 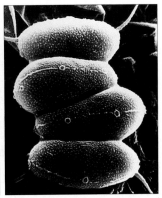

10 µm

a Light micrograph (phase-contrast process)

b Light micrograph (Nomarski process)

c Transmission electron micrograph, thin section

d Scanning electron micrograph

Figure 4.8 How different microscopes reveal different aspects of the same organism—a green alga (*Scenedesmus*). All four images are at the same magnification. (**a**,**b**) Light micrographs. (**c**) Transmission electron micrograph. (**d**) Scanning electron micrograph. A horizontal bar below a micrograph, as in (**d**), provides a visual reference for size. One micrometer (µm) is 1/1,000,000 of 1 meter. Using the scale bar, can you estimate the length and width of a *Scenedesmus* cell?

4.3 All Living Cells Have Membranes

Cell membranes consist of a lipid bilayer in which many different kinds of proteins are embedded. The membrane is a continuous boundary layer across which the flow of substances is selectively controlled.

Think back on the phospholipids, the most abundant components of cell membranes (Section 3.4). Each has one phosphate-containing head and two fatty acid tails attached to a glycerol backbone (Figure 4.9*a*). The head is hydrophilic; it dissolves fast in water. The two tails are hydrophobic; water repels them.

When you immerse many phospholipid molecules in water, they interact with water molecules and with one another until they spontaneously cluster into a sheet or film at the water's surface. Some even line up as two layers, with their fatty acid tails sandwiched between their outward-facing hydrophilic heads. This arrangement, called a **lipid bilayer**, is the structural basis of every cell membrane (Figure 4.9*b,c*).

Figure 4.10 shows the **fluid mosaic model**. By this model, a cell membrane has a mixed composition—a

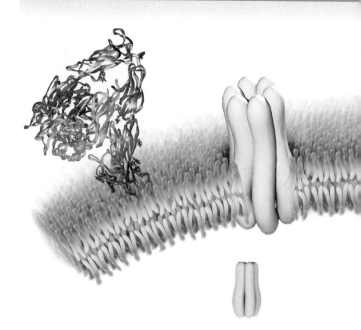

adhesion proteins

Adhesion proteins project outward from plasma membranes of multicelled species especially. They help cells of the same type stick together in the proper tissues.

communication proteins

Communication proteins of two adjoining cells match up, forming a direct channel between their cytoplasms. Signals flow through the channel. This channel is part of a gap junction between two heart muscle cells.

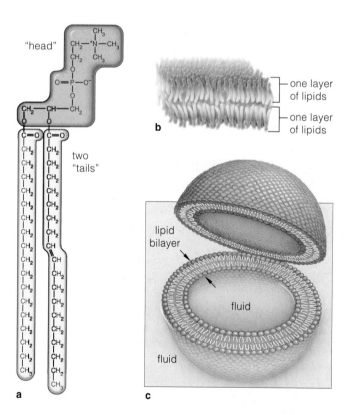

Figure 4.9 Lipid bilayer organization of cell membranes. (**a**) One of the phospholipids, the most abundant membrane components. (**b**,**c**) These lipids and others are arranged as two layers. Their hydrophobic tails are sandwiched between their hydrophilic heads in the bilayer.

mosaic—of phospholipids, glycolipids, sterols, and proteins. Its phospholipids are diverse, with different kinds of heads and with tails that vary in length and saturation. Unsaturated fatty acids have one or more double covalent bonds in their carbon backbone, and fully saturated fatty acids have none (Section 3.4).

Also by this model, a membrane is *fluid* because of the motions and interactions of its components. Most phospholipids drift sideways, spin on their long axes, and flex their tails, so they don't bunch up as a solid layer. Most membrane phospholipids have at least one kinked (unsaturated) fatty acid tail.

Hydrogen bonds and other weak interactions help proteins associate with the phospholipids. Many of the membrane proteins span the bilayer, with hydrophilic parts extending past both of its surfaces. Others are anchored to underlying cell structures.

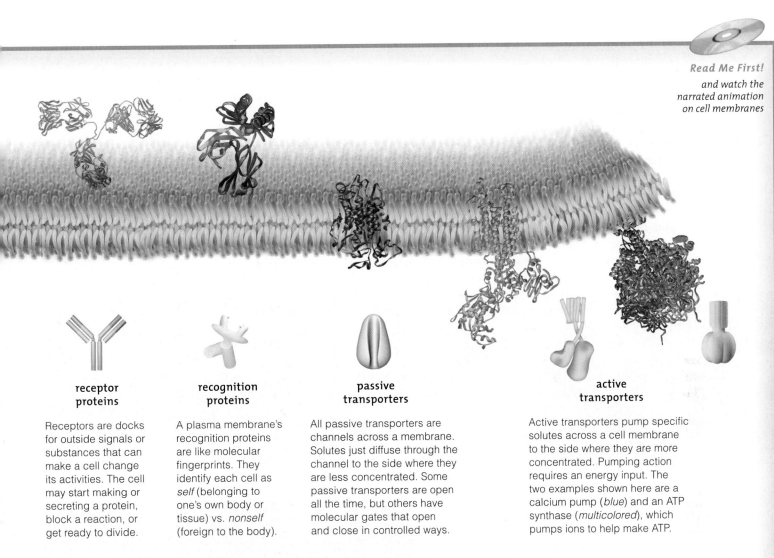

Read Me First!

*and watch the
narrated animation
on cell membranes*

**receptor
proteins**

Receptors are docks
for outside signals or
substances that can
make a cell change
its activities. The cell
may start making or
secreting a protein,
block a reaction, or
get ready to divide.

**recognition
proteins**

A plasma membrane's
recognition proteins
are like molecular
fingerprints. They
identify each cell as
self (belonging to
one's own body or
tissue) vs. *nonself*
(foreign to the body).

**passive
transporters**

All passive transporters are
channels across a membrane.
Solutes just diffuse through the
channel to the side where they
are less concentrated. Some
passive transporters are open
all the time, but others have
molecular gates that open
and close in controlled ways.

**active
transporters**

Active transporters pump specific
solutes across a cell membrane
to the side where they are more
concentrated. Pumping action
requires an energy input. The
two examples shown here are a
calcium pump (*blue*) and an ATP
synthase (*multicolored*), which
pumps ions to help make ATP.

Figure 4.10 Part of a plasma membrane. It consists of a lipid bilayer and far more proteins
than we can show here. Later chapters use the icons below these protein ribbon models.

The lipid bilayer functions mainly as a barrier to water-soluble substances. Proteins carry out nearly all other membrane tasks. Many proteins are receptors for signals. Others transport specific solutes across the bilayer. Some transport the solutes passively; others require an energy input. Still other proteins function as enzymes that mediate events at the membrane.

Especially among multicelled species, the plasma membrane bristles with diverse proteins. Recognition proteins identify the cell as belonging to the body, and other kinds help defend it against attacks. Special proteins even help different cells communicate with one another or stick together in tissues. Figure 4.10 introduces important categories of membrane proteins and gives a brief description of their functions.

The fluid mosaic model is a good starting point for thinking about cell membranes. But keep in mind that membranes have different types and arrangements of molecules. Even the two surfaces of the same bilayer are not exactly alike. For example, carbohydrate side chains that are attached to many proteins and lipids project from the cell, not into it. All such differences among plasma membranes and internal membranes correlate with their functions.

All cell membranes consist of two layers of lipids—mainly phospholipids—and diverse proteins. Hydrophobic parts of the lipids are sandwiched between hydrophilic parts, which are dissolved in cytoplasmic fluid or in extracellular fluid.

All cell membranes have protein receptors, transporters, and enzymes. The plasma membrane also incorporates adhesion, communication, and recognition proteins.

4.4 Introducing Prokaryotic Cells

The word prokaryote is taken to mean "before the nucleus." The name reminds us that bacteria and then archaea originated before cells with a nucleus evolved.

Prokaryotes are the smallest known cells. As a group they are the most metabolically diverse forms of life on Earth. Different kinds can exploit energy and raw materials in nearly all environments, from dry deserts to hot springs to mountain ice.

We recognize two domains of prokaryotic cells: the eubacteria, or true bacteria, and archaea (Sections 1.3 and 19.1). Cells of both groups are alike in outward appearance, size, and where they live. Even so, they differ in major ways at the molecular level. Bacteria start synthesizing each new polypeptide chain with a modified amino acid, formylmethionine. Archaea, like eukaryotes, start chains with methionine. They also have a few proteins called histones that interact with their DNA. Eukaryotic DNA has a great many histone molecules attached; bacterial DNA has none.

Most prokaryotic cells are not much wider than one micrometer; rod-shaped species are at most a few micrometers long (Figures 4.11 and 4.12). Structurally, these are the simplest cells. A semirigid or rigid wall around the plasma membrane helps impart shape to most species. Also, just under the plasma membrane,

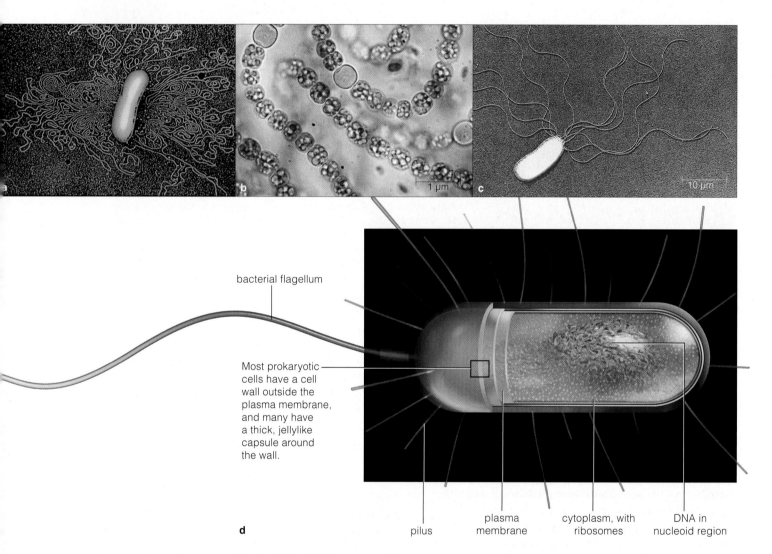

bacterial flagellum

Most prokaryotic cells have a cell wall outside the plasma membrane, and many have a thick, jellylike capsule around the wall.

d

pilus

plasma membrane

cytoplasm, with ribosomes

DNA in nucleoid region

Figure 4.11 (**a**) Micrograph of *Escherichia coli*. Researchers manipulated this bacterial cell to release its single, circular molecule of DNA. (**b**) Cells of various bacterial species are shaped like balls, rods, or corkscrews. Ball-shaped cells of *Nostoc*, a photosynthetic bacteria, stick together in a thick, jellylike sheath of their own secretions. Chapter 19 gives other examples. (**c**) Like this *Pseudomonas marginalis* cell, many species have one or more bacterial flagella that propel the cell body in fluid environments. (**d**) Generalized sketch of a typical prokaryotic body plan.

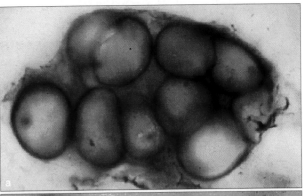

Figure 4.12 From Bitter Springs, Australia, fossilized bacteria dating back to about 850 million years ago, in Precambrian times: (**a**) a colonial form, most likely *Myxococcoides minor*, and (**b**) cells of a filamentous species (*Palaeolyngbya*).

(**c**) One of the structural adaptations seen among archaea. Many of these prokaryotic species live in extremely hostile habitats, such as the ones thought to have prevailed when life originated. Most archaea and some bacteria have a dense lattice of proteins anchored to the outer surface of their plasma membranes. The unique composition of some of these lattices may help cells withstand the insults of extreme environments, such as the near-boiling, mineral-rich water spewing from hydrothermal vents on the ocean floor.

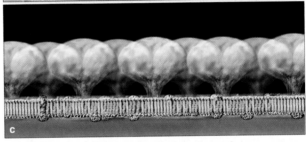

arrays of protein filaments in the cytoplasm compose a simple internal "skeleton," a bit like the cytoskeleton of eukaryotic cells.

Sticky polysaccharides that often envelop bacterial cell walls help them attach to interesting surfaces such as river rocks, teeth, and the vagina. Many disease-causing (pathogenic) bacteria have a thick protective capsule of jellylike polysaccharides around their wall.

All cell walls are permeable to dissolved substances, which are free to move to and away from the plasma membrane. However, eukaryotic cell walls differ in their structure, as you'll see in Section 4.11.

One or more bacterial flagella often project above the cell wall. Bacterial flagella are motile but differ in structure from eukaryotic flagella (Section 4.10); they do not have an orderly, inner array of microtubules. They help cells move about in fluid habitats, including animal body fluids. Other surface projections include pili (singular, pilus). These protein filaments help many kinds of bacterial cells attach to surfaces and to one another, sometimes for transfer of genetic material.

Like eukaryotic cells, bacteria and archaea depend on their plasma membrane to selectively control the flow of substances into and out of the cytoplasm. The lipid bilayer bristles with diverse protein channels, transporters, and receptors. It incorporates built-in machinery for reactions. For example, photosynthesis proceeds at the plasma membrane in many bacterial species. Organized arrays of proteins harness light energy and convert it to chemical energy in the form of ATP, which is used to build sugars.

The cytoplasm holds many ribosomes on which polypeptide chains are built. DNA is concentrated in an irregularly shaped region of cytoplasm called the nucleoid. Prokaryotic cells inherit one molecule of DNA, in the form of a circle. We call it a bacterial chromosome. The cytoplasm of some species also holds plasmids: far smaller circles of DNA that carry just a few genes. Typically, plasmid genes confer selective advantages, such as antibiotic resistance.

One more intriguing point: In cyanobacteria, part of the plasma membrane projects into the cytoplasm, where it repeatedly folds back on itself. As it happens, pigments and other molecules of photosynthesis are embedded in the membrane, as they are in the inner membrane of chloroplasts. Were ancient cyanobacteria the forerunners of chloroplasts? Section 18.4 looks at this possibility. It is one aspect of a remarkable story about how prokaryotes gave rise to all protists, plants, fungi, and animals.

Bacteria and archaea are different groups of prokaryotic cells; their DNA is not housed inside a nucleus. Most have a permeable cell wall around their plasma membrane that structurally supports and imparts shape to the cell.

These are the simplest cells, but as a group they show the most metabolic diversity. Their metabolic activities proceed at the plasma membrane and within the cytoplasm.

4.5 Introducing Eukaryotic Cells

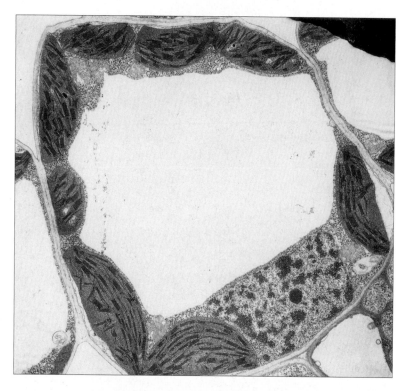

Figure 4.13 Transmission electron micrograph of a plant cell, cross-section. This is a photosynthetic cell from a blade of timothy grass.

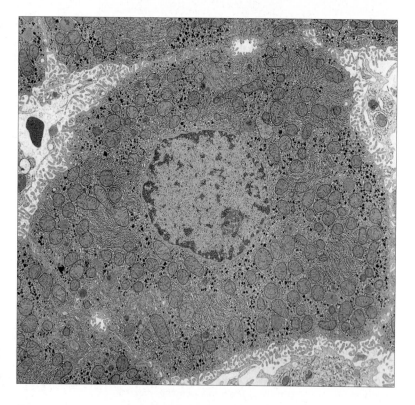

Figure 4.14 Transmission electron micrograph of an animal cell, cross-section. This is a cell from a rat liver.

All cells engage in biosynthesis, dismantling tasks, and energy production, but eukaryotic cells compartmentalize these operations. Their interior is subdivided into a nucleus and other organelles having specialized functions.

Like the prokaryotes, eukaryotic cells have ribosomes in the cytoplasm. Unlike them, eukaryotic cells have an intricate internal skeleton of proteins; we call it a cytoskeleton. They also start out life with **organelles**: internal compartments such as the nucleus. *Eu–* means true; and *karyon*, meaning kernel, refers to a nucleus. Figures 4.13 and 4.14 show two eukaryotic cells.

What advantages do organelles offer? Their outer membrane encloses and sustains a microenvironment. Membrane components selectively control the types and amounts of substances entering or leaving. Their action concentrates substances for metabolic reactions, isolates toxic or disruptive ones, and exports others.

For instance, organelles called mitochondria and chloroplasts concentrate hydrogen ions in ways that lead to the formation of ATP molecules. Enzymes in lysosomes can digest large organic compounds, and they would digest the whole cell if they escaped.

In addition, just as your organ systems interact in controlled ways to keep your whole body running, specialized organelles interact in ways that keep the whole cell running. Ions and molecules move out of one organelle and into another. They move to and from the plasma membrane.

Some substances move through the cytoplasm by a series of organelles. One series functions as a *secretory* pathway. It moves new polypeptide chains from ribosomes through organelles known as ER, then through Golgi bodies, then on to the plasma membrane for release from the cell. Another series is an *endocytic* pathway; it moves substances into the cell. The substances don't travel unescorted; they are enclosed in sacs (vesicles) that have pinched off from organelle membranes or the plasma membrane. Section 4.9 is a visual summary of eukaryotic cell components.

All eukaryotic cells start out life with a nucleus and other organelles, as well as ribosomes and a cytoskeleton. Specialized cells typically incorporate additional kinds of organelles and structures.

Organelles physically separate chemical reactions, many of which are incompatible.

Organelles organize events, as when they assemble, store, or move substances along pathways to and from the plasma membrane or to specific destinations in the cytoplasm.

4.6 The Nucleus

Constructing, operating, and reproducing cells can't be done without carbohydrates, lipids, proteins, and nucleic acids. It takes a class of proteins—enzymes— to build and use these molecules. Said another way, a cell's structure and function start with proteins. And instructions for building proteins are located in DNA.

Unlike prokaryotes, eukaryotic cells have their genetic material distributed among a number of linear DNA molecules of different lengths. The term **chromosome** refers to one double-stranded DNA molecule together with the many histones and other protein molecules attached to it. Each human body cell, for instance, has forty-six chromosomes; frog cells have twenty-six. **Chromatin** is the name for the collection of DNA and proteins in any nucleus of a eukaryotic cell.

The nucleus has two functions. First, it isolates the cell's DNA from potentially damaging reactions in the cytoplasm. Second, it allows or restricts access to DNA's hereditary information through controls over receptors, transport proteins, and pores at its surface. This structural and functional separation makes it far easier to keep DNA molecules organized and also to copy them before a cell divides.

When eukaryotic cells are not dividing, you can't see individual DNA molecules. The nucleus just looks grainy in micrographs, as in Figures 4.14 and 4.15. When cells divide, they duplicate their DNA. During actual division stages, the duplicated DNA molecules become more condensed and compact, like tiny rods. At such times, the DNA no longer looks grainy; each molecule becomes visible in micrographs.

A **nuclear envelope** encloses the semifluid interior of the nucleus (nucleoplasm). It consists of two lipid bilayers studded with proteins. Many of the proteins are organized in complexes that form pores across the envelope (Figure 4.15*b*). A nucleus also contains at least one nucleolus (plural, nucleoli), a construction site where large and small subunits of ribosomes are assembled from RNA and proteins. The subunits pass through pores and enter the cytoplasm. There, large and small subunits join briefly as intact ribosomes.

The outer envelope of the nucleus keeps DNA molecules separated from the cytoplasmic machinery and thus controls access to a cell's hereditary information.

With this separation, DNA is easier to keep organized and to copy before a parent cell divides into daughter cells.

Pores across the nuclear envelope help control the passage of many substances between the nucleus and cytoplasm.

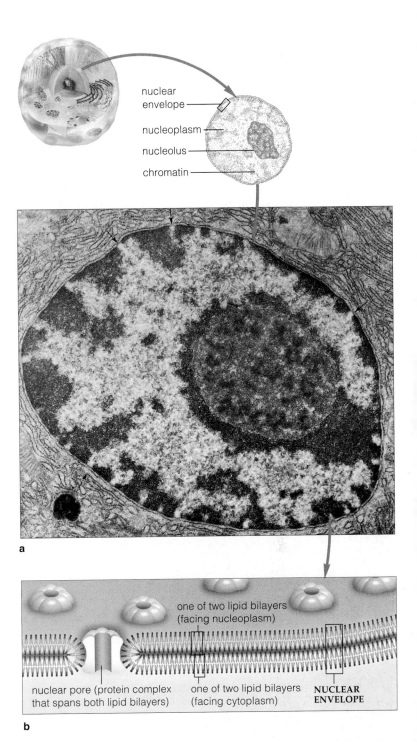

nuclear envelope

nucleoplasm

nucleolus

chromatin

a

one of two lipid bilayers (facing nucleoplasm)

nuclear pore (protein complex that spans both lipid bilayers)

one of two lipid bilayers (facing cytoplasm)

NUCLEAR ENVELOPE

b

Figure 4.15 (**a**) Pancreatic cell nucleus. Small arrows on the transmission electron micrograph point to pores where control systems selectively restrict or allow passage of specific substances across the nuclear envelope. (**b**) Sketch of part of the nuclear envelope. Each pore is an organized cluster of membrane proteins.

4.7 The Endomembrane System

New polypeptide chains become folded into proteins. Some proteins are stockpiled in the cytoplasm or used at once. Others enter flattened sacs and tubes of the endomembrane system: ER, Golgi bodies, and vesicles. All proteins that are destined for export or for insertion into cell membranes pass through this system.

ENDOPLASMIC RETICULUM

Endoplasmic reticulum, or **ER**, is a channel that starts at the nuclear envelope and extends through part of the cytoplasm. Here, polypeptide chains are processed into final proteins, and lipids are assembled. Vesicles deliver many proteins and lipids to Golgi bodies.

Rough ER consists of flattened sacs and tubes with ribosomes attached to their outer surface, as in Figure 4.16c. Newly forming polypeptide chains enter it or become inserted into its membrane. They can do so only if they contain a built-in signal (a special sequence of fifteen to twenty amino acids). Enzymes in the channel often modify polypeptide chains into final form. You'll see a lot of rough ER in cells that make, store, and secrete proteins. Example: ER-rich gland cells in your pancreas make and secrete enzymes that end up in your small intestine and help digest meals.

Smooth ER is ribosome-free (Figure 4.16d). It makes lipid molecules that become part of cell membranes. The ER also takes part in fatty acid breakdown and degrades some toxins. Sarcoplasmic reticulum, a type of smooth ER, functions in muscle contraction.

GOLGI BODIES

Patches of ER membrane bulge and break away as vesicles, each with proteins inside or incorporated in its membrane. Many vesicles fuse with **Golgi bodies**. These organelles are folded into flattened, membrane-bound sacs (Figure 4.16e). Golgi bodies attach sugar

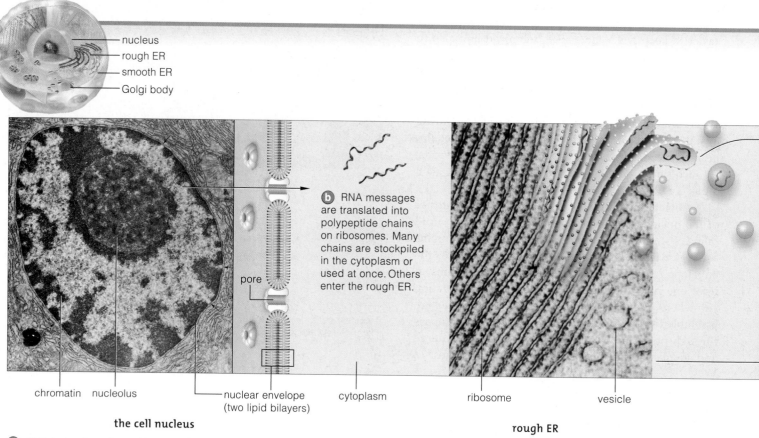

nucleus
rough ER
smooth ER
Golgi body

b RNA messages are translated into polypeptide chains on ribosomes. Many chains are stockpiled in the cytoplasm or used at once. Others enter the rough ER.

pore

chromatin   nucleolus

nuclear envelope (two lipid bilayers)

cytoplasm

ribosome

vesicle

the cell nucleus

rough ER

a DNA instructions for making proteins are transcribed in the nucleus and moved to the cytoplasm. RNAs are the messengers and protein builders.

c Flattened sacs of rough ER form one continuous channel between the nucleus and smooth ER. Polypeptide chains that enter the channel undergo modification. They will be inserted into organelle membranes or will be secreted from the cell.

Figure 4.16 Endomembrane system. Here, many proteins are processed, lipids are assembled, and both products are sorted and shipped to cellular destinations or to the plasma membrane for export.

side chains to ER proteins and lipids. They also cleave some proteins. The finished products are packaged in vesicles and then shipped to lysosomes, to the plasma membrane, or to the outside of the cell.

MEMBRANOUS SACS WITH DIVERSE FUNCTIONS

Vesicles help organize metabolic activities. Different kinds bud from ER, Golgi, or plasma membranes. For instance, the **lysosomes** that bud from Golgi bodies contain enzymes that digest carbohydrates, proteins, nucleic acids, and lipids. Different vesicles transport proteins and other substances between organelles or to the outer membrane where they are expelled.

The vesicles called **peroxisomes** hold enzymes that digest fatty acids and amino acids. An important function is the breakdown of hydrogen peroxide, a toxic product of metabolism. Enzyme action converts

hydrogen peroxide to water and oxygen or uses it in reactions that break down alcohol and other toxins. Drink alcohol, and peroxisomes of liver and kidney cells normally will degrade nearly half of it.

Some vesicles fuse and form large vacuoles, such as the **central vacuole** of mature plant cells. Ions, amino acids, sugars, and toxic substances accumulate in the fluid-filled interior of a central vacuole, which expands and forces the pliable cell wall to enlarge. One benefit is an increase in cell surface area.

Endoplasmic reticulum is a membrane-bound channel where polypeptide chains are processed and lipids are assembled. Golgi bodies further modify many of the proteins and lipids.

Vesicles help integrate cell activities. Different kinds transport substances around the cell, and break down nutrients and toxins. In plant cells, the central vacuole functions in storage and in increasing the cell surface area.

Read Me First!
and watch the narrated animation on the endomembrane system

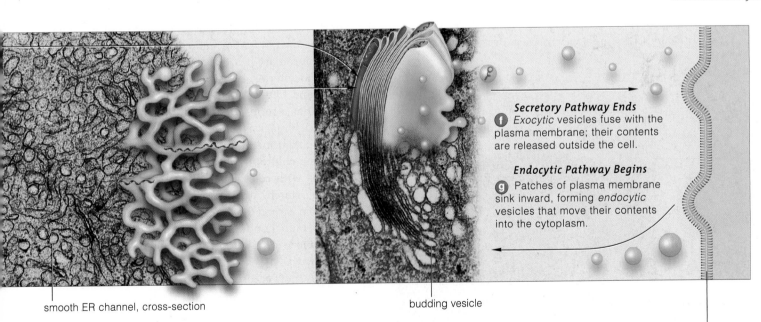

smooth ER channel, cross-section

budding vesicle

Secretory Pathway Ends
f *Exocytic* vesicles fuse with the plasma membrane; their contents are released outside the cell.

Endocytic Pathway Begins
g Patches of plasma membrane sink inward, forming *endocytic* vesicles that move their contents into the cytoplasm.

smooth ER
d Some proteins in the channel continue on to smooth ER, becoming membrane proteins or smooth ER enzymes. Some of these enzymes make lipids and inactive toxins.

Golgi body
e A Golgi body receives, processes, and repackages substances that arrive in vesicles from the ER. Different vesicles transport the substances to other parts of the cell.

plasma membrane
h Exocytic vesicles release cell products and wastes to the outside. Endocytic vesicles move nutrients, water, and other substances into the cytoplasm from outside (Section 5.5).

4.8 Mitochondria and Chloroplasts

ATP, recall, is the energy carrier that jump-starts most of the reactions in cells. So how do cells get ATP in the first place? All of them make ATP by aerobic respiration, which is completed in mitochondria. Algae and photosynthetic plant cells also contain ATP-making organelles called chloroplasts.

MITOCHONDRIA

ATP-forming reactions of aerobic respiration end in the **mitochondrion** (plural, mitochondria). Compared to prokaryotic cells, these organelles make far more ATP from the same compounds. A much-folded inner membrane divides the interior of the mitochondrion into two compartments (Figure 4.17). Hydrogen ions released from the breakdown of organic compounds accumulate in the inner compartment by operation of transport systems, of the sort described in Sections 5.6 and 6.3. As they flow back to the outer compartment, they drive the formation of ATP. Oxygen accepts the spent electrons and keeps the reactions going. Each time you breathe in, you are securing oxygen mainly for the mitochondria in your many trillions of cells.

All eukaryotic cells have one or more mitochondria. The cells that require a great deal of energy, such as those of your liver, heart, and skeletal muscles, may each contain a thousand or more.

CHLOROPLASTS

Many plant cells have plastids, which are organelles of photosynthesis, storage, or both. **Chloroplasts** are important plastids, and only photosynthetic eukaryotic cells have them. In these organelles, energy from the sun drives the formation of ATP and NADPH, which are then used in the formation of organic compounds.

A chloroplast has two outer membranes around a semifluid interior, the stroma, which bathes an inner membrane. Often this single membrane is folded back on itself as a series of stacked, flattened disks (Figure 4.18). Each stack is called a thylakoid. Embedded in the thylakoid membrane are light-trapping pigments, including chlorophylls, as well as enzymes and other proteins with roles in photosynthesis. Glucose, then sucrose, starch, and other organic compounds are built from carbon dioxide and water in the stroma.

Both mitochondria and chloroplasts are a lot like bacteria in size, structure, and biochemistry. Both have their own DNA, RNA, and ribosomes. Coincidence? Probably not, according to the theories discussed in Section 18.4.

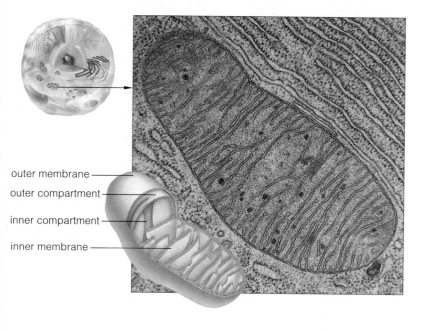

outer membrane
outer compartment
inner compartment
inner membrane

Figure 4.17 Typical mitochondrion. This organelle specializes in producing ATP.

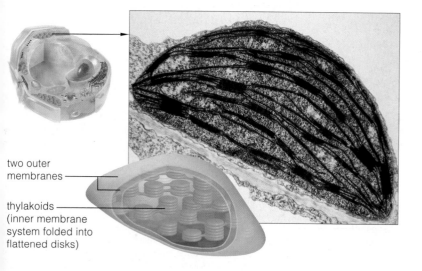

two outer membranes

thylakoids (inner membrane system folded into flattened disks)

Figure 4.18 Typical chloroplast, the key defining feature of photosynthetic eukaryotic cells.

Reactions that release energy from organic compounds occur at the compartmented, internal membrane of mitochondria. The reactions, which require oxygen, produce far more ATP than can be produced by any other cellular reaction.

Photosynthetic eukaryotic cells contain chloroplasts, which specialize in making sugars and other carbohydrates.

4.9 Visual Summary of Eukaryotic Cell Components

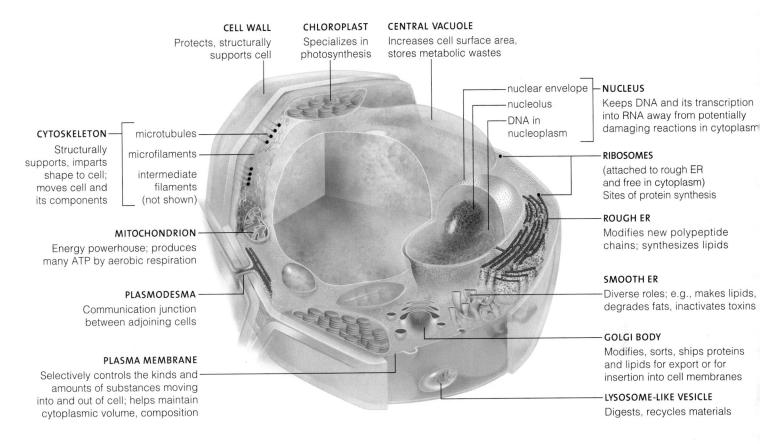

CELL WALL
Protects, structurally supports cell

CHLOROPLAST
Specializes in photosynthesis

CENTRAL VACUOLE
Increases cell surface area, stores metabolic wastes

nuclear envelope
nucleolus
DNA in nucleoplasm

NUCLEUS
Keeps DNA and its transcription into RNA away from potentially damaging reactions in cytoplasm

CYTOSKELETON
Structurally supports, imparts shape to cell; moves cell and its components

microtubules
microfilaments
intermediate filaments (not shown)

RIBOSOMES
(attached to rough ER and free in cytoplasm)
Sites of protein synthesis

ROUGH ER
Modifies new polypeptide chains; synthesizes lipids

MITOCHONDRION
Energy powerhouse; produces many ATP by aerobic respiration

SMOOTH ER
Diverse roles; e.g., makes lipids, degrades fats, inactivates toxins

PLASMODESMA
Communication junction between adjoining cells

GOLGI BODY
Modifies, sorts, ships proteins and lipids for export or for insertion into cell membranes

PLASMA MEMBRANE
Selectively controls the kinds and amounts of substances moving into and out of cell; helps maintain cytoplasmic volume, composition

LYSOSOME-LIKE VESICLE
Digests, recycles materials

Figure 4.19 Typical organelles and structures of plant cells.

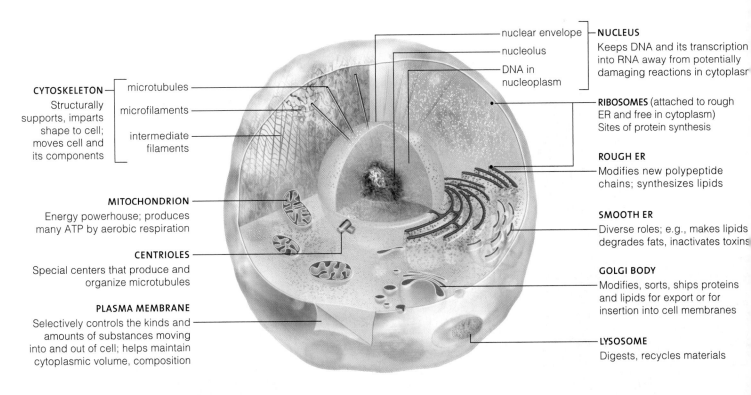

nuclear envelope
nucleolus
DNA in nucleoplasm

NUCLEUS
Keeps DNA and its transcription into RNA away from potentially damaging reactions in cytoplasm

CYTOSKELETON
Structurally supports, imparts shape to cell; moves cell and its components

microtubules
microfilaments
intermediate filaments

RIBOSOMES (attached to rough ER and free in cytoplasm)
Sites of protein synthesis

ROUGH ER
Modifies new polypeptide chains; synthesizes lipids

MITOCHONDRION
Energy powerhouse; produces many ATP by aerobic respiration

SMOOTH ER
Diverse roles; e.g., makes lipids degrades fats, inactivates toxins

CENTRIOLES
Special centers that produce and organize microtubules

GOLGI BODY
Modifies, sorts, ships proteins and lipids for export or for insertion into cell membranes

PLASMA MEMBRANE
Selectively controls the kinds and amounts of substances moving into and out of cell; helps maintain cytoplasmic volume, composition

LYSOSOME
Digests, recycles materials

Figure 4.20 Typical organelles and structures of animal cells.

4.10 The Cytoskeleton

Like you, all eukaryotic cells have an internal structural framework—a skeleton. Unlike your skeleton, theirs has elements that are not permanently rigid; they assemble and disassemble at different times.

tubulin subunits

In between the nucleus and plasma membrane of all eukaryotic cells is a **cytoskeleton**—an interconnected system of many protein filaments. Different parts of the system reinforce, organize, and move structures, and often the whole cell. Many parts are permanent; others form at certain times in a cell's life. Figure 4.21 shows an example from one kind of animal cell. The two major cytoskeletal elements—microtubules and microfilaments—have diverse functions. Another type, intermediate filaments, strengthens some animal cells.

Microtubules are long, hollow cylinders of tubulin subunits (Figure 4.21*a*). They organize the cell interior and form a dynamic framework that moves structures such as chromosomes to specific locations. Controls govern which microtubules grow or fall apart at any given time. Those growing in a specific direction—say, the forward end of a prowling amoeba—might get a protein cap that keeps them intact. Those at the trailing end aren't used, aren't capped, and fall apart.

Colchicine, made by the autumn crocus (*Colchicum autumnale*), is a poison. It blocks microtubule assembly, so the cells of animals that eat the plant can't divide. Western yews (*Taxus brevifolia*) make taxol, another microtubule poison. Taxol can stop the uncontrolled cell divisions that give rise to some kinds of cancers.

Microfilaments consist of two coiled-up polypeptide chains of actin monomers, as in Figure 4.21*b*. They often reinforce cell shape or cause it to change. For example, crosslinked, bundled, and gel-like arrays of microfilaments make up a reinforcing **cell cortex** that underlies the plasma membrane. Also, microfilaments anchor proteins and assist in muscle contraction. An animal cell divides as microfilaments around its midsection contract, pinching the cell in two. Although prokaryotic cells lack a cytoskeleton, some types do have microfilament-like proteins that reinforce the cell body.

The microtubules and microfilaments found in all eukaryotic cells are similar. How can they do so many different things if they are so uniform? Other proteins assist them. Among these *accessory* proteins are **motor proteins**, which move cell parts along microtubules when repeatedly energized by ATP.

Intermediate filaments are the most stable parts of some cytoskeletons (Figure 4.21*c*). They strengthen and help maintain cell structures. One type, the lamins, anchor actin and myosin of contractile units found in muscle cells. Other types anchor cells in tissues.

One or at most two kinds of intermediate filaments occur in certain animal cells. Researchers use them to identify the type of cell. *Cell typing* is a useful tool in diagnosing the tissue origin of diverse cancers.

MOVING ALONG WITH MOTOR PROTEINS

Think about the bustle at a train station during the busiest holiday season, and you get an idea of what goes on in cells. Microtubules and microfilaments are the cell's tracks. Kinesins, dyneins, myosins, and other motor proteins are the freight engines (Figure 4.22). ATP is the fuel for movement.

Some motor proteins move chromosomes. Others slide one microtubule over another, or chug along tracks inside nerve cells that extend from your spine to your toes. Many engines are organized in series, each moving some vesicle partway along the track before giving it up to the next in line. Kinesins in

a 25 nm

actin subunit

one polypeptide chain

8–12 nm

b 5–7 nm **c**

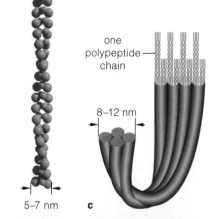

Figure 4.21 Subunits and structure of (**a**) microtubules, (**b**) microfilaments, and (**c**) one kind of intermediate filament. The micrograph at left shows intermediate filaments (*red*) of cultured kangaroo rat cells. The *blue*-stained organelle inside each cell is the nucleus.

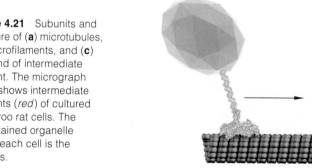

Figure 4.22 A motor protein, kinesin, on a microtubule. Kinesin scoots along the length of the microtubule in a hand-over-hand motion. If the microtubule is anchored near the cell's center, the kinesin moves its freight away from the center.

Figure 4.23 (**a**) Internal organization of flagella and cilia. Inside both motile structures is a 9+2 array: a ring of nine pairs of microtubules around one pair at the core. All are connected by spokes and linking elements that restrict the range of sliding. (**b**) Cilia (*gold*) on cells lining an airway that leads to human lungs.

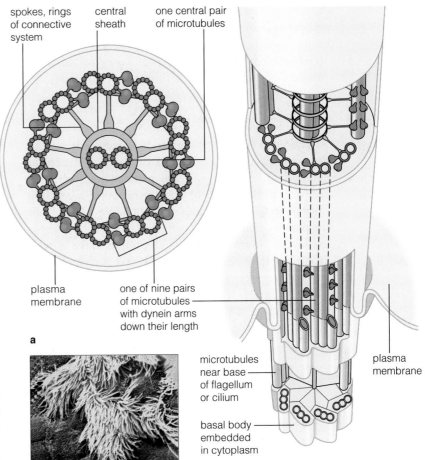

spokes, rings of connective system

central sheath

one central pair of microtubules

plasma membrane

one of nine pairs of microtubules with dynein arms down their length

a

b

microtubules near base of flagellum or cilium

basal body embedded in cytoplasm

plasma membrane

plant cells drag chloroplasts to new positions that are more efficient for light interception as the angle of the sun changes overhead.

Different myosins can move structures along microfilaments or slide one microfilament over another. For example, muscle cells contain long fibers divided into contractile units. Each unit has side-by-side arrays of microfilaments and myosin filaments. When ATP activates it, myosin slides all microfilaments in directions that shorten each unit. When all of the units shorten, the cell itself shortens; it contracts.

CILIA, FLAGELLA, AND FALSE FEET

Besides moving internal parts, many cells move their body or extend parts of it. First, consider **flagella** (singular, flagellum) and **cilia** (singular, cilium). Both are motile structures that project from the cell surface.

Eukaryotic flagella usually are longer and not as profuse as cilia. Many eukaryotic cells swim with the help of whiplike flagella. Sperm do this. The ciliated protozoans swim by beating many cilia in synchrony. In the airways to your lungs, cilia beat nonstop; their coordinated movement sweeps out airborne bacteria and particles that otherwise might reach the lungs (Figure 4.23b).

Inside these motile structures is a ring of nine pairs of microtubules around a central pair. Protein spokes and links stabilize the *9+2 array*, which starts at a **centriole** (Figure 4.23a). This barrel-shaped structure produces and organizes microtubules, then it remains positioned below the finished array as a **basal body**.

Flagella and cilia move by a sliding mechanism. All pairs of microtubules extend the same distance into the motile structure's tip. Stubby dynein arms project from each pair in the outer ring. When ATP energizes them, the arms grab the microtubule pair in front of them, tilt in a short, downward stroke, then let go. As the bound pair slides down, its arms bind the pair in front of it, forcing it to slide down also—and so on around the ring. The microtubules can't slide too far, but each *bends* a bit. Their sliding motion is converted to a bending motion.

As a final example, some free-living cells, such as macrophages and amoebas, form **pseudopods** ("false feet"). These temporary, irregular lobes project from the cell and function in locomotion and prey capture. Pseudopods move as microfilaments elongate inside them. Motor proteins attached to the microfilaments drag the plasma membrane with them.

A cytoskeleton of protein filaments is the basis of eukaryotic cell shape, internal structure, and movement. Accessory proteins extend the range of functions for those filaments.

Microtubules move cell components. Microfilaments form flexible, linear bundles and networks that reinforce and restructure the cell surface. Intermediate filaments strengthen and maintain shapes of some animal cells.

Cell contractions and migrations, chromosome movements, and other forms of cell movements arise at organized arrays of microtubules, microfilaments, and accessory proteins.

When energized by ATP, motor proteins move in specific directions, along tracks of microtubules and microfilaments. They deliver cell components to new locations.

4.11 Cell Surface Specializations

Our survey of eukaryotic cells concludes with a look at cell walls and other specialized surface structures. Many of these architectural marvels are made primarily of cell secretions. Others are clusters of membrane proteins that connect neighboring cells, structurally and functionally.

EUKARYOTIC CELL WALLS

Single-celled eukaryotic species are directly exposed to the environment. Many have a **cell wall**, a structural component that encloses the plasma membrane. A cell wall protects and physically supports a cell. It's porous, so water and solutes easily move to and from the plasma membrane. A cell would die without these exchanges. Many single-celled protists have a wall around their plasma membranes. So do plant cells and many types of fungal cells.

For example, in the growing parts of multicelled plants, young cells secrete molecules of pectin and other glue-like polysaccharides, as well as cellulose. The cellulose molecules are laid down in the gluey matrix as ropelike strands. All of these materials are components of the plant cell's **primary wall** (Figure 4.24). The sticky primary wall cements abutting cells together. Being thin and pliable, it permits the cell to enlarge under the pressure of incoming water.

Cells that have only a thin primary wall retain the capacity to divide or change shape as they grow and develop. Many types stop enlarging when they are mature. Such cells secrete material on the primary wall's inner surface. These deposits form a lignified, rigid **secondary wall** that reinforces cell shape (Figure 4.24d). Secondary wall deposits are extensive and contribute more to structural support.

In woody plants, up to 25 percent of the secondary wall is made of lignin. This organic compound makes plant parts more waterproof, less susceptible to plant-attacking organisms, and stronger.

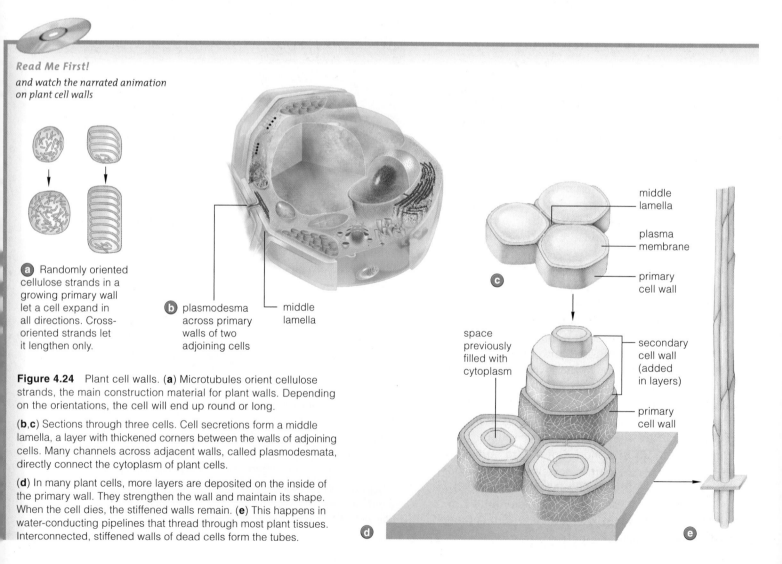

Read Me First!
and watch the narrated animation on plant cell walls

(**a**) Randomly oriented cellulose strands in a growing primary wall let a cell expand in all directions. Cross-oriented strands let it lengthen only.

(**b**) plasmodesma across primary walls of two adjoining cells — middle lamella

(**c**) middle lamella / plasma membrane / primary cell wall

space previously filled with cytoplasm

secondary cell wall (added in layers) / primary cell wall

Figure 4.24 Plant cell walls. (**a**) Microtubules orient cellulose strands, the main construction material for plant walls. Depending on the orientations, the cell will end up round or long.

(**b,c**) Sections through three cells. Cell secretions form a middle lamella, a layer with thickened corners between the walls of adjoining cells. Many channels across adjacent walls, called plasmodesmata, directly connect the cytoplasm of plant cells.

(**d**) In many plant cells, more layers are deposited on the inside of the primary wall. They strengthen the wall and maintain its shape. When the cell dies, the stiffened walls remain. (**e**) This happens in water-conducting pipelines that thread through most plant tissues. Interconnected, stiffened walls of dead cells form the tubes.

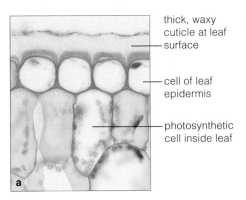

thick, waxy
cuticle at leaf
surface

cell of leaf
epidermis

photosynthetic
cell inside leaf

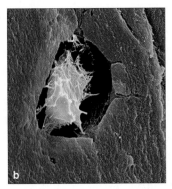

Figure 4.25 (**a**) Section through a plant cuticle, an outer surface layer of cell secretions. (**b**) A living cell inside bone tissue, the stuff of vertebrate skeletons.

At plant surfaces exposed to air, waxes and other cell secretions build up, forming a protective cuticle. This type of semitransparent surface covering limits water losses from aboveground parts during hot, dry days (Figure 4.25*a*).

MATRIXES BETWEEN ANIMAL CELLS

Animal cells have no cell walls. Intervening between many of them are matrixes made of cell secretions and of materials absorbed from the surroundings. For example, cartilage at the knobby ends of leg bones consists of scattered cells and protein fibers embedded in a ground substance of firm polysaccharides. Living cells also secrete the extensive, hardened matrix that we call bone tissue (Figure 4.25*b*).

CELL JUNCTIONS

Even when a wall or some other structure imprisons a cell in its own secretions, the cell still has contact with the outside world at its plasma membrane. Also, in multicelled species, membrane components extend into adjoining cells or the surrounding matrix. Among the components are **cell junctions**: molecular structures where a cell sends or receives signals or materials, or recognizes and cements itself to cells of the same type.

In plants, for instance, channels extend across the primary wall of adjacent living cells and interconnect the cytoplasm of both (Figure 4.24*b*). Each channel is a plasmodesma (plural, plasmodesmata). Substances flow quickly from cell to cell across these junctions.

In most animal tissues, three types of cell-to-cell junctions are common (Figure 4.26). *Tight* junctions link cells of most body tissues, including epithelia that line outer surfaces, internal cavities, and organs. The junctions seal abutting cells together so water-soluble substances cannot pass between them. That is why gastric fluid does not leak across the stomach lining

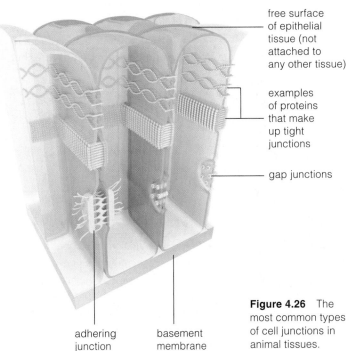

free surface
of epithelial
tissue (not
attached to
any other tissue)

examples
of proteins
that make
up tight
junctions

gap junctions

adhering
junction

basement
membrane

Figure 4.26 The most common types of cell junctions in animal tissues.

and damage internal tissues. *Adhering* junctions occur in skin, the heart, and in other organs subjected to stretching. *Gap* junctions link the cytoplasm of certain adjoining cells. They are open channels for a rapid flow of substances, most notably in heart muscle.

A variety of protistan, plant, and fungal cells have a porous wall that surrounds the plasma membrane.

Young plant cells have a thin primary wall pliable enough to permit expansion. Some mature cells also deposit a lignin-reinforced secondary wall that affords structural support.

Animal cells have no walls, but they and many other cells often secrete substances that help form matrixes of tissues. Junctions often occur between cells of multicelled organisms.

Summary

Section 4.1   The cell is the smallest unit that still displays the properties of life. The surface-to-volume ratio constrains size increases. All cells start out life with an outer plasma membrane, cytoplasm, and a nucleus or nucleoid area that contains DNA.

Section 4.2   Most cells are microscopically small. Different microscopes reveal cell shapes and structures.

Section 4.3   Cell membranes consist mainly of lipids and proteins. A lipid bilayer gives a membrane its fluid properties and prevents water-soluble substances from freely crossing it. Proteins embedded in the bilayer or positioned at its surfaces carry out many functions.

Section 4.4   Bacteria and archaea are prokaryotic. They have no nucleus and are the smallest, structurally simplest cells known (Table 4.1).

Sections 4.5, 4.6   Eukaryotic cells generally have diverse organelles: membranous sacs that divide the cell's interior into functional compartments (Table 4.1). Organelles physically separate chemical reactions from the rest of the cell. A nucleus isolates and protects the cell's genetic material.

Section 4.7   In the endomembrane system's ER and Golgi bodies, new polypeptide chains take on final form and lipids are assembled; both get packaged into vesicles for transport, storage, and other cell activities.

Section 4.8   The final reactions of aerobic respiration occur in mitochondria, where many ATP form. The chloroplasts of photosynthetic plant and algal cells use energy from the sun to make sugars.

Section 4.10   Eukaryotic cells have a cytoskeleton of microtubules, microfilaments, and intermediate filaments. It imparts shape and supports and moves cell parts, motile structures, and often the whole cell.

Section 4.11   Many bacterial, protistan, fungal, and plant cells have a wall around the plasma membrane. In multicelled organisms, adjoining cells form diverse structural and functional connections.

Table 4.1   Summary of Typical Components of Prokaryotic and Eukaryotic Cells

Cell Component	Function	Prokaryotic — Bacteria, Archaea	Eukaryotic — Protists	Fungi	Plants	Animals
Cell wall	Protection, structural support	✓*	✓*	✓	✓	None
Plasma membrane	Control of substances moving into and out of cell	✓	✓	✓	✓	✓
Nucleus	Physical separation and organization of DNA	None	✓	✓	✓	✓
DNA	Encoding of hereditary information	✓	✓	✓	✓	✓
RNA	Transcription, translation of DNA messages into polypeptide chains of specific proteins	✓	✓	✓	✓	✓
Nucleolus	Assembly of subunits of ribosomes	None	✓	✓	✓	✓
Ribosome	Protein synthesis	✓	✓	✓	✓	✓
Endoplasmic reticulum (ER)	Initial modification of many of the newly forming polypeptide chains of proteins; lipid synthesis	None	✓	✓	✓	✓
Golgi body	Final modification of proteins, lipids; sorting and packaging them for use inside cell or for export	None	✓	✓	✓	✓
Lysosome	Intracellular digestion	None	✓	✓*	✓*	✓
Mitochondrion	ATP formation	**	✓	✓	✓	✓
Photosynthetic pigments	Light–energy conversion	✓*	✓*	None	✓	None
Chloroplast	Photosynthesis; some starch storage	None	✓*	None	✓	None
Central vacuole	Increasing cell surface area; storage	None	None	✓*	✓	None
Bacterial flagellum	Locomotion through fluid surroundings	✓*	None	None	None	None
Flagellum or cilium with 9+2 microtubular array	Locomotion through or motion within fluid surroundings	None	✓*	✓*	✓*	✓
Complex cytoskeleton	Cell shape; internal organization; basis of cell movement and, in many cells, locomotion	Rudimentary***	✓*	✓*	✓*	✓

* Known to be present in cells of at least some groups.
** Many groups use oxygen-requiring (aerobic) pathways of ATP formation, but mitochondria are not involved.
*** Protein filaments form a simple scaffold that helps support the cell wall in at least some species.

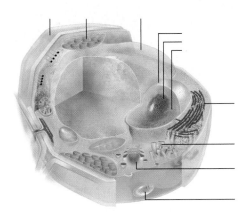
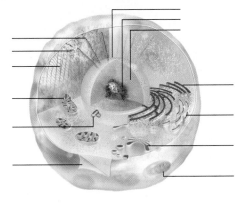
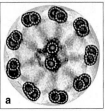
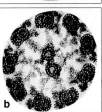

Figure 4.27 Cross-sections through the flagellum of a sperm cell from (**a**) a male with Kartagener syndrome and (**b**) an unaffected male. Notice the dynein arms that extend from the paired microtubules.

Self-Quiz

Answers in Appendix III

1. Cell membranes consist mainly of a _____ .
   a. carbohydrate bilayer and proteins
   b. protein bilayer and phospholipids
   c. lipid bilayer and proteins

2. Identify the components of the cells shown above.

3. Organelles _____ .
   a. are membrane-bound compartments
   b. are typical of eukaryotic cells, not prokaryotic cells
   c. separate chemical reactions in time and space
   d. All of the above are features of organelles.

4. Cells of many protists, plants, and fungi, but not animals, commonly have _____ .
   a. mitochondria   c. ribosomes
   b. a plasma membrane   d. a cell wall

5. Is this statement true or false: The plasma membrane is the outermost component of all cells. Explain your answer.

6. Unlike eukaryotic cells, prokaryotic cells _____ .
   a. lack a plasma membrane   c. have no nucleus
   b. have RNA, not DNA   d. all of the above

7. Match each cell component with its function.
   ____ mitochondrion   a. protein synthesis
   ____ chloroplast   b. initial modification of new
   ____ ribosome   polypeptide chains
   ____ rough ER   c. modification of new proteins;
   ____ Golgi body   sorting, shipping tasks
                        d. photosynthesis
                        e. formation of many ATP

Critical Thinking

1. Why is it likely that you will never meet a two-ton amoeba on a sidewalk?

2. Your professor shows you an electron micrograph of a cell with many mitochondria, Golgi bodies, and a lot of rough ER. What kinds of cellular activities would require such an abundance of the three kinds of organelles?

3. *Kartagener syndrome* is a genetic disorder caused by a mutated form of the protein dynein. Affected people have chronically irritated sinuses, and mucus builds up in the airways to their lungs. Bacteria form huge populations in the thick mucus. Their metabolic by-products and the inflammation they trigger combine to damage tissues. Males affected by the syndrome make sperm but are infertile (Figure 4.27). Some have become fathers with the help of a procedure that injects sperm cells directly into eggs. Explain how an abnormal dynein molecule could cause the observed effects.

Media Menu

Student CD-ROM

Impacts, Issues Video
   Where Did Cells Come From?
Big Picture Animation
   The unity and diversity of cells
Read-Me-First Animation
   Cell membranes
   The endomembrane system
   Plant cell walls
Other Animations and Interactions
   Surface-to-volume ratio   Light microscopy
   Lipid bilayer organization   Electron microscopy
   Eukaryotic organelles   Flagella structure

InfoTrac
   • Secrets of a Rock. *Newsweek International*, March 2002.
   • Cell Fantastyk. *Natural History*, May 2000.
   • Scientists Give Golgi Apparatus Its Own Identity. *Cancer Weekly*, December 2000.
   • Symbionts and Assassins. *Natural History*, July 2000.
   • Integral Connections. *The Scientist*, August 2001.

Web Sites
   • Cells Alive: www.cellsalive.com
   • Inside a Cell: gslc.genetics.utah.edu/units/basics/cell
   • What Is a Cell?:
     www.ncbi.nlm.nih.gov/About/primer/genetics_cell.html

How Would You Vote?

Scientists are trying to create a "minimal organism" from a living cell that has a small number of genes. They remove its genes one at a time until they have the simplest possible hereditary package that still allows survival and reproduction. Some people think it is wrong or dangerous to create "new" life forms. Do you think the research should continue?

IMPACTS, ISSUES   *Alcohol, Enzymes, and Your Liver*

Consider the cells that are supposed to keep a heavy drinker alive. It makes little difference whether a drinker gulps down 12 ounces of beer, 5 ounces of wine, or 1–1/2 ounces of eighty-proof vodka. Each drink has the same amount of "alcohol" or, more precisely, ethanol.

Ethanol molecules—CH_3CH_2OH—have water-soluble and fat-soluble components, which the stomach and small intestine quickly absorb. The bloodstream moves more than 90 percent of these components to the liver, where enzymes speed their breakdown to a nontoxic form called acetate (acetic acid). However, the liver's alcohol-metabolizing enzymes can detoxify only so much in a given hour.

One of the enzymes you'll read about in this chapter is catalase, a foot soldier against toxin attacks on the body (Figure 5.1). Catalase is thought to assist alcohol dehydrogenase. When alcohol circulates in blood, these enzymes convert it to acetaldehyde. Reactions can't end there, however, because acetaldehyde is toxic at high concentrations. In healthy people at least, another kind of enzyme speeds its breakdown to nontoxic forms.

Given the liver's central role in alcohol metabolism, habitually heavy drinkers gamble with alcohol-induced liver diseases. Over time, the capacity to tolerate alcohol diminishes because there are fewer and fewer liver cells —hence fewer enzymes—for detoxification.

In *alcoholic hepatitis*, inflammation and destruction of liver tissue is widespread. Another disease, *alcoholic cirrhosis*, permanently scars the liver. In time, the liver just stops working, with devastating effects.

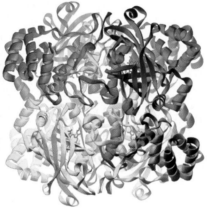

Figure 5.1 Ribbon model of catalase, an enzyme that helps detoxify many substances that can damage the body, such as the alcohol in beer, martinis, and other drinks.

the big picture

The One-Way Flow of Energy   Energy, the capacity to do work, can be converted from one form to another but can't be created from scratch. It flows in one direction, from usable to less usable forms. Some is lost as heat with each conversion.

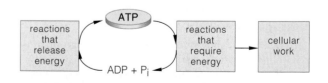

How Cells Use Energy   Energy flows into the web of life, mainly from the sun, and flows out of it. Cells tap into the one-way flow by energy-acquiring processes, starting with photosynthesis. They convert inputs of energy to forms that keep them alive and working properly.

The liver is the largest gland in the human body, and its activity impacts everything else. You'd have a hard time digesting and absorbing food without it. Your cells would have a hard time synthesizing and taking up carbohydrates, lipids, and proteins, and staying alive.

There's more. The liver makes plasma proteins. These proteins circulate in blood and are vital for blood clotting, immunity, maintaining the fluid volume of the internal environment, and other tasks. Also, liver enzymes get rid of a lot more toxic compounds than acetaldehyde.

Binge drinking—consuming large amounts of alcohol in a brief period—is now most serious drug problem on campuses in the United States. Consider: 44 percent of nearly 17,600 students surveyed at 140 colleges and universities are caught up in the culture of drinking. They report having five alcoholic drinks a day, on average.

Binge drinking does more than damage the liver. Put aside the related 500,000 injuries from accidents, the 70,000 cases of date rape, and the 400,000 cases of (whoops) unprotected sex among students in an average year. Binge drinking can kill before you know what hit you. Drink too much, too fast, and you can abruptly stop the beating of your heart. Think about it.

With this example, we turn to **metabolism**, the cell's capacity to acquire energy and use it to build, degrade, store, and release substances in controlled ways. At times, the activities of your cells may seem remote from your interests. But they help define who you are and what you will become, liver and all.

 How Would You Vote?

Some people have damaged their liver because they drank too much alcohol. Others have a diseased liver. There aren't enough liver donors for all the people waiting for liver transplants. Should life-style be a factor in deciding who gets a transplant? See the Media Menu for details, then vote online.

How Enzymes Work   Without enzymes, substances would not react fast enough to maintain living cells, hence life itself. Controls over enzyme action also maintain life through adjustments in the concentration of substances moving across cell membranes.

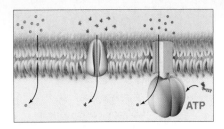

Membranes and Metabolism   Cells have built-in mechanisms that increase and decrease concentrations of substances across their membranes. The adjustments are essential for metabolic reactions and metabolic pathways.

5.1 Inputs and Outputs of Energy

Cells secure energy from their surroundings and use it for thousands of tasks. Energy drives metabolism—chemical work that stockpiles, builds, rearranges, and breaks down substances. It drives the mechanical work of moving cell parts, body parts, or the whole organism. It drives the electrochemical work of moving charged substances across membranes, as happens when cells make ATP.

THE ONE-WAY FLOW OF ENERGY

Energy is a capacity to do work, and you can't create it out of nothing. By the **first law of thermodynamics**, any isolated system has a finite amount of energy that cannot be added to or lost. Energy *can* be converted from one form to another. However, the total amount in the system stays the same. Motion, chemical bonds, heat, electricity, sound, nuclear forces, and gravity are examples of different forms of energy.

ENERGY LOST
Energy continually flows from the sun.

ENERGY GAINED
Sunlight energy reaches environments on Earth. Producers of nearly all ecosystems secure some and convert it to stored forms of energy. They and all other organisms convert stored energy to forms that can drive cellular work.

ENERGY LOST
With each conversion, there is a one-way flow of a bit of energy back to the environment. Nutrients cycle between producers and consumers.

producers

NUTRIENT CYCLING

consumers

"Entropy" is a measure of the degree of a system's disorder. By the **second law of thermodynamics**, the entropy, or disorder, of the universe always increases. Think of Egyptian pyramids—once highly organized, now crumbling, and thousands of years from now, dust. According to the second law, pyramids and all other things are on their way toward maximum entropy.

Energy is part of this big picture. It spontaneously flows toward its most disorganized form—heat. Why? Converting energy from one form to another is never 100 percent efficient. Although energy is conserved in any exchange, at least some of it dissipates as heat. It is not easy to convert heat to a different form of energy.

Can life be one glorious pocket of resistance to this depressing flow toward maximum entropy? After all, new bonds hold atoms together in orderly patterns in each new organism. Molecules get more organized and have richer stores of energy, not poorer.

Even so, the second law does apply to life on Earth. Life's main energy source is the sun, which has been losing energy ever since it formed about 5 billion years ago. Photosynthetic cells intercept light energy from the sun and convert it to chemical bond energy in sugars, starches, and other compounds. Organisms that eat plants get at the stored chemical energy by breaking and rearranging chemical bonds. With each conversion, however, a bit of energy escapes as heat. Cells don't convert that heat to other forms of energy. They simply can't use it to do work.

Overall, then, energy flows in one direction. Life can maintain its astounding organization only because it is being continually resupplied with energy that is being lost from someplace else (Figure 5.2).

UP AND DOWN THE ENERGY HILLS

Cells store and retrieve energy when they convert one molecule to another. In photosynthetic cells, sunlight energy drives ATP formation, then energy from ATP drives glucose formation (Figure 5.3*a*). Six molecules of carbon dioxide (CO_2) and six of water (H_2O) are converted to one molecule of glucose ($C_6H_{12}O_6$) and six of oxygen (O_2). Photosynthetic reactions require energy input; they are *endergonic* (meaning energy in).

Figure 5.2 A one-way flow of energy into ecosystems compensates for the one-way flow of energy out of it.

We think of glucose as a high-energy compound because it can be converted to more stable molecules for a net gain of energy. It does take an investment of energy to get the conversion reactions started, but the formation of more stable end products releases more energy than the amount invested. For example, CO_2 and H_2O are all that's left of glucose at the end of aerobic respiration. Both still have energy stored in covalent bonds, but the two products are so stable that cells cannot gain energy by converting them to something else. It's as if carbon dioxide and water are at the base of an "energy hill."

Aerobic respiration releases energy bit by bit, with many conversion steps, so cells can capture some of it efficiently. This metabolic process is like a downhill run, from high-energy glucose to low-energy carbon dioxide and water (Figure 5.3b). Such reactions, which show a net energy release, are said to be *exergonic*.

ATP—THE CELL'S ENERGY CURRENCY

All cells stay alive by *coupling* energy inputs to energy outputs, mainly with adenosine triphosphate, or **ATP**. This nucleotide consists of a five-carbon sugar (ribose), a base (adenine), and three phosphate groups (Figure 5.4a). ATP readily gives up a phosphate group to other molecules and primes them to react. Such phosphate-group transfers are known as **phosphorylations**.

ATP is the currency in a cell's economy. Cells earn it by investing in energy-releasing reactions. They spend it in energy-requiring reactions that keep them alive. We use a cartoon coin to symbolize ATP.

Because ATP is the main energy carrier for so many reactions, you might infer—correctly—that cells have ways to renew it. When ATP gives up a phosphate group, ADP (adenosine diphosphate) forms. ATP can re-form when ADP binds to inorganic phosphate (P_i) or to a phosphate group that was split from a different molecule. Regenerating ATP by this **ATP/ADP cycle** helps drive most metabolic reactions (Figure 5.4b).

Energy is the capacity to do work. It flows in one direction, from more usable to less usable forms. Heat is the least usable form of energy. Organisms maintain complex organization by being resupplied with energy from someplace else.

All organisms secure energy from outside sources. The sun is the primary source of energy for the web of life. All organisms use and store energy in chemical bonds.

ATP is the main energy carrier in all living cells. It couples energy-releasing and energy-requiring reactions. ATP primes molecules to react by transferring a phosphate group to them.

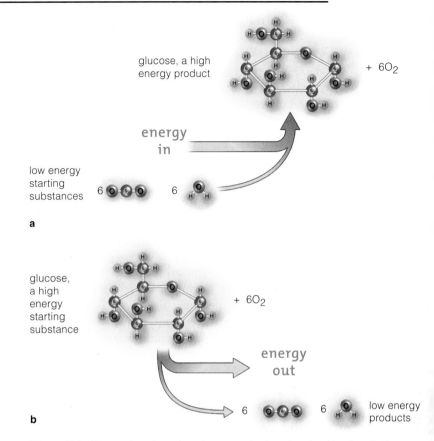

Figure 5.3 Two main categories of energy changes involved in chemical work. (**a**) Endergonic reactions, which won't run without an energy input. (**b**) Exergonic reactions, which end with a net release of usable energy.

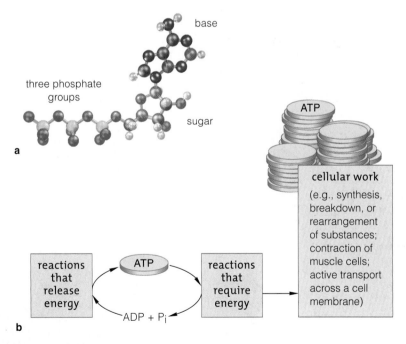

Figure 5.4 (**a**) Ball-and-stick model for ATP, an energy carrier. (**b**) ATP couples energy-releasing reactions with energy-requiring ones. In the ATP/ADP cycle, recurring phosphate-group transfers turn ATP into ADP, and back again to ATP.

5.2 Inputs and Outputs of Substances

How cells get energy is only one aspect of metabolism. Another is the accumulation, conversion, and disposal of materials by energy-driven reactions. Most reactions are part of stepwise metabolic pathways.

THE NATURE OF METABOLIC REACTIONS

For any metabolic reaction, the starting substances are called *reactants*. Substances formed during a reaction sequence are *intermediates*, and those left at the end are the *products*. ATP and other *energy carriers* activate enzymes and other molecules by making phosphate-group transfers. *Enzymes* are catalysts: They can speed specific reactions enormously. *Cofactors* are metal ions and coenzymes such as NAD^+. They help enzymes by moving functional groups, atoms, and electrons from one reaction site in an enzyme to another. *Transport proteins* help solutes across membranes. Controls over transport proteins adjust concentrations of substances required for reactions, and so influence the timing and direction of metabolism.

Bear in mind, metabolic reactions don't always run from reactants to products. They might start out in this "forward" direction. But most also run in reverse, with products being converted back to reactants. Such reversible reactions tend to run spontaneously toward **chemical equilibrium**, when the reaction rate is about the same in both directions. For most reactions, the amounts of reactant and product molecules differ at that time (Figure 5.5). It is like a party where people drift between two rooms. The number in each room stays the same—say, thirty in one and ten in the other—even as individuals move back and forth.

Why bother to think about this? *Each cell can bring about big changes in its activities by controlling a few steps of reversible metabolic pathways.*

For instance, when your cells need a quick bit of energy, they rapidly split glucose into two pyruvate molecules. They do so by a sequence of nine enzyme-mediated steps of a pathway called glycolysis. When glucose supplies are too low, cells quickly reverse this pathway and build glucose from pyruvate and other substances. How? Six steps of the pathway happen to be reversible, and the other three are bypassed. An input of energy from ATP drives the bypass reactions in the uphill (energetically unfavorable) direction.

What if cells did not have this reverse pathway? They wouldn't be able to build glucose fast enough to compensate for episodes of starvation, when glucose supplies in blood become dangerously low.

REDOX REACTIONS

Energy flows from the environment through all living things by way of photosynthesis and other metabolic pathways. Individual cells capture free energy, store it, then release it in manageable bits. They *control* the energy they require to grow and reproduce.

Cells release energy efficiently by electron transfers, or **oxidation–reduction reactions**. In these "redox" reactions, one molecule gives up electrons (is oxidized) and another gains them (is reduced). Commonly, hydrogen atoms are released at the same time, thus becoming H^+. Being attracted to the opposite charge of the electrons, H^+ tags along with them.

highly spontaneous

equilibrium

highly spontaneous

Figure 5.5 Chemical equilibrium. With a high concentration of reactant molecules (represented as wishful frogs), a reaction runs most strongly in the forward direction, to products (the princes). When the concentration of product molecules is high, it runs most strongly in reverse. At equilibrium, the rates of the forward and reverse reactions are the same.

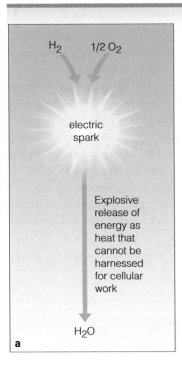

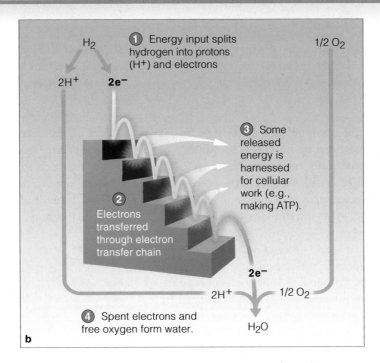

H_2 $1/2 O_2$

electric spark

Explosive release of energy as heat that cannot be harnessed for cellular work

H_2O

a

1 Energy input splits hydrogen into protons (H^+) and electrons

H_2 $1/2 O_2$

$2H^+$ $2e^-$

3 Some released energy is harnessed for cellular work (e.g., making ATP).

2 Electrons transferred through electron transfer chain

$2e^-$

$2H^+$ $1/2 O_2$

4 Spent electrons and free oxygen form water.

H_2O

b

Read Me First!
and watch the narrated animation on controlling energy release

Figure 5.6 Uncontrolled versus controlled energy release. (**a**) Free hydrogen and oxygen exposed to an electric spark react and release energy all at once. (**b**) Electron transfer chains let the same reaction proceed in small, more manageable steps that can access the released energy.

Start thinking about redox reactions, because they are central to photosynthesis and aerobic respiration. In the next two chapters, you'll see how coenzymes pick up electrons and H^+ stripped from substrates, then deliver them to **electron transfer chains**. Such chains are membrane-bound arrays of enzymes and other molecules that accept and give up electrons in sequence. Electrons are at a higher energy level when they enter a chain than when they leave. Think of the electrons as descending a staircase and stingily losing a bit of energy at each step (Figure 5.6). For these two pathways, stepwise electron transfers concentrate H^+ in ways that contribute to ATP formation.

TYPES OF METABOLIC PATHWAYS

We've mentioned metabolic pathways in passing, but let's now formally define them. **Metabolic pathways** are enzyme-mediated sequences of reactions in cells. Many are *biosynthetic* (or anabolic), and they require energy inputs. Examples are the assembly of glucose, starch, proteins, and other high-energy molecules from small molecules. The main biosynthetic pathway in the biosphere is photosynthesis (Figure 5.7).

Degradative (or catabolic) pathways are exergonic, overall. These reactions can break down molecules to smaller, lower energy products. Aerobic respiration releases a lot of usable energy (ATP) in the step-by-step enzymatic breakdown of glucose. It is the main degradative pathway in the biosphere (Figure 5.7).

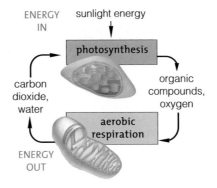

ENERGY IN   sunlight energy

photosynthesis

carbon dioxide, water

organic compounds, oxygen

aerobic respiration

ENERGY OUT

Figure 5.7 The main metabolic pathways in ecosystems. Energy input from the sun drives photosynthesis, and aerobic respiration yields a lot of usable energy. ATP forms in both pathways by way of redox reactions.

Not all metabolic pathways are linear, a straight line from the reactants to products. In cyclic pathways, the final step regenerates a reactant that is the point of entry for the reaction sequence. In branched pathways, reactants or intermediates are channeled into two or more different reaction sequences.

Metabolic pathways are orderly, enzyme-mediated reaction sequences, some biosynthetic, others degradative.

Control over a key step of a metabolic pathway can bring about rapid shifts in cell activities.

Many aspects of metabolism involve electron transfers, or oxidation–reduction reactions. Electron transfer chains are important sites of energy exchange in both photosynthesis and aerobic respiration.

5.3 How Enzymes Make Substances React

What would happen if you left a cupful of glucose out in the open? Not much. Years would pass before you would see evidence of its conversion to carbon dioxide and water. Yet that same conversion takes only a few seconds in your body. Enzymes make the difference.

Enzymes, again, are catalytic molecules; they speed rates of specific reactions by hundreds to millions of times. Enzymes chemically recognize, bind, and alter specific reactants. They remain unchanged, and so can mediate the same reaction over and over again. Except for a few RNAs, enzymes are proteins.

Regardless of whether a reaction is spontaneous or enzyme-mediated, it won't proceed unless the starting substances have enough internal energy to overcome repulsive forces that otherwise keep molecules apart. All molecules have internal energy that is affected by temperature and pressure. **Activation energy** refers to the minimum amount of internal energy that molecules must have before a reaction gets going.

Activation energy is an energy barrier—something like a hill or a brick wall (Figures 5.8 and 5.9). One way or another, that barrier must be surmounted before the reaction will proceed. Enzymes lower the barrier. How? *Compared to the surrounding environment,*

they offer a stable microenvironment that is more favorable for reaction. Enzymes are far larger than **substrates**, another name for the reactants that bind to a specific enzyme. Each enzyme has one or more **active sites**: pockets or crevices where substrates bind and where specific reactions are catalyzed (Figure 5.10).

Part of the substrate is complementary in shape, size, solubility, and charge to the active site. Because of this fit, each enzyme can recognize and bind its substrate among thousands of substances in cells.

Think back on the main types of enzyme-mediated reactions (Section 3.1). In *functional group transfers,* one

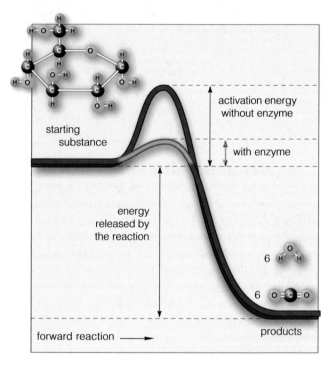

Figure 5.8 Activation energy. Reactants must have a minimum amount of internal energy before a given reaction will run to products. Sometimes they need an input of energy to get there. An enzyme enhances the reaction rate by lowering the amount of activation energy required. It makes the energy hill smaller.

Figure 5.9 A simple way to think about the energy required to get a reaction going without an enzyme (**a**) and with the help of an enzyme (**b**).

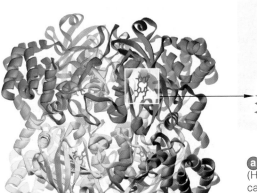

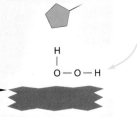

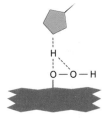

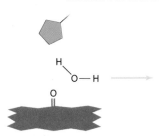

a Hydrogen peroxide (H_2O_2) enters a cavity in catalase. It is the substrate for a reaction aided by an iron molecule in a heme group (*red*).

b A hydrogen of the peroxide is attracted to histidine, an amino acid projecting into the cavity. One oxygen binds the iron.

c This binding destabilizes the peroxide bond, which breaks. Water (H_2O) forms. In a later reaction, another H_2O_2 will pull the oxygen from iron, which will then be free to act again.

Figure 5.10 How catalase works. This enzyme has four polypeptide chains and four heme groups.

molecule gives up a functional group to another. In *electron transfers*, one or more electrons stripped from one molecule are donated to another. In *rearrangements*, a juggling of internal bonds converts one molecule to another. In *condensation*, two molecules are covalently bound together as a larger molecule. Finally, in *cleavage* reactions, a larger molecule splits into smaller ones.

When we talk about activation energy, *we really are talking about the energy it takes to align reactive chemical groups, briefly destabilize electric charges, and break bonds.*

Enzymes lower activation energy by restraining a reactant molecule. Binding to the active site stretches and squeezes the reactant into a certain shape, maybe next to another molecule or reactive group. This puts a substrate at its **transition state**, meaning its bonds are at the breaking point and the reaction can run easily to product.

The binding between an enzyme and its substrate is weak, and temporary (that's why the reaction does not change the enzyme). But energy is released when weak bonds form. This "binding energy" stabilizes the transition state long enough to keep the enzyme and its substrate together for the reaction.

Four mechanisms work alone or in combination to get substrates to the transition state:

Helping substrates get together. Substrate molecules rarely react at low concentrations. Binding to an active site boosts local substrate concentration by as much as ten millionfold.

Orienting substrates in positions favoring reaction. On their own, substrates collide from random directions. By contrast, weak but extensive bonds at an active site put reactive groups close together.

Shutting out water. Because of its ability to form hydrogen bonds so easily, water can interfere with the breaking and formation of bonds during reactions. Some active sites contain mostly nonpolar amino acids. The hydrophobic groups keep water away from the active site and reactions.

Inducing changes in enzyme shape. Weak interactions between the enzyme and its substrate may induce the enzyme to change its shape. By the **induced-fit model**, a substrate is not quite complementary to an active site. The enzyme bends and optimizes the fit; in doing so, it pulls the substrate to the transition state.

On their own, chemical reactions occur too slowly to sustain life. Enzymes greatly increase reaction rates by lowering the activation energy—the minimum amount of energy required to align reactive groups, destabilize electric charges, and break bonds so that products can form from reactants.

Enzymes drive their substrates to a transition state, when the reaction can most easily run to completion. This happens in the enzyme's active site.

In the active site, substrates move to the transition state by mechanisms that concentrate and orient them, that exclude water, and that induce an optimal fit with the active site.

5.4 Enzymes Don't Work In a Vacuum

Controls over enzyme function help cells respond quickly to changing conditions by triggering adjustments in metabolic reactions. Feedback mechanisms that can activate or inhibit enzymes conserve resources. Cells synthesize what conditions require—no more, no less.

HELP FROM COFACTORS

Cofactors (specific metal ions or coenzymes) help out at the active site of enzymes or taxi electrons, H^+, or functional groups to a different location. **Coenzymes** are a class of organic compounds that may or may not have a vitamin component.

One or more metal ions assist nearly a third of all known enzymes. Metal ions easily give up and accept electrons. As part of coenzymes, they help products form by shifting electron arrangements in substrates or intermediates. That is what goes on at the hemes in catalase. Heme, an organic ring structure, incorporates iron at its center. Figure 5.10 shows how iron atoms in heme coenzymes help catalase break down hydrogen peroxide to water.

Like vitamin E, catalase is one of the **antioxidants**: It helps neutralize free radicals. *Free radicals* are atoms with unpaired electrons—reactive, unbound fragments left over from reactions. As we age, we make less and less catalase, so free radicals accumulate. They attack the structure of DNA and other biological molecules.

Some coenzymes are tightly bound to an enzyme. Others, such as NAD^+ and $NADP^+$, can diffuse freely through a cell membrane or cytoplasm. Either way, coenzymes participate intimately in a reaction. Unlike enzymes, many become modified during the reaction, but they are regenerated elsewhere.

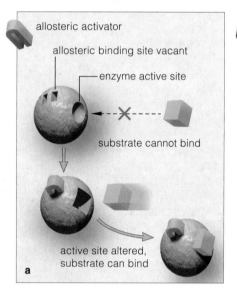
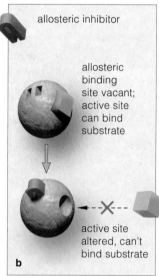

Figure 5.11 Allosteric control over enzyme activity. (**a**) An active site is unblocked when an activator binds to a vacant allosteric site. (**b**) An active site is blocked when an inhibitor binds to a vacant allosteric site.

CONTROLS OVER ENZYMES

Many controls over enzymes maintain, lower, and raise the concentrations of substances. Others adjust how fast enzyme molecules are synthesized, and they activate or inhibit the ones already built.

In some cases, a molecule that acts as an activator or inhibitor reversibly binds to its own *allosteric* site, not the active site, on the enzyme (*allo*–, other; *steric*, structure). Binding alters the enzyme's shape in a way that hides or exposes the active site (Figure 5.11).

Picture a bacterial cell making tryptophan and other amino acids—the building blocks for proteins. Even when the cell has made enough proteins, tryptophan synthesis continues until its increasing concentration causes **feedback inhibition**. This means a change that results from a specific activity *shuts down the activity*.

A feedback loop starts and ends at many allosteric enzymes. In this case, unused tryptophan binds to an allosteric site on one of the enzymes in a tryptophan biosynthesis pathway. It blocks the active site, so less tryptophan is made (Figure 5.12). At times when not many tryptophan molecules are around, more active

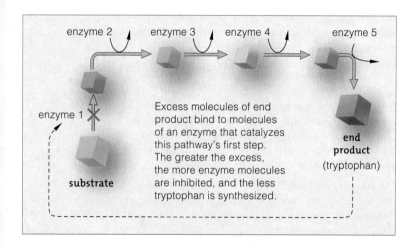

Figure 5.12 Feedback inhibition of a metabolic pathway. Five kinds of enzymes act in sequence to convert a substrate to tryptophan.

sites remain exposed, and so the synthesis rate picks up. In such ways, feedback loops quickly adjust the concentrations of substances.

In humans and other multicelled species, enzyme controls are just amazing. They keep individual cells functioning in ways that benefit the whole body!

EFFECTS OF TEMPERATURE, PH, AND SALINITY

Temperature is a measure of molecular motion. As it rises, it boosts reaction rates both by increasing the likelihood that a substrate will bump into an enzyme and by raising a substrate molecule's internal energy. Remember, the more energy a reactant molecule has, the closer it gets to jumping that activation energy barrier and taking part in a reaction.

Above or below the range of temperature that an enzyme can tolerate, weak bonds break, and enzyme shape changes. Substrates no longer can bind to the active site, and the reaction rate falls sharply (Figure 5.13). Such declines typically occur with fevers above 44°C (112°F), which people usually cannot survive.

Enzyme action is also affected by pH (Figure 5.14). In the human body, most enzymes work best when the pH is between 6 and 8. For instance, trypsin is active in the small intestine (pH of 8 or so).

One of the notable exceptions is pepsin, a protein-digesting enzyme. Pepsin is a nonspecific protease; it chews up any proteins. It is produced in inactive form and normally becomes activated only in gastric fluid, in the stomach. Gastric fluid happens to be a highly acidic environment (pH 1–2). It's a good thing that activated pepsin is confined to the stomach. If it were to leak out (as happens with peptic ulcers), it could digest a lot of you instead of proteins in your food.

Most enzymes don't work well when the fluids in which they are dissolved are saltier or less salty than their range of tolerance. Too much or too little salt interferes with the hydrogen bonds that help hold an enzyme in its three-dimensional shape. By doing so, it inactivates the enzyme.

Many enzymes are assisted by cofactors, which are specific metal ions or coenzymes.

Enzyme action adjusts the concentrations and kinds of substances available in cells. Controls over enzymes enhance or inhibit their activity.

Enzymes work best when the cellular environment stays within limited ranges of temperature, pH, and salinity. The actual ranges differ from one type of enzyme to the next.

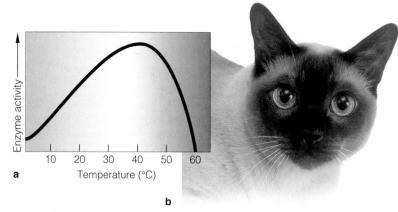

Figure 5.13 Enzymes and the environment. (**a**) How increases in temperature affect one enzyme's activity. (**b**) Temperature outside the body affects the fur color of Siamese cats. Epidermal cells that give rise to the cat's fur produce a brownish-black pigment, melanin. Tyrosinase, an enzyme in the melanin production pathway, is heat-sensitive in the Siamese. It becomes inactive in warmer parts of the cat's body, which end up with less melanin, and lighter fur. Put this cat in booties for a few weeks and its warm feet will turn white.

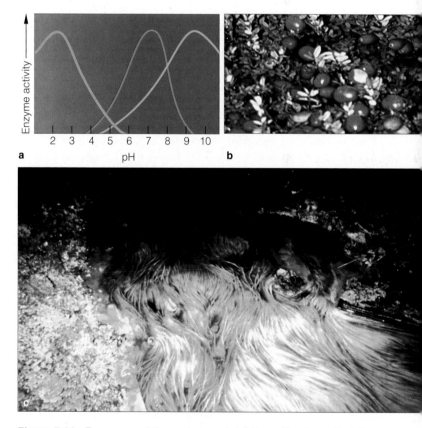

Figure 5.14 Enzymes and the environment. (**a**) How pH values affect three enzymes. (**b**) Cranberry plants grow best in acidic bogs. Unlike most plants, they have no nitrate reductase. This enzyme converts nitrate (NO_3) found in typical soils to metabolically useful ammonia (NH_3). Nitrogen in highly acidic soils is already in the form of ammonia (NH_4^+). (**c**) Life in wastewater from a copper mine in California. The slime streamers are microbial communities dominated by an archaean, which makes unique enzymes that help it live in this toxic, highly acidic environment.

5.5 Diffusion, Membranes, and Metabolism

What determines whether a substance will move one way or another to and from a cell, across that cell's membranes, or through the cell itself? Part of the answer has to do with something called diffusion.

Think about the water bathing the surfaces of a cell membrane. Plenty of substances are dissolved in it, but the kinds and amounts close to its two surfaces differ. The membrane itself set up the difference and is busy maintaining it. How? Each cell membrane has

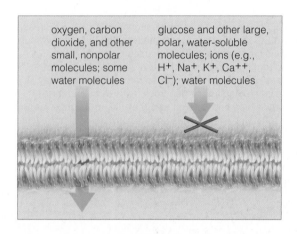

Figure 5.15 Selective permeability of cell membranes. Small, nonpolar molecules and some water molecules can cross the lipid bilayer. Ions and large, polar, water-soluble molecules and the water dissolving them cross with the help of transport proteins.

selective permeability. Its molecular structure allows some substances but not others to cross it in certain ways, at certain times.

Lipids of a membrane's bilayer are mostly nonpolar, so they let small, nonpolar molecules such as O_2 and CO_2 slip across. Water molecules are polar, but some slip through gaps that form as the hydrophobic tails of many lipids flex and bend. The bilayer itself is not permeable to ions or large, polar molecules such as glucose; these cross with the help of proteins. Water often crosses with them (Figure 5.15).

Membrane barriers and crossings are vital, because metabolism depends on the cell's capacity to increase, decrease, and maintain concentrations of molecules and ions required for reactions. They also supply cells or organelles with raw materials, get rid of wastes, and collectively maintain the cell's volume and pH.

WHAT IS A CONCENTRATION GRADIENT?

Now picture molecules or ions of some substance near a membrane. They move constantly, collide at random, and bounce off one another. When the concentration in one region is not the same as in an adjoining region, this condition is a *gradient*. A **concentration gradient** is a difference in the number per unit volume of ions or molecules of a substance between adjoining regions.

In the absence of other forces, a substance tends to move from a region where it is more concentrated to a region where it is less concentrated. At temperatures characteristic of life, *thermal energy that is inherent in molecules drives this movement.* Although the molecules are colliding and careening back and forth millions of times per second, their *net* movement is away from the place where they are most concentrated.

Diffusion is the name for the net movement of like molecules or ions down a concentration gradient. It is a factor in how substances move into, through, and out of cells. In multicelled species, it moves substances between body regions and between the body and its environment. For instance, when oxygen builds up in leaf cells, it may diffuse into air inside the leaf, then into air outside, where its concentration is lower.

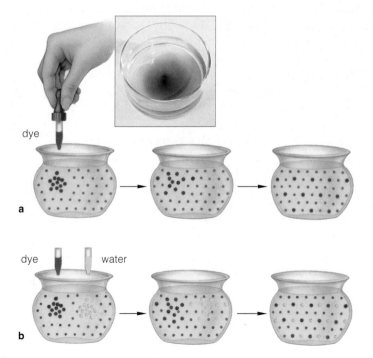

Figure 5.16 Two cases of diffusion. (**a**) A drop of dye enters a bowl filled with water. Gradually, the dye molecules become evenly dispersed through the molecules of water. (**b**) The same thing happens with water molecules. Here, dye (*red*) and water (*yellow*) are added to the same bowl. Each substance will show a net movement down its own concentration gradient.

Like other substances, oxygen tends to diffuse in a direction set by its *own* concentration gradient, not by gradients of other solutes. You can see the outcome of this tendency by squeezing a drop of dye into water. The dye molecules diffuse into the region where they are not as concentrated, and water molecules move into the region where *they* are not as concentrated. Figure 5.16 shows simple examples of diffusion.

WHAT DETERMINES DIFFUSION RATES?

How fast a particular solute diffuses depends on the steepness of its concentration gradient, its size, the temperature, and electric or pressure gradients that may be present.

First, rates are high with steep gradients, because more molecules are moving out of a region of greater concentration compared to the number moving into it. Second, more heat energy in warmer regions makes molecules move faster and collide more often. Third, smaller molecules diffuse faster than large ones do.

Fourth, an electric gradient may alter the rate and direction of diffusion. An **electric gradient** is simply a difference in electric charge between adjoining regions. For example, each ion dissolved in fluids bathing a cell membrane contributes to an electric charge at one side or the other. Opposite charges attract. Therefore, the fluid with more negative charge overall exerts the greatest pull on positively charged substances, such as sodium ions. Later chapters explain how many cell activities, including ATP formation and the sending and receiving of signals in nervous systems, are based on the force of electric and concentration gradients.

Fifth, as you will see shortly, diffusion also may be affected by a **pressure gradient**. This is a difference in the exerted force per unit area in two adjoining regions.

MEMBRANE CROSSING MECHANISMS

Before getting into the actual mechanisms that move substances across membranes, study the overview in Figure 5.17. These mechanisms help supply cells and organelles with raw materials and get rid of wastes. Collectively, they help maintain the volume and pH of cells or organelles within functional ranges.

Small, nonpolar molecules such as oxygen diffuse across the membrane's lipid bilayer. Polar molecules and ions diffuse through the interior of transport proteins that span the bilayer. Passive transporters simply allow a substance to follow its concentration gradient across a membrane. The mechanism is called *passive transport*, or "facilitated" diffusion.

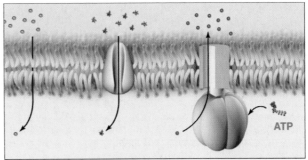

| Diffusion of lipid-soluble substances across bilayer | Passive transport of water-soluble substances through channel protein; no energy input needed | Active transport through ATPase; requires energy input from ATP |

High

Concentration gradient across cell membrane

Low

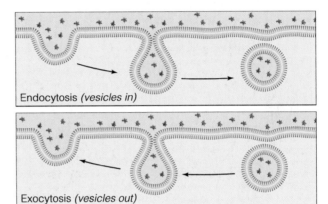

Endocytosis *(vesicles in)*

Exocytosis *(vesicles out)*

Figure 5.17 Overview of membrane crossing mechanisms.

Polar molecules cross the membrane through the interior of active transporters. The net direction of movement is against the concentration gradient, and it requires an input of energy. We call this mechanism *active transport*. Energy-activated transporters move a substance against its concentration gradient.

Other mechanisms move substances in bulk into or out of cells. *Exocytosis* involves fusion of the plasma membrane and a membrane-bound vesicle that formed inside the cytoplasm. *Endocytosis* involves an inward sinking of a patch of plasma membrane, which seals back on itself to form a vesicle inside the cytoplasm.

Diffusion is the net movement of molecules or ions of a substance into an adjoining region where they are not as concentrated.

The force of a concentration gradient can drive the directional movement of a substance across membranes. The gradient's steepness, temperature, molecular size, and electric and pressure gradients affect diffusion rates.

Cellular mechanisms increase and decrease concentration gradients across cell membranes.

5.6 How the Membrane Transporters Work

Read Me First!
and watch the narrated animation on passive transport

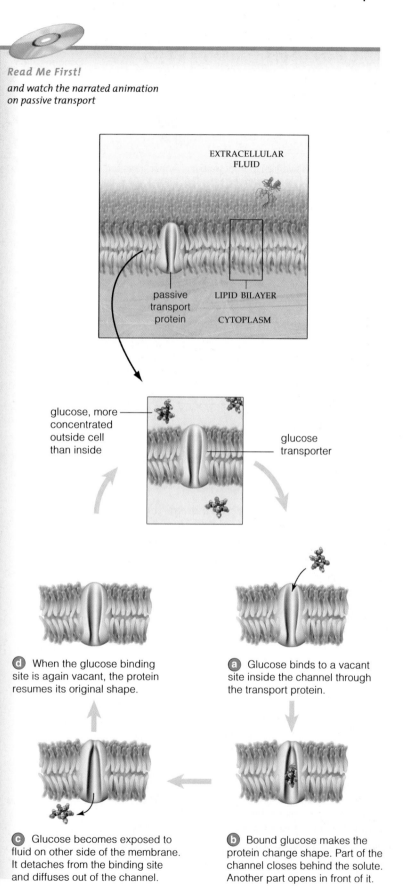

glucose, more concentrated outside cell than inside

glucose transporter

d When the glucose binding site is again vacant, the protein resumes its original shape.

a Glucose binds to a vacant site inside the channel through the transport protein.

c Glucose becomes exposed to fluid on other side of the membrane. It detaches from the binding site and diffuses out of the channel.

b Bound glucose makes the protein change shape. Part of the channel closes behind the solute. Another part opens in front of it.

Large, polar molecules and ions can't cross a lipid bilayer; they require the help of transport proteins.

Many kinds of solutes cross a membrane by diffusing through a channel or tunnel inside transport proteins. When one solute molecule or ion enters the channel and weakly binds to the protein, the protein's shape changes. The channel closes behind the bound solute and opens in front of it, which exposes the solute to the fluid environment on the opposite side of the membrane. There, the binding site reverts to what it was before, so the solute is released.

PASSIVE TRANSPORT

In **passive transport**, a concentration gradient, electric gradient, or both drive the diffusion of a substance across a membrane, through the interior of a transport protein. The protein does not require an energy input to assist the directional movement. That is why this mechanism is also known as facilitated diffusion.

Some passive transporters are open channels, and some are channels with gates that can be opened or closed when conditions change. Others, including the glucose transporter illustrated in Figure 5.18, assist solutes across by undergoing reversible changes in their shape.

The *net* direction of movement depends on how many molecules or ions of the solute are randomly colliding with the transporters. Encounters are more frequent on the side of the membrane where the solute concentration is greatest. The solute's *net* movement tends to be toward the side of the membrane where it is less concentrated.

If nothing else were going on, passive transport would continue until concentrations on both sides of a cell membrane became equal. But other processes affect the outcome. For instance, glucose transporters help glucose from blood move into cells, which use it for biosynthesis and for quick energy. How? As fast as glucose molecules are diffusing into cells, others are being used up. By using up glucose, then, these cells maintain the gradient that favors the uptake of *more* glucose.

Figure 5.18 Passive transport. This model shows one of the glucose transporters that span the plasma membrane. Glucose crosses in both directions. The *net* movement is down its concentration gradient until its concentrations are equal on both sides of the membrane.

ACTIVE TRANSPORT

Only in a dead cell have solute concentrations become equal on both sides of membranes. Living cells never stop expending energy to pump solutes into and out of their interior. With **active transport**, energy-driven protein motors help move a specific solute across the cell membrane *against* its concentration gradient.

Only specific solutes can bind to functional groups that line the interior channel of an active transporter. When the solute enters the channel and binds to one of those groups, the transporter accepts a phosphate group from an ATP molecule. The phosphate-group transfer changes the transporter's shape in a way that releases the solute on the other side of the membrane.

Figure 5.19 focuses on a **calcium pump**. This active transporter helps keep the concentration of calcium in a cell at least a thousand times lower than outside. A different active transporter, the **sodium–potassium pump**, mediates the movement of two kinds of ions, in opposite directions. Sodium ions (Na^+) from the cytoplasm diffuse into the open channel of the pump, where they bind to functional groups. A phosphate-group transfer by ATP prompts the pump to change shape and release the sodium ions outside the cell.

The channel through the activated pump is now open to the outside of the cell. Potassium ions (K^+) diffuse into the pump and bind to functional groups inside. The phosphate group is released from the pump, which reverts to its original shape. When it does, the potassium ions are released to the cytoplasm.

Active transport systems help maintain membrane gradients that are essential to many processes, such as muscle contraction and nerve cell (neuron) function.

> *Some transport proteins are open or gated channels across cell membranes. Others change shape when solutes bind to them.*
>
> *In passive transport, a solute simply diffuses through the interior of a transporter; an energy input is not necessary.*
>
> *In active transport, the net diffusion of a specific solute is against its concentration gradient. The transporter must be activated by an energy input from ATP to counter the force inherent in the gradient.*

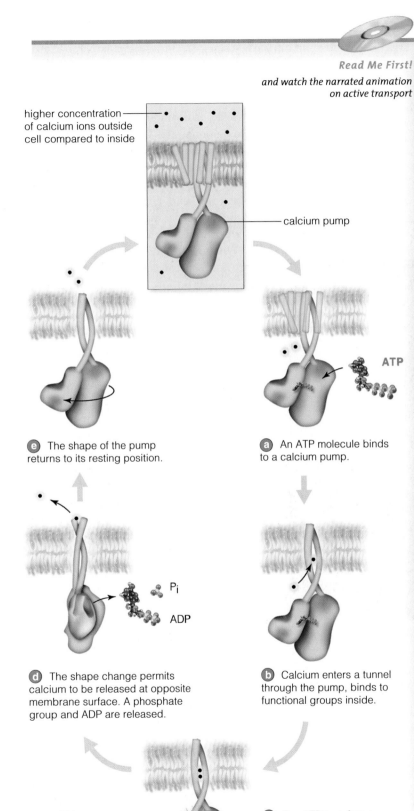

Read Me First!
and watch the narrated animation on active transport

higher concentration of calcium ions outside cell compared to inside

calcium pump

ATP

e The shape of the pump returns to its resting position.

a An ATP molecule binds to a calcium pump.

P_i

ADP

d The shape change permits calcium to be released at opposite membrane surface. A phosphate group and ADP are released.

b Calcium enters a tunnel through the pump, binds to functional groups inside.

c The ATP transfers a phosphate group to pump. The energy input will cause pump's shape to change.

Figure 5.19 Active transport by a calcium pump. This sketch shows its channel for calcium ions. ATP transfers a phosphate group to the pump, thus providing energy that can drive the movement of calcium *against* a concentration gradient across the cell membrane.

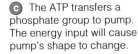

5.7 Which Way Will Water Move?

By far, more water diffuses across cell membranes than any other substance, so the main factors that influence its directional movement deserve special attention.

MOVEMENT OF WATER

Something as trickly as a running faucet or as mighty as Niagara Falls demonstrates **bulk flow**, or the mass movement of one or more substances in response to pressure, gravity, or another external force. Bulk flow accounts for some water movement in big multicelled organisms. A beating heart generates fluid pressure that pumps blood, which is mostly water. Sap flows inside tubes in trees, and this, too, is bulk flow.

What about the movement of water into and out of cells and organelles? If the concentration of water is not equal across a cell membrane, osmosis tends to occur. **Osmosis** is the diffusion of water across a selectively permeable membrane, to a region where the water concentration is lower.

You may be asking: How can water, a liquid, be more or less "concentrated"? Its concentration actually is influenced by the concentration of *solutes* on both sides of the membrane. If you pour glucose or some other solute into a glass of water, you will increase the volume of liquid in the glass. Now the same number of water molecules will become less concentrated than they were before; they will diffuse through the larger volume of space.

Now suppose you divide the interior of a glass container with a selectively permeable membrane, one that permits the diffusion of water but not glucose (a large, polar molecule) across it. You have created a water concentration gradient. More water molecules will diffuse across the membrane, into the solution, than will diffuse back (Figure 5.20).

In cases of osmosis, "solute concentration" refers to the *total number* of molecules or ions in a specified volume of a solution. It doesn't matter whether the dissolved substance is glucose, urea, or anything else; the *type* of solute doesn't dictate water concentration.

EFFECTS OF TONICITY

Suppose you decide to test the statement that water tends to move to a region where solutes are more concentrated. You make three sacs from a membrane that water but not sucrose can cross. You fill each sac with a solution that's 2 percent sucrose, then immerse one in a liter of water. You immerse another sac in a solution that is 10 percent sucrose. And you immerse the third sac in a solution that is 2 percent sucrose.

In each experiment, tonicity dictates the extent and direction of water movement across the membrane, as Figure 5.21 shows. *Tonicity* refers to the relative solute concentrations of two fluids. When two fluids that are on opposing sides of a membrane differ in their solute concentrations, the **hypotonic solution** is the one with fewer solutes. The one having more solutes is a **hypertonic solution**. And water tends to diffuse from a hypotonic fluid to a hypertonic one. **Isotonic solutions** show no net osmotic movement.

Normally, the fluid inside your cells is isotonic with tissue fluid outside. If the fluid outside becomes far too hypotonic, too much water will diffuse into those cells and make them burst. If it gets too hypertonic, water will diffuse out, and the cells will shrivel.

Most cells have built-in mechanisms that adjust to changes in tonicity. Red blood cells don't. Figure 5.21 shows what happens to them when tonicity changes.

EFFECTS OF FLUID PRESSURE

Selective transport of solutes across the plasma membrane keeps animal cells from bursting. Cells of plants and many protists, fungi, and bacteria avoid bursting with the help of pressure on their cell walls.

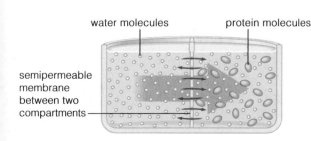

water molecules   protein molecules

semipermeable membrane between two compartments

Figure 5.20 Solute concentration gradients and osmosis. A membrane divides this container. Water, but not proteins, can cross it. Pour 1 liter of water in the left compartment and 1 liter of a protein-rich solution in the right one. The proteins occupy some of the space in the right one. The net diffusion of water in this case is from left to right (large *gray* arrow).

Pressure differences as well as solute concentrations influence osmosis. Take a look at Figure 5.22. It shows how water will diffuse across a membrane between a hypotonic and a hypertonic solution until the solute concentration is the same on both sides. As you can see, the *volume* of the formerly hypertonic solution has increased (because its solutes cannot diffuse out).

Hydrostatic pressure is the force that any volume of fluid exerts against a wall, a membrane, or some other structure enclosing it. (In plants, this pressure is called *turgor*.) Hydrostatic pressure that has built up in a cell can counter the further inward diffusion of water. This **osmotic pressure** is the amount of force preventing any further increase in volume.

Think of the pliable primary wall of a young plant cell. As it matures, many vesicles start to coalesce into a large central vacuole. During cell growth, water diffuses into the vacuole and puts more fluid pressure on the cell wall. The wall expands, so the cell volume increases. Continued expansion of the wall (and of the cell) ends when enough internal fluid pressure develops to counter the water uptake.

Plant cells are vulnerable to water losses, which can occur when soil dries out or becomes too salty. Water stops diffusing in and starts diffusing out, so internal fluid pressure falls and the cytoplasm shrinks.

In later chapters, you'll see how fluid pressure has a role in the distribution of water and solutes inside the body of plants and animals.

> Osmosis is a net diffusion of water between two solutions that differ in solute concentration and are separated by a selectively permeable membrane. The greater the number of molecules and ions dissolved in a given amount of water, the lower the water concentration will be.
>
> Water tends to move osmotically to regions of greater solute concentration (from hypotonic to hypertonic solutions). There is no net diffusion between isotonic solutions.
>
> Fluid pressure that a solution exerts against a membrane or wall influences the osmotic movement of water.

Read Me First!

and watch the narrated animation on tonicity and water movement

2% sucrose solution

1 liter of distilled water

1 liter of 10% sucrose solution

1 liter of 2% sucrose solution

Hypotonic Conditions
Water diffuses into red blood cells, which swell up

Hypertonic Conditions
Water diffuses out of the cells, which shrink

Isotonic Conditions
No net movement of water, no change in cell size or shape

Figure 5.21 Tonicity and the direction of water movement. In each of three containers, arrow widths signify the direction and the relative amounts of flow. The micrographs below each sketch show the shape of a human red blood cell that is immersed in fluids of higher, lower, or equal concentrations of solutes. The solutions inside and outside red blood cells are normally balanced. This type of cell has no way to adjust to drastic change in solute levels in its fluid surroundings.

Figure 5.22 Experiment showing an increase in fluid volume as an outcome of osmosis. A semipermeable membrane separates two compartments. Over time, the net diffusion will be the same in both directions across the membrane, but the fluid volume in the second compartment will be greater because there are more solute molecules in it.

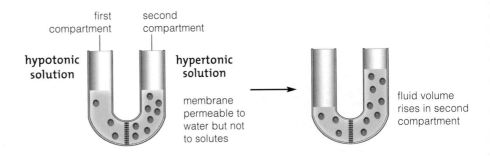

first compartment

second compartment

hypotonic solution

hypertonic solution

membrane permeable to water but not to solutes

fluid volume rises in second compartment

5.8 Membrane Traffic To and From the Cell Surface

We leave this chapter with another look at exocytosis and endocytosis. By these mechanisms, vesicles move substances to and from the plasma membrane. Vesicles help the cell take in and expel materials in amounts that are more than transport proteins can handle.

ENDOCYTOSIS AND EXOCYTOSIS

Think back on the membrane traffic to and from a cell surface (Figure 5.17). By **exocytosis**, a vesicle moves to the surface, and the protein-studded lipid bilayer of its membrane fuses with the plasma membrane. As this exocytic vesicle is losing its identity, its contents are released to the outside (Figures 5.23 and 5.24).

There are three pathways of **endocytosis**, but all take up substances near the cell surface. A small patch of plasma membrane balloons inward and pinches off inside the cytoplasm, forming an endocytic vesicle that moves its contents to some organelle or stores them in a cytoplasmic region (Figure 5.23).

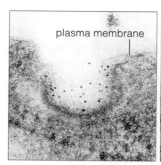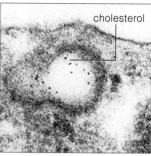

Figure 5.23 Endocytosis of cholesterol molecules.

With *receptor-mediated* endocytosis, receptors at the membrane bind to molecules of a hormone, vitamin, mineral, or another substance. A tiny pit forms in the plasma membrane beneath the receptors. The pit sinks into the cytoplasm and closes back on itself, and in this way it becomes a vesicle (Figure 5.24).

Phagocytosis ("cell eating") is a common endocytic pathway. Phagocytes such as amoebas engulf microbes, food particles, or cellular debris. In multicelled species, macrophages and some other white blood cells do this to pathogenic viruses or bacteria, cancerous body cells, and other threats.

Phagocytosis also involves receptors. Receptors that bind a target cause microfilaments to form a mesh just beneath the phagocyte's plasma membrane. When the microfilaments contract, they squeeze some cytoplasm toward the margins of the cell, forming a bulging lobe called a pseudopod (Figure 5.25). Pseudopods flow all around the target and form a vesicle. This sinks into the cell and fuses with lysosomes, the organelles of intracellular digestion. Lysosomes digest the trapped items into fragments and smaller, reusable molecules.

Bulk-phase endocytosis is not as selective. A vesicle forms around a small volume of the extracellular fluid regardless of the kinds of substances dissolved in it. This pathway continually removes patches of plasma membrane, balancing the steady additions that arrive in the form of exocytic vesicles from the cytoplasm.

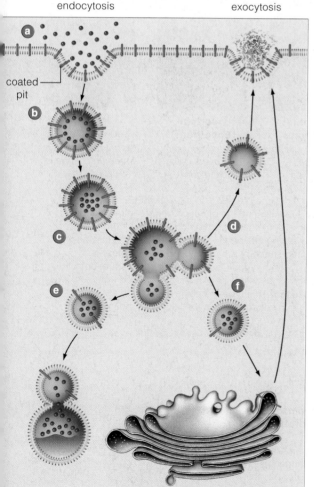

endocytosis   exocytosis

a Molecules get concentrated inside coated pits of plasma membrane.

b Endocytic vesicles form from the pits.

c Enclosed molecules are sorted and often released from receptors.

d Many sorted molecules are cycled back to the plasma membrane.

e,f Many other sorted molecules are delivered to lysosomes and stay there or are degraded. Still others are routed to spaces in the nuclear envelope and inside ER membranes, and others to Golgi bodies.

Figure 5.24 Cycling of membrane lipids and proteins. This sketch starts with receptor-mediated endocytosis. Patches of the plasma membrane form endocytic vesicles. New membrane arrives as exocytic vesicles that budded from ER membranes and Golgi bodies. The membrane initially used for endocytic vesicles will cycle receptor proteins and lipids back to the plasma membrane.

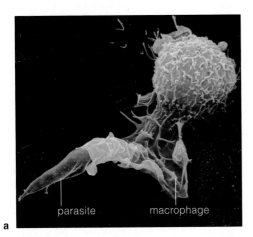

a

parasite   macrophage

b   bacterium   phagocytic vesicle

Figure 5.25 (**a**) A macrophage engulfing *Leishmania mexicana*. This parasitic protozoan causes leishmaniasis, a disease that can be fatal. Bites from infected sandflies transmit the parasite to humans.

(**b**) Phagocytosis. Lobes of an amoeba's cytoplasm surround a target. The plasma membrane of the extensions fuses to form a phagocytic vesicle. In the cytoplasm, this endocytic vesicle fuses with lysosomes, which digest its contents.

MEMBRANE CYCLING

For as long as a cell remains alive, exocytosis and endocytosis continually replace and withdraw patches of its plasma membrane, as in Figure 5.24. And they apparently do so at rates that can maintain the plasma membrane's total surface area.

As one example, neurons release neurotransmitters in bursts of exocytosis. Each neurotransmitter is a type of signaling molecule that acts on neighboring cells. An intense burst of endocytosis counterbalances each major burst of exocytosis.

Whereas transport proteins in a cell membrane deal only with ions and small molecules, exocytosis and endocytosis move large packets of materials across a plasma membrane.

By exocytosis, a cytoplasmic vesicle fuses with the plasma membrane, and its contents are released outside the cell.

By endocytosis, a small patch of the plasma membrane sinks inward and seals back on itself, forming a vesicle inside the cytoplasm. Membrane receptors often mediate this process.

Summary

Section 5.1 Cells engage in metabolism, or chemical work. They obtain and use energy to stockpile, build, rearrange, and break apart substances.

Energy in biological systems flows in one direction, from usable to less usable forms. Life maintains its complex organization by being resupplied with energy lost from someplace else. Sunlight is the ultimate energy source for the web of life.

ATP, the main energy carrier, couples reactions that release energy with reactions that require it. It primes molecules to react through phosphate-group transfers.

Section 5.2 Metabolic pathways are orderly, enzyme-mediated reaction sequences. Photosynthesis and other energy-requiring, *biosynthetic* pathways build large molecules with high energy from smaller ones. Energy-releasing, *degradative* pathways such as aerobic respiration break down large molecules to small products with lower bond energies. Table 5.1 lists the participants.

Cells increase, maintain, and lower concentrations of substances by coordinating thousands of reactions. They rapidly shift rates of metabolism by controlling a few steps of reversible pathways.

Electron transfers, or oxidation–reduction reactions, often proceed in series at cell membranes.

Section 5.3 Enzymes are catalysts; they enormously enhance rates of specific reactions and are not altered by their function. Pockets or cavities in these big molecules create favorable microenvironments for the reaction; these are the active sites.

Table 5.1	Summary of the Main Participants in Metabolic Reactions	
Reactant	Substance that enters a metabolic reaction or pathway; also called the substrate of a specific enzyme
Intermediate	Substance formed between the reactants and end products of a reaction or pathway
Product	Substance at the end of a reaction or pathway
Enzyme	A protein that greatly enhances reaction rates; a few RNAs also do this
Cofactor	Coenzyme (such as NAD^+) or metal ion; assists enzymes or taxis electrons, hydrogen, or functional groups between reaction sites
Energy carrier	Mainly ATP; couples energy-releasing reactions with energy-requiring ones
Transport protein	Protein that passively assists or actively pumps specific solutes across a cell membrane

Activation energy is the minimum internal energy that reactant molecules must have for a reaction to occur. Enzymes lower it by boosting substrate concentrations in the active site, by orienting substrates, by shutting out most or all water, and by inducing a precise fit with them.

Section 5.4 Cofactors (metal ions, coenzymes, or both) help an enzyme catalyze a reaction. Controls over enzyme action influence the kinds and amounts of substances available. Enzymes function best within a limited range of temperature, pH, and salinity.

Section 5.5 Diffusion is the movement of molecules or ions toward an adjoining region where they are less concentrated. The steepness of the concentration gradient, temperature, molecular size, and gradients in electrical charge and pressure influence diffusion rates.

Built-in cellular mechanisms work with and against gradients to move solutes across membranes.

Molecular oxygen, carbon dioxide, and other small nonpolar molecules diffuse across a membrane's lipid bilayer. Ions and large, polar molecules such as glucose cross it with the help of transport proteins. Some water moves through proteins and some through the bilayer.

Section 5.6 Many solutes cross membranes through transport proteins that act as open or gated channels or that reversibly change shape. Passive transport does not require energy input; a solute is free to follow its own concentration gradient across the membrane. Active transport requires an energy input from ATP to move a specific solute against its concentration gradient.

Section 5.7 Osmosis is the diffusion of water across a selectively permeable membrane, down the water concentration gradient. Pressure gradients can affect it.

Section 5.8 By exocytosis, a cytoplasmic vesicle fuses with the plasma membrane, and its contents are released outside. By endocytosis, a patch of plasma membrane forms a vesicle that sinks into the cytoplasm.

Self-Quiz
Answers in Appendix III

1. _____ is life's primary source of energy.
   a. Food   b. Water   c. Sunlight   d. ATP

2. Which of the following statements is *not* correct? A metabolic pathway _____ .
   a. has an orderly sequence of reaction steps
   b. is mediated by only one enzyme that starts it
   c. may be biosynthetic or degradative, overall
   d. all of the above

3. An enzyme _____ .
   a. is a protein
   b. lowers the activation energy of a reaction
   c. is destroyed by the reaction it catalyzes
   d. a and b

4. Immerse a living cell in a hypotonic solution, and water will tend to _____ .
   a. diffuse into the cell   c. show no net movement
   b. diffuse out of the cell   d. move in by endocytosis

5. _____ can readily diffuse across a lipid bilayer.
   a. Glucose   c. Carbon dioxide
   b. Oxygen   d. b and c

6. Sodium ions cross a membrane at transport proteins that receive an energy boost. This is a case of _____ .
   a. passive transport   c. facilitated diffusion
   b. active transport   d. a and c

7. Vesicle formation occurs in _____ .
   a. membrane cycling   c. endocytosis, exocytosis
   b. phagocytosis   d. all of the above

8. The rate of diffusion is affected by _____ .
   a. temperature   c. molecular size
   b. electrical gradients d. all of the above

9. Match the substance with its suitable description.
   _____ coenzyme or metal ion   a. reactant
   _____ adjusts gradients at membrane b. enzyme
   _____ substance entering a reaction c. cofactor
   _____ substance formed during   d. intermediate
        a reaction   e. product
   _____ substance at end of reaction   f. energy carrier
   _____ enhances reaction rate   g. transporter
   _____ mainly ATP   proteins

Critical Thinking

1. Cyanide, a toxic compound, binds irreversibly to an enzyme that is a component of electron transfer chains. The outcome is *cyanide poisoning*. Binding prevents the enzyme from donating electrons to a nearby acceptor molecule in the system. What effect will this have on ATP formation? From what you know of ATP's function, what effect will this have on a person's health?

2. In cells, superoxide dismutase (*below*) has a quaternary structure—it consists of two polypeptide chains. In each chain, a strandlike domain is arrayed as a barrel around a copper ion and a zinc ion (coded *red* and *blue*).

   Which part of the barrel is probably hydrophobic? Which part is hydrophilic? Do you suppose substrates bind inside or outside the barrels? Do the metal ions have a role in catalysis?

3. Catalase breaks down hydrogen peroxide, a reactive by-product of aerobic metabolism, to water and oxygen (Figure 5.10). It is a very efficient enzyme: One molecule of catalase can break down 6 million hydrogen peroxide molecules every minute. It is found in most organisms that live under aerobic conditions because hydrogen

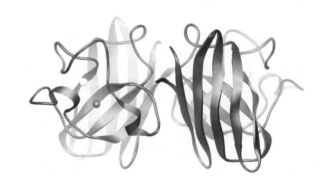

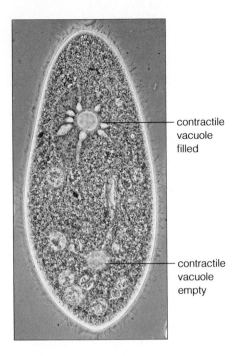

contractile
vacuole
filled

contractile
vacuole
empty

Figure 5.26 *Paramecium*
contractile vacuoles.

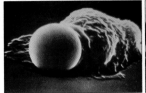

Figure 5.27 Go ahead, name the mystery membrane mechanism.

peroxide is toxic—cells must dispose of it quickly or
they risk being damaged. Peroxide is catalase's substrate;
but by a neat trick, it also can inactivate other toxins,
including alcohol. Can you guess what the trick is?

4. Nutritional supplements often include plant enzymes.
Explain why it is not likely that plant enzymes will aid
your digestion.

5. Why does applying lemon juice to sliced apples keep
them from turning brown?

6. Explain why hydrogen peroxide bubbles when you
dribble it on an open cut but does not bubble on skin
that is unbroken.

7. Most of the cultivated fields in California are heavily
irrigated. Over the years, most of the imported water
has evaporated from the soil, leaving behind solutes.
What problems will the altered soil cause plants?

8. Water moves osmotically into *Paramecium*, a single-
celled aquatic protist. If unchecked, the influx would
bloat the cell and rupture its plasma membrane, killing
the cell. An energy-requiring mechanism that involves
contractile vacuoles expels excess water (Figure 5.26).
Water enters the vacuole's tubelike extensions and
collects inside. A full vacuole contracts and squirts
water out of the cell through a pore. Are *Paramecium*'s
surroundings hypotonic, hypertonic, or isotonic?

9. Imagine you're a juvenile shrimp living in an *estuary*,
where freshwater draining from the land mixes with
saltwater from the sea. Many people own homes near a
lake and want boat access to the sea. They ask their city
for permission to build a canal to your estuary. If they
succeed, what may happen to you?

10. Is the white blood cell shown in Figure 5.27 disposing
of a worn-out red blood cell by endocytosis,
phagocytosis, or both?

Media Menu

Student CD-ROM

Impacts, Issues Video
   Alcohol, Enzymes, and Your Liver
Big Picture Animation
   Energy, enzymes, and movement across membranes
Read-Me-First Animation
   Controlling energy release
   Catalase action
   Passive transport
   Active transport
   Tonicity and water movement
Other Animations and Interactions
   Activation energy interaction
   Allosteric activation
   Feedback inhibition

InfoTrac

- Harnessing the Energy. *World and I*, October 2001.
- Ion Channel Protein Contraceptive Target. *Drug Discovery & Technology News*, October 2001.
- Drug Abuse During 1970s and 1980s May Explain Doubling of Deaths from Alcoholic Liver Disease. *Hepatitis Weekly*, August 2002.

Web Sites

- National Institute on Alcohol Abuse and Alcoholism: www.niaaa.nih.gov
- Adenosine Triphosphate—ATP: www.bris.ac.uk/Depts/Chemistry/MOTM/atp/atp1.htm
- Introduction to Enzymes: www.worthington-biochem.com/introBiochem/introEnzymes.html
- Pumping Ions: www.mbl.edu/publications/LABNOTES/ 10.1/pumping_ions.html

How Would You Vote?

The only cure for liver failure, regardless of its cause, is a
liver transplant. A shortage of livers means many potential
transplant recipients die waiting. How should these organs be
allocated? Should people who invited liver failure by their own
abusive life-style be a lower priority for transplants than those
with failure brought on by a transfusion or a genetic disorder?

IMPACTS, ISSUES *Pastures of the Seas*

Think about the last bit of apple, celery, chicken, pizza, or any other food you ate. Where did it come from? Look past the refrigerator, the market or restaurant, or even the farm. Look to individual plants, the starting point for nearly all of your food.

Plants, and many bacteria and protists, are "self-nourishing" organisms, or **autotrophs**. They tap into an environmental energy source and use it to *make* food from simple materials. By contrast, most bacteria and protists, all fungi, and all animals are **heterotrophs**. They are not self-nourishing; they cannot make their own food. They must eat autotrophs, one another, and organic wastes. (*Hetero*– means other; in this case, "being nourished by others.")

Plants do something you'll never do. By the process of **photosynthesis**, they make food by using no more than sunlight energy, water, and carbon dioxide (CO_2). Each year, they produce 220 billion tons of sugar, enough to make 300 quadrillion sugar cubes. These photosynthetic autotrophs have been doing so for more than a billion years. That is a LOT of sugar.

Uncountable numbers of photosynthesizers also abound in the seas. A cupful of seawater may hold more than 24 million microscopically small cells of different species! Most are bacteria and protists that form "pastures of the seas"—the producers that feed most other marine organisms. Like plants, they too "bloom" in spring, when nutrients churned up from the deep support rapid population growth. Figure 6.1 is a record of an algal bloom that stretched from North Carolina to Spain.

Atlantic Ocean in Winter

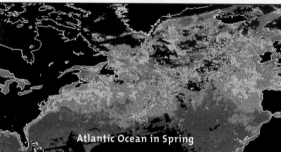

Atlantic Ocean in Spring

Figure 6.1 Satellite images that convey the magnitude of photosynthetic activity during springtime in the North Atlantic Ocean. Sensors responded to concentrations of chlorophyll, which were greatest in regions coded *red*.

the big picture

Catching the Rainbow Energy enters the world of life when chlorophyll and other photosynthetic pigments absorb energy in the sun's rays.

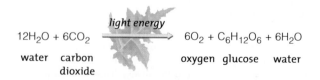

$$12H_2O + 6CO_2 \xrightarrow{\text{light energy}} 6O_2 + C_6H_{12}O_6 + 6H_2O$$

water   carbon dioxide   oxygen   glucose   water

Overview of Photosynthesis Photosynthesis occurs in two stages in chloroplasts. Energy from the sun is converted to chemical energy and stored in ATP and NADPH. These molecules are later used to assemble sugars from carbon dioxide and water.

Imagine zooming in on just one small patch of "pasture" in an Antarctic sea. There, tiny shrimplike crustaceans are rapidly eating tinier photosynthesizers, including algal cells of the sort shown in the filmstrip. Dense concentrations of such crustaceans, known as krill, are feeding other animals, including fishes, penguins, seabirds, and the immense blue whale. A single, mature whale is straining four tons of krill from the water today, as it has been doing for months. And before they themselves were eaten, the four tons of krill had munched through *1,200 tons* of the pasture!

Another point: Collectively, photosynthetic cells on land and in the seas handle staggering numbers of reactant and product molecules. By doing so, they even help shape the global climate. They also sponge up nearly half of the CO_2 we humans release each year, as by burning fossil fuels. Without them, CO_2 would accumulate faster and warm the atmosphere, which already is warming too fast.

In short, *photosynthesis is the main pathway by which energy and carbon enter the web of life.* Photosynthetic autotrophs make, use, and store organic compounds, the food for most heterotrophs. And *all* organisms release that stored energy for cellular work, mainly by aerobic respiration.

There are different types of photoautotrophs, and they perform photosynthesis in different ways. In this chapter we focus on oxygenic (oxygen-producing) photosynthesis in plants and algae.

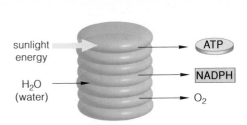

How Would You Vote?

Crop plants feed most of the human population. Limits on the activity of some enzymes can limit crop production. Should we genetically engineer plants to boost photosynthesis and get higher crop yields? See the Media Menu for details, then vote online.

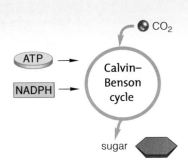

Making ATP and NADPH   In the first stage of photosynthesis, sunlight energy becomes converted to chemical bond energy of ATP. Water molecules are broken apart, NADPH forms, and oxygen escapes into the air.

Making Sugars   The second stage is the "synthesis" part of photosynthesis. ATP delivers energy to reaction sites where sugars are built with atoms of hydrogen (delivered by NADPH), carbon, and oxygen (from carbon dioxide in the air).

6.1 Sunlight As an Energy Source

*Photosynthesis runs on a fraction of the electromagnetic spectrum, or the full range of energy radiating from the sun. Radiant energy undulates across space, something like waves crossing a sea. The horizontal distance between two successive waves is a **wavelength**.*

PROPERTIES OF LIGHT

Our story starts with energy in the sun's rays—not all of it, just light of wavelengths between 380 and 750 nanometers. These are wavelengths of visible light, the ones that drive photosynthesis.

Light is made of *photons*, which are individual packets of electromagnetic energy traveling in waves. The shorter a photon's wavelength, the higher its energy (Figure 6.2). For example, blue light has a shorter wavelength and more energy than red light:

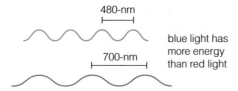

480-nm

blue light has more energy than red light

700-nm

Photons with wavelengths shorter than violet light are energetic enough to disrupt DNA of living cells.

PIGMENTS—THE RAINBOW CATCHERS

Pigments are a class of molecules that absorb photons with particular wavelengths. Photons that a pigment cannot absorb bounce off or continue on through it; they are reflected or transmitted.

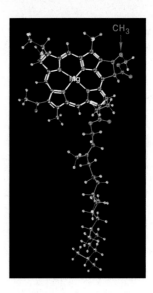

Figure 6.3 Ball-and-stick model for chlorophylls *a* and *b*, which differ by only a single functional group. In chlorophyll *b*, the group is —COO⁻, not the —CH₃ shown. The light-catching portion is the flattened ring structure—which is similar to a heme except it holds a magnesium atom instead of iron. The hydrocarbon backbone readily dissolves in the lipid bilayers of cell membranes.

Certain pigments are the molecular bridges from sunlight to photosynthesis. **Chlorophyll *a*** is the most abundant type in plants, green algae, and a number of photoautotrophic bacteria (Figure 6.3). It is the best at absorbing red and violet wavelengths. Chlorophyll *b* absorbs light at slightly different wavelengths. It is an *accessory* pigment, meaning that it enhances efficiency of photosynthesis reactions by capturing additional wavelengths. All chlorophylls reflect or transmit green wavelengths, which is why plant parts that are rich in chlorophylls appear green to us.

Accessory pigments include the **carotenoids**, which absorb blue-violet and blue-green wavelengths, and reflect red, orange, and yellow ones. Beta-carotene is a carotenoid that colors carrots and other plant parts

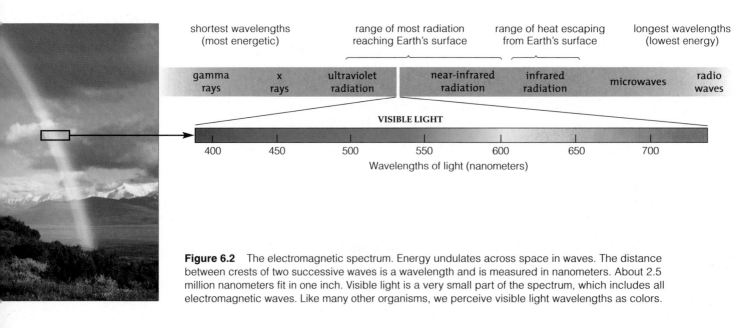

shortest wavelengths (most energetic)		range of most radiation reaching Earth's surface		range of heat escaping from Earth's surface		longest wavelengths (lowest energy)
gamma rays	x rays	ultraviolet radiation	near-infrared radiation	infrared radiation	microwaves	radio waves

VISIBLE LIGHT

400   450   500   550   600   650   700

Wavelengths of light (nanometers)

Figure 6.2 The electromagnetic spectrum. Energy undulates across space in waves. The distance between crests of two successive waves is a wavelength and is measured in nanometers. About 2.5 million nanometers fit in one inch. Visible light is a very small part of the spectrum, which includes all electromagnetic waves. Like many other organisms, we perceive visible light wavelengths as colors.

Figure 6.4 (**a**) Absorption spectra reveal the efficiency with which chlorophylls *a* and *b* absorb wavelengths of visible light. Peaks in the graphs reveal the wavelengths that each type of pigment absorbs best.

(**b**) Absorption spectra for beta-carotene (a carotenoid) and phycobilin. As Figure 6.6 describes, before scientists devised ways to measure absorption efficiencies, the botanist T. Engelmann figured out which colors of light were best at driving photosynthesis in a green alga.

Collectively, these and other photosynthetic pigments can capture almost the entire spectrum of visible light.

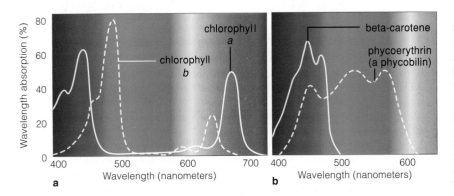

Figure 6.5 Leaf color. In spring and summer, intensely green leaves have an abundance of chlorophylls, which mask the presence of carotenoids, xanthophylls, and other accessory pigments.

In many kinds of plants, chlorophyll synthesis lags behind its breakdown in autumn, so more stable pigments show through. Cold, sunny days trigger the production of water-soluble anthocyanins in leaf cells. The anthocyanins act like a sunscreen; they protect leaves from ultraviolet radiation.

Figure 6.6 T. Englemann's study of photosynthesis in *Spirogyra*, a strandlike green alga. A long time ago, most people assumed plants withdrew raw materials for photosynthesis from soil. By 1882 a few chemists suspected that plants use light, water, and something in the air. Englemann wondered: What parts of sunlight do plants favor?

As he knew, free oxygen is released during photosynthesis. He also knew some bacteria use oxygen during aerobic respiration, as most organisms do. He hypothesized: If bacteria require oxygen, then we can expect them to gather in places where the most photosynthesis is going on. He put a water droplet containing bacterial cells on a microscope slide with the green alga *Spirogyra*. He used a crystal prism to break up a beam of sunlight and cast a spectrum of colors across the slide.

Bacteria gathered mostly where violet and red light fell on the green alga. Algal cells released more oxygen in the part illuminated by light of those colors—the very best light for photosynthesis. Compare Figure 6.4.

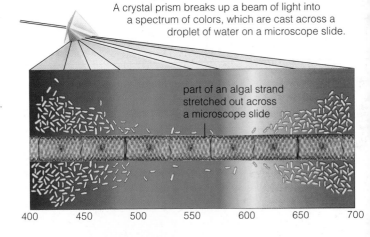

A crystal prism breaks up a beam of light into a spectrum of colors, which are cast across a droplet of water on a microscope slide.

part of an algal strand stretched out across a microscope slide

orange. **Xanthophylls** are yellow, brown, purple, or blue accessory pigments; **phycobilins** are red or blue-green. Absorption spectra (singular, spectrum) give us a picture of how such photosynthetic pigments absorb different wavelengths of visible light (Figure 6.4).

The chlorophyll content in the leaves of deciduous species declines in autumn and lets the carotenoids, xanthophylls, and **anthocyanin**, a red-purple pigment, show through (Figure 6.5). Each year in New England, tourists spend a billion dollars to watch a three-week display of red, orange, and gold leaves of maples and other trees. We also can thank the deep red to purple anthocyanins for the visual appeal of many flowers and food, including blueberries, red grapes, cherries, red cabbage, and rhubarb.

Such photosynthetic pigments do not work alone. Organized arrays of them work together and harvest energy from the sun. For now, start thinking about the structure of that chlorophyll molecule in Figure 6.3—particularly the flattened ring. Here, alternating single and double covalent bonds share electrons. And these are the electrons which, when excited by inputs of energy, get photosynthesis going.

Light from the sun travels through space in waves, and wavelengths of visible light correspond to specific colors.

Chlorophyll a and diverse accessory pigments absorb specific wavelengths of visible light. They are the molecular bridge between the sun and photosynthesis.

6.2 What Is Photosynthesis and Where Does It Happen?

Sit outdoors on a warm, sunny day and you will never build your own food but you will get hot. Plants plug into the sun's energy usefully, without getting cooked.

TWO STAGES OF REACTIONS

Photosynthesis proceeds through two reaction stages. The first stage, the **light-dependent reactions**, converts light energy to chemical bond energy of ATP. Also, water molecules are split, and the coenzyme NADP+ picks up the released electrons and hydrogen. We call its reduced form NADPH. The oxygen atoms released from water molecules escape into the surroundings.

In the second stage, called the **light-independent reactions**, energy from ATP jump-starts reactions that form glucose and other carbohydrates. At these same sites, NADPH gives up electrons and hydrogen ions, which bond with carbon and oxygen to form glucose.

Here is a simple way to summarize the reactions of photosynthesis:

$$12H_2O + 6CO_2 \xrightarrow[\text{enzymes}]{\text{light energy}} 6O_2 + C_6H_{12}O_6 + 6H_2O$$

water   carbon dioxide   oxygen   glucose   water

A LOOK INSIDE THE CHLOROPLAST

Photosynthetic reactions differ among certain bacteria, protists, and plants. For now, focus on what goes on in **chloroplasts**, the organelles of photosynthesis in plants and algae. Each chloroplast has two outer membranes, which enclose a semifluid interior, the stroma (Figure 6.7c). Inside the stroma is the **thylakoid membrane**, a third membrane folded in ways that form a single compartment. Often the folds look like flattened channels between stacks of flattened sacs (thylakoids). The space inside the sacs is part of one continuous compartment. Sugars are built outside this compartment, in the stroma (Figure 6.8).

Embedded in all the thylakoids are **photosystems**: clusters of 200 to 300 pigments and other molecules that trap energy from the sun. Chloroplasts have two types of photosystems, called I and II (Figure 6.7d).

PHOTOSYNTHESIS CHANGED THE BIOSPHERE

Before zooming down further, to the mechanisms of photosynthesis, zoom out in your mind to the global impact of one of the steps involved. About 3.2 billion

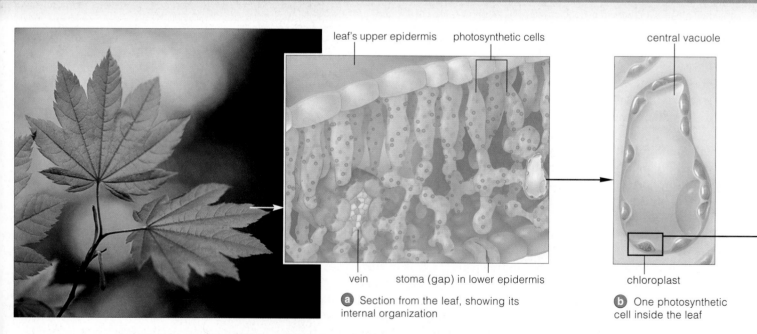

leaf's upper epidermis   photosynthetic cells   central vacuole

vein   stoma (gap) in lower epidermis   chloroplast

a Section from the leaf, showing its internal organization

b One photosynthetic cell inside the leaf

Figure 6.7 Zooming in on sites of photosynthesis in a typical plant leaf. Two thousand chloroplasts, lined up single file, would be no wider than a dime. Think of all the chloroplasts in a corn or rice plant—each a tiny sugar-making factory—to get a sense of the magnitude of metabolic events required to feed you and every other living thing.

years ago, oxygen released by photosynthetic bacteria started accumulating in the atmosphere, which before then held little of it. As the atmosphere changed, so did the world of life. All that free oxygen favored the evolution of a novel pathway—aerobic respiration—that efficiently releases a great deal of energy from organic compounds. An oxygen-rich atmosphere was a key environmental factor in the evolution of large, active animals, which the aerobic pathway sustains. Breathing in oxygen helps keep them alive.

In the first stage of photosynthesis, sunlight energy drives ATP and NADPH formation, and oxygen is released. In chloroplasts, this stage occurs at the thylakoid membrane.

Embedded in the membrane are photosystems—clusters of pigments and other molecules—where light energy is captured.

The second stage occurs in the stroma. Energy from ATP drives the synthesis of sugars. Carbon dioxide provides carbon and oxygen atoms for the reactions. NADPH delivers the required electrons and hydrogen atoms.

The atmosphere was free of oxygen before photosynthesis evolved. Oxygen released by emerging photosynthesizers slowly accumulated. It changed the atmosphere and became a selective force in the evolution of aerobic respiration.

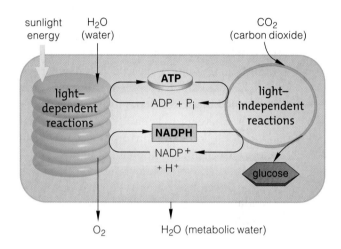

Figure 6.8 Overview of the two stages of photosynthesis in a chloroplast. The first stage, the light-dependent reactions, occurs at the thylakoid membrane. The second stage (light-independent reactions that produce sugars) occurs in the stroma.

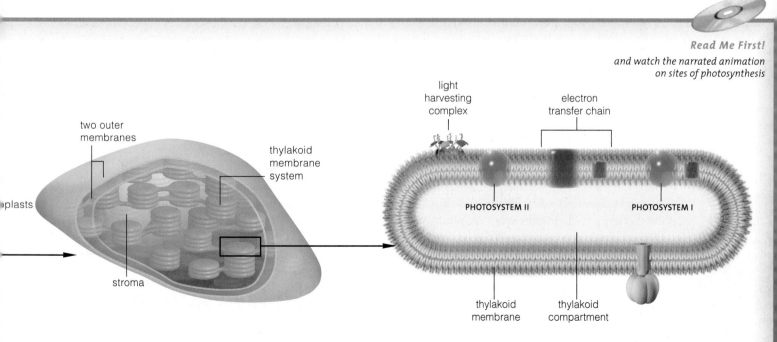

Read Me First!

and watch the narrated animation on sites of photosynthesis

c Closer look at one chloroplast. It has two outer membranes and an inner *thylakoid* membrane in its semifluid interior (the stroma). In many cells, the inner membrane resembles stacks of flattened sacs connected by channels. The interiors of all sacs and channels interconnect, forming a single compartment.

d Components of the thylakoid membrane system that carry out the first stage of photosynthesis—the light-dependent reactions. Light-harvesting complexes capture photon energy and pass it to two types of photosystems. Electron transfer chains embedded in the membrane have roles in ATP and NADPH formation.

6.3 Light-Dependent Reactions

In the first stage of photosynthesis, the sunlight energy harvested at photosystems drives ATP formation. Water molecules are split, and their oxygen diffuses away. NADP$^+$, a coenzyme, picks up the electrons and hydrogen, which will be used in the second stage to form sugars.

TRANSDUCING THE ABSORBED ENERGY

Suppose a photon collides with a pigment molecule that absorbs it. The photon's energy will boost one of the pigment's electrons to a higher energy level. If nothing else happens, the electron quickly will drop back to its unexcited state, losing the extra energy as it does. The energy is emitted as heat, or as another photon. Photon emissions from electrons losing extra energy are visible as fluorescent light.

In the thylakoid membrane, however, energy that excited electrons give up is kept in play. Embedded in the membrane are many photosystems. Surrounding them are hundreds of light-harvesting complexes, or circular clusterings of pigments and other proteins (Figure 6.9a). Pigments in light-harvesting complexes also absorb photon energy, but they don't waste it. Electrons of these pigments can hold on to energy by passing it back and forth, like a volleyball. The energy released from one cluster is passed to another, which passes it on to another, and so on until it reaches a photosystem—a reaction center.

Look back on Figure 6.3, which shows the structure of chlorophyll. Two molecules of chlorophyll *a* are at the center of every photosystem. Their flat rings face each other so closely that electrons in both rings are destabilized. When light-harvesting neighbors pass on photon energy to a photosystem, electrons come right off of that special pair of chlorophylls.

The freed electrons immediately enter an electron transfer chain positioned next to the photosystem in the thylakoid membrane. *The entry of electrons from a photosystem into an electron transfer chain is the first step in the light-dependent reactions*—in the conversion of photon energy to chemical energy for photosynthesis.

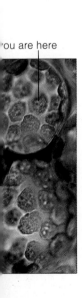
ou are here

MAKING ATP AND NADPH

Let's use Figure 6.9 to track electrons that a type II photosystem gives up. **Electron transfer chains**, recall, are cell membrane components. Each is an organized array of enzymes, coenzymes, and other proteins through which electrons are transferred step-by-step. In the process of moving electrons, molecules of the chain pick up hydrogen ions (H$^+$) from the stroma, cart them across the thylakoid membrane, and release

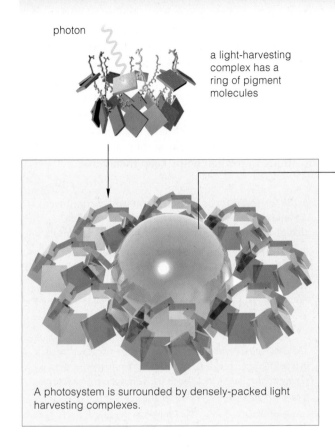
photon

a light-harvesting complex has a ring of pigment molecules

A photosystem is surrounded by densely-packed light harvesting complexes.

a In the thylakoid membrane of chloroplasts, rings of pigments can intercept photons coming from any direction. They pass captured photon energy to nearby photosystems. Each photosystem collects energy from hundreds of light-harvesting complexes surrounding it; a few are shown here.

Figure 6.9 How ATP and NADPH form during photosynthesis in chloroplasts.

them to the inner compartment. Their repeated action causes concentration and electric gradients to build up across the membrane. The combined force of those gradients attracts H$^+$ back toward the stroma.

The H$^+$ ions can only cross the membrane with the help of **ATP synthases**, as explained in Section 4.3. Ion flow through these membrane proteins causes the attachment of inorganic phosphate to a molecule of ADP in the stroma. In this way, ATP forms.

As long as electrons flow through transfer chains, the cell can keep on producing ATP. But where do the electrons come from in the first place? By the process of *photolysis*, photosystem II replaces its lost electrons by pulling them from water molecules—which then dissociate into hydrogen ions and molecular oxygen. The free oxygen diffuses out of the chloroplast, then

Read Me First!
and watch the narrated animation on photosynthetic
pathways for making ATP and NADPH

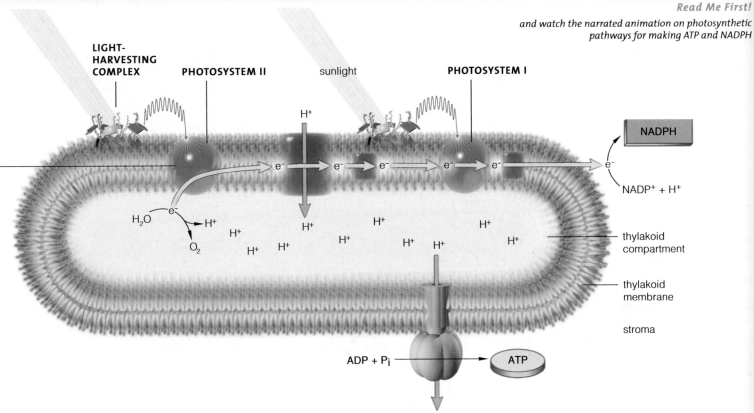

b Photon energy (*red*) causes photosystem II to lose electrons. It replaces them by pulling electrons from water molecules, which then split into oxygen and hydrogen ions (H+). Oxygen leaves the cell as O_2.

c Electrons from photosystem II enter an electron transfer chain, which also moves H+ from the stroma into the thylakoid compartment. Electrons continue on to photosystem I.

d H+ concentration and electric gradients build up across the thylakoid membrane. The force of these gradients propels H+ through ATP synthases, driving ATP formation.

e Photon energy (*red*) also triggers the loss of electrons from photosystem I. Through an intermediary molecule, the electrons are transferred to NADP+, which also picks up H+ and thereby becomes NADPH.

out of the cell and into the air. Hydrogen ions remain in the thylakoid compartment, and they contribute to the gradients that drive ATP formation.

So where do the electrons end up? After passing through the electron transfer chain, they continue on to photosystem I. There, light-harvesting complexes volley energy to a special pair of chlorophylls at the photosystem's reaction center, causing them to release electrons. An intermediary molecule transfers them to NADP+, which attracts hydrogen ions at the same time. In this way, NADPH forms.

Photosystem I also runs independently in a more ancient cyclic pathway. Electrons freed from it enter an adjoining transfer chain, which moves hydrogen ions into the thylakoid compartment. As before, the resulting gradient drives ATP formation. At the end

of this chain, however, electrons are cycled back to photosystem I, and no NADPH forms.

These "noncyclic" and "cyclic" pathways operate at the same time in many photosynthetic organisms. Which one dominates at a particular time depends on metabolic demands for ATP and NADPH.

In the light-dependent reactions, sunlight energy drives the formation of ATP, NADPH, or both.

Both ATP and NADPH form by a noncyclic pathway in which electrons are pulled from water molecules, then flow through two types of photosystems, and finally to NADP+. This is the photosynthetic pathway that releases free oxygen.

ATP alone forms in a cyclic pathway that starts and ends at photosystem I.

6.4 A Case of Controlled Energy Release

One of the themes threading through this book is that organisms convert one form of energy to another in highly controlled ways. The light-dependent reactions are a classic example of such conversions. Figure 6.10 walks you step-by-step through these conversions.

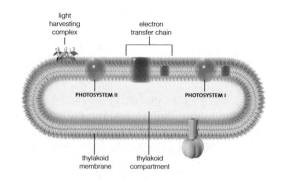

Read Me First!

and watch the narrated animation on energy release in photosynthesis

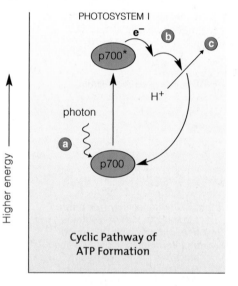

Cyclic Pathway of ATP Formation

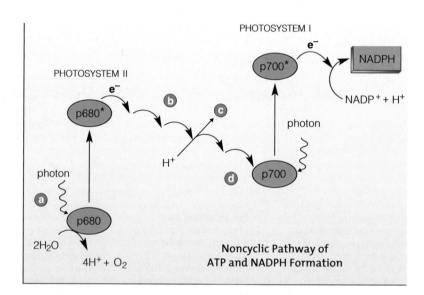

Noncyclic Pathway of ATP and NADPH Formation

a Photosystem I gets a boost of photon energy from a light-harvesting cluster. It loses an electron.

b The electron passes from one molecule to another in an electron transfer chain that is embedded in the thylakoid membrane. It loses a little energy with each transfer, and ends up being reused by photosystem I.

c Molecules in the transfer chain ferry H^+ across the thylakoid membrane into the inner compartment. Hydrogen ions accumulating in the compartment create an electrochemical gradient across the membrane that drives ATP synthesis, as shown in Figure 6.9.

a Photosystem II gets a boost of photon energy from a light-harvesting cluster, then loses an electron. Here, too, the electron moves through a different electron transfer chain and loses a little energy with each transfer. It ends up at photosystem I.

b Photosystem I gets a boost of photon energy from a light-harvesting complex, then loses electrons. The freed electrons, along with hydrogen ions, are used in the formation of NADPH from $NADP^+$.

c As in the cyclic pathway, operation of the electron transfer chain puts hydrogen ions into the thylakoid compartment. In this case, hydrogens released from dissociated water molecules also enter the compartment. The H^+ concentration and electric gradient across the membrane are tapped for ATP formation (Figure 6.9).

d Electrons lost from photosystem I are replaced by the electrons lost from photosystem II. Electrons lost from photosystem II are replaced by electrons from water. (Photolysis pulls water molecules apart into electrons, H^+ and O_2.)

Figure 6.10 Energy transfers in the light-dependent reactions. The pair of chlorophyll *a* molecules at the center of photosystem I is designated p700. The pair in photosystem II is designated p680. The pairs respond most efficiently to wavelengths of 700 and 680 nanometers, respectively.

6.5 Light-Independent Reactions: The Sugar Factory

The chloroplast is a sugar factory, and the Calvin–Benson cycle is its machinery. These cyclic, light-independent reactions are the "synthesis" part of photosynthesis.

Sugars form in the **Calvin–Benson cycle**, which runs inside the stroma of chloroplasts (Figure 6.11). This cyclic pathway uses ATP and NADPH from the light-dependent reactions. We call them light-*independent* because they also can run in the dark, as long as ATP and NADPH are available.

ATP energy drives these sugar-building reactions, and NADPH donates hydrogen and electrons. Plants get carbon and oxygen building blocks from carbon dioxide (CO_2) in the air. Algae of aquatic habitats get them from CO_2 dissolved in water.

Rubisco, an enzyme, transfers a carbon from CO_2 to five-carbon ribulose biphosphate, or RuBP. The resulting unstable compound is the entry point for the Calvin–Benson cycle. It splits at once into two stable molecules of phosphoglycerate (PGA), each having a backbone of three carbons. The process of securing carbon from the environment by incorporating it in a stable organic compound is called **carbon fixation**.

Each PGA gets a phosphate group from ATP, and hydrogen and electrons from NADPH. For every six CO_2 fixed, twelve phosphoglyceraldehydes (PGAL) form. Ten PGAL become rearranged in a way that regenerates RuBP. The other two combine to make a six-carbon glucose with a phosphate group attached.

Most of the glucose is converted at once to sucrose or starch by other pathways that conclude the light-independent reactions. Sucrose is the main form in which carbohydrate is transported in plants; starch is the main storage form. Cells convert excess PGAL to starch, which they briefly store as starch grains in the stroma. After the sun goes down, starch is converted to sucrose for export to other cells in leaves, stems, and roots. Photosynthetic products and intermediates end up as energy sources or building blocks for all the lipids, amino acids, and other organic compounds that plants require for growth, survival, and reproduction.

Driven by ATP energy, the light-independent reactions make sugars with hydrogen and electrons from NADPH, and with carbon and oxygen from carbon dioxide.

Read Me First!
and watch the narrated animation on the Calvin–Benson cycle

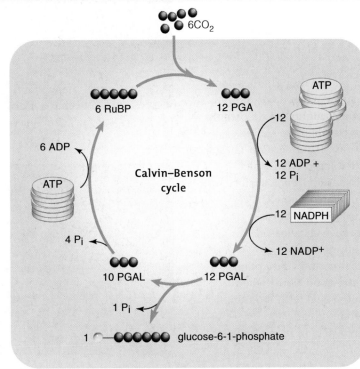

f It takes six turns of the Calvin–Benson cycle (six carbon atoms) to make one glucose molecule.

e Ten of the PGAL get phosphate groups from ATP. In terms of energy, this primes them for an uphill run—for synthesis reactions that regenerate RuBP.

d The phosphorylated glucose enters reactions that form carbohydrate products—mainly sucrose, starch, and cellulose.

a CO_2 in air spaces inside a leaf diffuses into a photosynthetic cell. Rubisco attaches the carbon atom of CO_2 to RuBP, which starts the Calvin–Benson cycle. Each resulting intermediate splits at once into two PGAs.

b Each PGA molecule gets a phosphate group from ATP, plus hydrogen and electrons from NADPH. The resulting intermediate, PGAL, is thus primed for reaction.

c Two of the twelve PGAL molecules combine to form one molecule of glucose with an attached phosphate group.

Figure 6.11 Light-independent reactions of photosynthesis. *Brown* circles signify carbon atoms. Appendix V details the reaction steps.

6.6 Different Plants, Different Carbon-Fixing Pathways

If sunlight intensity, air temperature, rainfall, and soil composition never varied, photosynthesis might be the same in all plants. But environments differ, and so do details of photosynthesis. For example, you see such differences on hot days when water is scarce.

Take a look at the leaves in Figure 6.12. They all have a waxy cuticle that restricts water loss. Water and gases move into and out of leaves across tiny openings called **stomata** (singular, stoma). Stomata close on hot, dry days. Water and O_2 can't get out, and CO_2 can't get in. A plant's capacity to make sugars declines when its photosynthetic cells are exposed to too much O_2 and not enough CO_2.

That's why beans, sunflowers, and many other plants don't grow well in hot, dry climates unless they are steadily irrigated. We call them **C3 plants**, because the *three*-carbon PGA is the first stable intermediate of the Calvin–Benson cycle. Remember the enzyme that fixes carbon for this cycle? When oxygen builds up in leaves of C3 plants, rubisco uses oxygen—not CO_2—in an alternate reaction that yields only one molecule of PGA (Figure 6.12*a*).

In **C4 plants**, *four*-carbon oxaloacetate forms first in reactions that fix carbon twice (Figure 6.12*b*). In mesophyll cells, the C4 cycle fixes carbon no matter how much O_2 there is. This reaction delivers CO_2 directly to bundle-sheath cells, where it enters the Calvin–Benson cycle (Figure 6.12*b*). The C4 cycle keeps the CO_2 level near rubisco high enough to stop the competing reaction. C4 plants do use an extra ATP. Compared to C3 plants, though, they lose less water and make more sugar when days are dry.

CAM plants open stomata at night and fix carbon by repeated turns of a C4 cycle, then the Calvin–Benson cycle runs the next day (Figure 6.12*c*). These plants include cacti and other succulents, which have juicy, water-storing tissues and thick surface layers adapted to hot, dry climates. Some CAM plants survive prolonged droughts by closing stomata even at night. They fix CO_2 released by aerobic respiration, which supports slow growth.

In short, C3 plants, C4 plants, and CAM plants respond differently to hot, dry conditions, when their photosynthetic cells must deal with too much oxygen and not enough carbon dioxide.

The C4 cycle evolved separately in many lineages, over millions of years. Before then, CO_2 levels in air were higher, so C3 plants had the advantage in hot climates. Which cycle will be best in the future? CO_2 levels have been rising for decades and may double in fifty years. C3 plants may again have the edge.

Leaves of basswood (*Tilia americana*), a typical C3 plant.

Leaves of corn (*Zea mays*), a typical C4 plant

Beavertail cactus (*Opuntia basilaris*), one of the CAM plants

Figure 6.12 Comparison of carbon-fixing adaptations in three kinds of plants.

Read Me First!
*and watch the narrated animation
on carbon-fixing adaptations*

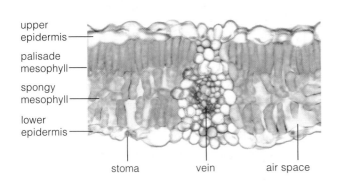

upper
epidermis

palisade
mesophyll

spongy
mesophyll

lower
epidermis

stoma   vein   air space

Basswood leaf, cross-section.

stomata closed,
no CO_2 uptake

RuBP   PGA
Calvin–
Benson
cycle

sugar

a Many C3 plants evolved in moist temperate zones. The basswood tree is one of them. On hot, dry days, it can't grow as well as C4 plants because its rubisco uses O_2 in an inefficient reaction that competes with the Calvin–Benson cycle. Not as many sugars are produced.

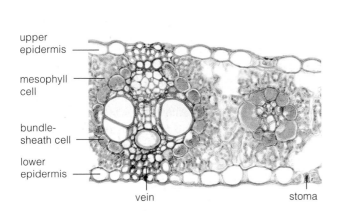

upper
epidermis

mesophyll
cell

bundle-
sheath cell

lower
epidermis

vein   stoma

Corn leaf, cross-section.

stomata closed,
no CO_2 uptake

C4
cycle   oxaloacetate   mesophyll
cell

CO_2

RuBP   PGA
Calvin–
Benson
cycle   bundle-
sheath
cell

sugar

b How C4 plants fix carbon in hot, dry weather, when there is too little CO_2 and too much O_2 inside leaves. A C4 cycle is common in grasses, corn, and other plants that evolved in the tropics. In their mesophyll cells, CO_2 gets fixed by an enzyme that ignores O_2. That reaction releases carbon dioxide in adjoining bundle sheath cells, where the Calvin–Benson cycle runs.

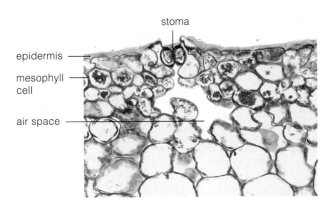

stoma

epidermis

mesophyll
cell

air space

Cacti have photosynthetic, fleshy stems, not leaves. This cross-section shows a stoma and mesophyll cells inside.

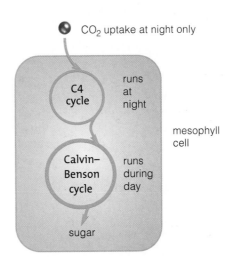

CO_2 uptake at night only

C4
cycle   runs
at
night

Calvin–
Benson   runs
cycle   during
day   mesophyll
cell

sugar

c How CAM plants fix carbon in hot, dry climates. Their stomata limit water loss by opening only at night. That is when CO_2 enters and O_2 departs. The CO_2 is fixed by a C4 cycle that runs at night. The fixed carbon enters the Calvin–Benson cycle in the same cell during daylight hours.

Summary

Section 6.1 Photosynthesis starts with the absorption of light energy by pigment molecules. Chlorophyll *a*, the main photosynthetic pigment, is best at absorbing violet and red wavelengths. Carotenoids and other pigments absorb characteristic wavelengths.

Section 6.2 Photosynthesis has two stages: the light-dependent and the light-independent reactions. This equation and Figure 6.13 summarize the process:

$$12H_2O + 6CO_2 \xrightarrow{\text{light energy}} 6O_2 + C_6H_{12}O_6 + 6H_2O$$

water   carbon   oxygen   glucose   water
       dioxide

In plants and algae, the light-dependent reactions occur at the thylakoid membrane, which forms a continuous compartment in the semifluid interior (stroma) of the chloroplast. Starting long ago, oxygen released by these reactions has accumulated in the atmosphere. Without it, aerobic respiration would not have evolved.

Sections 6.3, 6.4 Many clusters of pigments in the thylakoid membrane absorb photons and pass the energy to many photosystems. The light-dependent reactions start when electrons released from photosystems enter electron transfer chains. Operation of the transfer chains results in the formation of the energy carrier ATP and the reduced coenzyme NADPH.

The released electrons can move through a noncyclic or a cyclic pathway. In the noncyclic reactions, electrons lost from photosystem II enter an electron transfer chain. Electron flow through the chain causes hydrogen ions to accumulate in the thylakoid compartment. Light energy prompts photosystem I to lose electrons which, along with hydrogen ions, convert $NADP^+$ to NADPH.

Electrons lost from photosystem I are replaced by electrons from photosystem II. Photosystem II replaces its lost electrons by pulling them away from water molecules. This dissociates them into H^+ and O_2, a process called photolysis.

In the cyclic reactions, electrons from photosystem I enter a different electron transfer chain, then are recycled back to the same photosystem.

In both pathways, H^+ accumulation in the thylakoid compartment forms concentration and electric gradients across the thylakoid membrane. H^+ flows in response to the gradients, through ATP synthases. The flow causes P_i to be attached to ADP in the stroma, forming ATP.

Section 6.5 Light-independent reactions, the synthesis part of photosynthesis, occur in the stroma. In C3 plants, the enzyme rubisco attaches carbon to RuBP to start the Calvin–Benson cycle. In this cyclic pathway, energy from ATP, carbon and oxygen from CO_2, and hydrogen and electrons from NADPH are used to make glucose, which immediately enters reactions that form the end products of photosynthesis (e.g., sucrose, cellulose, and starch).

Section 6.6 On hot, dry days, plants close stomata and conserve water, so oxygen from photosynthesis builds up in leaves. When that happens, rubisco uses oxygen instead of CO_2, which slows sugar production. C4 plants fix carbon twice, in two cell types. CAM plants close stomata during the day and fix carbon at night.

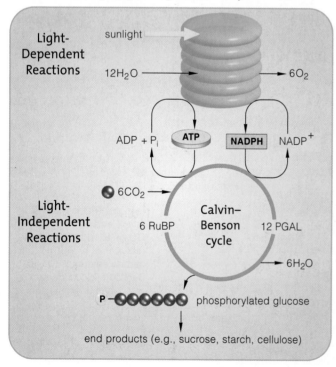

Figure 6.13 Visual summary of photosynthesis.

Self-Quiz
Answers in Appendix III

1. Photosynthetic autotrophs use _____ from the air as a carbon source and _____ as their energy source.

2. Light-*dependent* reactions in plants occur at the _____ .
   a. thylakoid membrane   c. stroma
   b. plasma membrane   d. cytoplasm

3. In the light-*dependent* reactions, _____ .
   a. carbon dioxide is fixed c. CO_2 accepts electrons
   b. ATP and NADPH form   d. sugars form

4. What accumulates inside the thylakoid compartment during the light-*dependent* reactions?
   a. glucose   c. hydrogen ions
   b. RuBP   d. carbon dioxide

5. Light-*independent* reactions proceed in the _____ .
   a. cytoplasm   b. plasma membrane   c. stroma

6. The Calvin–Benson cycle starts when _____ .
   a. light is available
   b. carbon dioxide is attached to RuBP
   c. electrons leave photosystem II

7. Match each event with its most suitable description.
   _____ ATP formation only a. rubisco required
   _____ CO_2 fixation   b. ATP, NADPH required
   _____ PGAL formation   c. electrons cycled back
                                   to photosystem I

Critical Thinking

1. Imagine walking through a garden of red, white, and blue petunias. Explain each of the colors in terms of which wavelengths of light the flower is absorbing.

2. While gazing into an aquarium, you observe bubbling from an aquatic plant (Figure 6.14). What's going on?

3. In the laboratory, Krishna invites plants to take up a carbon radioisotope ($^{14}CO_2$). In which compound will the labeled carbon appear first?

4. About 200 years ago, Jan Baptista van Helmont did experiments on the nature of photosynthesis. He wanted to know where growing plants get the materials necessary for increases in size. He planted a tree seedling weighing 5 pounds in a barrel filled with 200 pounds of soil. He watered the tree regularly. Five years passed. Then van Helmont weighed the tree and the soil. The tree weighed 169 pounds, 3 ounces. The soil weighed 199 pounds, 14 ounces. Because the tree gained so much weight and the soil lost so little, he concluded the tree had gained weight by absorbing the water he had added to the barrel. Given what you know about the composition of biological molecules, why was he misguided? Knowing what you do about photosynthesis, what really happened?

5. The green alga in Figure 6.15a lives in seawater. Its main pigments absorb red light. Its accessory pigments help harvest energy in sunlit waters, and some shield it against ultraviolet radiation. Other green algae live in ponds, lakes, on rocks, even in snow. The red alga in Figure 6.15b grows on tropical reefs in clear, warm water. Its phycobilins absorb green and blue-green wavelengths that penetrate deep water. Some of its relatives live in deep, dimly lit waters; their pigments are nearly black.

If wavelengths are such a vital source of energy, why aren't all pigments black?

Hint: If photoautotrophs first evolved in the seas, then their pigment molecules must also have evolved in the seas. We have evidence that life arose near hydrothermal vents on the seafloor. Survival may have depended on being able to move away from weak infrared radiation (heat energy), which has been measured at vents, to keep from being boiled alive. Millions of years later, bacterial descendants were evolving near the sea surface. By one hypothesis, light-sensing machinery in deep-sea bacteria became modified for shallow-water photosynthesis.

6. Only about eight classes of pigment molecules are known, but this limited group gets around in the world. For example, animals synthesize the brownish-black melanin and some other pigments, but not carotenoids. Photoautotrophs make carotenoids, which move up through food webs, as when tiny aquatic snails graze on green algae and then flamingos eat the snails.

Flamingos modify ingested carotenoids in plenty of ways. For instance, their cells split beta-carotene to form two molecules of vitamin A. This vitamin is the precursor of retinol, a visual pigment that transduces light into electric signals in the flamingo's eyes. Beta-carotene also gets dissolved in fat reservoirs under the skin. From there they are taken up by cells that give rise to bright pink feathers. Choose an animal and do some research into its life cycle and diet. Use your research to identify possible sources for the pigments that color its surfaces.

Figure 6.14 Leaves of *Elodea*, an aquatic plant.

Figure 6.15 (**a**) A green alga (*Codium*) from shallow coastal waters. (**b**) Red alga from a tropical reef.

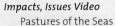

IMPACTS, ISSUES *When Mitochondria Spin Their Wheels*

In the early 1960s, Swedish physician Rolf Luft reflected on some odd symptoms of a young patient. The woman felt weak and too hot all the time. Even on the coldest winter days, she couldn't stop sweating and her skin was flushed. She was thin in spite of a huge appetite.

Luft inferred that his patient's symptoms pointed to a metabolic disorder. Her cells seemed to be spinning their wheels. They were active, but a lot of activity was being dissipated as metabolic heat. He ordered tests designed to detect her metabolic rates. The patient's oxygen consumption was the highest ever recorded!

Microscopic examination of a tissue sample from the patient's skeletal muscles revealed mitochondria, the cell's ATP-producing powerhouses. But there were far too many of them, and they were abnormally shaped. Other studies showed that the mitochondria were engaged in aerobic respiration—yet very little ATP was forming.

The disorder, now called *Luft's syndrome*, was the first to be linked directly to a defective organelle. By analogy, someone with this mitochondrial disorder functions like a city with half of its power plants shut down. Skeletal and heart muscles, the brain, and other hard-working body parts with the highest energy demands are hurt the most.

More than a hundred other mitochondrial disorders are now known. One, a heritable genetic disease called *Friedreich's ataxia*, runs in families (Figure 7.1). Affected people develop weak muscles, loss of coordination (ataxia), and visual problems. Many die when they are young adults because of heart muscle irregularities.

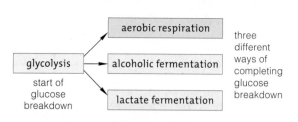

Figure 7.1 Photogenic siblings with Friedreich's ataxia. Leah (*left*) began to lose balance and coordination when she was 5. She was in a wheelchair by the time she was 11. She is now diabetic, and has lost part of her hearing. Joshua (*right*) was 3 when his symptoms began. By the time he was 11, he was unable to walk. He is now legally blind.

Both young people have a heart condition called hypertrophic cardiomyopathy. Both had spinal fusion surgery. Although they have lost a large part of their fine motor skills, with the aid of adaptive equipment they continue to go to school and work in productive jobs. Leah has a part-time modeling career.

the big picture

aerobic respiration

glycolysis → alcoholic fermentation

start of glucose breakdown

lactate fermentation

three different ways of completing glucose breakdown

It All Starts With Glycolysis All cells make ATP by breaking down organic compounds, which releases energy stored in chemical bonds. The main pathways all start in the cytoplasm, with glycolysis.

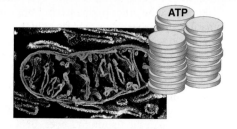

How the Aerobic Route Ends In aerobic respiration alone, glucose breakdown is completed in mitochondria. This pathway has the greatest net energy yield from each glucose molecule.

A mutant gene and its abnormal protein product give rise to Friedreich's ataxia. The abnormal protein causes iron to accumulate inside mitochondria. Iron is required for electron transfers that drive ATP formation. But too much invites an accumulation of **free radicals**— unbound molecular fragments with the wrong number of electrons. These highly reactive fragments can attack all of the molecules of life.

Type 1 diabetes, atherosclerosis, amyotrophic lateral sclerosis (Lou Gehrig's disease), Parkinson's, Alzheimer's, and Huntington's diseases—defective mitochondria contribute to every one of these age-related problems. So when you consider mitochondria in this chapter, don't assume they are too remote from your interests. Without them, you wouldn't make enough ATP even to read about how they do it.

The preceding chapter described how plants and all other photosynthetic organisms get energy from the sun. You and all the other heterotrophs around you get some of the energy that they captured secondhand, thirdhand, and so on. Regardless of its source, energy must first be put into a form that can drive thousands of different life-sustaining reactions. That form is ATP's chemical bond energy.

You already read about the way ATP molecules form during photosynthesis. Turn now to how all organisms make ATP by tapping into the chemical bond energy of organic compounds—especially glucose.

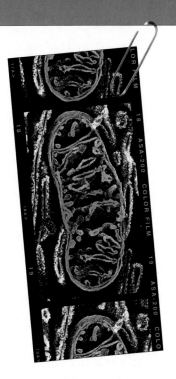

 How Would You Vote?

Developing new drugs is costly. There's little incentive for pharmaceutical companies to target ailments, such as Friedreich's ataxia, that affect relatively few individuals. Should the government provide some funding to private companies that search for cures for diseases affecting only a small number of people? See the Media Menu for details, then vote online.

How Fermentation Routes End

In lactate and alcoholic fermentation, glucose breakdown starts *and* ends in the cytoplasm. The net energy yield is small.

What Cells Do With Food

Big meals, small meals, no meals— cells shunt carbohydrates, lipids, and proteins into breakdown pathways.

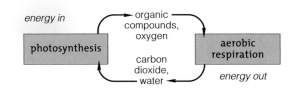

Evolutionary Connections Aerobic respiration and photosynthesis are connected on a global scale, and that connection can be traced to the evolution of novel metabolic pathways.

7.1 Overview of Energy-Releasing Pathways

Plants make ATP during photosynthesis and use it to synthesize glucose and other carbohydrates. But all organisms, plants included, can make ATP by breaking down carbohydrates, lipids, and proteins.

Organisms stay alive by taking in energy. Plants and all other photosynthetic autotrophs get energy from the sun. Heterotrophs get energy by eating plants and one another. Regardless of its source, the energy must be in a form that can drive thousands of diverse life-sustaining reactions. Energy that becomes converted into chemical bond energy of adenosine triphosphate —ATP—serves that function.

COMPARISON OF THE MAIN TYPES OF ENERGY-RELEASING PATHWAYS

The first energy-releasing metabolic pathways were operating billions of years before Earth's oxygen-rich atmosphere evolved, so we can expect that they were *anaerobic*; the reactions did not use free oxygen. Many prokaryotes and protists still live in places where oxygen is absent or not always available. They make ATP by fermentation and other anaerobic pathways. Many eukaryotic cells still use fermentation, including skeletal muscle cells. However, the cells of nearly all species extract energy efficiently from glucose by way of **aerobic respiration**, an oxygen-dependent pathway. Each breath you take provides your actively respiring cells with a fresh supply of oxygen.

Make note of this point: *In all cells, all of the main energy-releasing pathways start with the same reactions in the cytoplasm.* During the initial reactions, **glycolysis**, enzymes cleave and rearrange a glucose molecule into two molecules of **pyruvate**, an organic compound that has a three-carbon backbone.

Once glycolysis is over, energy-releasing pathways differ. Only the aerobic pathway continues and ends in mitochondria (Figure 7.2). There, oxygen accepts and removes electrons that drove the reactions.

Only aerobic respiration delivers enough ATP to build and maintain big multicelled organisms, including redwoods and highly active animals, such as people and Canada geese.

As you examine the energy-releasing pathways in sections to follow, keep in mind that enzymes catalyze each step, and intermediates formed at one step serve as substrates for the next enzyme in the pathway.

OVERVIEW OF AEROBIC RESPIRATION

Of all energy-releasing pathways, aerobic respiration gets the most ATP for each glucose molecule. Whereas anaerobic routes have a net yield of two ATP, aerobic respiration typically yields thirty-six or more. If you were a bacterium, you would not require much ATP. Being far larger, more complex, and highly active, you depend on the aerobic pathway's high yield. When a molecule of glucose is used as the starting material, aerobic respiration can be summarized this way:

$$C_6H_{12}O_6 \ + \ 6O_2 \ \longrightarrow \ 6CO_2 \ + \ 6H_2O$$

glucose   oxygen   carbon   water
                                   dioxide

Figure 7.2 Where the main energy-releasing pathways of ATP formation start and finish.

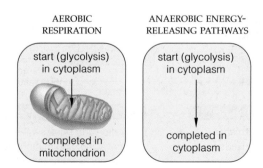

Read Me First!
and watch the narrated animation
on aerobic respiration

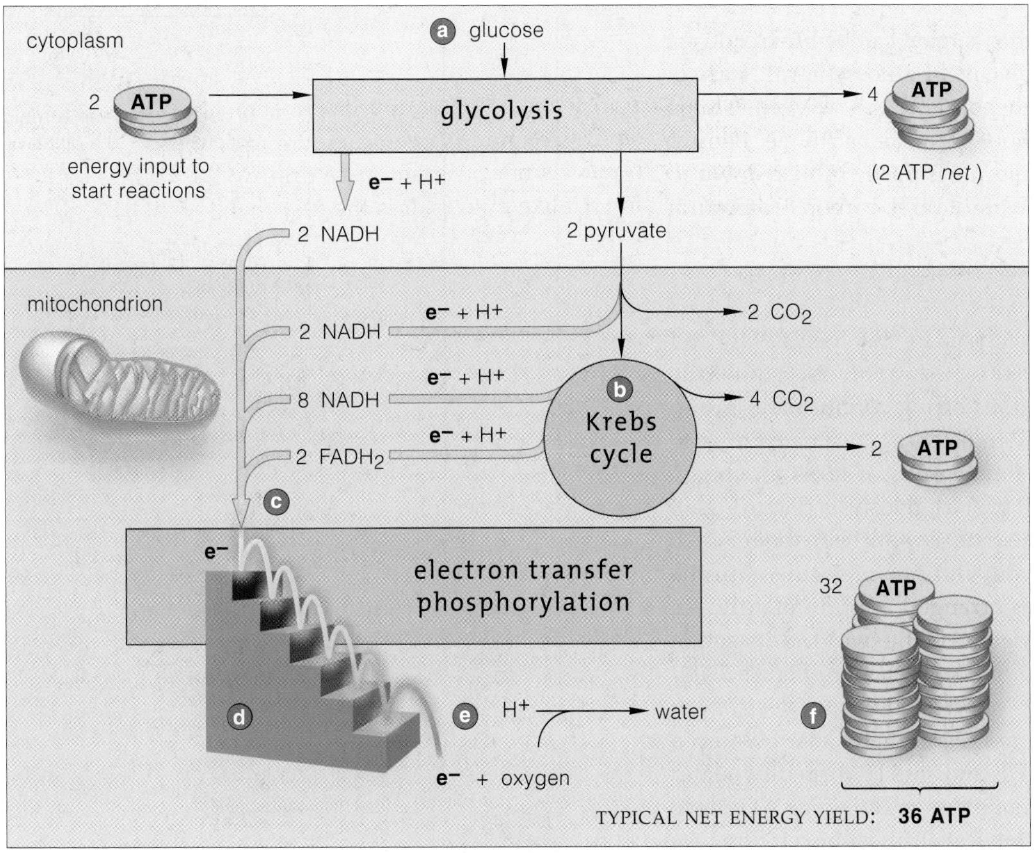

cytoplasm

(a) glucose

2 **ATP** → **glycolysis** → 4 **ATP**

energy input to
start reactions

(2 ATP *net*)

e⁻ + H⁺

2 NADH

2 pyruvate

mitochondrion

2 NADH → **e⁻ + H⁺** → 2 CO₂

8 NADH → **e⁻ + H⁺**

(b) Krebs cycle → 4 CO₂

2 FADH₂ → **e⁻ + H⁺**

→ 2 **ATP**

(c)

e⁻

(d) electron transfer phosphorylation

32 **ATP**

(e) H⁺ → water

(f)

e⁻ + oxygen

TYPICAL NET ENERGY YIELD: **36 ATP**

Figure 7.3 Overview of aerobic respiration. Reactions start in the cytoplasm and end in mitochondria.

(**a**) In the first stage, glycolysis, enzymes partly break down glucose to pyruvate.

(**b**) In the second stage, enzymes break down pyruvate to carbon dioxide.

(**c**) NAD⁺ and FAD pick up the electrons and hydrogen stripped from intermediates in both stages.

(**d**) The final stage is electron transfer phosphorylation. The reduced coenzymes NADH and FADH₂ give up electrons to electron transfer chains. H⁺ tags along with electrons. Electron flow through the chains sets up H⁺ gradients, which are tapped to make ATP.

(**e**) Oxygen accepts electrons at the end of the third stage, forming water.

(**f**) From start to finish, a typical net energy yield from a glucose molecule is thirty-six ATP.

However, as you can see, the summary equation only tells us what the substances are at the start and finish of the pathway. In between are three reaction stages.

Figure 7.3 is your overview of aerobic respiration. Glycolysis, again, is the first stage. The second stage is a cyclic pathway, the **Krebs cycle**. Enzymes break down pyruvate to carbon dioxide and water, which releases many electrons and hydrogen atoms.

As you track the reactions, you'll come across two enzyme helpers, the coenzymes **NAD⁺** (nicotinamide adenine dinucleotide) and **FAD** (flavin adenine dinucleotide). Both accept electrons and hydrogen derived from intermediates of glucose breakdown. Unbound hydrogen atoms are simply hydrogen ions (H⁺), or naked protons. When the two coenzymes are carrying electrons and hydrogen, they are in a reduced form and may be abbreviated NADH and FADH₂.

Few ATP form during glycolysis or the Krebs cycle. The big energy harvest comes in the third stage, after the coenzymes give up the electrons and hydrogen to

electron transfer chains. The chains are the machinery of **electron transfer phosphorylation**. They set up H⁺ concentration and electric gradients, which drive ATP formation at nearby membrane proteins. It is in this final stage that so many ATP molecules are produced. As it ends, oxygen inside the mitochondrion accepts the "spent" electrons from the last component of each transport system. Oxygen picks up H⁺ at the same time and thereby forms water.

Nearly all metabolic reactions run on energy released from glucose and other organic compounds. The main energy-releasing pathways start in the cytoplasm with glycolysis, a stage of reactions that break down glucose to pyruvate.

Anaerobic pathways have a small net energy yield, typically two ATP per glucose.

Aerobic respiration, an oxygen-dependent pathway, runs to completion in mitochondria. From start (glycolysis) to finish, it typically has a net energy yield of thirty-six ATP.

7.2 The First Stage: Glycolysis

Let's track what happens to a glucose molecule in the first stage of aerobic respiration. Remember, the same steps happen in anaerobic energy-releasing pathways.

Any of several six-carbon sugars can be broken down in glycolysis. Each molecule of glucose, recall, has six carbon, twelve hydrogen, and six oxygen atoms (Section 3.3). The carbons form its backbone. During glycolysis, this one molecule is partly broken down to two molecules of pyruvate, a three-carbon compound:

glucose ⟶ ⓟ–glucose ⟶ 2 pyruvate

The initial steps of gycolysis are *energy-requiring*, and that energy is delivered by ATP. One ATP molecule activates glucose by transferring a phosphate group to it. Then another ATP transfers a phosphate group to the intermediate that forms. Thus, it takes an energy investment of two ATP to start glycolysis (Figure 7.4*a*).

The second intermediate is split into one PGAL (phosphoglyceraldehyde) and one molecule with the same number of atoms arranged a bit differently. An enzyme can reversibly convert the two, and its action delivers two PGAL for the next reaction (Figure 7.4*b*).

In the first *energy-releasing* step of glycolysis, both PGALs are converted to intermediates that give up a phosphate group to ADP, and so ATP forms. Two later intermediates do the same thing. Thus four ATP have been formed by **substrate-level phosphorylation**. We define this metabolic event as the direct transfer of a phosphate group from the substrate of a reaction to some other molecule—in this case, to ADP.

Meanwhile, the coenzyme NAD^+ accepts electrons and hydrogens from each PGAL, becoming NADH.

By this time, a total of four molecules of ATP have formed, but remember that two ATP were invested to get the reactions going. The *net* yield of glycolysis is two ATP and two NADH.

To summarize, glycolysis converts the bond energy of glucose to bond energy of ATP—a transportable form of energy. The electrons and hydrogen stripped from glucose and picked up by NAD^+ will enter the next stage of reactions. And so will the end products of glycolysis—two pyruvate molecules.

Glycolysis is a series of reactions that partially break down glucose or other six-carbon sugars to two molecules of pyruvate. It takes two ATP to jump-start the reactions.

Two NADH and four ATP form. However, when we subtract the two ATP required to start the reactions, the net energy yield of glycolysis is two ATP from one glucose molecule.

GLUCOSE

Figure 7.4 Glycolysis. This first stage of the main energy-releasing pathways occurs in the cytoplasm of all prokaryotic and eukaryotic cells. Glucose is the reactant in this example. Appendix V gives the structural formulas of intermediates that form during its breakdown. Two pyruvate, two NADH, and four ATP form in glycolysis. Cells invest two ATP to start the reactions however, so the *net* energy yield is two ATP.

Depending on the type of cell and environmental conditions, the pyruvate may enter the second set of reactions of the aerobic pathway, including the Krebs cycle. Or it may be used in other reactions, such as those of fermentation.

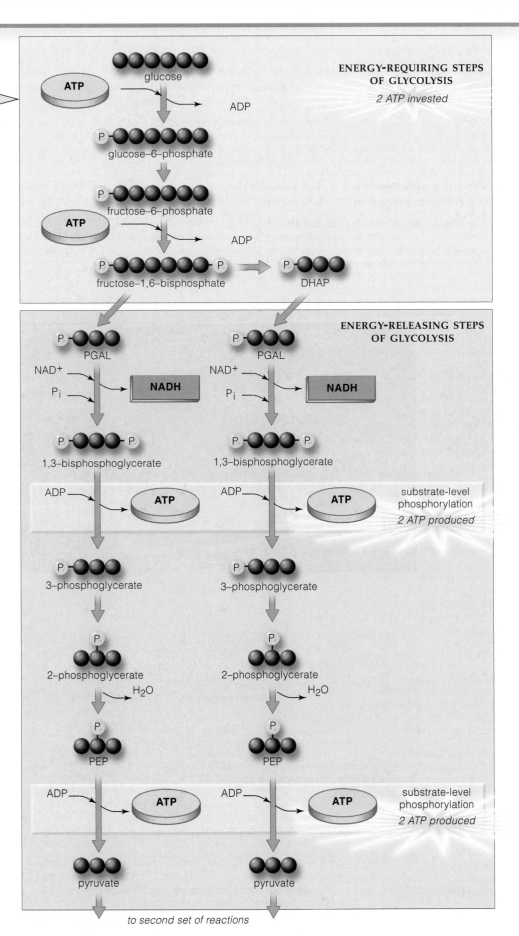

to second set of reactions

ENERGY-REQUIRING STEPS OF GLYCOLYSIS

2 ATP invested

glucose

ADP

glucose–6–phosphate

fructose–6–phosphate

ADP

fructose–1,6–bisphosphate   DHAP

ENERGY-RELEASING STEPS OF GLYCOLYSIS

PGAL

NAD⁺

Pi

NADH

1,3–bisphosphoglycerate

ADP

ATP

3–phosphoglycerate

2–phosphoglycerate

H_2O

PEP

ADP

ATP

pyruvate

substrate-level phosphorylation

2 ATP produced

substrate-level phosphorylation

2 ATP produced

Read Me First!

and watch the narrated animation on glycolysis

Track the six carbon atoms (*brown circles*) of glucose. Glycolysis requires an energy investment of two ATP:

a One ATP transfers a phosphate group to glucose, jump-starting the reactions.

b Another ATP transfers a phosphate group to an intermediate, causing it to split into two three-carbon compounds: PGAL and DHAP (dihydroxyacetone phosphate). Both have the same atoms, arranged differently. They are interconvertible, but only PGAL can continue on in glycolysis. DHAP gets converted, so two PGAL are available for the next reaction.

c Two NADH form when each PGAL gives up two electrons and a hydrogen atom to NAD⁺.

d Two intermediates each transfer a phosphate group to ADP. *Thus, two ATP have formed by direct phosphate group transfers.* The original energy investment of two ATP is now paid off.

e Two more intermediates form. Each gives up one hydrogen atom and an —OH group. These combine as water. Two molecules called PEP form by these reactions.

f Each PEP transfers a phosphate group to ADP. *Once again, two ATP have formed by substrate-level phosphorylation.*

In sum, glycolysis has a net energy yield of two ATP for each glucose molecule. Two NADH also form during the reactions, and two molecules of pyruvate are the end products.

7.3 Second Stage of Aerobic Respiration

The two pyruvate molecules formed by glycolysis can leave the cytoplasm and enter a mitochondrion. There they enter reactions that get the Krebs cycle going. Many coenzymes pick up the electrons and hydrogens released when the two pyruvates are dismantled.

ACETYL–CoA FORMATION

Start with Figure 7.5, which shows the structure of a typical mitochondrion. Figure 7.6 zooms in on part of the interior where the second-stage reactions occur. At the start of these reactions, enzyme action strips one carbon atom from each pyruvate and attaches it to oxygen, forming CO_2. Each two-carbon fragment combines with a coenzyme (designated A) and forms acetyl–CoA, a type of cofactor that can get the Krebs cycle going. The initial breakdown of each pyruvate also yields one NADH (Figure 7.7).

THE KREBS CYCLE

The two acetyl–CoA molecules enter the Krebs cycle separately. Each transfers its two-carbon acetyl group to four-carbon oxaloacetate. Incidentally, this cyclic pathway is also called the citric acid cycle, after the first intermediate that forms (citric acid, or citrate).

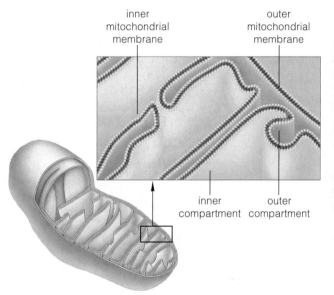

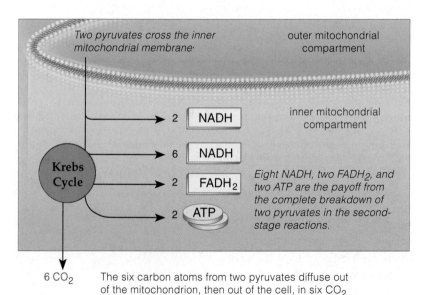

Figure 7.5 *Above,* functional zones inside the mitochondrion. An inner membrane system divides this organelle's interior into an inner and an outer compartment. The second and third stages of aerobic respiration play out at this membrane.

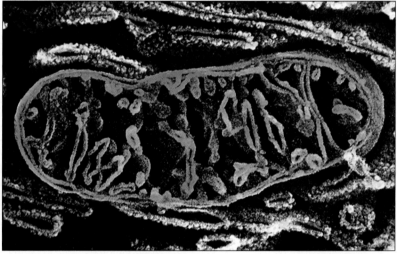

Figure 7.6 *Right:* Overview of the number of ATP molecules and coenzymes that form in the second stage of aerobic respiration. The reactions start with two molecules of pyruvate from glycolysis. Pyruvate moves from the cytoplasm, then across the outer and inner mitochondrial membranes, into the inner compartment where the reactions take place.

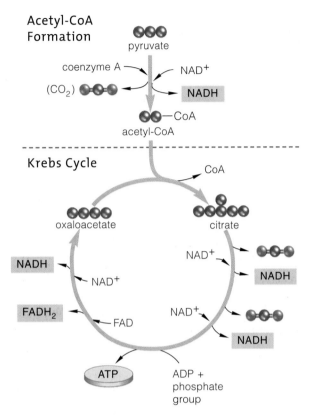

a One carbon atom is stripped from each pyruvate and is released as CO_2. The remaining fragment binds with coenzyme A, forming acetyl–CoA.

h The final steps regenerate oxaloacetate. NAD^+ picks up hydrogen and electrons, forming NADH. *At this point in the cycle, three NADH and one FADH$_2$ have formed.*

g FADH$_2$ forms as the coenzyme FAD picks up electrons and hydrogen.

b NAD^+ picks up hydrogen and electrons, forming one NADH.

c In the first step of the Krebs cycle, acetyl–CoA transfers two carbons to oxaloacetate, forming citrate.

d In rearrangements of intermediates, another carbon atom is released as CO_2, and NADH forms as NAD^+ picks up hydrogen and electrons.

e Another carbon atom is released as CO_2. Another NADH forms. *Three carbon atoms now have been released.* This balances out the three carbons that entered (in one pyruvate).

f A phosphate group is attached to ADP. At this point, one ATP has formed by substrate-level phosphorylation.

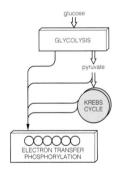

Figure 7.7 Aerobic respiration's second stage: formation of acetyl–CoA and the Krebs cycle. The reactions occur in a mitochondrion's inner compartment. It takes two turns of the cycle to break down the two pyruvates from glucose. A total of two ATP, eight NADH, two FADH$_2$, and six CO_2 molecules form. Organisms release the CO_2 from the reactions into their surroundings.

It takes two turns of the Krebs cycle to completely break down two molecules of pyruvate to CO_2 and water. Only two ATP form, which doesn't add much to the small net yield from glycolysis. However, in addition to those two NADH produced during the formation of acetyl–CoA, six more NADH and two FADH$_2$ are produced in the cycle. With their cargo of electrons and hydrogen atoms, these ten coenzymes constitute a big potential payoff for the cell.

Four more CO_2 molecules form as the Krebs cycle turns. In total, *six* carbon atoms (from two pyruvates) depart during the second stage of aerobic respiration, in six molecules of CO_2 (Figures 7.6 and 7.7). And so glucose from glycolysis has lost all of its carbons; it has become fully oxidized.

For interested students, Appendix V has a closer look at the steps of these remarkable reactions.

Aerobic respiration's second stage starts after two pyruvate molecules from glycolysis move from the cytoplasm, across the outer and inner mitochondrial membranes, and into the inner mitochondrial compartment.

Here, pyruvate is converted to acetyl–CoA, which starts the Krebs cycle. A total of two ATP and ten coenzymes (eight NADH, two FADH$_2$) form. All of pyruvate's carbons depart, in the form of carbon dioxide.

Together with two coenzymes (NADH) that formed during glycolysis, the ten from the second stage will deliver electrons and hydrogen to the third and final stage.

7.4 Third Stage of Aerobic Respiration—The Big Energy Payoff

In the aerobic pathway's third stage, energy release goes into high gear. Coenzymes from the first two stages provide the hydrogen and electrons that drive the formation of many ATP. Electron transfer chains and ATP synthases function as the machinery.

ELECTRON TRANSFER PHOSPHORYLATION

The third stage starts as coenzymes donate electrons to electron transfer chains that are located in the inner mitochondrial membrane (Figure 7.8). The flow of electrons through the chains drives the attachment of phosphate to ADP molecules. Hence the name *electron transfer phosphorylation.*

Incremental energy release, recall, is more efficient than one big burst of energy that would result in little more than a lot of unusable heat (Section 5.2). When electrons flow through transfer chains, they give up energy bit by bit, in usable parcels, to substances that can briefly store it.

The two NADH that formed in the cytoplasm (by glycolysis) can't reach the ATP-producing machinery directly. They give up their electrons and hydrogen to transport proteins, which shuttle them into the inner compartment. There, NAD+ or FAD inside pick them up. Eight NADH and two FADH$_2$ from the second stage are already inside.

When all of these coenzymes turn over electrons to transfer chains, they release hydrogen ions (H+) at the same time. Electrons passing through the chains lose a bit of energy at each step. In three parts of the chain, that energy drives the pumping of H+ into the outer compartment. There, accumulation of H+ sets up an electrochemical gradient across the inner membrane.

H+ can't diffuse across membranes. The only way it can follow the gradients, which lead back to the inner compartment, is by flowing through the interior of ATP synthases (Figures 7.8 and 7.9). H+ flow through these transport proteins drives the formation of ATP from ADP and unbound phosphate.

The last molecules in the electron transfer chains pass electrons to gaseous oxygen, which forms water after combining with H+. *Oxygen is the final acceptor of electrons stripped from glucose.* In oxygen-starved cells, electrons in the transfer chain have nowhere to go. The whole chain backs up with electrons all the way to NADPH, so no H+ gradient forms, and no ATP is made. Cells of complex organisms don't survive long without oxygen, because they can't produce enough ATP to sustain life processes.

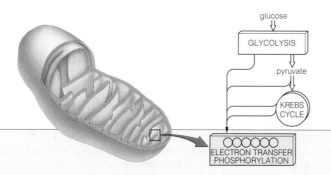

Figure 7.8 Electron transfer phosphorylation, the third and final stage of aerobic respiration.

At the inner mitochondrial membrane, NADH and FADH$_2$ give up electrons to the transfer chains. When electrons are transferred through the chains, unbound hydrogen (H+) is shuttled across the membrane to the outer compartment:

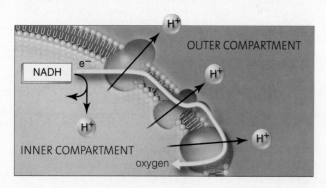

H+ concentration is now greater in the outer compartment. Concentration and electric gradients across the membrane have been set up. H+ follows these gradients through the interior of ATP synthases. The flow drives the formation of ATP from ADP and unbound phosphate (P$_i$).

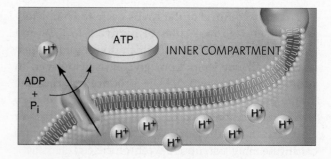

Do these events sound familiar? They should. ATP forms in much the same way inside chloroplasts. H+ concentration and electric gradients across the inner thylakoid membrane drive ATP formation. In thylakoids, H+ flows in the opposite direction compared to the flow in chloroplasts.

Read Me First!
and watch the narrated animation on third-stage reactions

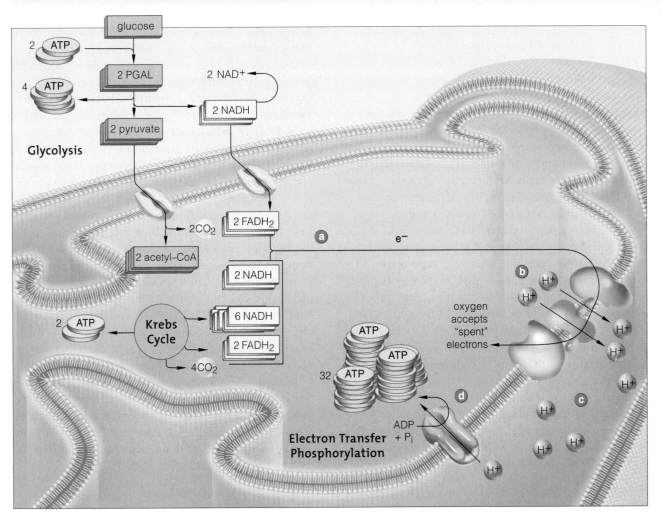

a Electrons and hydrogen from NADH and FADH$_2$ that formed during the first and second stages enter electron transfer chains.

b As electrons are transferred through the chains, H$^+$ ions are shuttled across the inner membrane, into the outer compartment.

c H$^+$ concentration becomes greater in the outer compartment than the inner one. Chemical and electrical gradients have been established.

d Hydrogen ions follow the gradients through the interior of ATP synthases, driving ATP synthesis from ADP and phosphate (P$_i$).

Figure 7.9 Summary of the transfers of electrons and hydrogen from coenzymes involved in ATP formation in mitochondria.

SUMMING UP: THE ENERGY HARVEST

Thirty-two ATP typically form in the third stage. Add in the four produced in the first and second stages, and aerobic respiration has netted thirty-six ATP from one glucose molecule. That's a lot of ATP! Anaerobic pathways may use up eighteen glucose molecules to get the same net yield.

The actual yield varies. Shifting concentrations of reactants, intermediates, and products affect it. So does the shuttling of electrons and hydrogen from NADH that forms in the cytoplasm. Shuttling mechanisms are not the same in all cell types.

In aerobic respiration's third stage, electrons and hydrogen from coenzymes (NADH and FADH$_2$) interact with electron transfer chains in the mitochondrion's inner membrane.

Electron flow through transfer chains makes H$^+$ accumulate in the outer mitochondrial compartment. The resulting chemical and electrical gradients across the inner membrane drive the synthesis of thirty-two ATP.

Aerobic respiration typically nets thirty-six ATP molecules from each glucose molecule metabolized.

7.5 Fermentation Pathways

We turn now to the use of glucose as a substrate for fermentation pathways. These are anaerobic pathways. They don't use oxygen as the final acceptor of electrons that ultimately drive the ATP-forming machinery.

Diverse organisms are fermenters. Many are protists and bacterial species that live in marshes, bogs, mud, ocean sediments, the animal gut, canned foods, sewage treatment ponds, and other oxygen-free places. Some die when exposed to free oxygen. Bacterial species that cause botulism and many other diseases are like this. Other fermenters are indifferent to oxygen's presence. Still other kinds use oxygen, but they also can switch to fermentation when oxygen becomes scarce.

Glycolysis is the first stage of fermentation, as it is in aerobic respiration (Figure 7.4). Here, too, pyruvate and NADH form, and the net energy yield is two ATP. But fermentation reactions cannot completely degrade glucose (to carbon dioxide and water). They produce no more ATP beyond the small yield from glycolysis. *The final steps simply regenerate NAD+, the coenzyme that is essential for the breakdown reactions.* The regeneration allows glycolysis reactions to continue production of small amounts of ATP in the absence of oxygen.

Fermentation yields enough energy to sustain many single-celled anaerobic organisms. It even helps some aerobic cells when oxygen levels are stressfully low. But it isn't enough to sustain large, multicelled organisms, this being why you'll never see anaerobic elephants.

ALCOHOLIC FERMENTATION

In **alcoholic fermentation**, the three-carbon backbone of the two pyruvate molecules from glycolysis is split. The reactions result in two molecules of acetaldehyde (an intermediate having a two-carbon backbone), and two of carbon dioxide. Next, the acetaldehydes accept electrons and hydrogen from NADH, thus becoming an alcohol product called ethanol (Figure 7.10).

Some single-celled fungi called yeasts are famous for their use of this pathway. One type, *Saccharomyces cerevisiae,* makes bread dough rise. Bakers mix it with sugar, then blend both into dough. Fermenting yeast cells release carbon dioxide, and the dough expands (rises) as the gas forms bubbles in it. Oven heat forces the bubbles out of spaces they had occupied in the dough, and the alcohol product evaporates away.

Wild and cultivated strains of *Saccharomyces* are used to produce alcohol in wine. Crushed grapes are left in vats along with the yeast, which converts sugar in the juice to ethanol. Ethanol is toxic to microbes. When a fermenting brew's ethanol content nears 10 percent, yeast cells start dying and fermentation ends.

Birds get drunk when they eat too many naturally fermented berries. Landscapers avoid planting berry-producing shrubs along highways because inebriated birds fly into windshields. Also, wild turkeys, robins, and other birds get tipsy on fermenting fruit that has dropped from orchard trees.

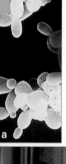

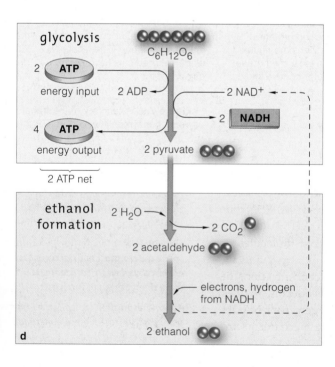

Figure 7.10 A look at alcoholic fermentation. (**a**) Yeasts, single-celled organisms, make ATP by this anaerobic pathway.

(**b**) A vintner examining the color and clarity of one fermentation product of *Saccharomyces.* Strains of this yeast live on the sugar-rich tissues of ripe grapes.

(**c**) Carbon dioxide released from cells of *S. cerevisiae* makes bread dough rise in this bakery.

(**d**) Alcoholic fermentation. The intermediate acetaldehyde functions as the final electron acceptor. The end product of the reactions is ethanol.

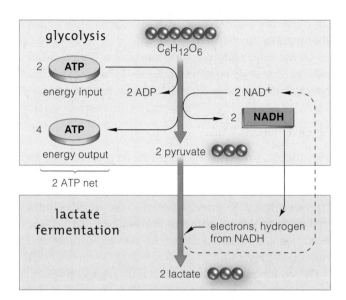

Figure 7.11 Lactate fermentation. In this anaerobic pathway, the product (lactate) is the final acceptor of electrons originally stripped from glucose. The reactions have a net energy yield of two ATP (from glycolysis).

Figure 7.12 Sprinters, calling upon lactate fermentation in their muscles. The micrograph is a cross-section through part of a muscle showing three types of fibers. The lighter fibers contribute to muscle speed by producing ATP with lactate fermentation when demands for energy are high. Darker fibers use aerobic respiration and support greater levels of endurance.

LACTATE FERMENTATION

In **lactate fermentation**, NADH gives up electrons and hydrogen to two pyruvate molecules from glycolysis. The transfer converts each pyruvate to lactate, a three-carbon compound (Figure 7.11). You've probably heard of lactic acid, the non-ionized form of this compound, but lactate is by far the most common form inside living cells, which is our focus here.

Lactobacillus and some other bacteria use lactate fermentation. Their fermenting action can spoil food, yet some species have commercial uses. For instance, huge populations that break down glucose in milk give us cheeses, yogurt, buttermilk, and other dairy products. Fermenters also help in curing meats and in pickling some fruits and vegetables, such as sauerkraut. Lactate is an acid; it gives these foods a sour taste.

Lactate fermentation as well as aerobic respiration yields ATP for muscles that are partnered with bones. These skeletal muscles contain a mixture of cell types. Cells composing *slow-twitch* muscle fibers support light, steady, prolonged activity, as during marathon runs or bird migrations. Slow-twitch muscle cells make ATP only by the aerobic respiration pathway, and so they have many mitochondria. They are dark red because they contain large amounts of myoglobin, a pigment related to hemoglobin that is used to store oxygen for aerobic respiration.

By contrast, cells of pale *fast-twitch* muscle fibers have few mitochondria and no myoglobin, and use lactate fermentation to produce ATP. They are useful when demands for energy are immediate and intense, such as in weight lifting or sprints (Figure 7.12). Lactate fermentation works quickly but not for long—it does not produce enough ATP to sustain activity. That is one reason you don't see migrating chickens. Flight muscles in a chicken are the white breast meat, containing mostly fast-twitch fibers.

Short bursts of flight evolved in the ancestors of chickens, perhaps as a way of escaping predators or improving agility during territorial battles. Chickens do walk or sprint; hence the "dark meat" (slow-twitch muscle) in their thighs and legs. So what sort of breast meat can you expect to find in a migrating duck?

Section 32.5 is an overview of alternative energy pathways for muscle cells.

In fermentation pathways, an organic substance that forms during the reactions is the final acceptor of electrons originally derived from glucose.

Alcoholic fermentation and lactate fermentation both have a net energy yield of two ATP for each glucose molecule metabolized. That ATP forms during glycolysis. The remaining reactions regenerate NAD⁺, the coenzyme that keeps these pathways operating.

7.6 Alternative Energy Sources in the Body

So far, you've looked at what happens after glucose molecules enter an energy-releasing pathway. Now start thinking about what cells do when they have too much or too little glucose.

THE FATE OF GLUCOSE AT MEALTIME AND IN BETWEEN MEALS

What happens to glucose at mealtime? While you and all other mammals are eating, glucose and other small organic molecules are being absorbed across the gut lining, and your blood is transporting them through the body. The rising glucose concentration in blood prompts an organ, the pancreas, to secrete insulin. This hormone makes cells take up glucose faster.

Cells trap the incoming glucose by converting it to glucose–6–phosphate. This is the first intermediate of glycolysis, formed by a phosphate group transfer from ATP (Figures 7.4 and 7.13). Phosphorylated glucose can't be transported out of the cell.

When glucose intake exceeds cellular demands for energy, the body's ATP-producing machinery goes into high gear. Unless a cell is using ATP rapidly, the ATP concentration in cytoplasm rises, and glucose–6–phosphate is diverted into a biosynthesis pathway. Glucose gets stored as glycogen, one of the storage polysaccharides found in animals (Section 3.3). Liver cells and muscle cells especially favor this alternative pathway. Together, these two types of cells maintain the largest stores of glycogen in the body.

Between meals, the blood level of glucose declines. If the decline were not countered, that would be bad news for the brain, your body's glucose hog. At any time, your brain is taking up more than two-thirds of the freely circulating glucose. Why? The brain's many hundreds of millions of nerve cells (neurons) use this sugar as their preferred energy source.

The pancreas responds to glucose decline by secreting glucagon. This hormone causes liver cells to convert stored glycogen to glucose and send it back to the blood. Only liver cells do this; muscle cells won't give it up. The blood glucose level rises, and brain cells keep on functioning. Thus, *hormones control whether your cells use free glucose as an energy source or tuck it away.*

Don't let this explanation lead you to believe that your cells squirrel away huge amounts of glycogen. Glycogen makes up only 1 percent or so of the adult body's total energy reserves, the energy equivalent of two cups of cooked pasta. Unless you eat on a regular basis, you'll end up depleting your liver's small glycogen stores in less than twelve hours.

Of the total energy reserves in, say, a typical adult who eats well, 78 percent (about 10,000 kilocalories) is concentrated in body fat and 21 percent in proteins.

ENERGY FROM FATS

How does a human body access its fat reservoir? A fat molecule, recall, has a glycerol head and one, two, or three fatty acid tails. The body stores most fats as triglycerides, with three tails each. Triglycerides build up inside of the fat cells of adipose tissue. This tissue is strategically located under the skin of buttocks and other body regions.

When the blood glucose level falls, triglycerides are tapped as an energy alternative. Enzymes in fat cells cleave bonds between glycerol and fatty acids, which both enter the blood. Enzymes in the liver convert the glycerol to PGAL. And PGAL, recall, is one of the key intermediates for glycolysis (Figure 7.4). Nearly all cells of your body take up circulating fatty acids, and enzymes inside them cleave the fatty acid backbones. The fragments are converted to acetyl–CoA, which can enter the Krebs cycle.

Compared to glucose, a fatty acid tail has far more carbon-bound hydrogen atoms, so it yields more ATP. Between meals or during steady, prolonged exercise, fatty acid conversions supply about half of the ATP that muscle, liver, and kidney cells require.

What happens if you eat too many carbohydrates? Aerobic respiration, remember, converts glucose to pyruvate, then to acetyl–CoA, which enters the Krebs cycle. When too much glucose is circulating through the body, acetyl–CoA is diverted to a pathway that synthesizes fatty acids. *Too much glucose ends up as fat.*

ENERGY FROM PROTEINS

Some enzymes in your digestive system split dietary proteins into their amino acid subunits, which are then absorbed into the bloodstream. Cells use amino acids to build other proteins or nitrogen-containing compounds. Even so, if you eat more protein than your body needs, amino acids will be broken down further. Their $-NH_3^+$ group is pulled off, forming ammonia (NH_3). Depending on the types of amino acids, the leftover carbon backbones are broken down to either acetyl–CoA, pyruvate, or one of the intermediates of the Krebs cycle. Your cells can funnel any of these compounds into the Krebs cycle.

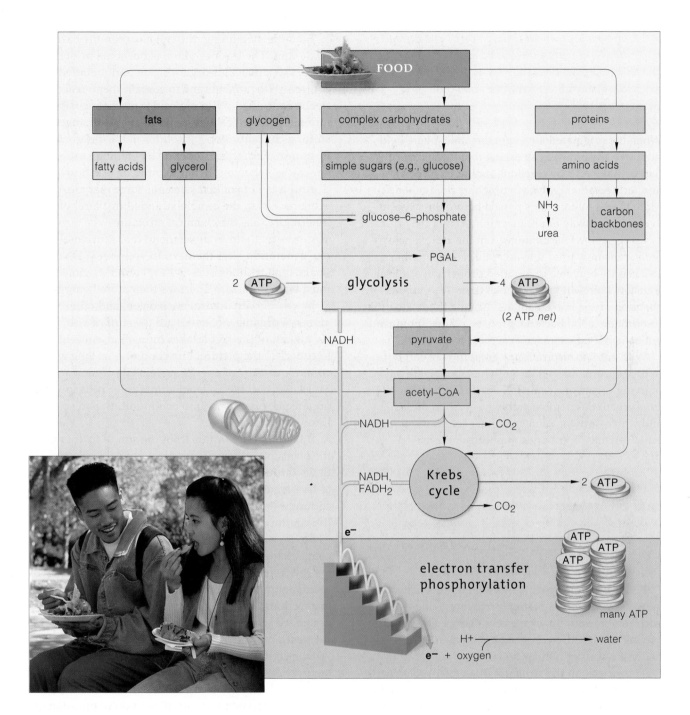

Figure 7.13 Reaction sites where a variety of organic compounds can enter the different stages of aerobic respiration. The compounds shown are alternative energy sources in humans and other mammals.

Notice how complex carbohydrates, fats, and proteins cannot enter the aerobic pathway directly. The digestive system, then individual cells, must first break apart these molecules to simpler compounds that the pathway can dismantle further.

As you can see, maintaining and accessing energy reserves is complicated business. Controlling the use of glucose is special because it is the fuel of choice for the brain. However, providing all of your cells with energy starts with the kinds of food you eat.

In humans and other mammals, the entrance of glucose or other organic compounds into an energy-releasing pathway depends on the kinds and proportions of carbohydrates, fats, and proteins in the diet.

7.7 Perspective on Life

In this unit you read about photosynthesis and aerobic respiration—the main pathways by which cells trap, store, and release energy. What you may not know is that the two pathways became linked, on a grand scale, over evolutionary time.

When life originated long ago, the atmosphere held little free oxygen. We can expect that those first cells had to make ATP by reactions similar to glycolysis, and fermentation pathways probably dominated. More than a billion years passed before the oxygen-evolving pathway of photosynthesis emerged.

Oxygen slowly accumulated in the atmosphere. Some cells now used it to accept electrons, perhaps as a chance outcome of mutated proteins in electron transfer chains. In time, some of their descendants abandoned anaerobic habitats. Among them were the forerunners of all bacteria, protists, plants, fungi, and animals that now engage in aerobic respiration.

With aerobic respiration, a great flow of carbon, hydrogen, and oxygen through metabolic pathways of living organisms came full circle. For the final products of this aerobic pathway—carbon dioxide and water—are the same materials necessary to build organic compounds in photosynthesis:

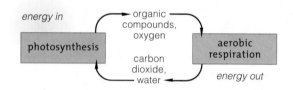

Perhaps you have difficulty seeing the connection between yourself—a highly intelligent being—and such remote-sounding events as energy flow and the cycling of carbon, hydrogen, and oxygen. Is this really the stuff of humanity?

Think back on the structure of a water molecule. Two hydrogen atoms sharing electrons with oxygen may not seem close to your daily life. Yet, through that sharing, water molecules show polarity and hydrogen-bond with one another. Their chemical behavior is a beginning for the organization of lifeless matter that leads in turn to the organization of all living things.

For now you can visualize other diverse molecules interspersed through water. Nonpolar kinds resist interaction with water; polar kinds dissolve in it. On their own, the phospholipids among them assemble into a two-layered film. Such lipid bilayers, recall, are the framework of cell membranes, hence all cells.

From the beginning, the cell has been the basic *living* unit. The essence of life is not some mysterious force; it is molecular organization and metabolic control. With a membrane to contain them, reactions *can* be controlled. With molecular mechanisms built into membranes, cells respond to energy changes and shifting concentrations of solutes in the environment. Response mechanisms operate by "telling" proteins—enzymes—when and what to build or tear down.

And it is not some mysterious force that creates proteins. DNA, the double-stranded treasurehouse of inheritance, has the chemical structure—*the chemical message*—that allows molecule to reproduce molecule, one generation after the next. In your body, DNA strands tell trillions of cells how countless molecules must be built or torn apart for their stored energy.

So yes, carbon, hydrogen, oxygen, and other atoms of organic molecules are the stuff of you, and us, and all of life. Yet it takes more than molecules to complete the picture. Life continues as long as a continuous flow of energy sustains its organization. Molecules become assembled into cells, cells into organisms, organisms into communities, and so on through the biosphere.

It takes energy inputs from the sun to maintain the levels of biological organization. And energy flows through time in one direction—from organized to less organized forms. Only as long as energy continues to flow into the great web of life can life continue in all its rich expressions.

So life is no more *and no less* than a marvelously complex system for prolonging order. Sustained with energy transfusions from the sun, life continues by its capacity for self-reproduction. With the hereditary instructions of DNA, energy and materials become organized, generation after generation. Even with the death of individuals, life elsewhere is prolonged. With each death, molecules are released and may be recycled as raw materials for new generations.

With this flow of energy and cycling of material through time, each birth is affirmation of our ongoing capacity for organization, each death a renewal.

Summary

Section 7.1 All organisms, including photosynthetic types, make ATP by the breakdown of glucose and other organic compounds. Glycolysis, the initial breakdown of one glucose to two pyruvate molecules, takes place in the cytoplasm. It is the first stage of all the main energy-releasing pathways, and it doesn't require free oxygen.

Anaerobic pathways end in the cytoplasm, and the net yield of ATP is small. An oxygen-requiring pathway called aerobic respiration continues in mitochondria, and it releases far more ATP energy from glucose.

Section 7.2 The first steps of glycolysis require an energy input of 2 ATP. Phosphate-group transfers from ATP drive the breakdown of a molecule of glucose (or another sugar) to two molecules of pyruvate, each with a three-carbon backbone. Two molecules of the coenzyme NAD^+ pick up electrons and hydrogen stripped from reaction intermediates, forming two NADH. Four ATP form during glycolysis, but the net energy yield is two ATP (because two ATP had to be invested up front).

Section 7.3 If the two pyruvates from glycolysis enter a mitochondrion, they will be fully degraded, as part of the second and third stages of aerobic respiration.

The second stage consists of acetyl–CoA formation and the Krebs cycle. Two pyruvates are converted to acetyl–CoA, and two carbon atoms depart in the form of CO_2. In two turns of the Krebs cycle (one for each pyruvate), intermediates are degraded; four more carbons escape (as CO_2). Coenzymes NAD^+ and FAD pick up electrons and hydrogen from intermediates. Two ATP form.

In total, eight NADH, two $FADH_2$, two ATP, and six CO_2 form during the aerobic pathway's second stage.

Section 7.4 The third stage of aerobic respiration proceeds at electron transfer chains and ATP synthases in the inner mitochondrial membrane. Electron transfer chains accept electrons and hydrogen from the NADH and $FADH_2$ that formed in the first two stages. Electron flow through the chains causes H^+ to accumulate in the inner mitochondrial compartment, so H^+ concentration and electric gradients build up across the membrane. H^+ flows down the gradients, through the interior of ATP synthases. This flow drives the attachment of unbound phosphate to ADP, forming many ATP.

Free oxygen picks up the electrons at the end of the transfer chains and combines with H^+, forming water.

Aerobic respiration has a typical net energy yield of thirty-six ATP for each glucose molecule metabolized.

Section 7.5 Fermentation pathways do not require oxygen, and they take place only in the cytoplasm. They use the pyruvate and ATP that formed during the first stage of reactions (glycolysis). The remaining reactions regenerate NAD^+. No more ATP forms. The net energy yield is only the two ATP that formed in glycolysis.

In alcoholic fermentation, the two pyruvates from glycolysis are converted to two acetaldehyde and two CO_2 molecules. When NADH transfers electrons and hydrogen to acetaldehyde, two ethanol molecules form and NAD^+ is regenerated.

In lactate fermentation, NAD^+ is regenerated when electrons and hydrogen are transferred from NADH to the two pyruvate molecules from glycolysis, which forms two lactate molecules as end products.

Slow-twitch and fast-twitch skeletal muscle cells support different levels of activity. Aerobic respiration and lactate fermentation occur in different cells that make up these muscles.

Section 7.6 In the human body, simple sugars from carbohydrates, glycerol and fatty acids from fats, and carbon backbones of amino acids from proteins can enter the aerobic pathway as alternative energy sources.

Section 7.7 Life's diversity, interconnections, and continuity arise from its unity at the molecular level.

Self-Quiz

Answers in Appendix III

1. Glycolysis starts and ends in the _____ .
   a. nucleus   c. plasma membrane
   b. mitochondrion   d. cytoplasm

2. Which of the following molecules does not form during glycolysis?
   a. NADH   b. pyruvate   c. $FADH_2$ d. ATP

3. Aerobic respiration is completed in the _____ .
   a. nucleus   c. plasma membrane
   b. mitochondrion   d. cytoplasm

4. In the third stage of aerobic respiration, _____ is the final acceptor of electrons from glucose.
   a. water   b. hydrogen   c. oxygen   d. NADH

5. Fill in the blanks in the diagram below.

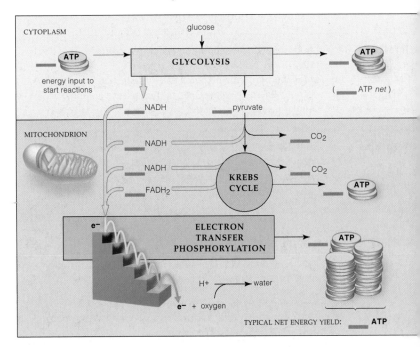

6. In alcoholic fermentation, _____ is the final acceptor of electrons stripped from glucose.
   a. oxygen
   b. pyruvate
   c. acetaldehyde
   d. sulfate

7. Fermentation pathways produce no more ATP beyond the small yield from glycolysis. The remaining reactions _____ .
   a. regenerate FAD
   b. regenerate NAD^+
   c. regenerate NAD
   d. regenerate $FADH_2$

8. In certain organisms and under certain conditions, _____ can be used as an energy alternative to glucose.
   a. fatty acids
   b. glycerol
   c. amino acids
   d. all of the above

9. Match the event with its most suitable description.
   ____ glycolysis
   ____ fermentation
   ____ Krebs cycle
   ____ electron transfer phosphorylation

   a. ATP, NADH, $FADH_2$, CO_2, and water form
   b. glucose to two pyruvates
   c. NAD^+ regenerated, two ATP net
   d. H^+ flows through ATP synthases

Media Menu

Student CD-ROM

Impacts, Issues Video
   When Mitochondria Spin Their Wheels
Big Picture Animation
   Energy-releasing pathways and links to photosynthesis
Read-Me-First Animation
   Aerobic respiration
   Glycolysis
   The Krebs cycle
   Third-stage reactions
Other Animations and Interactions
   Comparison of energy-releasing pathways
   Structure and function of a mitochondrion
   Fermentation pathways
   Alternative energy sources

InfoTrac
   • My Personal Challenge. *The Exceptional Parent*, August 1998.
   • Mitochondria: Cellular Energy Co.—Researchers Strive to Keep the Energy Pipeline Open in the Face of Damaging Cellular Insults. *The Scientist*, June 2002.

Web Sites
   • United Mitochondrial Disease Foundation: www.umdf.org
   • Friedreich's Ataxia Research Alliance: www.frda.org
   • National Organization for Rare Disorders: www.raredisorders.org

How Would You Vote?

Friedreich's ataxia is devastating but relatively rare. In the United States, it affects 1 individual in 50,000. This is good news for most of us, but means that there is relatively little incentive for companies to develop treatments. Who should fund this research? Should we provide tax incentives to companies that work to find cures for rare diseases?

Critical Thinking

1. Living cells of your body absolutely do not use their nucleic acids as alternative energy sources. Suggest why.

2. Suppose you start a body-building program. You are already eating plenty of carbohydrates. Now a qualified nutritionist recommends that you start a protein-rich diet that includes protein supplements. Speculate on how extra dietary proteins will be put to use, and in which tissues.

3. Each year, Canada geese lift off in precise formation from their northern breeding grounds. They head south to spend the winter months in warmer climates. Then they make the return trip in spring. As is the case for other migratory birds, their flight muscle cells are efficient at using fatty acids as an energy source. Remember, the carbon backbone of fatty acids can be cleaved into small fragments that can be converted to acetyl–CoA for entry into the Krebs cycle.

   Suppose a lesser Canada goose from Alaska's Point Barrow has been steadily flapping along for about three thousand kilometers and is approaching Klamath Falls, Oregon. It looks down and notices a rabbit sprinting from a coyote with a taste for rabbit.

   With a stunning burst of speed, the rabbit reaches the safety of its burrow.

   Which energy-releasing pathway predominated in muscle cells in the rabbit's legs? Why was the Canada goose relying on a different pathway for most of its journey? And why wouldn't the pathway of choice in goose flight muscle cells be much good for a rabbit making a mad dash from its enemy?

4. At high altitudes, oxygen levels are low. Mountain climbers risk altitude sickness, which is characterized by shortness of breath, weakness, dizziness, and confusion.

   Curiously, early symptoms of *cyanide poisoning* are similar to altitude sickness. This highly toxic poison binds tightly to a cytochrome, the last molecule in mitochondrial electron transfer chains. When cyanide becomes bound to it, cytochrome can't transfer electrons to the next component of the chain. Explain why cytochrome shutdown might cause the same symptoms as altitude sickness.

5. ATP form in mitochondria. In warm-blooded animals, so does a lot of heat, which can be circulated in ways that help regulate body temperature. Cells of brown adipose tissue (fat) make a protein that disrupts the formation of electron transfer chains in mitochondrial membranes. H^+ gradients are affected, so fewer ATP form; electrons in the transfer chains give up more of their energy as heat. Because of this, some researchers are hypothesizing that brown adipose tissue may not function like white adipose tissue, which is an energy reservoir. Brown adipose tissue may function in thermogenesis, or heat production.

   Mitochondria, recall, contain their own DNA, which may have mutated independently in human populations that evolved in the Arctic and in the hot tropics. If that is so, then mitochondrial function may be adapted to climate.

   How do you suppose such a mitochondrial adaptation might affect people living where the temperature range no longer correlates with their ancestral heritage? Would you expect people whose ancestors evolved in the Arctic to be more or less likely to put on a lot of weight than those whose ancestors lived in the tropics? See *Science*, January 9, 2004: 223–226 for more information.

II Principles of Inheritance

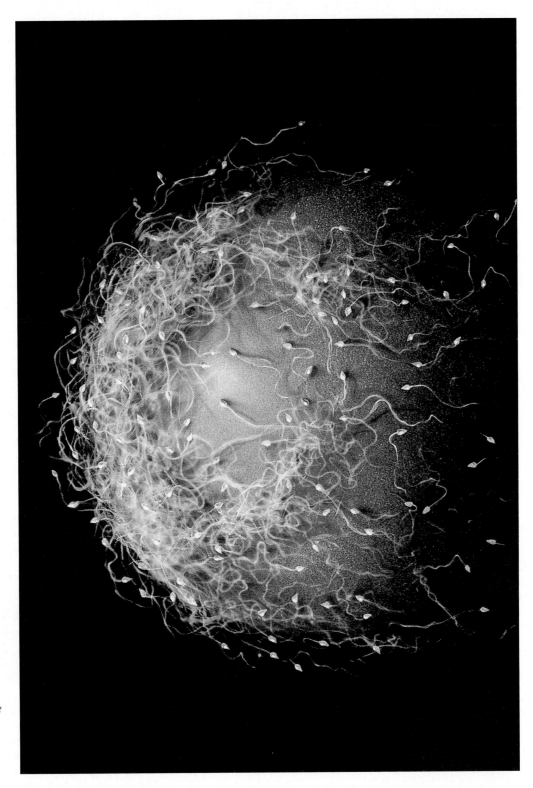

Human sperm, one of which will penetrate this mature egg and so set the stage for the development of a new individual in the image of its parents. This exquisite art is based on a scanning electron micrograph.

IMPACTS, ISSUES *Henrietta's Immortal Cells*

Each human starts out as a fertilized egg. By the time of birth, cell divisions and other processes have given rise to a body of about a trillion cells. Even in the adult, billions of cells are still dividing and replacing their damaged or worn-out predecessors.

In 1951, George and Margaret Gey of Johns Hopkins University were trying to develop a way to keep human cells dividing outside the body. An "immortal" cell lineage could help researchers study basic life processes as well as cancer and other diseases. Using cells to study cancer would be a far better alternative than experimenting directly on patients and risking their lives.

For almost thirty years, the Geys tried to grow normal and diseased human cells. But they could not stop the cellular descendants from dying within a few weeks.

Mary Kubicek, a lab assistant, tried again and again to establish a self-perpetuating lineage of cultured human cancer cells. She was about to give up, but she prepared one last sample and named them HeLa cells. The code name signified the first two letters of the patient's first and last names.

Those HeLa cells began to divide. Four days later, there were so many cells that the researchers subdivided them into more culture tubes. The cells grew at a phenomenal rate; they divided every twenty-four hours and coated the surface of the tubes within days.

Sadly, cancer cells in the patient were dividing just as often. Six months after she had been diagnosed with cancer, malignant cells had infiltrated tissues all through her body. Two months after that, Henrietta Lacks, a young woman from Baltimore, was dead.

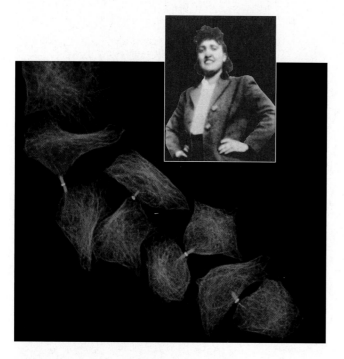

Figure 8.1 Dividing HeLa cells—a legacy of Henrietta Lacks, who was a casualty of cancer. Her cellular contribution to science is still helping others every day.

the big picture

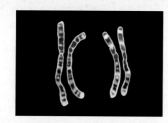

What Divides, and When Eukaryotic cells reproduce by duplicating their chromosomes, getting them into genetically identical parcels by mitosis or meiosis, and dividing the parcels as well as cytoplasm among daughter cells. Prokaryotic cells divide by a different mechanism.

Mitosis Mitosis, a nuclear division mechanism, has four continuous stages: prophase, metaphase, anaphase, and telophase. During these stages, a microtubular spindle moves duplicated chromosomes so that they end up in two genetically identical nuclei.

Although Henrietta passed away, her cells lived on in the Geys' laboratory (Figure 8.1). In time, HeLa cells were shipped to research laboratories all over the world. The Geys used HeLa cells to identify precisely the viral strains that cause polio, which was rampant at the time. Tissue culture techniques developed in their laboratory were used to grow a vaccine. Other scientists used the cells to study mechanisms of cancer, viral growth, the effects of radiation, protein synthesis, and more. Some HeLa cells even traveled into space for experiments on the *Discoverer XVII* satellite. Each year, hundreds of important research projects move forward, thanks to Henrietta's immortal cells.

Henrietta was only thirty-one when runaway cell divisions killed her. Decades later, her legacy continues to help humans everywhere, through her cellular descendants that are still dividing day after day.

Understanding cell division—and, ultimately, how new individuals are put together in the image of their parents—starts with answers to three questions. *First*, what kind of information guides inheritance? *Second*, how is the information copied in a parent cell before being distributed into daughter cells? *Third*, what kinds of mechanisms actually parcel out the information to daughter cells?

We will need more than one chapter to survey the nature of cell reproduction and other mechanisms of inheritance. This chapter introduces the structures and mechanisms that cells use to reproduce.

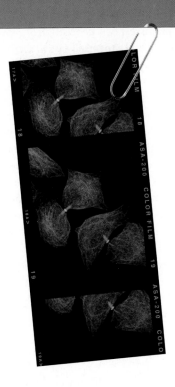

 How Would You Vote?

It is illegal to sell your organs, but you can sell your cells, including eggs, sperm, and blood cells. HeLa cells continue to be sold all over the world by cell culture firms. Should the family of Henrietta Lacks share in the profits? See the Media Menu for details, then vote online.

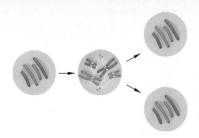

Cytoplasmic Division After nuclear division, the cytoplasm divides in a way that typically puts a nucleus in each daughter cell. The cytoplasm of an animal cell is simply pinched in two. In a plant cell, a cross-wall forms in the cytoplasm and divides it.

The Cell Cycle and Cancer The cell cycle has built-in checkpoints, or mechanisms that monitor and control the timing and rate of cell division. On rare occasions, these surveillance mechanisms fail, and cell division becomes uncontrollable. Tumor formation is the outcome.

8.1 Overview of Cell Division Mechanisms

*The continuity of life depends on **reproduction**. By this process, parents produce a new generation of cells or multicelled individuals like themselves. Cell division is the bridge between generations.*

A dividing cell faces a challenge. Each of its daughter cells must get information encoded in the parental DNA and enough cytoplasm to start up its own operation. DNA "tells" it which proteins to build. Some of the proteins are structural materials; others are enzymes that speed construction of organic compounds. If the cell does not inherit all of the required information, it will not be able to grow or function properly.

In addition, the parent cell's cytoplasm already has enzymes, organelles, and other metabolic machinery. When a daughter cell inherits what looks like a blob of cytoplasm, it really is getting start-up machinery that will keep it running until it can use information in DNA for growing on its own.

MITOSIS, MEIOSIS, AND THE PROKARYOTES

Eukaryotic cells can't just split in two, because a single nucleus holds the DNA. They do split their cytoplasm into daughter cells. But they don't do this until *after* their DNA has been copied, sorted out, and packaged by way of mitosis or meiosis.

Mitosis is a nuclear division mechanism that occurs in *somatic* cells (body cells) of multicelled eukaryotes. It is the basis of increases in body size during growth, replacements of worn-out or dead cells, and tissue repair. Many plants, animals, fungi, and single-celled protists also reproduce asexually, or make copies of themselves, by way of mitosis (Table 8.1).

Meiosis is a different nuclear division mechanism. It functions only in sexual reproduction, and it precedes the formation of gametes (such as sperm and eggs) or spores. In complex animals, gametes form from *germ* cells. As you will see in this chapter and the one that follows, meiosis and mitosis have a lot in common, but the outcomes differ.

What about prokaryotic cells—the archaea and the eubacteria? They reproduce asexually by an entirely different mechanism called prokaryotic fission. We will consider prokaryotic fission later, in Section 19.1.

KEY POINTS ABOUT CHROMOSOME STRUCTURE

Every eukaryotic cell has a characteristic number of DNA molecules, each with many attached proteins. Together, a molecule of DNA and its proteins are one **chromosome**. Chromosomes are duplicated before the cell enters nuclear division. Each chromosome and its copy stay attached to each other as **sister chromatids** until late in the nuclear division process. Think of each chromatid as one arm and leg of a sunbather stretched out on the sand (Figure 8.2).

Early in mitosis or meiosis, a chromosome coils back on itself repeatedly, to a highly condensed form, by interactions between its proteins and DNA. At high magnification, you can see the histone proteins, which look like beads on a string (Figure 8.3*d*). DNA winds

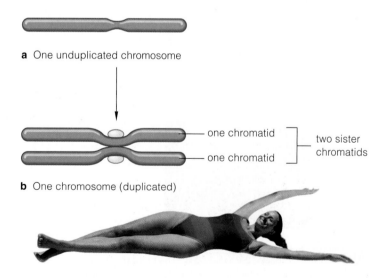

a One unduplicated chromosome

one chromatid
one chromatid
} two sister chromatids

b One chromosome (duplicated)

Figure 8.2 A simple way to visualize a eukaryotic chromosome in the unduplicated state and duplicated state. Eukaryotic cells are duplicated before mitosis or meiosis.

Table 8.1	Cell Division Mechanisms
Mechanisms	Functions
Mitosis, cytoplasmic division	In *all* multicelled eukaryotes, the basis of the following: 1. Increases in body size during growth. 2. Replacement of dead or worn-out cells. 3. Repair of damaged tissues. In single-celled and many multicelled eukaryotes, *also* the basis of asexual reproduction.
Meiosis, cytoplasmic division	In single-celled and multicelled eukaryotes, the basis of sexual reproduction; precedes gamete or spore formation (Chapter 9).
Prokaryotic fission	In bacteria and archaea only, the basis of asexual reproduction (Section 19.1).

Read Me First!
and watch the narrated animation on
chromosome structural organization

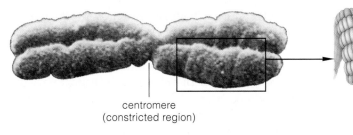

centromere
(constricted region)

a A duplicated human chromosome in its most condnsed form.

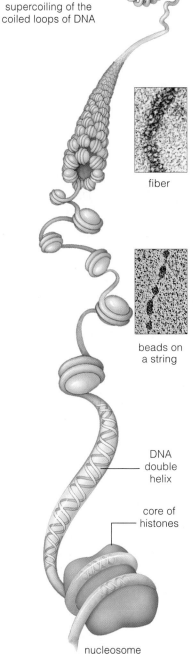

supercoiling of the
coiled loops of DNA

b At times when a chromosome is most condensed, the proteins associated with it interact in ways that package loops of already coiled DNA into "supercoils."

fiber

c At a deeper level of structural organization, the chromosomal proteins and DNA are organized as a cylindrical fiber.

beads on
a string

d Immerse a chromosome in saltwater and it loosens to a beads-on-a-string organization What appears to be a "string" is one DNA molecule. Each "bead" is a nucleosome.

DNA
double
helix

core of
histones

nucleosome

e A nucleosome consists of part of a DNA molecule looped twice around a core of histone proteins.

Figure 8.3 (**a**) Scanning electron micrograph of a duplicated human chromosome in its most condensed form. (**b**,**c**) Interacting proteins hold loops of coiled DNA in the supercoiled array of a cylindrical fiber. (**d**,**e**) The most basic unit of organization is the nucleosome: part of a DNA molecule looped twice around a core of histones. The transmission electron micrographs correspond to organizational levels (**c**) and (**d**).

twice around histone "spools." A histone–DNA spool is a **nucleosome**, a unit of structural organization.

While each duplicated chromosome is condensing, a pronounced constriction appears in a predictable location along its length. At this constriction, the **centromere**, the chromosome's sister chromatids are attached to each other (Figure 8.3). On its surface, we find kinetochores: docking sites for microtubules that will move the chromosome during nuclear division. The centromere's location is different for each type of chromosome and is one of its defining characteristics.

So what is the point of the structural organization? Tight packaging might help keep chromosomes from getting tangled up while they are moved and sorted out into parcels *during* nuclear division. Also, *between* divisions, nucleosome packaging can be loosened up in selected regions, giving enzymes access to required bits of information in the DNA.

When a cell divides, each daughter cell receives a required number of chromosomes and some cytoplasm. In eukaryotic cells, this involves nuclear and cytoplasmic division.

One nuclear division mechanism, mitosis, is the basis of bodily growth, cell replacements, tissue repair, and often asexual reproduction in eukaryotes.

Meiosis, another nuclear division mechanism, is the basis of sexual reproduction. It precedes gamete or spore formation.

8.2 Introducing the Cell Cycle

Let's start thinking about cell reproduction as a recurring series of events, a cycle. This isn't the same as a life cycle, which is a sequence of stages through which individuals of a species pass during their lifetime.

A **cell cycle** is a series of events from one cell division to the next (Figure 8.4). It starts when a new daughter cell forms by mitosis and cytoplasmic division; it ends when the cell divides. Mitosis, cytoplasmic division, and then interphase constitute one turn of the cycle.

THE WONDER OF INTERPHASE

During **interphase**, a cell increases in mass, roughly doubles the number of its cytoplasmic components, and duplicates its DNA. For most cells, interphase is the longest portion of the cell cycle. Biologists divide it into three stages:

G1 Interval ("Gap") of cell growth and functioning before the onset of DNA replication

S   Time of "Synthesis" (DNA replication)

G2 Second interval (Gap), after DNA replication when the cell prepares for division

G1, S, and G2 are code names for some events that are just amazing, considering how much DNA is stuffed in a nucleus. For example, if you could stretch out all the DNA molecules from one of your somatic cells in a single line, they would extend past the fingertips of an outstretched arm. A line of all the DNA from one salamander cell would stretch about 540 feet!

The wonder is, enzymes and other proteins in cells *selectively* access, activate, and silence information in all that DNA. They also make base-by-base copies of every DNA molecule before they divide. Most of this cellular work is completed in interphase.

G1, S, and G2 of interphase have distinct patterns of biosynthesis. Most of your cells remain in G1 while they are building proteins, carbohydrates, and lipids. Cells destined to divide enter S, when they copy their DNA and the proteins attached to it. During G2, they make the proteins that will drive mitosis.

Once S begins, DNA replication usually proceeds at about the same rate and is completed before mitosis. The rate holds for all cells of a species, so you might well wonder if the cell cycle has built-in molecular brakes. It does. Apply the brakes that are supposed to work in G1, and the cycle stalls in G1. Lift the brakes, and the cell cycle runs to completion. Said another way, *control mechanisms govern the rate of cell division.*

Imagine a car losing its brakes just as it starts down a steep mountain road. As you will read later in the chapter, that's how cancer starts. Crucial controls over division are lost, and the cell cycle can't stop turning.

The cell cycle lasts about the same amount of time for cells of the same type but varies among different types. For example, all neurons (nerve cells) in your brain remain in G1 of interphase, and usually they will not divide again. By contrast, every second, 2 to 3 million precursors of red blood cells form to replace worn-out ones circulating in your body. Early in the development of a sea urchin embryo, the number of cells doubles every two hours.

Adverse conditions often disrupt the cell cycle. When deprived of a vital nutrient, for example, the free-living cells called amoebas do not leave interphase. Even so, when any cell moves past a certain point in interphase, the cycle normally will continue regardless of the conditions outside because of built-in controls over its duration.

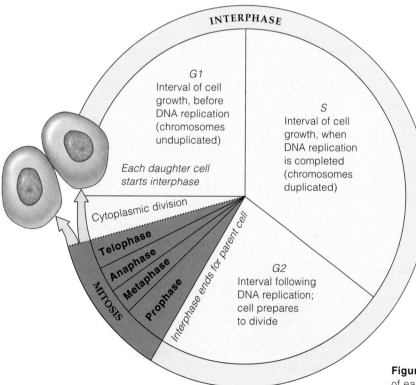

Figure 8.4 Eukaryotic cell cycle, generalized. The length of each interval differs among different cell types.

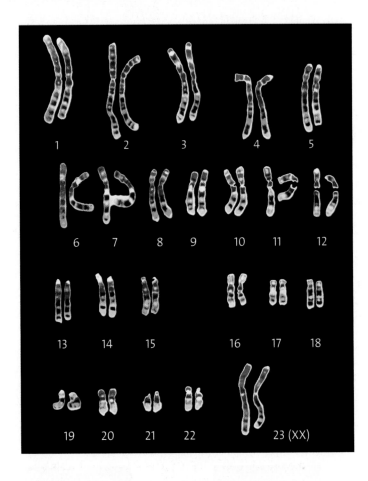

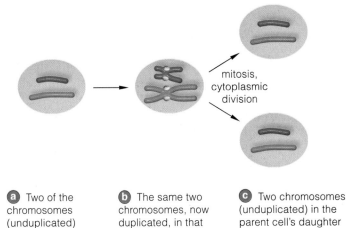

(a) Two of the chromosomes (unduplicated) in a parent cell at interphase

(b) The same two chromosomes, now duplicated, in that cell at interphase, prior to mitosis

(c) Two chromosomes (unduplicated) in the parent cell's daughter cells, which both start life in interphase

Figure 8.5 *Above:* One way to think about how mitosis maintains a parental chromosome number, one generation to the next.

Left: Here's an example. These are twenty-three pairs of metaphase chromosomes from a diploid cell of a human female. The last two are a pair of sex chromosomes. (In human females, such cells have an XX pairing; in males, they have an XY pairing.) When all goes well, each time a somatic cell in this female undergoes mitosis and cytoplasmic division, the daughter cells will always end up with an unduplicated set of these twenty-three pairs of chromosomes.

MITOSIS AND THE CHROMOSOME NUMBER

To know what mitosis does, you have to know that each species has a characteristic **chromosome number**, or the sum of all chromosomes in cells of a given type. Body cells of gorillas and chimpanzees have 48, pea plants have 14, and humans have 46 (Figure 8.5).

Actually, your cells have a **diploid number** (2n) of chromosomes; there are two of each type. Those 46 are like volumes of two sets of books numbered from 1 to 23. You have two volumes of, say, chromosome 22—*a pair of them.* Except for one sex chromosome pairing (XY), both have the same length and shape, and carry the same hereditary information about the same traits.

Think of them as two sets of books on how to build a house. Your father gave you one set. Your mother had her own ideas about wiring, plumbing, and so on. She gave you an alternate edition on the same topics, but it says slightly different things about many of them.

With mitosis, a diploid parent cell can produce two diploid daughter cells. This doesn't mean each merely gets forty-six or forty-eight or fourteen chromosomes. If only the total mattered, then one cell might get, say, two pairs of chromosome 22 and no pairs whatsoever of chromosome 9. But neither cell could function like its parent *without two of each type of chromosome.*

Mitosis has four stages: *prophase, metaphase, anaphase,* and *telophase.* All use a **bipolar mitotic spindle.** This dynamic structure is made of microtubules that grow or shrink as tubulin subunits are added or lost from their ends. The spindle forms as microtubules grow toward each other from two poles until they overlap. Some tether the duplicated chromosomes.

microtubule of bipolar spindle

One chromatid of each chromosome gets attached to microtubules extending from one spindle pole, its sister gets attached to microtubules from the other pole, then they are dragged apart. A complete set of (now-unduplicated) chromosomes ends up in each half of the cell before the cytoplasm divides. That is how mitosis can maintain a parental chromosome number through turn after turn of the cell cycle (Figure 8.5).

Interphase, mitosis, and cytoplasmic division constitute one turn of the cell cycle.

During interphase, a new cell increases its mass, roughly doubles the number of its cytoplasmic components, and duplicates its chromosomes. The cycle ends after the cell undergoes mitosis and then divides its cytoplasm.

8.3 A Closer Look at Mitosis

Let's focus on a "typical" animal cell to see how mitosis can keep the chromosome number constant, division after division, from one cell generation to the next.

By the time a cell enters **prophase**—the first stage of mitosis—its chromosomes are already duplicated, with sister chromatids joined at the centromere. They are in threadlike form, but now they start to twist and fold. By the end of prophase, they will be condensed into thick, compact, rod-shaped forms (Figure 8.6*a–c*).

Also before prophase, two barrel-shaped centrioles and two centrosomes started duplicating themselves next to the nucleus. A centriole, recall, gives rise to a cilium or flagellum. In animal cells, it is embedded in a centrosome, which it helps organize. A **centrosome** is a site where microtubules originate. In prophase, the duplicated centrioles move apart—as do the two centrosomes—until they are on opposite sides of the nucleus. Microtubules grow out of each centrosome. *These are the microtubules that form the bipolar spindle.*

As prophase ends, the nuclear envelope starts to break up into tiny flattened vesicles. The microtubules now interact with the chromosomes and one another. Some tether chromosomes at the docking sites called kinetochores. Others tether the chromosome arms. And still others keep on growing from centrosomes until they overlap midway between the two spindle poles. Driven by ATP energy, motor proteins (dyneins and kinesins) produce the force necessary to assemble the spindle, and to bind and move the chromosomes.

Microtubules from one pole tether one chromatid of each chromosome; microtubules from the opposite pole tether the other. They engage in a tug-of-war, growing and shrinking until they are the same length. At that point, **metaphase**, all duplicated chromosomes are aligned midway between the spindle poles. The alignment is crucial for the next stage of mitosis.

At **anaphase**, the kinetochores of sister chromatids detach from each other and take off toward opposite spindle poles. Driven by motor proteins, they move

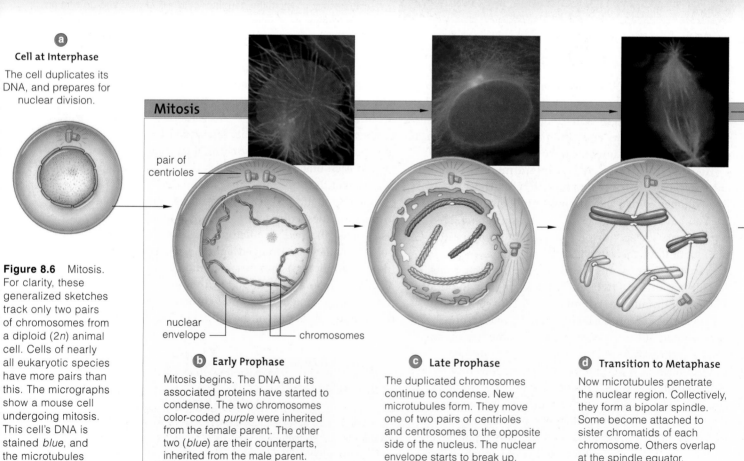

a
Cell at Interphase

The cell duplicates its DNA, and prepares for nuclear division.

Mitosis

pair of centrioles

nuclear envelope — chromosomes

Figure 8.6 Mitosis. For clarity, these generalized sketches track only two pairs of chromosomes from a diploid (2*n*) animal cell. Cells of nearly all eukaryotic species have more pairs than this. The micrographs show a mouse cell undergoing mitosis. This cell's DNA is stained *blue*, and the microtubules are stained *green*.

b Early Prophase

Mitosis begins. The DNA and its associated proteins have started to condense. The two chromosomes color-coded *purple* were inherited from the female parent. The other two (*blue*) are their counterparts, inherited from the male parent.

c Late Prophase

The duplicated chromosomes continue to condense. New microtubules form. They move one of two pairs of centrioles and centrosomes to the opposite side of the nucleus. The nuclear envelope starts to break up.

d Transition to Metaphase

Now microtubules penetrate the nuclear region. Collectively, they form a bipolar spindle. Some become attached to sister chromatids of each chromosome. Others overlap at the spindle equator.

along microtubules toward the opposite spindle poles, dragging the chromatids with them. At the same time, the microtubules are shortening at both ends even as chromatids remain attached to them. The net effect is that sister chromatids are reeled in to opposite poles.

Also at the same time, microtubules that overlap midway between the spindle poles are ratcheting past one another. Motor proteins drive their interactions, which push the two spindle poles farther apart.

Sister chromatids, recall, are genetically identical. Once they detach from each other at anaphase, each is a separate chromosome in its own right.

Telophase gets under way when one of each type of chromosome reaches a spindle pole. Each half of the cell now contains two genetically identical clusters of chromosomes. Now all the chromosomes decondense. Vesicles derived from the old nuclear envelope fuse and form patches of membrane around each cluster. Patch joins with patch until a new nuclear envelope encloses each cluster. And so two nuclei form (Figure

8.6*g*). In our example, the parent cell had a diploid number of chromosomes. So does each nucleus.

Once two nuclei have formed, telophase is over— and so is mitosis.

Prior to mitosis, each chromosome in a cell's nucleus is duplicated, so it consists of two sister chromatids.

In prophase, chromosomes condense to rodlike forms, and microtubules form a bipolar spindle. The nuclear envelope breaks up. Some microtubules harness the chromosomes.

At metaphase, all chromosomes are aligned midway between the spindle's poles, at its equator.

At anaphase, microtubules move sister chromatids of each chromosome apart, to opposite spindle poles.

At telophase, a new nuclear envelope forms around each of two clusters of decondensing chromosomes.

Thus mitosis forms two daughter nuclei. Each has the same chromosome number as the parent cell's nucleus.

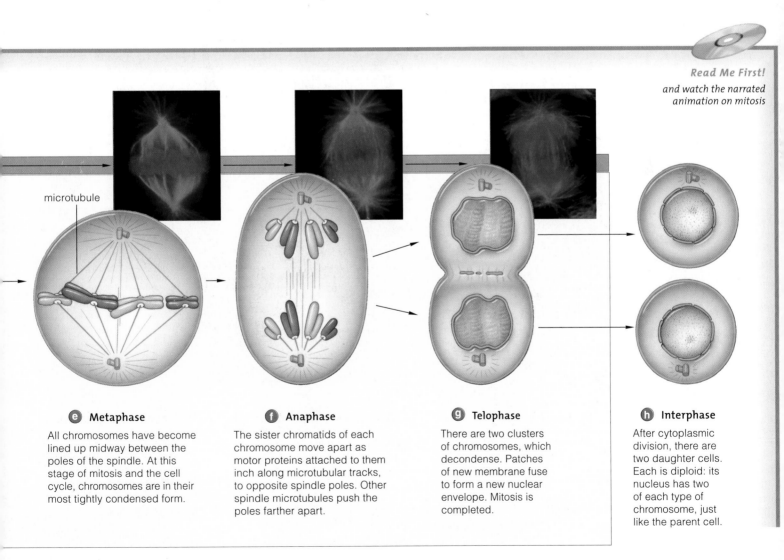

Read Me First!
and watch the narrated animation on mitosis

microtubule

ⓔ Metaphase

All chromosomes have become lined up midway between the poles of the spindle. At this stage of mitosis and the cell cycle, chromosomes are in their most tightly condensed form.

ⓕ Anaphase

The sister chromatids of each chromosome move apart as motor proteins attached to them inch along microtubular tracks, to opposite spindle poles. Other spindle microtubules push the poles farther apart.

ⓖ Telophase

There are two clusters of chromosomes, which decondense. Patches of new membrane fuse to form a new nuclear envelope. Mitosis is completed.

ⓗ Interphase

After cytoplasmic division, there are two daughter cells. Each is diploid: its nucleus has two of each type of chromosome, just like the parent cell.

8.4 Division of the Cytoplasm

The cytoplasm usually divides at some time between late anaphase and the end of telophase. The actual mechanism of cytoplasmic division—or, as it is often called, cytokinesis—differs among species.

CLEAVAGE IN ANIMALS

An animal cell divides by **cleavage**, a mechanism that pinches its cytoplasm in two. Typically, the plasma membrane starts to sink inward as a thin indentation about halfway between the cell's two poles (Figure 8.7a). This cleavage furrow is the first visible sign that the cytoplasm in an animal cell is dividing. The furrow advances until it extends all the way around the cell. As it does, it deepens along a plane that corresponds to the equator of the former microtubular spindle.

How does this happen? In the cytoplasm just under the plasma membrane, microfilaments organized in a thin, ringlike band generate the contractile force for the cut (Figure 8.8). These cytoskeletal elements are attached to the plasma membrane. They slide past one another, as outlined in Section 4.10. As they do, they drag the plasma membrane deeper and deeper inward until the cytoplasm is partitioned. Each of the two

Read Me First!

and watch the narrated animation on cytoplasmic division

 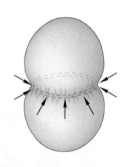 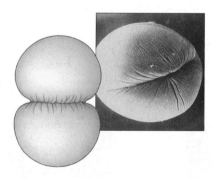 

1 Mitosis is over, and the spindle is disassembling.

2 At the former spindle equator, a ring of microfilaments attached to the plasma membrane contracts.

3 As the microfilament ring shrinks in diameter, it pulls the cell surface inward.

4 Contractions continue; the cell is pinched in two.

a Animal cell division

 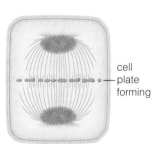 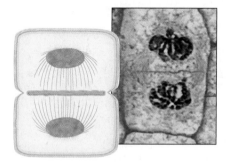 

cell plate forming

1 As mitosis ends, vesicles cluster at the spindle equator. They contain materials for a new primary cell wall.

2 Vesicle membranes fuse. The wall material is sandwiched between two new membranes that lengthen along the plane of a newly forming cell plate.

3 Cellulose is deposited inside the sandwich. In time, these deposits will form two cell walls. Others will form the middle lamella between the walls and cement them together.

4 A cell plate grows at its margins until it fuses with the parent cell plasma membrane. The primary wall of growing plant cells is still thin. New material is deposited on it.

b Plant cell division

Figure 8.7 Cytoplasmic division of an animal cell (**a**) and a plant cell (**b**).

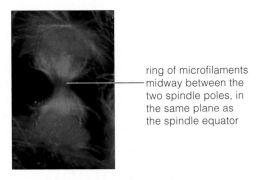

ring of microfilaments midway between the two spindle poles, in the same plane as the spindle equator

Figure 8.8 Cleavage. Inside this animal cell, a ring of microfilaments is pinching the cytoplasm in two.

daughter cells that forms this way ends up with a nucleus, some cytoplasm, and plasma membrane.

CELL PLATE FORMATION IN PLANTS

Plant cells cannot divide the same way your cells do, because most of them have a cell wall. That wall prevents their cytoplasm from simply pinching in two.

Instead, cytoplasmic division of plant cells involves **cell plate formation**, as shown in Figure 8.7b. By this mechanism, tiny vesicles packed with wall-building materials fuse with one another and with remnants of the microtubular spindle. Together, deposits of the materials form a disklike structure called a cell plate. Deposits of cellulose accumulate at the plate. In time, they thicken enough to form a cross-wall through the cell. New plasma membrane extends across both sides of it. This wall grows until it bridges the cytoplasm and divides the parent cell in two.

APPRECIATE THE PROCESS!

Take a moment to look closely at your hands. Visualize the cells making up your palms, thumbs, and fingers. Now imagine the mitotic divisions that produced all of the cell generations that preceded them while you were developing, early on, inside your mother (Figure 8.9). And be grateful for the astonishing precision of mechanisms that led to their formation at prescribed times, in prescribed numbers, for the alternatives can be terrible indeed.

Why? Good health and survival itself depend on the proper timing and completion of cell cycle events. Some genetic disorders arise as a result of mistakes that happened during the duplication or distribution of even one chromosome. Unchecked cell divisions often destroy surrounding tissues and, ultimately, the

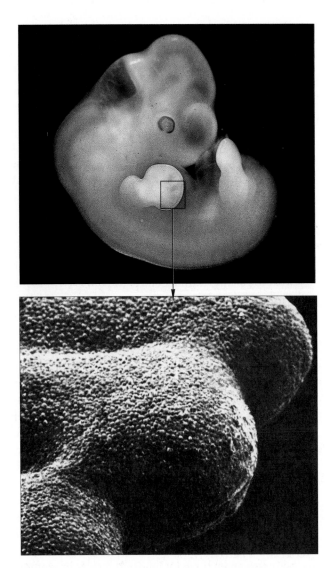

Figure 8.9 Transformation of a paddlelike structure into a human hand through mitosis, cytoplasmic divisions, and other processes of embryonic development. The scanning electron micrograph shows individual cells.

individual. Such losses can start in body cells. They can start in the germ cells that give rise to sperm and eggs, although rarely. The last section of this chapter can give you a sense of the consequences.

After mitosis, a separate mechanism cuts the cytoplasm into two daughter cells, each with a daughter nucleus.

Cleavage is a form of cytoplasmic division in animal cells. Microfilaments banded around a cell's midsection slide past one another in a way that pinches the cytoplasm in two.

Cytoplasmic division in plants often involves the formation of a cross-wall between the new plasma membranes of adjoining daughter cells.

8.5 When Control Is Lost

Growth and reproduction depend on controls over cell division. On rare occasions, something goes wrong in a somatic cell or germ cell. Cancer may be the outcome.

THE CELL CYCLE REVISITED

Millions of cells in your skin, bone marrow, gut lining, liver, and elsewhere divide and replace their worn-out, dead, and dying predecessors every second. They don't divide willy-nilly; many cellular mechanisms control cell growth, DNA replication, and division. They also control when the division machinery is put to rest.

What happens when something goes wrong? For example, if sister chromatids do not separate as they should during mitosis, one daughter cell may end up with too many chromosomes, the other with too few. Chromosomal DNA can be attacked by free radicals or peroxides, two metabolic by-products. It can be damaged by cosmic radiation, which bombards us all the time. Problems are frequent, inevitable, and must be corrected quickly.

The cell cycle has built-in checkpoints that keep errors from getting out of hand. Certain proteins—products of checkpoint genes—monitor whether the DNA gets fully replicated, whether it gets damaged, even whether nutrient concentrations are sufficient to support cell growth. The surveillance helps cells identify and correct problems.

Some checkpoint proteins make the cell cycle advance; their absence arrests it. The ones called *growth factors* invite transcription of genes that help the body grow. For instance, epidermal growth factor activates an enzyme by binding to cells in epithelial tissues; it is a signal to start mitotic cell divisions.

Other proteins inhibit cell cycle changes. Several checkpoint gene products put the brakes on mitosis when chromosomal DNA gets damaged (Figure 8.10). Some of the *kinases*, enzymes that phosphorylate other molecules, act as checkpoint gene products. When DNA is broken or incomplete, they activate other proteins in a cascade of signaling events that ultimately stop the cell cycle or induce cell death.

CHECKPOINT FAILURE AND TUMORS

Sometimes a checkpoint gene mutates so that its protein product no longer functions properly. When all checkpoint mechanisms for a particular process fail, the cell loses control over its replication cycle. Figures 8.11 through 8.13 show a few of the outcomes.

In some cases it gets stuck in mitosis and divides over and over again, with no interphase. In other cases, damaged chromosomes are replicated or cells don't die as they are supposed to, because signals calling for cell death are disabled. A growing mass of a cell's defective descendants may invade other tissues in the body, as a tumor.

In most tumor cells, at least one checkpoint protein is missing. That is why checkpoint gene products that *inhibit* mitosis are called tumor suppressors. Checkpoint genes encoding proteins that *stimulate* mitosis are called oncogenes. Mutations that affect oncogene products or the rate at which they form help transform a normal cell into a tumor cell. Mutant checkpoint genes are linked with increased risk of tumors, and sometimes they run in families.

Moles and other tumors are **neoplasms**—abnormal masses of cells that lost controls over how they grow

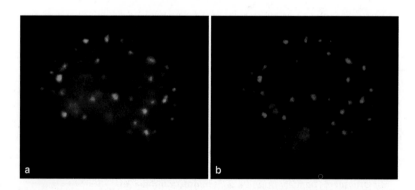

Figure 8.10 Protein products of checkpoint genes in action. DNA in the nucleus of this cell has been damaged by ionizing radiation. (**a**) *Green* spots pinpoint the location of *53BP1*, and (**b**) *red* spots pinpoint the location of *BRCA1*. Both proteins have clustered around the same chromosome breaks in a single cell nucleus. The integrated action of these proteins and others can arrest mitosis until the DNA breaks are fixed.

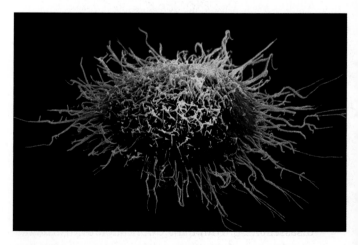

Figure 8.11 Scanning electron micrograph of a cervical cancer cell, the kind that killed Henrietta Lacks.

and divide. Ordinary skin moles and other *benign*, or noncancerous, neoplasms grow very slowly, and their cells retain the surface recognition proteins that are supposed to keep them in a home tissue (Figure 8.12). Unless a benign neoplasm grows too large or becomes irritating, it poses no threat to the body.

CHARACTERISTICS OF CANCER

Cancers are abnormally growing and dividing cells of a *malignant* neoplasm. They disrupt surrounding tissues, both physically and metabolically. Cancer cells are grossly disfigured. They can break loose from their home tissues. They can slip into and out of blood vessels and lymph vessels, and invade other tissues where they do not belong (Figure 8.12).

All cancer cells display four characteristics. *First,* they grow and divide abnormally. The controls on overcrowding in tissues are lost and cell populations reach abnormally high densities. The number of tiny blood vessels that service the growing cell mass also increases abnormally.

Second, the cytoplasm and plasma membrane of cancer cells become grossly altered. The membrane becomes leaky and has abnormal or lost proteins. The cytoskeleton shrinks, becomes disorganized, or both. Enzyme action shifts, as in an amplified reliance on ATP formation by glycolysis.

Third, cancer cells have a weakened capacity for adhesion. Recognition proteins are lost or altered, so they can't stay anchored in proper tissues. They break away and may establish growing colonies in distant tissues. *Metastasis* is the name for this process of abnormal cell migration and tissue invasion.

Fourth, cancer cells usually have lethal effects. Unless they are eradicated by surgery, chemotherapy, or other procedures, their uncontrollable divisions put an individual on a painful road to death.

Each year in the developed countries alone, cancers cause 15 to 20 percent of all deaths. And cancer is not just a human problem. Cancers are known to occur in most of the animal species studied to date.

Cancer is a multistep process. Researchers have already identified many of the mutant genes that contribute to it. They also are working to identify drugs that specifically target and destroy cancer cells or stop them from dividing.

HeLa cells, for instance, were used in early tests of taxol, an anticancer drug that stops spindles from disassembling. With this kind of research, we may one day have drugs that can put the brakes on cancer cells. We return to this topic in later chapters.

Read Me First!
and watch the narrated animation on cancer

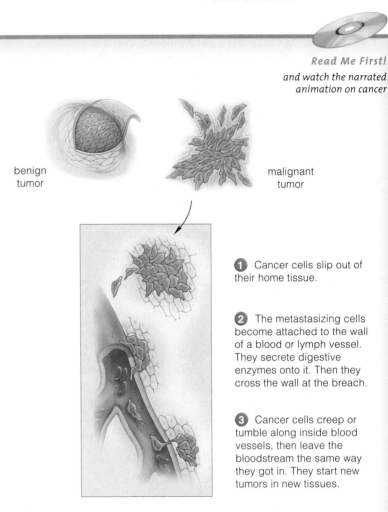

benign tumor

malignant tumor

1 Cancer cells slip out of their home tissue.

2 The metastasizing cells become attached to the wall of a blood or lymph vessel. They secrete digestive enzymes onto it. Then they cross the wall at the breach.

3 Cancer cells creep or tumble along inside blood vessels, then leave the bloodstream the same way they got in. They start new tumors in new tissues.

Figure 8.12 Comparison of benign and malignant tumors. Benign tumors typically are slow-growing and stay put in their home tissue. Cells of a malignant tumor can migrate abnormally through the body and establish colonies even in distant tissues.

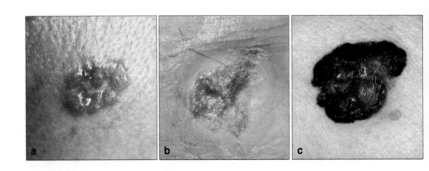

Figure 8.13 Skin cancers. (**a**) A *basal cell carcinoma* is the most common type. This slow-growing, raised lump is typically uncolored, reddish-brown, or black.

(**b**) The second most common form is *squamous cell carcinoma*. This pink growth, firm to the touch, grows fast under the surface of skin exposed to the sun.

(**c**) *Malignant melanoma* spreads fastest. Cells form dark, encrusted lumps. They may itch like an insect bite or bleed easily.

Summary

Section 8.1 The continuity of life depends on reproduction. By this process, parents produce a new generation of individuals like themselves. Cell division is the bridge between generations. When a cell divides, its daughters each receive a required number of DNA molecules and some cytoplasm.

Mitosis and meiosis occur only in eukaryotic cells. These nuclear division mechanisms sort out a parent cell's chromosomes into daughter nuclei. A separate mechanism divides the cytoplasm. Prokaryotic cells divide by a different mechanism.

Mitosis is the basis of multicellular growth, cell replacements, and tissue repair. Many eukaryotic organisms also reproduce *asexually* by mitosis.

Meiosis, the basis of sexual reproduction, precedes the formation of gametes or spores.

A chromosome is a molecule of DNA and associated proteins. When duplicated, it consists of two sister chromatids, both attached to its centromere region by kinetochores. These are docking sites for microtubules.

Section 8.2 Each cell cycle starts when a new cell forms. It proceeds through interphase and ends when the cell reproduces by nuclear and cytoplasmic division. A cell carries out its functions in interphase. Before it divides, it increases in mass, roughly doubles the number of its cytoplasmic components, then duplicates each of its chromosomes.

Section 8.3 The sum of all chromosomes in cells of a given type is the chromosome number. Human body cells have a diploid chromosome number of 46, or two copies of 23 types of chromosome. Mitosis maintains the chromosome number, one generation to the next.

Mitosis has four continuous stages:

a. Prophase. The duplicated, threadlike chromosomes start to condense. With the help of motor proteins, new microtubules start forming a bipolar mitotic spindle. The nuclear envelope starts to break apart into tiny vesicles.

Some microtubules growing from one spindle pole tether one chromatid of each chromosome; others that are growing from the opposite pole tether its sister chromatid. Still other microtubules extending from both poles grow until they overlap at the midpoint of the newly forming spindle.

b. Metaphase. At metaphase, all chromosomes have become aligned at the spindle's midpoint.

c. Anaphase. Kinetochores detach from chromosomes, dragging the chromatids with them along microtubules, which are shortening at both ends. The microtubules that overlap ratchet past each other, pushing the spindle poles farther apart. Different motor proteins drive the movements. One of each type of parental chromosome ends up clustered together at each spindle pole.

d. Telophase. Chromosomes decondense to threadlike form. A new nuclear envelope forms around each cluster. Both nuclei have the parental chromosome number.

Fill in the blanks of the diagram below to check your understanding of the four stages of mitosis.

Section 8.4 Cytoplasmic division mechanisms differ. Animal cells undergo cleavage. A microfilament ring under the plasma membrane contracts, pinching the cytoplasm in two. In plant cells, a cross-wall forms in the cytoplasm and divides it.

Section 8.5 Checkpoint gene products are part of mechanisms that control the cell cycle. The mechanisms can stimulate or arrest the cell cycle, or even prompt cell death. Mutant checkpoint genes cause tumors to form by disrupting normal cell cycle controls.

Cancer is a multistep process involving altered cells that grow and divide abnormally. Such cells have a weakened ability to stick to one another in tissues, and sometimes they migrate to new tissues.

Self-Quiz   *Answers in Appendix III*

1. Mitosis and cytoplasmic division function in _____ .
   a. asexual reproduction of single-celled eukaryotes
   b. growth, tissue repair, often asexual reproduction
   c. gamete formation in prokaryotes
   d. both a and b

2. A duplicated chromosome has _____ chromatid(s).
   a. one   b. two   c. three   d. four

3. The basic unit that structurally organizes a eukaryotic chromosome is the _____ .
   a. supercoil   c. nucleosome
   b. bipolar mitotic spindle   d. microfilament

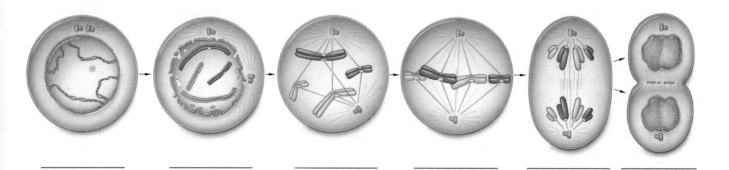

4. The chromosome number is _____ .
   a. the sum of all chromosomes in cells of a given type
   b. an identifiable feature of each species
   c. maintained by mitosis
   d. all of the above

5. A somatic cell having two of each type of chromosome has a(n) _____ chromosome number.
   a. diploid   b. haploid   c. tetraploid   d. abnormal

6. Interphase is the part of the cell cycle when _____ .
   a. a cell ceases to function
   b. a germ cell forms its spindle apparatus
   c. a cell grows and duplicates its DNA
   d. mitosis proceeds

7. After mitosis, the chromosome number of a daughter cell is _____ the parent cell's.
   a. the same as   c. rearranged compared to
   b. one-half   d. doubled compared to

8. Only _____ is not a stage of mitosis.
   a. prophase   b. interphase   c. metaphase   d. anaphase

9. Match each stage with the events listed.
   ____ metaphase   a. sister chromatids move apart
   ____ prophase   b. chromosomes start to condense
   ____ telophase   c. daughter nuclei form
   ____ anaphase   d. all duplicated chromosomes are
                        aligned at the spindle equator

Critical Thinking

1. Figure 8.14 shows metaphase chromosomes. Name their levels of structural organization, starting with DNA molecules and histones.

2. Pacific yews (*Taxus brevifolius*) are among the slowest growing trees, which makes them vulnerable to extinction. People started stripping their bark and killing them when they heard that *taxol,* a chemical extracted from the bark, may work against breast and ovarian cancer. It takes bark from about six trees to treat one patient. Do some research and find out why taxol has potential as an anticancer drug and what has been done to protect the trees.

3. X-rays emitted from some radioisotopes damage DNA, especially in cells undergoing DNA replication. Humans exposed to high levels of x-rays face *radiation poisoning.* Hair loss and a damaged gut lining are early symptoms. Speculate why. Also speculate on why radiation exposure is used as a therapy to treat some cancers.

4. Suppose you have a way to measure the amount of DNA in a single cell during the cell cycle. You first measure the amount at the G1 phase. At what points during the remainder of the cycle would you predict changes in the amount of DNA per cell?

5. The cervix is part of the uterus, a chamber in which embryos develop. The *Pap smear* is a screening procedure that can detect *cervical cancer* in its earliest stages.
   Treatments range from freezing precancerous cells or killing them with a laser beam to removal of the uterus (a hysterectomy). The treatments are more than 90 percent effective when this cancer is detected early. Survival chances plummet to less than 9 percent after it spreads.
   Most cervical cancers develop slowly. Unsafe sex increases the risk. A key risk factor is infection by human

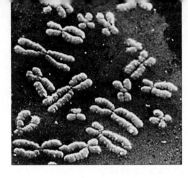

Figure 8.14 Human chromosomes at metaphase, each in the duplicated state.

papillomaviruses (HPV), which cause genital warts. Viral genes coding for the tumor-inducing proteins get inserted into the DNA of cervical cells. In one study, 91 percent of patients with cervical cancer had been infected with HPV.
   Not all women request Pap smears. Many wrongly believe the procedure is costly. Many don't recognize the importance of abstinence or "safe" sex. Others simply don't want to think about whether they have cancer. Knowing what you've learned so far about the cell cycle and cancer, what would you say to a woman who falls into one or more of these groups?

Media Menu

Student CD-ROM

Impacts, Issues Video
  Henrietta's Immortal Cells
Big Picture Animation
  Normal cell division and cancer
Read-Me-First Animation
  Chromosome structural organization
  Mitosis
  Cytoplasmic division
  Cancer
Other Animations and Interactions
  The cell cycle

InfoTrac

- Cell Cycle Circuits Mapped. *Applied Genetics News,* October 2001.
- HIV Protein Stops Cell Division. *Virus Weekly,* April 2002.
- Familiar Proteins Play Unfamiliar Role In Cell Division. *Stem Cell Week,* January 2002.
- How You Can Lower Your Cancer Risk. *Harvard Health Letter,* August 2002.

Web Sites

- Talking Genetic Glossary: www.genome.gov/glossary.cfm
- Mitosis World: www.bio.unc.edu/faculty/salmon/lab/mitosis
- Animated Cell Cycle: www.cellsalive.com/cell_cycle.htm
- The Cytokinetic Mafia Home Page: www.bio.unc.edu/faculty/salmon/lab/mafia/

How Would You Vote?

When she died, Henrietta Lacks left behind a husband and five children. The scientists who propagated the HeLa cell line never told her or her family how they were using her tissues. Today, HeLa cells are sold by cell culture firms around the world. Should her survivors get a share of the profits?

IMPACTS, ISSUES   *Why Sex?*

Women and men, does and bucks, geese and ganders. Most of us take it for granted that it takes two to make offspring, and among eukaryotes it usually does—at least some of the time. Sexual reproduction combines DNA from individuals of two mating types. It started many hundreds of millions of years ago among tiny, single-celled eukaryotes, although no one knows how. An unsolved puzzle is why it happened at all. Asexual reproduction, whereby an individual makes offspring that are copies of itself, is far more efficient.

Protists and fungi routinely reproduce by mitosis. Plants and many invertebrates, including corals, sea stars, and flatworms, can form new individuals from parts that bud or break off. But almost all of these species also reproduce sexually.

For instance, some single-celled algae reproduce asexually again and again, by way of mitosis, and form huge populations exactly like themselves. Only when nitrogen is scarce do sexual cells of two types form. The fusion of two cells, one of each type, produces new individuals. The result is offspring that are not exact copies of one another or their parents.

Consider also the plant-sucking insects called aphids. In the summer nearly all are females. Each matures in less than a week and can produce as many as five new females a day from her unfertilized eggs (Figure 9.1). This process, called parthenogenesis, allows population sizes to soar rapidly. Only as autumn approaches do male aphids develop. Even then, females that manage to survive over the winter can do without the opposite

Figure 9.1 Sexual reproduction moments. (**a**) Mealybugs mating. (**b**) Poppy plant being helped by a beetle, which makes pollen deliveries for it. (**c**) Aphid giving birth. Like females of many other sexually reproducing species, this one also reproduces asexually, all by itself.

the big picture

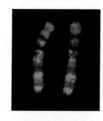

Sexual Reproduction   Sexual reproduction requires meiosis, gamete formation, and fertilization. Meiosis is a nuclear division mechanism that halves the parental chromosome number for forthcoming gametes.

Meiosis   Meiosis consists of two nuclear divisions, not one. There is no interphase between divisions. It results in four haploid nuclei. When cytoplasmic division follows, each of the resulting haploid cells may function as a gamete or spore.

sex. The next spring they begin another round of female production all by themselves.

There are even a few all-female species of fishes, reptiles, and birds. No mammal is parthenogenic in nature. In 2004, however, researchers at the University of Tokyo in Japan fused two mouse eggs in a test tube to produce an embryo with all-female DNA. The embryo developed into Kaguya—the world's first fatherless mammal. She grew to adulthood, mated with a male mouse, and produced offspring of her own, as shown in the filmstrip at right.

Does this mean males could soon be unneccessary? Hardly. It wasn't easy to produce a mouse that has all-female DNA. The researchers had to turn off genes in one egg. Even then, it took more than 600 attempts before they succeeded in producing two viable embryos. Besides, the prevalance of sexually reproducing species suggests that a division into two sexes must offer selective advantages.

With this chapter, we turn to the kinds of cells that serve as the bridge between generations of organisms. Three interconnected events—meiosis, the formation of gametes, and fertilization—are the hallmarks of sexual reproduction. As you will see in many chapters throughout the book, these events occur in the life cycle of almost all eukaryotic species. Through the production of offspring with new and unique traits, they have contributed immensely to the diversity of life.

✓ How Would You Vote?

Japanese researchers have successfully created a "fatherless" mouse that contains the genetic material from the eggs of two females. The mouse is healthy and fully fertile. Do you think researchers should be allowed to try the same process with human eggs? See the Media Menu for details, then vote online.

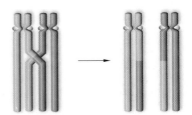

Gene Shufflings With Sex During meiosis, crossing over and the random alignment of chromosomes at metaphase puts different mixes of maternal and paternal genes in gametes. More mixing occurs at fertilization. Such events introduce variation in traits among offspring.

Meiosis in Life Cycles Plant and animal life cycles typically include fertilization, meiosis, and gamete formation. In plant life cycles, meiosis is followed by the formation of spores which, under favorable conditions, germinate and give rise to gamete-producing bodies.

9.1 An Evolutionary View

Asexual reproduction produces genetically identical copies of a parent. Sexual reproduction introduces variation in the details of traits among offspring.

When an orchid or aphid reproduces all by itself, what sort of offspring does it get? By the process of **asexual reproduction**, one alone produces offspring, and each offspring inherits the same number and kinds of genes as its parent. **Genes** are stretches of chromosomes—that is, of DNA molecules. The genes for each species contain all the heritable information necessary to make new individuals. Rare mutations aside, then, asexually produced individuals can only be *clones*, or genetically identical copies of the parent.

Inheritance gets far more interesting with **sexual reproduction**. The process involves meiosis, formation of gametes, and fertilization (union of the nuclei of two gametes). In most sexual reproducers, such as humans, the first cell of a new individual contains *pairs of genes* on pairs of chromosomes. Usually, one of each pair is maternal and the other paternal in origin (Figure 9.2).

If information in every pair of genes were identical down to the last detail, sexual reproduction would also produce clones. Just imagine—you, every person you know, the entire human population might be a clone, with everybody looking alike. But the two genes of a pair might *not* be identical. Why not? The molecular structure of a gene can change; it can mutate. So two genes that happen to be paired in a person's cells may "say" slightly different things about a trait. Each unique molecular form of the same gene is called an **allele**.

Such tiny differences affect thousands of traits. For example, whether your chin has a dimple depends on which pair of alleles you inherited at one chromosome location. One kind of allele at that location says "put a dimple in the chin." Another kind says "no dimple." This leads to one reason why the individuals of sexually reproducing species don't all look alike. *By sexual reproduction, offspring inherit new combinations of alleles, which lead to variations in the details of their traits.*

This chapter gets into the cellular basis of sexual reproduction. More importantly, it starts you thinking about far-reaching effects of gene shufflings at certain stages of the process. The process introduces variations in traits among offspring that are typically acted upon by agents of natural selection. Thus, *variation in traits is a foundation for evolutionary change.*

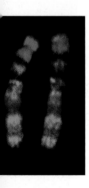

Figure 9.2
A maternal and a paternal chromosome. Any gene on one might be slightly different structurally than the same gene on the other.

> *Sexual reproduction introduces variation in traits by bestowing novel combinations of alleles on offspring.*

9.2 Overview of Meiosis

Meiosis is a nuclear division process that divides the parental chromosome number by half in specialized reproductive cells. It is central to sexual reproduction.

THINK "HOMOLOGUES"

Think back to the preceding chapter and its focus on mitotic cell division. Unlike mitosis, **meiosis** partitions chromosomes into parcels not once but *twice* prior to cytoplasmic division. Unlike mitosis, it is the first step leading to the formation of gametes. Male and female gametes, such as sperm and eggs, fuse to form a new individual. In most multicelled eukaryotes, cells that form in specialized reproductive structures or organs give rise to gametes. Figure 9.3 shows examples of where the cellular antecedents of gametes originate.

As you know, the **chromosome number** is the sum total of chromosomes in cells of a given type. If a cell has a **diploid number** ($2n$), it has a *pair* of each type of chromosome, often from two parents. Except for a pairing of nonidentical sex chromosomes, each pair has the same length, shape, and assortment of genes, and they line up with each other at meiosis. We call them **homologous chromosomes** (*hom–* means alike).

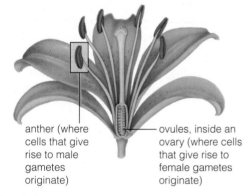

anther (where cells that give rise to male gametes originate)

ovules, inside an ovary (where cells that give rise to female gametes originate)

a Flowering plant

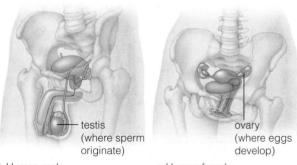

testis (where sperm originate)

ovary (where eggs develop)

b Human male   **c** Human female

Figure 9.3 Examples of reproductive organs, where cells that give rise to gametes originate.

Body cells of humans have 23 + 23 homologous chromosomes (Figure 9.4). So do the germ cells that give rise to human gametes. After a germ cell finishes meiosis, 23 chromosomes—one of each type—will end up in those gametes. Meiosis halves the chromosome number, so the gametes have a **haploid number** (*n*).

TWO DIVISIONS, NOT ONE

Meiosis is like mitosis in some ways, but the result is different. As in mitosis, a germ cell duplicates its DNA in interphase. The two DNA molecules and associated proteins stay attached at the centromere, the notably constricted region along their length. For as long as they remain attached, we call them **sister chromatids**:

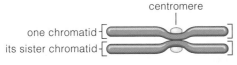

one chromosome in the duplicated state

As in mitosis, the microtubules of a spindle apparatus move the chromosomes in prescribed directions.

With meiosis, however, *chromosomes go through two consecutive divisions that end with the formation of four haploid nuclei.* There is no interphase between divisions, which we call meiosis I and meiosis II:

interphase (*DNA replication before meiosis I*)	MEIOSIS I	no interphase (*no DNA replication before meiosis II*)	MEIOSIS II
	PROPHASE I		PROPHASE II
	METAPHASE I		METAPHASE II
	ANAPHASE I		ANAPHASE II
	TELOPHASE I		TELOPHASE II

In meoisis I, each duplicated chromosome aligns with its partner, *homologue to homologue.* After the two chromosomes of every pair have lined up with each other, they are moved apart:

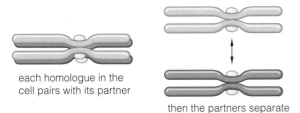

each homologue in the cell pairs with its partner

then the partners separate

The cytoplasm typically starts to divide at some point after each homologue detaches from its partner. The two daughter cells formed this way are haploid,

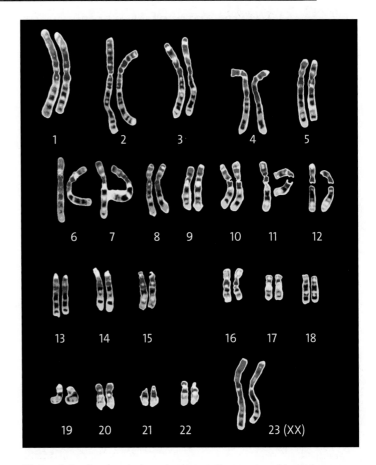

Figure 9.4 Another look at the twenty-three pairs of homologous human chromosomes. This example is from a human female, with two X chromosomes. Human males have a different pairing of sex chromosomes (XY). As in Figure 9.2, these chromosomees have been labeled with several fluorescent markers.

with *one* of each type of chromosome. Don't forget, these chromosomes are still in the duplicated state.

Next, during meiosis II, *the two sister chromatids of each chromosome are separated from each other:*

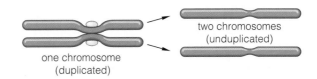

one chromosome (duplicated)

two chromosomes (unduplicated)

Each chromatid is now a separate chromosome. Next, four nuclei form, and the cytoplasm typically divides once more. The final outcome is four haploid cells. Figure 9.5, on the next two pages, offers a closer look at key events of meiosis and their consequences.

Meiosis, a nuclear division mechanism, reduces a parental cell's chromosome number by half—to a haploid number (n).

9.3 Visual Tour of Meiosis

Meiosis I

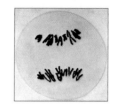
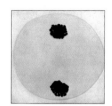

plasma membrane · newly forming microtubules in the cytoplasm

spindle equator (midway between the two poles) · one pair of homologous chromosomes

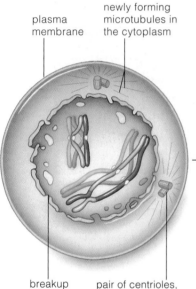
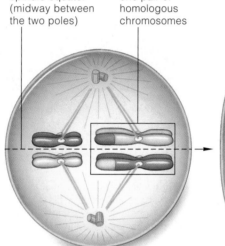
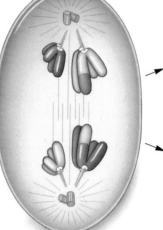
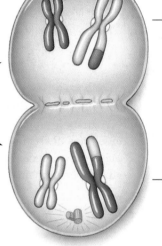

breakup of nuclear envelope · pair of centrioles, and a centrosome, moving to opposite sides of nucleus

a Prophase I

As prophase I begins, chromosomes become visible as threadlike forms. Each pairs with its homologue and usually swaps segments with it, as indicated by the breaks in color in the large chromosomes. Microtubules are forming a bipolar spindle (Section 8.3). If two pairs of centrioles are present, one pair is moved to the opposite side of the nuclear envelope, which is starting to break up.

b Metaphase I

Microtubules from one spindle pole have tethered one of each type of chromosome; microtubules from the other pole have tethered its homologue. By metaphase I, a tug-of-war between the two sets of microtubules has aligned all chromosomes midway between the poles.

c Anaphase I

Microtubules attached to each chromosome shorten and move it toward a spindle pole. Other microtubules, which extend from the poles and overlap at the spindle equator, ratchet past each other and push the two poles farther apart. Motor proteins drive the ratcheting.

d Telophase I

One of each type of chromosome has now arrived at the spindle poles. For most species, the cytoplasm divides at some point, forming two haploid cells. All chromosomes are still duplicated.

Figure 9.5 Sketches of meiosis in a generalized animal cell. This is a nuclear division mechanism. It reduces the parental chromosome number in immature reproductive cells by half, to the haploid number, for forthcoming gametes. To keep things simple, we track only two pairs of homologous chromosomes. Maternal chromosomes are shaded *purple* and paternal chromosomes *blue*.

Of the four haploid cells that form by way of meiosis and cytoplasmic divisions, one or all may develop into gametes and function in sexual reproduction. In plants, cells that form by way of meiosis may develop into spores, which take part in a stage of the life cycle that precedes gamete formation.

Read Me First!
and watch the narrated animation on meiosis

Meiosis II

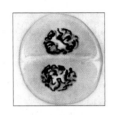 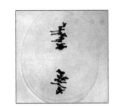  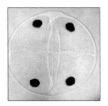

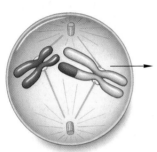 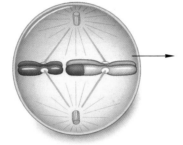 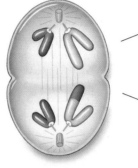 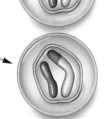

There is no DNA replication between the two nuclear divisions.

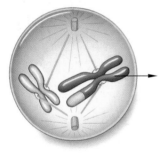 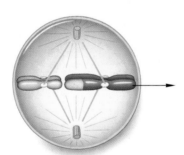 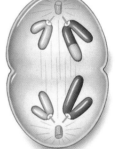 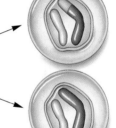

ⓔ Prophase II

A new bipolar spindle forms in each haploid cell. Microtubules have moved one member of the pair of centrioles to the opposite end of each cell. One chromatid of each chromosome becomes tethered to one spindle pole, and its sister chromatid becomes tethered to the opposite pole.

ⓕ Metaphase II

Microtubules from both spindle poles have assembled and disassembled in a tug-of-war that ended at metaphase II, when all chromosomes are positioned midway between the poles.

ⓖ Anaphase II

The attachment between sister chromatids of each chromosome breaks. Each is now a separate chromosome but is still tethered to microtubules, which move it toward a spindle pole. Other microtubules push the poles apart. A parcel of unduplicated chromosomes ends up near each pole. One of each type of chromosome is present in each parcel.

ⓗ Telophase II

In telophase II, four nuclei form as a new nuclear envelope encloses each cluster of chromosomes. After cytoplasmic division, each of the resulting daughter cells has a haploid (*n*) number of chromosomes.

9.4 How Meiosis Puts Variation in Traits

As Sections 9.2 and 9.3 make clear, the overriding function of meiosis is the reduction of a parental chromosome number by half. However, two other events that occur during meiosis have evolutionary consequences.

The preceding section mentioned in passing that pairs of homologous chromosomes swap parts of themselves during prophase I. It also showed how homologous chromosomes become aligned with their partner at metaphase I. Let's take a look at these two events, because they contribute enormously to variation in the traits of sexually reproducing species. They introduce novel combinations of alleles into the gametes that form after meiosis. Those combinations—and the way they are further mixed together at fertilization—are the start of a new generation of individuals that differ in the details of their shared traits.

CROSSING OVER IN PROPHASE I

Prophase I of meiosis is a time of much gene shuffling. Reflect on Figure 9.6a, which shows two chromosomes condensed to threadlike form. All chromosomes in a germ cell condense this way. When they do, each is drawn close to its homologue. Molecular interactions stitch homologues together point by point along their length with little space between them. The intimate, parallel orientation favors **crossing over**, a molecular interaction between a chromatid of one chromosome and a chromatid of its homologous partner. The two *nonsister* chromatids break at the same places along their length, then the two exchange corresponding segments; they swap genes.

Gene swapping would be pointless if each type of gene never varied. But remember, a gene can come in

Read Me First!

and watch the narrated animation on crossing over

a Both chromosomes shown here were duplicated during interphase, before meiosis. When prophase I is under way, sister chromatids of each chromosome are positioned so close together that they look like a single thread.

b Each chromosome becomes zippered to its homologue, so all four chromatids are tightly aligned. If the two sex chromosomes have different forms, such as X paired with Y, they still get zippered together, but only in a tiny region at their ends.

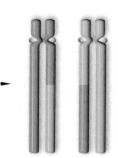

 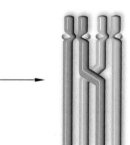  

c We show the pair of chromosomes as if they already condensed only to give you an idea of what goes on. They really are in a tightly aligned, threadlike form during prophase I.

d The intimate contact encourages one crossover (and usually more) to happen at various intervals along the length of nonsister chromatids.

e Nonsister chromatids exchange segments at the crossover sites. They continue to condense into thicker, rodlike forms. By the start of metaphase I, they will be unzipped from each other.

f Crossing over breaks up old combinations of alleles and puts new ones together in the cell's pairs of homologous chromosomes.

Figure 9.6 Key events of prophase I, the first stage of meiosis. For clarity, we show only one pair of homologous chromosomes and one crossover event. Typically, more than one crossover occurs. *Blue* signifies the paternal chromosome; *purple* signifies its maternal homologue.

slightly different forms: alleles. You can bet that some number of the alleles on one chromosome will *not* be identical to their partner alleles on the homologue. Every crossover is a chance to swap slightly different versions of hereditary instructions for gene products.

We will look at the mechanism of crossing over in later chapters. For now, just remember this: *Crossing over leads to recombinations among genes of homologous chromosomes, and to variation in traits among offspring.*

METAPHASE I ALIGNMENTS

Major shufflings of intact chromosomes start during the transition from prophase I to metaphase I. Suppose this is happening right now in one of your germ cells. Crossovers have already made genetic mosaics of the chromosomes, but put this aside to simplify tracking. Just call the twenty-three chromosomes you inherited from your mother the *maternal* chromosomes, and the twenty-three inherited from your father the *paternal* chromosomes.

At metaphase I, microtubules have tethered one chromosome of each pair to one spindle pole and its homologue to the other, and all are lined up at the spindle equator (Figure 9.5b). Have they tethered all maternal chromosomes to one pole and all paternal chromosomes to the other? Maybe, but probably not. As microtubules grow outward from the poles, they latch on to the first chromosome they contact. Because the tethering is random, there is no particular pattern to the metaphase I positions of maternal and paternal chromosomes. Carry this thought one step further. After a pair of homologous chromosomes are moved apart during anaphase I, *either one* of them can end up at either spindle pole.

Think of the possibilities while tracking just three pairs of homologues. By metaphase I, these three pairs may be arranged in any one of four possible positions (Figure 9.7). This means that eight combinations (2^3) are possible for forthcoming gametes.

Cells that give rise to human gametes have twenty-three pairs of homologous chromosomes, not three. So every time a human sperm or egg forms, you can expect a total of *8,388,608* (or 2^{23}) possible combinations of maternal and paternal chromosomes!

Moreover, in each sperm or egg, many hundreds of alleles inherited from the mother might not "say" the exact same thing about hundreds of different traits as alleles inherited from the father. Are you beginning to get an idea of why such fascinating combinations of traits show up the way they do among the generations of your own family tree?

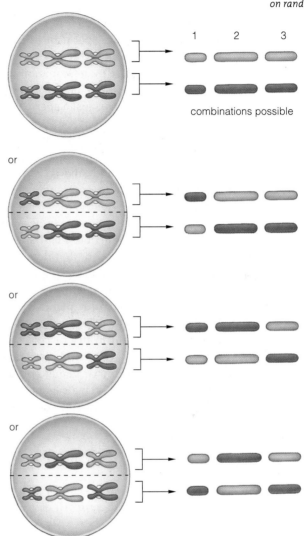

Figure 9.7 Possible outcomes for the random alignment of merely three pairs of homologous chromosomes at metaphase I. The three types of chromosomes are labeled 1, 2, and 3. With four alignments, eight combinations of maternal chromosomes (*purple*) and paternal chromosomes (*blue*) are possible in gametes.

Crossing over, an interaction between a pair of homologous chromosomes, breaks up old combinations of alleles and puts new ones together during prophase I of meiosis.

The random tethering and subsequent positioning of each pair of maternal and paternal chromosomes at metaphase I lead to different combinations of maternal and paternal traits in each new generation.

9.5 From Gametes to Offspring

What happens to the gametes that form after meiosis? Later chapters have specific examples. Here, just focus on where they fit in the life cycles of plants and animals.

Gametes are not all the same in their details. Human sperm have one tail, opossum sperm have two, and roundworm sperm have none. Crayfish sperm look like pinwheels. Most eggs are microscopic in size, yet an ostrich egg inside its shell is as big as a football. A flowering plant's male gamete is just a sperm nucleus.

GAMETE FORMATION IN PLANTS

Seasons vary for plants on land, and so fertilization must coincide with spring rains and other conditions that favor growth of the new individual. That is why life cycles of plants generally alternate between spore production and gamete production. Plant **spores** are haploid resting cells, often walled, that develop after meiosis (Figure 9.8*a*). They originate in reproductive structures of *sporophytes*, or spore-producing bodies. Pine trees, corn plants, and all other plants with roots, stems, and leaves are examples of sporophytes.

Plant spores stay dormant in dry or cold seasons. When they resume growth (germinate), they undergo mitosis and form *gametophytes*, or gamete-producing haploid bodies. For example, female gametophytes form on pine cone scales. In their tissues, gametes form by way of meiosis, as Chapter 27 explains.

GAMETE FORMATION IN ANIMALS

In animals, germ cells give rise to gametes. In a male reproductive system, a diploid germ cell develops into a large, immature cell: a primary spermatocyte. This cell enters meiosis and cytoplasmic divisions. Four haploid cells result, and they develop into spermatids (Figure 9.9). These cells undergo changes that include the formation of a tail. Each becomes a **sperm**, which is a common type of mature male gamete.

In female animals, a germ cell becomes an **oocyte**, or immature egg. Unlike sperm, an oocyte stockpiles many cytoplasmic components, and its four daughter cells differ in size and function (Figure 9.10).

As an oocyte divides after meiosis I, one daughter cell—the secondary oocyte—gets nearly all of the cytoplasm. The other cell, a first polar body, is small. Later, both of these haploid cells enter meiosis II, then cytoplasmic division. One of the secondary oocyte's daughter cells develops into a second polar body. The other receives most of the cytoplasm and develops into a gamete. A mature female gamete is called an ovum (plural, ova) or, more often, an **egg**.

And so we have one egg. The three polar bodies that formed don't function as gametes and aren't rich in nutrients or plump with cytoplasm. In time they degenerate. But the fact that they formed means the egg now has a haploid chromosome number. Also, by getting most of the cytoplasm, the egg has enough metabolic machinery to support the early divisions of the new individual.

MORE SHUFFLINGS AT FERTILIZATION

The chromosome number characteristic of the parents is restored at **fertilization**, a time when a female and male gametes unite and their haploid nuclei fuse. If meiosis did not precede it, fertilization would double

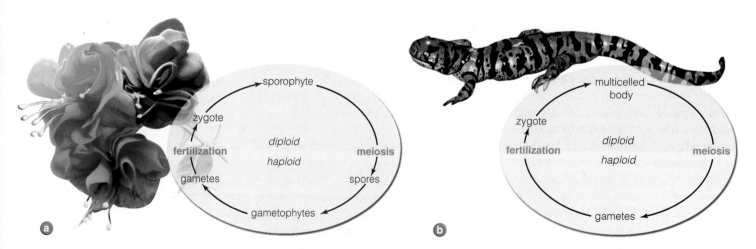

Figure 9.8 (**a**) Generalized life cycle for most plants. (**b**) Generalized life cycle for animals. The zygote is the first cell to form when the nuclei of two gametes fuse at fertilization.

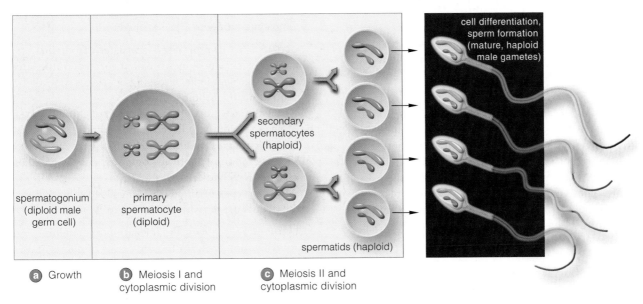

Figure 9.9 Generalized sketch of sperm formation in animals. Figure 38.16 shows a specific example (how sperm form in human males).

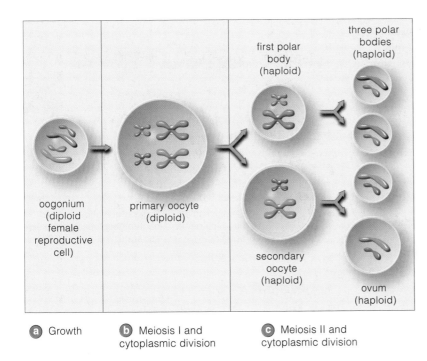

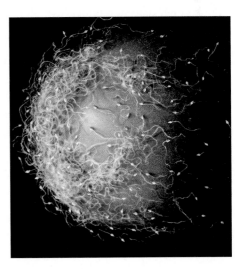

Figure 9.10 Animal egg formation. Eggs are far larger than sperm and larger than the three polar bodies. The painting above, based on a scanning electron micrograph, depicts human sperm surrounding an ovum.

the chromosome number each generation. Doublings would disrupt hereditary information, usually for the worse. Why? That information is like a fine-tuned set of blueprints that must be followed exactly, page after page, to build a normal individual.

Fertilization also adds to variation among offspring. Reflect on the possibilities for humans alone. During prophase I, each human chromosome undergoes an average of two or three crossovers. Even without these crossovers, random positioning of pairs of paternal and maternal chromosomes at metaphase I results in one of millions of possible chromosome combinations in each gamete. And of all male and female gametes that are produced, *which* two actually get together is a matter of chance. The sheer number of combinations that can exist at fertilization is staggering!

The distribution of random mixes of chromosomes into gametes, random metaphase chromosome alignments, and fertilization contribute to variation in traits of offspring.

Summary

Section 9.1 Alleles are slightly different molecular forms of the same gene, and they specify different versions of the same gene product.

Sections 9.2, 9.3 Meiosis, which consists of two nuclear divisions, is central to sexual reproduction. It halves the parental chromosome number (Figure 9.11).

Meiosis I, the first nuclear division, partitions homologous chromosomes into two clusters, both with one of each type of chromosome. All of the chromosomes were duplicated earlier, in interphase.

Prophase I: Chromosomes start condensing into rodlike forms. The nuclear envelope starts to break up. If duplicated pairs of centrioles are present, one pair moves to the opposite side of the nucleus along with a centrosome, from which new microtubules of a spindle originate. Crossing over occurs between homologues.

Metaphase I: All pairs of homologous chromosomes are positioned at the spindle equator. Microtubules have tethered the maternal or paternal chromosome of each pair to either pole, at random.

Anaphase I: Microtubules pull each chromosome away from its homologue, to opposite spindle poles.

Telophase I: Two haploid nuclei form. Cytoplasmic division typically follows.

In meiosis II, the second nuclear division, the sister chromatids of all the chromosomes are pulled away from each other and partitioned into two clusters. By the end of telophase II, four nuclei—each with a haploid chromosome number—have formed.

Section 9.4 In prophase I, *non*sister chromatids of homologous chromosomes break at corresponding sites and exchange segments. Crossing over puts new allelic combinations in chromosomes.

At metaphase I, maternal and paternal chromosomes have been randomly tethered to one spindle pole or the other, which mixes up allelic combinations even more. Alleles are randomly shuffled again when two gametes meet up at fertilization.

All three types of allele shufflings lead to variation in the details of shared traits among offspring.

Section 9.5 Meiosis, the formation of gametes, and fertilization occur in the life cycles of plants and animals. In plant sporophytes, meiosis is followed by haploid spore formation. Germinating spores give rise to gametophytes, where cells that give rise to gametes originate. In most animals, germ cells in reproductive organs give rise to sperm or eggs. Fusion of a sperm and egg nucleus at fertilization results in a zygote.

Figure 9.11 Comparison of the key features of mitosis and meiosis. We use a diploid cell with only two paternal and two maternal chromosomes. All of the chromosomes were duplicated during interphase, prior to nuclear division. Mitosis maintains the chromosome number. Meiosis halves it, to the haploid number.

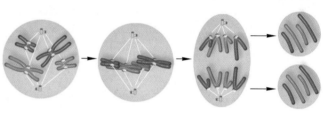

Mitosis

PROPHASE	METAPHASE	ANAPHASE	TELOPHASE
	Chromosomes align at spindle equator.	Sister chromatids of chromosomes separate.	two nuclei (2*n*)

Meiosis I

PROPHASE I	METAPHASE I	ANAPHASE I	TELOPHASE I
Crossing over occurs between homologues.	Homologous pairs align randomly.	Homologues separate from their partner.	typically two nuclei (*n*)

no interphase between nuclear divisions

Meiosis II

PROPHASE II	METAPHASE II	ANAPHASE II	TELOPHASE II
	Chromosomes align at spindle equator.	Sister chromatids of chromosomes separate.	four nuclei (*n*)

Self-Quiz

Answers in Appendix III

1. Meiosis and cytoplasmic division function in _____ .
   a. asexual reproduction of single-celled eukaryotes
   b. growth, tissue repair, often asexual reproduction
   c. sexual reproduction
   d. both b and c

2. A duplicated chromosome has _____ chromatid(s).
   a. one   b. two   c. three   d. four

3. A somatic cell having two of each type of chromosome has a(n) _____ chromosome number.
   a. diploid   b. haploid   c. tetraploid   d. abnormal

4. Sexual reproduction requires _____ .
   a. meiosis   c. gamete formation
   b. fertilization   d. all of the above

5. Generally, a pair of homologous chromosomes _____ .
   a. carry the same genes   c. interact at meiosis
   b. are the same length, shape d. all of the above

6. Meiosis _____ the parental chromosome number.
   a. doubles   b. halves   c. maintains   d. corrupts

7. Meiosis is a division mechanism that produces _____ .
   a. two cells   c. eight cells
   b. two nuclei   d. four nuclei

8. Pairs of duplicated, homologous chromosomes end up at opposite spindle poles during _____ .
   a. prophase I   c. anaphase I
   b. prophase II   d. anaphase II

9. Sister chromatids of each duplicated chromosome end up at opposite spindle poles during _____ .
   a. prophase I   c. anaphase I
   b. prophase II   d. anaphase II

10. Match each term with its description.
   ____ chromosome   a. different molecular forms
          number   of the same gene
   ____ alleles   b. none between meiosis I, II
   ____ metaphase I   c. all chromosomes aligned
   ____ interphase   at spindle equator
                       d. all chromosomes of a given type

Critical Thinking

1. Why can we expect meiosis to give rise to genetic differences between parent cells and their daughter cells in fewer generations than mitosis?

2. As mentioned in the chapter introduction, aphids can reproduce asexually and sexually at different times of year. How might their reproductive flexibility be an adaptation to seasonal change?

3. The bdelloid rotifer lineage started at least 40 million years ago (Figure 9.12). About 360 known species of these tiny animals are found in many aquatic habitats worldwide. Speculate on why scientists were surprised to discover that all bdelloid rotifers are female.

4. Actor Viggo Mortensen inherited a gene that makes his chin dimple. Figure 9.13*b* shows what he might have looked like with an ordinary form of that gene. What is the name for alternative forms of the same gene?

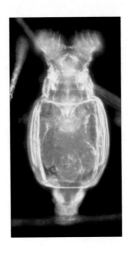

Figure 9.12 Bdelloid rotifer.

Figure 9.13 Viggo Mortensen (**a**) with and (**b**) without a chin dimple.

Media Menu

Student CD-ROM
Impacts, Issues Video
  Why Sex?
Big Picture Animation
  Meiosis and sexual reproduction
Read-Me-First Animation
  Meiosis
  Crossing over
  Random alignment
Other Animations and Interactions
  Variation in life cycles
  Sperm formation
  Egg formation

InfoTrac
• Bdelloids: No Sex for over 40 Million Years. *Science News*, May 2000.
• Crossover Interference in Humans. *American Journal of Human Genetics*, July 2003.
• Tracking Down a Cheating Gene. *American Scientist*, March 2000.

Web Sites
• Meselson Lab: golgi.harvard.edu/meselson/research.html
• Mitosis vs. Meiosis: www.pbs.org/wgbh/nova/miracle/divide.html

How Would You Vote?

Japanese researchers have created a "fatherless" mouse from two eggs. Other scientists have coaxed unfertilized human eggs to develop into embryos. Some people object to the use of any human embryo for research purposes, and some worry about the potential to produce "fatherless" humans. Would you support a ban on this technique?

IMPACTS, ISSUES *Menacing Mucus*

Cystic fibrosis (CF) is a debilitating and ultimately fatal genetic disorder. In 1989, researchers identified the mutated gene that causes it. In 2001, the American College of Obstetricians and Gynecologists suggested that all prospective parents be screened for mutated versions of the gene. The suggestion led to the first mass screening for carriers of a genetic disorder.

CFTR, the gene's product, is a membrane transport protein. It helps chloride and water move into and out of cells that secrete mucus or sweat. More than 10 million people in the United States inherited one normal and one abnormal copy of the CFTR gene. They do have sinus problems, but no other symptoms develop. Most do not even know they carry the gene.

CF develops in anyone who inherits a mutant form of the gene from both parents. Thick, dry mucus clogs bronchial airways to their lungs and makes it hard to breathe (Figure 10.1). The mucus coating the airways is supposed to be thin enough to trap airborne particles and pathogens, so that ciliated cells lining the airways can sweep them out. Bacterial populations thrive in the thick mucus of CF patients, shown in the filmstrip.

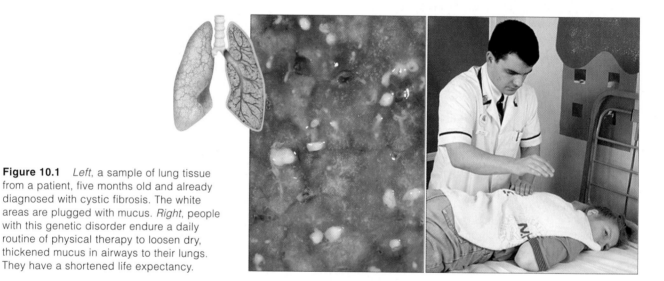

Figure 10.1 *Left*, a sample of lung tissue from a patient, five months old and already diagnosed with cystic fibrosis. The white areas are plugged with mucus. *Right*, people with this genetic disorder endure a daily routine of physical therapy to loosen dry, thickened mucus in airways to their lungs. They have a shortened life expectancy.

the big picture

An Experimental Approach Experiments with pea plants yielded the first observable evidence that parents transmit genes—units of information about heritable traits—to offspring. The experiments also revealed some underlying patterns of inheritance.

Two Theories Emerge As Mendel sensed, diploid organisms have pairs of genes and each gamete gets only one of the pairs. Also, genes on pairs of homologous chromosomes tend to be sorted out for distribution into gametes independently of gene pairs of other chromosomes.

Antibiotics help keep the pathogens under control but cannot get rid of them entirely. Also, to loosen the mucus, patients must go through daily routines of posture changes and thumps on the chest and back. Even with physiotherapy, most can expect lung failure. A double lung transplant can extend their life, but donor organs are scarce. Even if they do receive a transplant, few will live past their thirtieth birthday.

The severity of CF and the prevalence of carriers in the general population persuaded doctors to screen prospective parents—hundreds of thousands of them. By 2003, however, the law of unintended consequences took effect. Some people misunderstood the screening results. Some took unnecessary diagnostic tests to find out if their child would be normal. Confused by test results, a few may have aborted normal fetuses.

So here we are today, working our way through the genetic basis of our very lives. And where did it all start? It started in a small garden, with a monk named Gregor Mendel. By analyzing generation after generation of pea plants in experimental plots, he uncovered indirect but observable evidence of how parents bestow units of hereditary information—genes—on offspring.

This chapter starts out with the methods and some representative results of Mendel's experiments. His pioneering work remains a classic example of how a scientific approach can pry open important secrets about the natural world. To this day, it serves as the foundation for modern genetics.

 *How Would You Vote?*

Many advances in genetics, including the ability to detect mutant genes that cause severe disorders, raise bioethical questions. Should we encourage the mass screening of prospective parents for the alleles that cause cystic fibrosis? And should we as a society encourage women to give birth only if their child will not develop severe medical problems? See the Media Menu for details, then vote online.

Beyond Mendel The traits that Mendel studied happened to follow simple dominant-to-recessive patterns of gene expression. The expression of genes for most traits is not as straightforward. Incomplete dominance and codominance are cases in point.

Less Predictable Variation Although many genes have predictable, observable effects on traits, the expression of most genes is variable. Most traits are outcomes of interactions among the products of two or more genes. Environmental factors also influence gene expression.

10.1 Mendel's Insight Into Inheritance Patterns

We turn now to recurring inheritance patterns among humans and other sexually reproducing species. You already know meiosis halves the parental chromosome number, which is restored at fertilization. Here the story picks up with some observable outcomes of these events.

More than a century ago, people wondered about the basis of inheritance. As many knew, both sperm and eggs transmit information about traits to offspring, but few suspected that the information is organized in units (genes). By the prevailing view, the father's

Figure 10.2 Gregor Mendel, the founder of modern genetics.

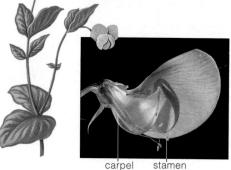
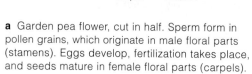
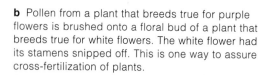

carpel   stamen

a Garden pea flower, cut in half. Sperm form in pollen grains, which originate in male floral parts (stamens). Eggs develop, fertilization takes place, and seeds mature in female floral parts (carpels).

b Pollen from a plant that breeds true for purple flowers is brushed onto a floral bud of a plant that breeds true for white flowers. The white flower had its stamens snipped off. This is one way to assure cross-fertilization of plants.

c Later, seeds develop inside pods of the cross-fertilized plant. An embryo within each seed develops into a mature pea plant.

d Each new plant's flower color is indirect but observable evidence that hereditary material has been transmitted from the parent plants.

Figure 10.3 Garden pea plant (*Pisum sativum*), which can self-fertilize or cross-fertilize. Experimenters can control the transfer of its hereditary material from one flower to another.

blob of information "blended" with the mother's blob at fertilization, like milk into coffee.

Carried to its logical conclusion, blending would slowly dilute a population's shared pool of hereditary information until there was only a single version of each trait. Freckled children would never pop up in a family of nonfreckled people. In time, all of the colts and fillies that are descended from a herd of white stallions and black mares would be gray. But freckles do show up, and not all horses are gray. The blending theory could scarcely explain the obvious variation in traits that people could observe with their own eyes. Even so, few disputed the theory.

"Blending" proponents dismissed Charles Darwin's theory of natural selection. According to the theory's key premise, individuals of a population vary in the details of the traits they have in common. Over the generations, variations that help an individual survive and reproduce show up among more offspring than variations that do not. Less helpful variations might persist, but among fewer individuals. They may even disappear. It is not that some versions of a trait are "blended out" of the population. Rather, *the frequency of each version of a trait among all individuals of the population may persist or change over time.*

Even before Darwin presented his theory, someone was gathering evidence that eventually would help support it. A monk, Gregor Mendel (Figure 10.2), had already guessed that sperm and eggs carry distinct "units" of information about heritable traits. After analyzing certain traits of pea plants generation after generation, he found indirect but *observable* evidence of how parents transmit genes to offspring.

MENDEL'S EXPERIMENTAL APPROACH

Mendel spent most of his adult life in Brno, a city near Vienna that is now part of the Czech Republic. Yet he was not a man of narrow interests who accidentally stumbled onto dazzling principles.

Mendel's monastery was close to European capitals that were centers of scientific inquiry. Having been raised on a farm, he was keenly aware of agricultural principles and their applications. He kept abreast of literature on breeding experiments. He also belonged to a regional agricultural society and even won awards for developing improved varieties of vegetables and fruits. Shortly after he entered the monastery, Mendel took a number of courses in mathematics, physics, and botany at the University of Vienna. Few scholars of his time showed interest in both plant breeding *and* mathematics.

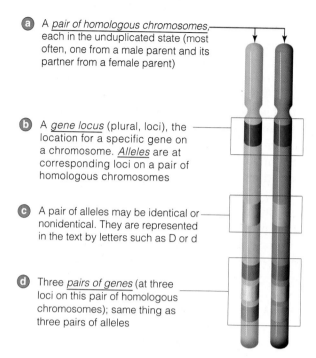

(a) A *pair of homologous chromosomes*, each in the unduplicated state (most often, one from a male parent and its partner from a female parent)

(b) A *gene locus* (plural, loci), the location for a specific gene on a chromosome. *Alleles* are at corresponding loci on a pair of homologous chromosomes

(c) A pair of alleles may be identical or nonidentical. They are represented in the text by letters such as D or d

(d) Three *pairs of genes* (at three loci on this pair of homologous chromosomes); same thing as three pairs of alleles

Figure 10.4 A few genetic terms. Garden peas and other species with a diploid chromosome number have pairs of genes, on pairs of homologous chromosomes. Most genes come in slightly different molecular forms called alleles. Different alleles specify different versions of the same trait. An allele at any given location on a chromosome may or may not be identical to its partner on the homologous chromosome.

Shortly after his university training, Mendel began studying *Pisum sativum*, the garden pea plant (Figure 10.3). This plant is self-fertilizing. Its male and female gametes—call them sperm and eggs—originate in the same flower, and fertilization can occur in the same flower. A lineage of pea plants can "breed true" for certain traits. This means successive generations will be just like parents in one or more traits, as when all offspring grown from seeds of self-fertilized, white-flowered parent plants also have white flowers.

Pea plants also cross-fertilize when pollen from one plant's flower reaches another plant's flower. Mendel knew he could open the flower buds of a plant that bred true for a trait, such as white flowers, and snip out its stamens. Pollen grains, in which sperm develop, originate in stamens. Then he could brush the buds with pollen from a plant that bred true for a *different* version of the same trait—say, purple flowers.

As Mendel hypothesized, such clearly observable differences might help him track a given trait through many generations. If there were patterns to the trait's inheritance, *then those patterns might tell him something about heredity itself.*

TERMS USED IN MODERN GENETICS

In Mendel's time, no one knew about genes, meiosis, or chromosomes. As we follow his thinking, we can clarify the picture by substituting some modern terms used in inheritance studies, as stated here and in Figure 10.4:

1. **Genes** are units of information about heritable traits, transmitted from parents to offspring. Each gene has a specific location (locus) on a chromosome.

2. Cells with a **diploid** chromosome number ($2n$) have pairs of genes, on pairs of homologous chromosomes.

3. **Mutation** alters a gene's molecular structure and its message about a trait. It may cause a trait to change, as when one gene for flower color specifies white and a mutant form specifies yellow. All molecular forms of the same gene are known as **alleles**.

4. When offspring inherit a pair of *identical* alleles for a trait generation after generation, we expect them to be a true-breeding lineage. Offspring of a cross between two individuals that breed true for different forms of a trait are **hybrids**; each one has inherited *nonidentical* alleles for the trait.

5. When a pair of alleles on homologous chromosomes are identical, this is a *homozygous* condition. When the two are not identical, this is a *heterozygous* condition.

6. An allele is *dominant* when its effect on a trait masks that of any *recessive* allele paired with it. We use capital letters to signify dominant alleles and lowercase letters for recessive ones. *A* and *a* are examples.

7. Pulling this all together, a **homozygous dominant** individual has a pair of dominant alleles (*AA*) for the trait being studied. A **homozygous recessive** individual has a pair of recessive alleles (*aa*). And a **heterozygous** individual has a pair of nonidentical alleles (*Aa*).

8. Two terms help keep the distinction clear between genes and the traits they specify. *Genotype* refers to the particular alleles that an individual carries. *Phenotype* refers to an individual's observable traits.

9. P stands for the parents, F_1 for their first-generation offspring, and F_2 for the second-generation offspring.

Mendel hypothesized that tracking clearly observable differences in forms of a given trait might reveal patterns of inheritance.

He predicted that hereditary information is transmitted from one generation to the next as separate units (genes) and is not "diluted" at fertilization.

10.2 Mendel's Theory of Segregation

Mendel used monohybrid crosses to test his hypothesis that pea plants inherit two "units" of information for a trait, one from each parent.

Monohybrid crosses use F_1 offspring of parents that breed true for different forms of a trait ($AA \times aa = Aa$). The experiment itself is a cross between two identical F_1 heterozygotes, which are the "monohybrids" ($Aa \times Aa$).

MONOHYBRID CROSS PREDICTIONS

Mendel tracked many traits over two generations. In one set of experiments, he crossed plants that bred true for purple *or* white flowers. All F_1 offspring had purple flowers. They self-fertilized, and some of the F_2 offspring had white flowers! What was going on?

Pea plants have pairs of homologous chromosomes. Assume one plant is homozygous dominant (AA) and another is homozygous recessive (aa) for flower color. Following meiosis in both plants, each sperm or egg that forms has only one allele for flower color (Figure 10.5). Thus, when a sperm fertilizes an egg, only one outcome is possible: $A + a = Aa$.

With his background in mathematics, Mendel knew about sampling error (Chapter 1). He crossed many thousands of plants. He also counted and recorded the number of dominant and recessive forms of traits. On average, three of every four F_2 plants were dominant, and one was recessive (Figure 10.6).

The ratio hinted that fertilization is a chance event having a number of possible outcomes. Mendel knew about probability, which applies to chance events *and so could help him predict possible outcomes of his genetic crosses.* **Probability** means this: The chance that each outcome of an event will occur is proportional to the number of ways in which the event can be reached.

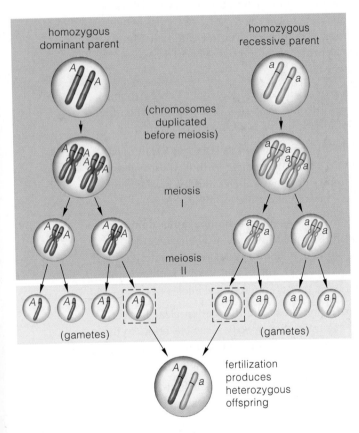

Figure 10.5 One gene of a pair segregating from the other gene in a monohybrid cross. Two parents that breed true for two versions of a trait produce only heterozygous offspring.

Figure 10.6 *Right*: Some monohybrid cross experiments with pea plants. Mendel's counts of F_2 offspring having dominant or recessive hereditary "units" (alleles). On average, the 3:1 phenotypic ratio held for traits.

Trait Studied	Dominant Form	Recessive Form	F_2 Dominant-to-Recessive Ratio
SEED SHAPE	5,474 round	1,850 wrinkled	2.96:1
SEED COLOR	6,022 yellow	2,001 green	3.01:1
POD SHAPE	882 inflated	299 wrinkled	2.95:1
POD COLOR	428 green	152 yellow	2.82:1
FLOWER COLOR	705 purple	224 white	3.15:1
FLOWER POSITION	651 along stem	207 at tip	3.14:1
STEM LENGTH	787 tall	277 dwarf	2.84:1

A **Punnett-square method**, explained and applied in Figure 10.7, shows the possibilities. If half of a plant's sperm or eggs are *a* and half are *A*, then we can expect four outcomes with each fertilization:

POSSIBLE EVENT	PROBABLE OUTCOME
sperm *A* meets egg *A*	1/4 *AA* offspring
sperm *A* meets egg *a*	1/4 *Aa*
sperm *a* meets egg *A*	1/4 *Aa*
sperm *a* meets egg *a*	1/4 *aa*

Each F₂ plant has 3 chances in 4 of inheriting at least one dominant allele (purple flowers). It has 1 chance in 4 of inheriting two recessive alleles (white flowers). That is a probable phenotypic ratio of 3:1.

Mendel's observed ratios were not *exactly* 3:1. Yet he put aside the deviations. To understand why, flip a coin several times. As we all know, a coin is as likely to end up heads as tails. But often it ends up heads, or tails, several times in a row. If you flip the coin only a few times, the observed ratio might differ a lot from the predicted ratio of 1:1. Flip it many times, and you are more likely to approach the predicted ratio.

That is why Mendel used rules of probability and counted so many offspring. He minimized sampling error deviations in the predicted results.

TESTCROSSES

Testcrosses supported Mendel's prediction. In such experimental tests, an organism shows dominance for a specified trait but its genotype is unknown, so it is crossed to a known homozygous recessive individual in a number of matings. Results may reveal whether it is homozygous dominant or heterozygous.

For example, Mendel crossed F₁ purple-flowered plants with true-breeding white-flowered plants. If all were homozygous dominant, then all the F₂ offspring would be purple flowered. If heterozygous, then only about half would. That is what happened. Half of the F₂ offspring had purple flowers (*Aa*) and half had white (*aa*). Go ahead and construct Punnett squares as a way to predict possible outcomes of this testcross.

Results from Mendel's monohybrid crosses became the basis of a theory of **segregation**, as stated here:

MENDEL'S THEORY OF SEGREGATION *Diploid cells have pairs of genes, on pairs of homologous chromosomes. The two genes of each pair are separated from each other during meiosis, so they end up in different gametes.*

Read Me First!
and watch the narrated animation on monohybrid crosses

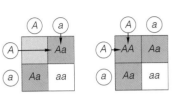

a Punnett-square method

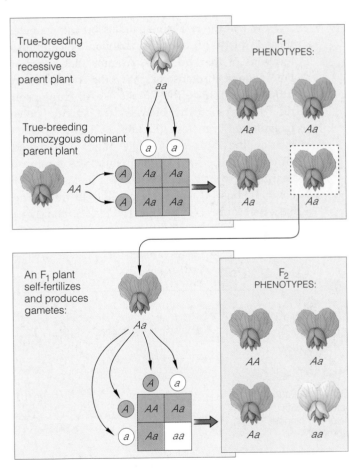

b Cross between two plants that breed true for different forms of a trait, followed by a monohybrid cross between their F₁ offspring

Figure 10.7 (**a**) Punnett-square method of predicting probable outcomes of genetic crosses. Circles signify gametes. *Italics* indicate dominant or recessive alleles. Possible genotypes among offspring are written in the squares. (**b**) Results from one of Mendel's monohybrid crosses. On average, the ratio of dominant-to-recessive that showed up among second-generation (F₂) plants was 3:1.

10.3 Mendel's Theory of Independent Assortment

In another set of experiments, Mendel used dihybrid crosses to explain how two pairs of genes assort into gametes.

*Di*hybrids are the offspring of parents that breed true for different versions of two traits. A **dihybrid cross** is an experimental intercross between F_1 dihybrids that are identically heterozygous for two pairs of genes.

Let's duplicate one of Mendel's dihybrid crosses for flower color (alleles *A* or *a*) and for height (*B* or *b*):

True-breeding parents:	AABB X aabb
Gametes:	AB AB ab ab
F_1 hybrid offspring:	AaBb

As Mendel would have predicted, F_1 offspring from this cross are all purple-flowered and tall (*AaBb*).

How will the two gene pairs assort into gametes in these F_1 plants? It depends partly on the chromosome locations of the two pairs. Assume that one pair of homologous chromosomes have the *Aa* alleles and a different pair have the *Bb* alleles. All chromosomes, recall, align midway between the spindle poles at metaphase I of meiosis (Figures 9.5 and 10.8). The one bearing the *A* or the *a* allele might be tethered to either pole. The same can happen to the chromosome bearing the *B* or *b* allele. Following meiosis, only four combinations of alleles are possible in the sperm or eggs that form: $1/4\,AB$, $1/4\,Ab$, $1/4\,aB$, and $1/4\,ab$.

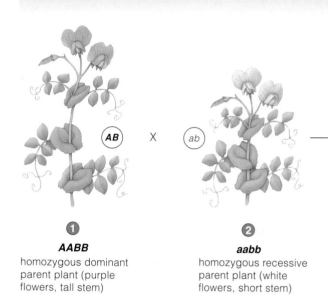

1 **AABB** homozygous dominant parent plant (purple flowers, tall stem)

2 **aabb** homozygous recessive parent plant (white flowers, short stem)

Figure 10.9 Results from Mendel's dihybrid cross starting with parent plants that bred true for different versions of two traits: flower color and plant height. *A* and *a* signify dominant and recessive alleles for flower color. *B* and *b* signify dominant and recessive alleles for height. The Punnett square shows the F_2 combinations possible:

- ☐ 9/16 or 9 purple flowered, tall
- ☐ 3/16 or 3 purple-flowered, dwarf
- ☐ 3/16 or 3 white-flowered, tall
- ☐ 1/16 or 1 white-flowered, dwarf

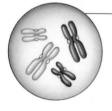

Nucleus of a diploid (2*n*) reproductive cell with two pairs of homologous chromosomes

Figure 10.8 An example of independent assortment at meiosis. Either chromosome of a pair may get tethered to either spindle pole. When just two pairs are tracked, two different metaphase I alignments are possible.

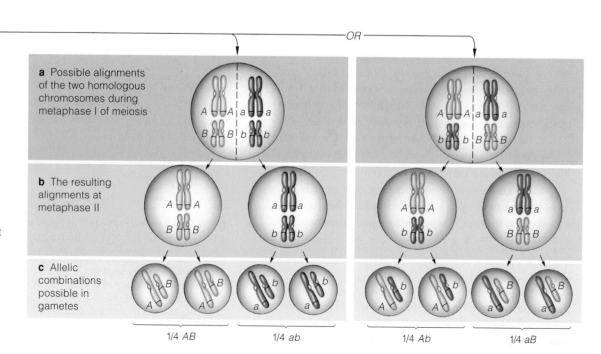

a Possible alignments of the two homologous chromosomes during metaphase I of meiosis

b The resulting alignments at metaphase II

c Allelic combinations possible in gametes

1/4 *AB*   1/4 *ab*   1/4 *Ab*   1/4 *aB*

Read Me First!
and watch the narrated
animation on dihybrid crosses

④ Possible outcomes of cross-fertilization of F₁ plants:

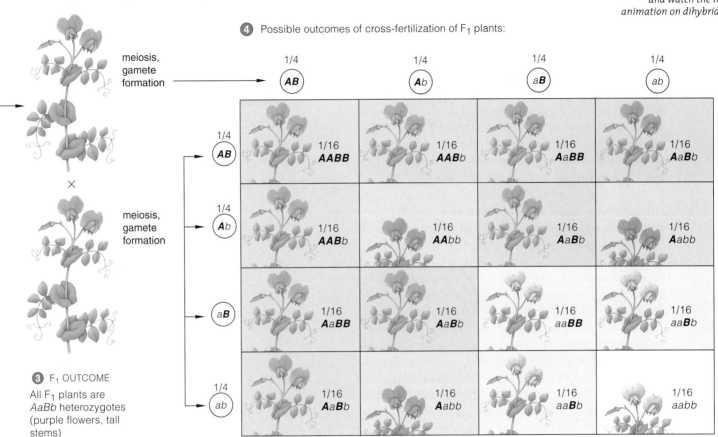

③ F₁ OUTCOME
All F₁ plants are
AaBb heterozygotes
(purple flowers, tall
stems)

Given the alternative metaphase I alignments, many allelic combinations can result at fertilization. Simple multiplication (four sperm types × four egg types) tells us that sixteen combinations of genotypes are possible among F₂ offspring of a dihybrid cross (Figure 10.9).

Adding all possible phenotypes gives us a ratio of 9:3:3:1. We can expect to see 9/16 tall purple-flowered, 3/16 dwarf purple-flowered, 3/16 tall white-flowered, and 1/16 dwarf white-flowered F₂ plants. Results from one dihybrid cross were close to this ratio.

Mendel could only analyze numerical results from such crosses because he did not know seven pairs of homologous chromosomes carry a pea plant's "units" of inheritance. He could do no more than hypothesize that the two units for flower color were sorted out into gametes independently of the two units for height.

In time, his hypothesis became known as the theory of **independent assortment**. In modern terms, after meiosis ends, the genes on each pair of homologous chromosomes are assorted into gametes independently

of how all the other pairs of homologues are sorted out. Independent assortment and hybrid intercrosses give rise to genetic variation. In a monohybrid cross for one gene pair, three genotypes are possible: *AA*, *Aa*, and *aa*. We represent this as 3^n, where *n* is the number of gene pairs. The more pairs, the more combinations are possible. If parents differ in twenty gene pairs, for instance, the number approaches 3.5 billion!

In 1866, Mendel published his idea, but apparently he was read by few and understood by no one. Today his theory of segregation still stands. However, his theory of independent assortment does not apply to *all* gene combinations, as you will see in Chapter 11.

MENDEL'S THEORY OF INDEPENDENT ASSORTMENT *As meiosis ends, genes on pairs of homologous chromosomes have been sorted out for distribution into one gamete or another, independently of gene pairs of other chromosomes.*

10.4 More Patterns Than Mendel Thought

Mendel happened to focus on traits that have clearly dominant and recessive forms. However, expression of genes for most traits is not as straightforward.

ABO BLOOD TYPES—A CASE OF CODOMINANCE

In *codominance*, a pair of nonidentical alleles affecting two phenotypes are both expressed at the same time in heterozygotes. For example, red blood cells have a type of glycolipid at the plasma membrane that helps give them their unique identity. The glycolipid comes in slightly different forms. An analytical method, *ABO blood typing*, reveals which form a person has.

An enzyme dictates the glycolipid's final structure. Humans have three alleles for this enzyme. Two, I^A and I^B, are codominant when paired. The third allele, *i*, is recessive; a pairing with I^A or I^B masks its effect. (If the letter for an allele is superscript, it signifies a lack of dominance.) Here we have a **multiple allele system**, the occurrence of three or more alleles for one gene locus among individuals of a population.

Each of these glycolipid molecules was assembled in the endomembrane system (Figure 4.16). First, an oligosaccharide chain was attached to a lipid, then a sugar was attached to the chain. But alleles I^A and I^B specify different versions of the enzyme that attaches the sugar. The two attach *different* sugars, which gives a glycolipid molecule a different identity: A or B.

Which alleles do you have? If you have I^AI^A or I^Ai, your blood is type A. With I^BI^B or I^Bi, it is type B. With codominant alleles I^AI^B, it is AB—you have both versions of the sugar-attaching enzyme. If you are homozygous recessive (*ii*), the glycolipid molecules never did get a final sugar side chain, so your blood type is not A or B. It is O (Figure 10.10).

homozygous parent   x   homozygous parent

All F₁ offspring heterozygous for flower color:

Cross two of the F₁ plants, and the F₂ offspring will show three phenotypes in a 1:2:1 ratio:

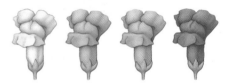

Figure 10.11 Incomplete dominance in heterozygous (*pink*) snapdragons, in which an allele that affects red pigment is paired with a "white" allele.

INCOMPLETE DOMINANCE

In *incomplete* dominance, one allele of a pair is not fully dominant over its partner, so the heterozygote's phenotype is *somewhere between* the two homozygotes. Cross true-breeding red and white snapdragons and their F₁ offspring will be pink-flowered. Cross two F₁ plants and you can expect to see red, white, and *pink* flowers in a certain ratio (Figure 10.11). Why the "odd" pattern? Red snapdragons have two alleles that let them make a lot of molecules of a red pigment. White snapdragons have two mutant alleles, and they are pigment-free. Pink snapdragons have one "red" allele and one "white" one. These heterozygotes make just enough pigment to color flowers pink, not red.

Two interacting gene pairs also can give rise to a phenotype that neither produces by itself. In chickens, interactions among *R* and *P* alleles specify the walnut, rose, pea, and single combs shown in Figure 10.12.

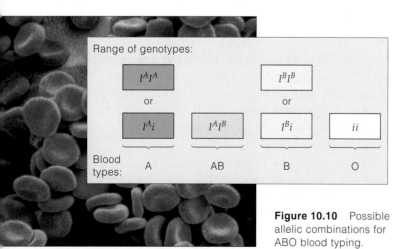

Range of genotypes:

I^AI^A			I^BI^B	
or			or	
I^Ai	I^AI^B	I^Bi		*ii*

Blood types: A   AB   B   O

Figure 10.10 Possible allelic combinations for ABO blood typing.

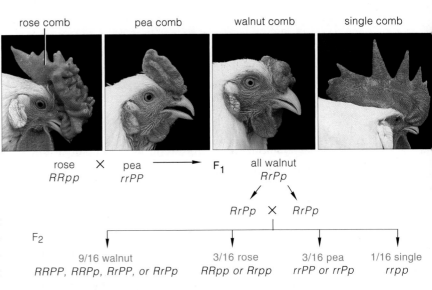

Figure 10.12 Interaction between two genes with variable effects on the comb on a chicken's head. The first cross is between a Wyandotte (rose comb) and a Brahma (pea comb). Check the outcomes by making a Punnett-square diagram.

rose comb   pea comb   walnut comb   single comb

rose   ×   pea   ⟶   F$_1$ all walnut
RRpp   *rrPP*   *RrPp*

RrPp × *RrPp*

F$_2$

9/16 walnut	3/16 rose	3/16 pea	1/16 single
RRPP, RRPp, RrPP, or *RrPp*	*RRpp* or *Rrpp*	*rrPP* or *rrPp*	*rrpp*

SINGLE GENES WITH A WIDE REACH

The alleles at one locus on a chromosome may affect two or more traits in good or bad ways. This outcome of the activity of one gene's product is **pleiotropy**. We see its effects in many genetic disorders, such as cystic fibrosis, sickle-cell anemia, and Marfan syndrome.

An autosomal dominant mutation in the gene for fibrillin causes *Marfan syndrome*. Fibrillin is a protein of connective tissues, the most abundant, widespread of all vertebrate tissues. We find many thin fibrillin strands, loose or cross-linked with the protein elastin, in the heart, blood vessels, and skin. They passively recoil after being stretched, as by the beating heart.

Altered fibrillin weakens the connective tissues in 1 of 10,000 men and women of any ethnicity. The heart, blood vessels, skin, lungs, and eyes are at risk. One of the mutations disrupts the synthesis of fibrillin 1, its secretion from cells, and its deposition. It skews the structure and function of smooth muscle cells inside the wall of the aorta, a big vessel carrying blood out of the heart. Cells infiltrate and multiply inside the wall's epithelial lining. Calcium deposits accumulate and the wall becomes inflamed. Elastic fibers split into fragments. The aorta wall, thinned and weakened, can rupture abruptly during strenuous exercise.

Until recent medical advances, Marfan syndrome killed most affected people before they were fifty years old. Flo Hyman was one of them (Figure 10.13).

WHEN PRODUCTS OF GENE PAIRS INTERACT

Traits also arise from interactions among products of two or more gene pairs. In some cases, two alleles can mask expression of another gene's alleles, and some expected phenotypes may not appear at all.

For example, several gene pairs govern fur color in Labrador retrievers. The fur appears black, yellow, or brown depending on how enzymes and other products of gene pairs synthesize melanin, a dark pigment, and deposit it in different body regions. Allele *B* (black) has a stronger effect and is dominant to *b* (brown). Alleles at another gene locus control how much melanin gets

Figure 10.13 Flo Hyman, at left, captain of the United States volleyball team that won an Olympic silver medal in 1984. Two years later, at a game in Japan, she slid to the floor and died. A dime-sized weak spot in the wall of her aorta had burst. We know at least two affected college basketball stars also died abruptly as a result of Marfan syndrome.

deposited in hair. Allele *E* permits full deposition. Two recessive alleles (*ee*) reduce it, so fur appears yellow.

Alleles at another locus (*C*) may override those two. They encode the first enzyme in a melanin-producing pathway. *CC* or *Cc* individuals do make the functional enzyme. An individual with two recessive alleles (*cc*) cannot. *Albinism*, the absence of melanin, is the result.

Some alleles are fully dominant, incompletely dominant, or codominant with a partner on the homologous chromosome.

With pleiotropy, alleles at a single locus have positive or negative impact on two or more traits.

Gene effects do not always appear together but rather appear over time. A gene's product may alter one trait, which may cause alteration in another trait, and so on.

10.5 Complex Variations in Traits

For most populations or species, individuals show rich variation for many of the same traits. Variation arises from gene mutations, cumulative gene interactions, and variations in environmental conditions.

REGARDING THE UNEXPECTED PHENOTYPE

As Mendel found out, phenotypic effects of one or two pairs of certain genes show up in predictable ratios. Two or more gene pairs also can produce phenotypes in predictable ratios. However, track some genes over the generations, and you might find that the resulting phenotypes were not what you expected.

As one example, *camptodactyly*, a rare abnormality, affects the shape and movement of fingers. Some of the people who carry a mutant allele for this heritable trait have immobile, bent fingers on both hands. Others have immobile, bent fingers on the left or right hand only. Fingers of still other people who have the mutant allele are not affected in any obvious way at all.

What causes such odd variation? Remember, most organic compounds are synthesized by a sequence of metabolic steps. *Different enzymes, each a gene product, control different steps.* Maybe one gene has mutated in a number of ways. Maybe a gene product blocks some pathway or makes it run nonstop or not long enough. Maybe poor nutrition or another variable factor in the individual's environment influences a crucial enzyme in the pathway. Such variable factors often introduce less predictable variations in the phenotypes that we otherwise associate with certain genes.

CONTINUOUS VARIATION IN POPULATIONS

Generally, individuals of a population display a range of small differences in most traits. This characteristic of natural populations, called **continuous variation**, depends mainly on how many gene products affect a given trait and on how many environmental factors impact them. The greater the number of genes

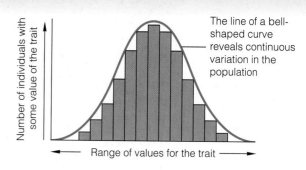

a Idealized bell-shaped curve for a population that displays continuous variation in a trait

The line of a bell-shaped curve reveals continuous variation in the population

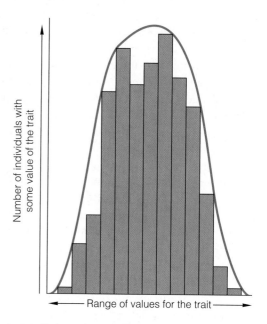

b A bell-shaped curve that corresponds to the height distribution among individual females in the far-right photograph in (**c**)

and environmental factors, the more continuous is the distribution of all versions of the trait.

Look in a mirror at your eye color. The colored part is the iris, a doughnut-shaped, pigmented structure just under the cornea. The color results from several gene products. Some products help make and distribute the light-absorbing pigment melanin, the same pigment that affects coat color in mammals. Almost black irises have dense melanin deposits, and melanin molecules absorb most of the incoming light. Deposits are not as great in brown eyes, so some unabsorbed light is reflected out. Light brown or hazel eyes have even less melanin (Figure 10.14).

Green, gray, or blue eyes do not have green, gray, or blue pigments. The iris has some melanin, but not

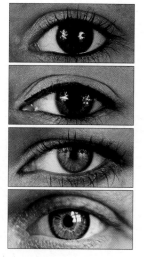

Figure 10.14 Examples from a range of continuous variation in human eye color. Products of different gene pairs interact in making and distributing the melanin that helps color the iris. Different combinations of alleles result in small color differences. The frequency distribution for the eye-color trait is continuous over a range from black to light blue.

Read Me First!
and watch the narrated animation
on continuous variation in traits

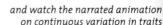

5'3" 5'4" 5'5" 5'6" 5'7" 5'8" 5'9" 5'10" 5'11" 6'0" 6'1" 6'2" 6'3" 6'4" 6'5"
Height (feet/inches)

Figure 10.15 Continuous variation in body height, one of the traits that help characterize the human population.

(**a**) A bar graph can depict continuous variation in a population. The proportion of individuals in each category is plotted against the range of measured phenotypes. The curved line above this particular set of bars is an idealized example of the kind of bell-shaped curve that emerges for populations showing continuous variation in a trait.

(**b,c**) Jon Reiskind and Greg Pryor wanted to show the frequency distribution for height among biology students at the University of Florida. They divided students into two groups: male and female. For each group, they divided the range of possible heights, measured the students, and assigned each to the appropriate category.

4'11" 5'0" 5'1" 5'2" 5'3" 5'4" 5'5" 5'6" 5'7" 5'8" 5'9" 5'10" 5'11"
Height (feet/inches)

c Two examples of continuous variation: Biology students (males, *left*; females, *right*) organized by height.

much. Many or most of the blue wavelengths of light that do enter the eyeball are simply reflected out.

How can you describe the continuous variation of some trait in a group? Consider the students in Figure 10.15. They range from short to tall, with average heights more common than the extremes. Start out by dividing the full range of phenotypes into measurable categories—for instance, number of inches. Next, count how many students are in each category to get the relative frequencies of all phenotypes across the range of measurable values.

The chart in Figure 10.15*b* is a plot of the number of students in each height category. The shortest bars represent categories having the fewest individuals. The tallest bar signifies the category with the most. In

this case, a graph line skirting the top of all the bars will be a bell-shaped curve. Such "bell curves" are typical of any trait that shows continuous variation.

> Enzymes and other gene products control each step of most metabolic pathways. Mutations, interactions among genes, and environmental conditions may affect one or more steps. The outcome is variation in phenotypes.
>
> For most traits, individuals of a population or species show continuous variation—a range of small differences.
>
> Usually, the greater the number of genes and environmental factors that influence a trait, the more continuous the distribution of versions of that trait.

10.6 Genes and the Environment

We have mentioned, in passing, that the environment often contributes to variable gene expression among a population's individuals. Now consider a few cases.

Possibly you have noticed a Himalayan rabbit's coat color. Like a Siamese cat, this mammal has dark hair in some parts of its body and lighter hair in others. The Himalayan rabbit is homozygous for the c^h allele of the gene specifying tyrosinase. Tyrosinase is one of the enzymes involved in melanin production. The c^h allele specifies a heat-sensitive form of this enzyme. And this form is active only when the air temperature around the body is below 33°C, or 91°F.

When cells that give rise to this rabbit's hair grow under warmer conditions, they cannot make melanin, so hairs appear light. This happens in body regions that are massive enough to conserve a fair amount of metabolic heat. The ears and other slender extremities tend to lose metabolic heat faster, so they are cooler. Figure 10.16 shows one experiment that demonstrated how environmental temperatures affect this allele.

One classic experiment identified environmental effects on yarrow plants. These plants can grow from cuttings, so they are a useful experimental organism. Why? Cuttings from the same plant all have the same genotype, so experimenters can discount genes as a basis for differences that show up among them.

In this case, three yarrow cuttings were planted at three elevations. Two plants that grew at the lowest elevation and highest elevation fared best; the one at the mid-elevation grew poorly (Figure 10.17).

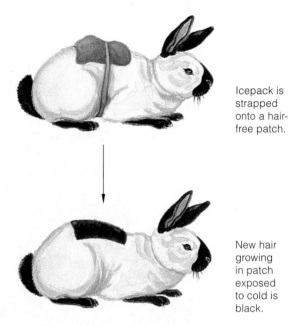

Icepack is strapped onto a hair-free patch.

New hair growing in patch exposed to cold is black.

Figure 10.16 Observable effect of an environmental factor that influences gene expression. A Himalayan rabbit normally has black hair only on its long ears, nose, tail, and leg regions farthest from the body mass. In one experiment, a patch of a rabbit's white coat was removed, then an icepack was secured over the hairless patch. Where the colder temperature had been maintained, the hairs that grew back were black.

Himalayan rabbits are homozygous for an allele of the gene for tyrosinase, an enzyme required to make melanin. As described in the text, this allele encodes a heat-sensitive form of the enzyme, which functions only when air temperature is below about 33°C.

a Mature cutting at high elevation (3,050 meters above sea level)

b Mature cutting at mid-elevation (1,400 meters above sea level)

c Mature cutting at low elevation (30 meters above sea level)

Figure 10.17 One experiment demonstrating the impact of environmental conditions of three different habitats on gene expression in yarrow (*Achillea millefolium*). Cuttings from the same parent plant were grown in the same soil batch but at three different elevations.

However, recall from Chapter 1 that sampling error can skew experimental results. The experimenters did the same growth experiments for *many* yarrow plants and found no consistent pattern; phenotypic variation was too great. For instance, a cutting from one plant did *best* at mid-elevation. The conclusion? For yarrow plants, at least, individuals with different genotypes react differently across a range of environments.

Similarly, plant a hydrangea in a garden and it may have pink flowers instead of the expected blue ones. Soil acidity affects the function of gene products that color hydrangea flowers.

What about humans? One of our genes codes for a transporter protein that moves serotonin across the plasma membrane of brain cells. This gene product has several effects, one of which is to counter anxiety and depression when traumatic events challenge us. For a long time, researchers have known that some people handle stress without getting too upset, while others spiral into a deep and lasting depression.

Mutation of the gene for the serotonin transporter compromises responses to stress. It is as if some of us are bicycling through life without an emotional helmet. Only when we take a fall does the phenotypic effect—depression—appear. Other genes also affect emotional states, but mutation of this one reduces our capacity to snap out of it when bad things happen.

And so we conclude this chapter, which introduces heritable and environmental factors that give rise to great variation in traits. What is the take-home lesson? Simply this: An individual's phenotype is an outcome of complex interactions among its genes, enzymes and other gene products, and the environment.

Variation in traits arises not only from gene mutations and interactions, but also in response to variations in environmental conditions that each individual faces.

Summary

Section 10.1 Genes are heritable units of information about traits. Each gene has its own locus on a particular chromosome. Different molecular forms of the same gene are known as alleles. Diploid cells have two copies of each gene, usually one inherited from each of two parents, on homologous chromosomes.

Offspring of a cross between two individuals that breed true for different forms of a trait are hybrids; each has inherited nonidentical alleles for the trait.

An individual with two dominant alleles for a trait (AA) is homozygous dominant. A homozygous recessive has two recessive alleles (aa). A heterozygote has two nonidentical alleles (Aa) for a trait. A dominant allele may mask the effect of a recessive allele partnered with it on the homologous chromosome.

Section 10.2 Results from Mendel's monohybrid crosses between F_1 offspring of true-breeding pea plants in time led to a theory of segregation: Paired genes on homologous chromosomes separate from each other at meiosis and end up in different gametes. The theory is based on a pattern of dominance and recessiveness that showed up among F_2 offspring of monohybrid crosses:

	A	*a*
A	*AA*	*Aa*
a	*Aa*	*aa*

AA (dominant)
Aa (dominant) } the expected
Aa (dominant) } phenotypic
aa (recessive) } ratio of 3:1

Section 10.3 Mendel did dihybrid crosses between F_1 offspring of parents that bred true for two different traits. The dihybrid cross results were close to a 9:3:3:1 ratio:

    9 dominant for both traits
    3 dominant for *A*, recessive for *b*
    3 dominant for *B*, recessive for *a*
    1 recessive for both traits

His results support a theory of independent assortment: Meiosis assorts gene pairs of homologous chromosomes for forthcoming gametes independently of how gene pairs of the other chromosomes are sorted out. This is an outcome of the random alignment of all pairs of homologous chromosomes at metaphase I.

Section 10.4 Inheritance patterns are not always straightforward. Some alleles are codominant or not fully dominant. Products of gene pairs often interact in ways that influence the same trait. A single gene may have effects on two or more traits. Products of pairs of genes often interact in ways that influence the same trait. One gene may have positive or negative effects on two or more traits, a condition called pleiotropy.

Section 10.5 Mutations and interactions among gene products contribute to variation in traits among the individuals of a population. Some traits show a range of small, incremental differences—continuous variation.

Section 10.6 Environmental conditions can alter gene expression. The individuals of most populations show complex variation in traits, a combination of gene expression and exposure to environmental factors.

Self-Quiz
Answers in Appendix III

1. Alleles are _____ .
   a. different molecular forms of a gene
   b. different phenotypes
   c. self-fertilizing, true-breeding homozygotes

2. A heterozygote has a _____ for a trait being studied.
   a. pair of identical alleles
   b. pair of nonidentical alleles
   c. haploid condition, in genetic terms
   d. a and c

3. The observable traits of an organism are its _____ .
   a. phenotype   c. genotype
   b. sociobiology   d. pedigree

4. Second-generation offspring from a cross are the _____ .
   a. F_1 generation   c. hybrid generation
   b. F_2 generation   d. none of the above

5. F_1 offspring of the monohybrid cross $AA \times aa$ are _____ .
   a. all AA c. all Aa
   b. all aa d. 1/2 AA and 1/2 aa

6. Refer to Question 5. Assuming complete dominance, the F_2 generation will show a phenotypic ratio of _____ .
   a. 3:1   b. 9:1   c. 1:2:1   d. 9:3:3:1

7. Crosses between F_1 pea plants resulting from the cross $AABB \times aabb$ lead to F_2 phenotypic ratios close to _____ .
   a. 1:2:1   b. 3:1   c. 1:1:1:1   d. 9:3:3:1

8. Match each example with the most suitable description.
   ____ dihybrid cross   a. *bb*
   ____ monohybrid cross   b. *AABB* × *aabb*
   ____ homozygous condition   c. *Aa*
   ____ heterozygous condition   d. *Aa* × *Aa*

Figure 10.18 Two albino organisms. By not posing his subjects as objects of ridicule, the photographer of human albinos is attempting to counter the notion that there is something inherently unbeautiful about them.

Genetics Problems
Answers in Appendix IV

1. A certain recessive allele *c* is responsible for *albinism*, an inability to produce or deposit melanin, a brownish-black pigment, in body tissues. Humans and a number of other organisms can have this phenotype. Figure 10.18 shows two stunning examples. In cases of albinism, what are the possible genotypes of the father, the mother, and their children?
   a. Both parents have normal phenotypes; some of their children are albino and others are unaffected.
   b. Both parents are albino and have albino children.
   c. The woman is unaffected, the man is albino, and they have one albino child and three unaffected children.

2. One gene has alleles *A* and *a*. Another has alleles *B* and *b*. For each genotype, what type(s) of gametes will form? Assume that independent assortment occurs.
   a. *AABB*   c. *Aabb*
   b. *AaBB*   d. *AaBb*

3. Refer to Problem 2. What will be the genotypes of offspring from the following matings? Indicate the frequencies of each genotype among them.
   a. *AABB* × *aaBB*   c. *AaBb* × *aabb*
   b. *AaBB* × *AABb*   d. *AaBb* × *AaBb*

4. Certain dominant alleles are so essential for normal development that an individual who is homozygous recessive for a mutant recessive form can't survive. Such recessive, *lethal alleles* can be perpetuated in the population by heterozygotes.
   Consider the Manx allele (M^L) in cats. Homozygous cats ($M^L M^L$) die when they are still embryos inside the mother cat. In heterozygotes ($M^L M$), the spine develops abnormally. The cats end up with no tail (Figure 10.19).
   Two $M^L M$ cats mate. What is the probability that any one of their *surviving* kittens will be heterozygous?

5. In one experiment, Mendel crossed a pea plant that bred true for green pods with one that bred true for yellow pods. All the F_1 plants had green pods. Which form of the trait (green or yellow pods) is recessive? Explain how you arrived at your conclusion.

6. Return to Problem 2. Assume you now study a third gene having alleles *C* and *c*. For each genotype listed, what type(s) of gametes will be produced?
   a. *AABBCC*   c. *AaBBCc*
   b. *AaBBcc*   d. *AaBbCc*

7. Mendel crossed a true-breeding tall, purple-flowered pea plant with a true-breeding dwarf, white-flowered plant. All F_1 plants were tall and had purple flowers. If an F_1 plant self-fertilizes, then what is the probability that a randomly selected F_2 offspring will be heterozygous for the genes specifying height and flower color?

8. *DNA fingerprinting* is a method of identifying individuals by locating unique base sequences in their DNA molecules (Section 15.4). Before researchers refined the method, attorneys often relied on the ABO blood-typing system to settle disputes over paternity. Suppose that you, as a geneticist, are asked to testify during a paternity case in which the mother has type A blood, the child has type O blood, and the alleged father has type B blood. How would you respond to the following statements?

a. Attorney of the alleged father: "The mother's blood is type A, so the child's type O blood must have come from the father. My client has type B blood; he could not be the father."

b. Mother's attorney: "Because further tests prove this man is heterozygous, he must be the father."

9. Suppose you identify a new gene in mice. One of its alleles specifies white fur. A second allele specifies brown fur. You want to determine whether the relationship between the two alleles is one of simple dominance or incomplete dominance. What sorts of genetic crosses would give you the answer? On what types of observations would you base your conclusions?

10. Your sister gives you a purebred Labrador retriever, a female named Dandelion. Suppose you decide to breed Dandelion and sell puppies to help pay for your college tuition. Then you discover that two of her four brothers and sisters show *hip dysplasia*, a heritable disorder arising from a number of gene interactions. If Dandelion mates with a male Labrador known to be free of the harmful alleles, can you guarantee to a buyer that her puppies will not develop the disorder? Explain your answer.

11. A dominant allele W confers black fur on guinea pigs. A guinea pig that is homozygous recessive (ww) has white fur. Fred would like to know whether his pet black-furred guinea pig is homozygous dominant (WW) or heterozygous (Ww). How might he determine his pet's genotype?

12. Red-flowering snapdragons are homozygous for allele R^1. White-flowering snapdragons are homozygous for a different allele (R^2). Heterozygous plants (R^1R^2) bear pink flowers. What phenotypes should appear among first-generation offspring of the crosses listed? What are the expected proportions for each phenotype?

a. $R^1R^1 \times R^1R^2$ c. $R^1R^2 \times R^1R^2$

b. $R^1R^1 \times R^2R^2$ d. $R^1R^2 \times R^2R^2$

(In cases of incomplete dominance, alleles are usually designated by superscript numerals, as shown here, not by the uppercase letters for dominance and lowercase letters for recessiveness.)

13. Two pairs of genes affect comb type in chickens (Figure 10.12). When both genes are recessive, a chicken has a single comb. A dominant allele of one gene, P, gives rise to a pea comb. Yet a dominant allele of the other (R) gives rise to a rose comb. An *epistatic* interaction occurs when a chicken has at least one of both dominants, $P\_\ R\_$, which gives rise to a walnut comb.

Predict the ratios resulting from a cross between two walnut-combed chickens that are heterozygous for both genes ($PpRr$).

14. As Section 3.6 explains, a single mutant allele gives rise to an abnormal form of hemoglobin (Hb^S instead of Hb^A). Homozygotes (Hb^SHb^S) develop sickle-cell anemia. Heterozygotes (Hb^AHb^S) show few obvious symptoms.

Suppose a woman's mother is homozygous for the Hb^A allele. She marries a male who is heterozygous for the allele, and they plan to have children. For *each* of her pregnancies, state the probability that this couple will have a child who is:

a. homozygous for the Hb^S allele
b. homozygous for the Hb^A allele
c. heterozygous Hb^AHb^S

Figure 10.19 The Manx, a breed of cat that has no tail.

IMPACTS, ISSUES *Strange Genes, Tortured Minds*

"This man is brilliant," was the entire text of a letter of recommendation from Richard Duffin, a mathematics professor at Carnegie Mellon University. Duffin wrote it in 1948 on behalf of John Forbes Nash, Jr. (Figure 11.1), who was twenty years old at the time and applying to Princeton University's graduate school.

In the next decade, Nash made brilliant contributions to the field of mathematics and was considered to be

Figure 11.1 John Forbes Nash, Jr., a prodigy who solved problems that had long baffled some of the greatest minds in mathematics. His early work in economic game theory won him a Nobel Prize. He is shown here at a premier of "A Beautiful Mind," an award-winning film based on his long, tormented battle with schizophrenia.

one of the nation's top scientists. Apart from his social awkwardness, which is common among highly gifted people, there was no warning that paranoid schizophrenia would debilitate him in his thirtieth year. Nash had to abandon his position at the Massachusetts Institute of Technology. Two decades would pass before he would return to his work in mathematics.

Of every hundred people worldwide, one is affected by *schizophrenia*, which is characterized by delusions, hallucinations, disorganized speech and behavior, and social dysfunction. Many researchers have speculated that extraordinary creativity is linked to schizophrenia and other neurobiological disorders (NBDs) including depression, bipolar disorder (manic depression), and autism.

Certainly not every individual with high IQ shows such a link, but a higher percentage of geniuses have NBDs compared to the general population. Creative writers alone are eighteen times more suicidal, ten times more likely to be depressed, and twenty times more likely to have bipolar disorder.

We now have evidence that highly creative, healthy people have more personality traits in common with the mentally ill than with normal, less creative people, particularly in their sensitivity to environmental stimuli. People with NBDs belong to an illustrious crowd that includes Socrates, Newton, Beethoven, Darwin, Lincoln, Poe, Dickens, Tolstoy, Van Gogh, Freud, Churchill, Einstein, Picasso, Woolf, Hemingway, and Nash.

the big picture

Focus on Chromosomes Males and females differ in their sex chromosomes, but all other homologous chromosomes are the same in both. All of their chromosomes are subject to crossing over and other changes, which diagnostic tools can detect.

Human Inheritance Patterns Family pedigrees often reveal patterns of autosomal dominant, autosomal recessive, and sex-linked inheritance. Such patterns underlie many genetic abnormalities and disorders.

Abnormal brain biochemistry underlies NBDs. For instance, people with *bipolar disorder* show extreme swings in mood, thoughts, energy, and behavior. In their brain cells, expression of some mitochondrial genes that control aerobic respiration and protein breakdown is markedly low.

Change in any step of a crucial biochemical pathway could impair the brain's wiring. Therefore, we can expect that alterations in genes contribute to the abnormal neurochemistry in NBDs. Indeed, NBDs tend to run in families. Geniuses and individuals with one or more types of NBD often appear in the same family.

We already know about several mutant genes that predispose individuals to neural disorders. We also know that their bearers do not always show severe symptoms. Individuals who push the envelope of human creativity walk a razor's edge of mental stability, and it may take interplays of gene products and environmental factors to knock them off.

This brief account of neurobiological disorders is a glimpse into the world of modern genetics research. It invites you to think about how far you have come in this unit of the book. You first looked at cell division, the starting point of inheritance. You looked at how chromosomes and the genes they carry are shuffled during meiosis, then at fertilization. You also mulled over Mendel's insights into patterns of inheritance and some exceptions to his conclusions. Turn now to the chromosomal basis of inheritance.

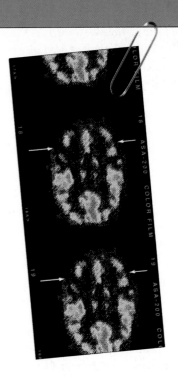

 **How Would You Vote?**

Diagnostic tests for predisposition to neurobiological disorders will soon be available. Individuals might use knowledge of their susceptibility to modify life-style choices. Insurance companies and employers might also use that information to exclude predisposed but otherwise healthy individuals. Would you support legislation governing these tests? See the Media Menu for details, then vote online.

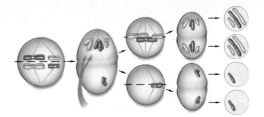

Chromosome Abnormalities   Certain genetic disorders arise from structural alterations of chromosomes or from abnormal changes in the chromosome number. Some changes occur spontaneously, and others result from exposure to harmful agents in the environment.

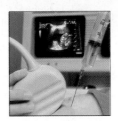

Prospects in Human Genetics   Some genetic disorders are treatable. Prospective parents who are at risk of transmitting a gene for a severe disorder often request genetic counseling or screening options, including prenatal and preimplantation diagnosis.

11.1 The Chromosomal Basis of Inheritance

You already know about chromosomes and what happens to them during meiosis. Now we'll start correlating chromosome structure to human inheritance patterns.

A REST STOP ON OUR CONCEPTUAL ROAD

Before driving on to the land of human inheritance, take a few minutes to check the following road map. It offers perspective on six important concepts:

1. A *gene*, again, is a unit of information about a heritable trait. The genes of eukaryotic cells are distributed among a number of chromosomes. Each gene has its own location, or locus, in one type of chromosome.

2. A cell with a diploid chromosome number, or 2*n*, has *pairs of homologous chromosomes*. All but one pair are normally the same in length, shape, and order of genes. The exception is a pairing of nonidentical sex chromosomes, such as X with Y in humans. Each chromosome becomes aligned with its homologous partner at metaphase I of meiosis.

3. Genes mutate, so a pair of genes on homologous chromosomes may or may not be the same. All of the slightly different molecular forms of a gene that occur among individuals of a population are called *alleles*.

4. A *wild-type* allele is a gene's most common form, in either a natural population or in a standardized, laboratory-bred strain of the species. A less common form of the gene is a *mutant* allele.

5. All genes on the same chromosome are physically connected. The farther apart any two genes are along the length of a chromosome, the more vulnerable they are to *crossing over*. By this event, a chromatid of one chromosome and a chromatid of its homologue swap corresponding segments (Figure 11.2). Crossing over between nonsister chromatids is a form of *genetic recombination* that introduces novel combinations of alleles in chromosomes.

6. On rare occasions, the *structure* of a chromosome or the parental *chromosome number* changes in mitosis or meiosis. Such chromosomal abnormalities can have severe phenotypic consequences.

AUTOSOMES AND SEX CHROMOSOMES

Some species show separation into sexes, and it all starts with genes on chromosomes. Say the species has a diploid chromosome number, so that body cells have pairs of homologous chromosomes. All but one pair are alike in length, shape, and gene sequence. A unique chromosome occurs in either females *or* males of many species, but not both.

For instance, a diploid cell in a human female has two X chromosomes (XX). A diploid cell in a human male has one X and one Y chromosome (XY). This is a common inheritance pattern among mammals, fruit flies, and many other animals. It is not the only one. In butterflies, moths, birds, and certain fishes, the two sex chromosomes are identical in males, and they are not identical in females.

Human X and Y chromosomes differ physically. The Y is a lot shorter, almost a remnant of the other in appearance. The two also differ in which genes they carry. They still synapse (zipper together briefly) in a small region. That bit of zippering allows them to interact as homologues during meiosis.

Human X and Y chromosomes fall into the more general category of **sex chromosomes**. When inherited in certain combinations, sex chromosomes determine a new individual's gender—whether a male or female will develop. All other chromosomes in a cell are the same in both sexes. We categorize them as **autosomes**.

Read Me First!

and watch the narrated animation on crossing over and genetic recombination

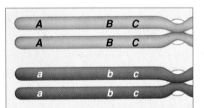

a A pair of duplicated homologous chromosomes (two sister chromatids each). In this example, nonidentical alleles occur at three gene loci (*A* with *a*, *B* with *b*, and *C* with *c*).

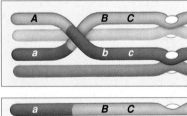

b In prophase I of meiosis, a crossover event occurs: Two nonsister chromatids exchange corresponding segments.

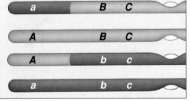

c What is the outcome of the crossover? Genetic recombination between nonsister chromatids (which are shown here, after meiosis, as two unduplicated, separate chromosomes).

Figure 11.2 Review of crossing over. As shown in Figure 9.6, this event occurs in prophase I of meiosis.

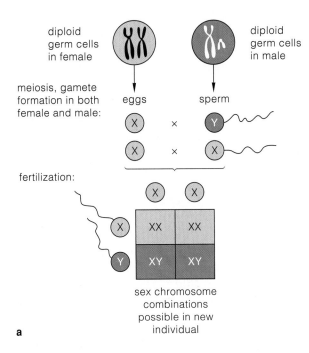

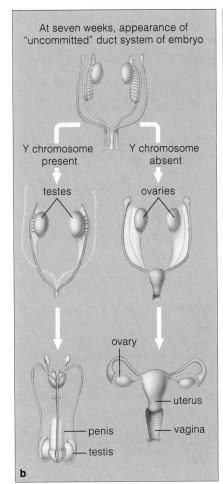

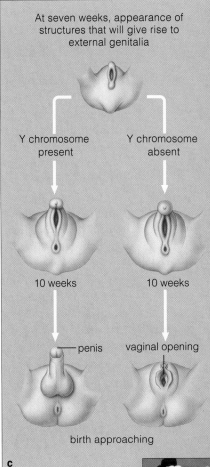

Figure 11.3 (**a**) Punnett-square diagram showing the sex determination pattern in humans.

(**b**) Early on, a human embryo is neither male nor female. Then tiny ducts and other structures that can develop into male *or* female reproductive organs start forming. In an XX embryo, ovaries form *in the absence of the SRY gene on the Y chromosome*. In an XY embryo, the gene product triggers the formation of testes. A hormone secreted from testes calls for development of male traits. (**c**) External reproductive organs in human embryos.

SEX DETERMINATION IN HUMANS

Each normal egg produced by a human female has one X chromosome. Half the sperm cells formed in a male carry an X chromosome, and half carry a Y. Say an X-bearing sperm fertilizes an X-bearing egg. The individual will develop into a female. If the sperm carries a Y chromosome, the individual will develop into a male (Figure 11.3*a*).

SRY, one of 330 genes in a human Y chromosome, is the master gene for male sex determination. Its expression in XY embryos triggers the formation of testes, the primary male reproductive organs (Figure 11.3*b*). Testes make testosterone, and this sex hormone governs the emergence of male sexual traits.

An XX embryo has no *SRY* gene, so primary female reproductive organs—ovaries—form instead. Ovaries make estrogens and other sex hormones that govern the development of female sexual traits.

The human X chromosome carries 2,062 genes. Like other chromosomes, it carries some genes associated with sexual traits, such as the distribution of body fat and hair. But most of its genes deal with *nonsexual* traits, such as blood-clotting functions. Such genes can be expressed in males as well as in females. Males, remember, also inherit one X chromosome.

Diploid cells have pairs of genes, on pairs of homologous chromosomes. The alleles (alternative forms of a gene) at a given locus may be identical or nonidentical.

As a result of crossing over and other events, offspring inherit combinations of alleles not found on parental chromosomes.

Abnormal events at meiosis or mitosis can change the structure and number of chromosomes.

Autosomes are pairs of chromosomes that are the same in males and females of a species. One other pairing, the sex chromosomes, differs between males and females.

The SRY gene on the human Y chromosome dictates that a new individual will develop into a male. In the absence of the Y chromosome (and the gene), a female develops.

11.2 Karyotyping Made Easy

Karyotyping is a diagnostic tool that allows us to check images of the structure and number of chromosomes in an individual's somatic cells.

How do we know so much about an individual's autosomes and sex chromosomes? *Karyotyping* is one diagnostic tool. A **karyotype** is a preparation of an individual's metaphase chromosomes, sorted out by their defining visual features. Any abnormalities in chromosome structure or number can be detected by comparing a standard karyotype for the species.

Chromosomes are in their most condensed form and easiest to identify when a cell enters metaphase. Technicians don't count on finding dividing cells in the body—they culture cells and induce mitosis artificially. They put a sample of cells, usually from blood, into a solution that stimulates growth and mitotic cell division. They add colchicine to arrest the cell cycle at metaphase. Colchicine, recall, is a microtubule poison that blocks spindle formation.

The cell culture is centrifuged to isolate all the metaphase cells (Figure 11.4). A hypotonic solution makes the cells swell, by osmosis. The cells, along with their chromosomes, move apart. Then they are mounted on slides, fixed, and stained.

The chromosomes are viewed and photographed through a microscope. The photograph is cut, either with scissors or on a computer, and the individual chromosomes are lined up by their size and shape.

Spectral karyotyping uses a range of colored fluorescent dyes that bind to specific regions of chromosomes. Analysis of the resulting rainbow-hued karyotype often reveals crossovers and abnormalities that would not be otherwise visible. You will see an example of a multicolor spectral karyotype in Section 11.7.

Read Me First!

and watch the narrated animation on karyotype preparation

Figure 11.4 Karyotyping. With this type of diagnostic tool, an image of metaphase chromosomes is cut apart. Individual chromosomes are aligned by their centromeres and arranged according to size, shape, and length.

(**a**) A sample of cells from an individual is added to a medium that stimulates cell growth and mitotic cell division. The cell cycle is arrested at metaphase, with colchicine. (**b**) The culture is subjected to *centrifugation*, which works because cells have greater mass and density than the solution bathing them. A centrifuge's spinning force moves the cells farthest from the center of rotation, so they collect at the base of the centrifuge tubes.

(**c**) The culture medium is removed; a hypotonic solution is added. As the cells swell, the chromosomes move apart. (**d**) The cells are mounted on a microscope slide, fixed by air-drying, and stained. Chromosomes show up.

(**e**) A photograph of one cell's chromosomes is cut up and organized, as in the human karyotype in (**f**), which shows 22 pairs of autosomes and 1 pair of sex chromosomes—XX *or* XY. Scissors or computers do the cuts.

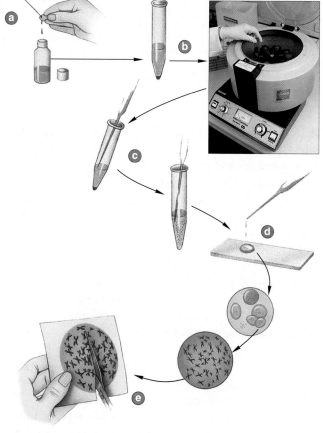

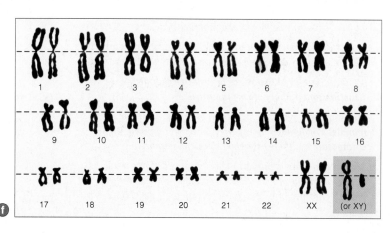

11.3 Impact of Crossing Over on Inheritance

Crossing over between homologous chromosomes is one of the main pattern-busting events in inheritance.

We now know there are many genes on each type of autosome and sex chromosome. All the genes on one chromosome are called a **linkage group**. For instance, the fruit fly (*Drosophila melanogaster*) has four linkage groups, corresponding to its four pairs of homologous chromosomes. Indian corn (*Zea mays*) has ten linkage groups, corresponding to its ten pairs, and so on.

If linked genes stayed connected through meiosis, then there would be no surprising mixes of parental traits. You could expect parental phenotypes among, say, F_2 offspring of dihybrid crosses to show up in a predictable ratio. As early experiments with fruit flies made clear, however, plenty of genes on the same chromosomes do *not* stay together through meiosis.

In one experiment, mutant female flies that bred true for white eyes and a yellow body were crossed with wild-type males (red eyes and gray body). As expected, 50 percent of the F_1 offspring had one or the other parental phenotype. However, 129 of the 2,205 F_2 offspring were recombinants! They had white eyes and a gray body, or red eyes and a yellow body.

Why? Some alleles tend to stay together more often than others through meiosis. They are closer together along the length of a chromosome and therefore less vulnerable to a crossover. *The probability that crossing over will disrupt the linkage between any two gene loci is proportional to the distance between them.*

If, say, genes *A* and *B* are twice as far apart as genes *C* and *D*, we can expect crossing over to disrupt the linkage between *A* and *B* far more frequently:

Two genes are very closely linked when the distance between them is small. Their combinations of alleles nearly always end up in the same gamete. Linkage is more vulnerable to crossing over when the distance between two gene loci is greater (Figure 11.5). When two loci are far apart, crossing over is so frequent that the genes assort independently into gametes.

Human gene linkages were identified by tracking phenotypes in families over generations. One thing is clear from such studies: Crossovers are not rare. For most eukaryotes, meiosis cannot even be completed properly until at least one crossover occurs between each pair of homologous chromosomes.

> All of the genes at different locations along the length of a chromosome belong to the same linkage group. They do not all assort independently at meiosis.
>
> Crossing over between homologous chromosomes disrupts gene linkages and results in nonparental combinations of alleles in chromosomes.
>
> The farther apart two genes are on a chromosome, the greater will be the frequency of crossing over and genetic recombination between them.

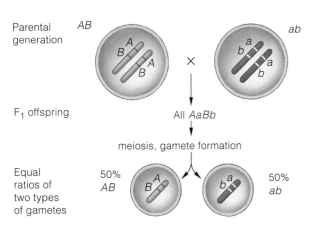

a Full linkage between two genes; no crossing over. Half of the gametes have one parental genotype, and half have the other. Genes that are very close together along the length of a chromosome typically stay together in gametes.

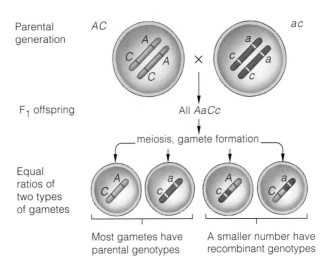

Most gametes have parental genotypes

A smaller number have recombinant genotypes

b Incomplete linkage; crossing over affected the outcome. Genes that are far apart along the length of a chromosome are more vulnerable to crossing over.

Figure 11.5 Examples of outcomes of crossing over between two gene loci.

11.4 Human Genetic Analysis

Some organisms, including pea plants and fruit flies, are ideal for genetic analysis. They do not have a lot of chromosomes. They grow and reproduce fast in small spaces, under controlled conditions. It doesn't take long to track a trait through many generations. Humans, however, are another story.

Unlike fruit flies in the laboratory, we humans live under variable conditions in diverse environments, and we live as long as the geneticists who study our traits. Most of us select our own mates and reproduce if and when we want to. Most families are not large, which means there are not enough offspring available for researchers to make easy inferences.

Geneticists often gather information from several generations to increase the numbers for analysis. If a trait follows a simple Mendelian inheritance pattern, they can be confident about predicting the probability of its showing up again. The pattern also can be a clue to the past (Figure 11.6).

Such information is often displayed in **pedigrees**, or charts of genetic connections among individuals. Standardized methods, definitions, and symbols that represent different kinds of individuals are used to

Figure 11.6 An intriguing pattern of inheritance. Eight percent of the men in Central Asia carry nearly identical Y chromosomes, which implies descent from a shared ancestor. If so, then 16 million males living between northeastern China and Afghanistan—close to 1 of every 200 men alive today—belong to a lineage that started with the warrior and notorious womanizer Genghis Khan. In time, his offspring ruled an empire that stretched from China all the way to Vienna.

construct these charts. Figure 11.7 gives an example. Those who analyze pedigrees rely on their knowledge of probability and Mendelian inheritance patterns that may yield clues to a trait. As you will see, they have traced many genetic abnormalities and disorders to a dominant or recessive allele, even to its location on an autosome or a sex chromosome.

Bear in mind, a genetic *abnormality* is simply a rare or uncommon version of a trait, as when a person is born with six digits on each hand or foot instead of the usual five. Whether we view such a condition as disfiguring or merely interesting is subjective; there is nothing inherently life-threatening about it. A **genetic disorder**, however, is a heritable condition that sooner or later gives rise to mild to severe medical problems. A set of symptoms, or **syndrome**, characterizes each abnormality or disorder. Table 11.1 gives examples.

You might be thinking that a disease, too, has a set of symptoms that arises from an abnormal change in how the body functions. However, each **disease** is an illness that results from an infection, dietary problems, or environmental factors—*not* from a heritable mutation. It might be appropriate to call it a *genetic* disease only when such factors alter previously workable genes in a way that disrupts body functions.

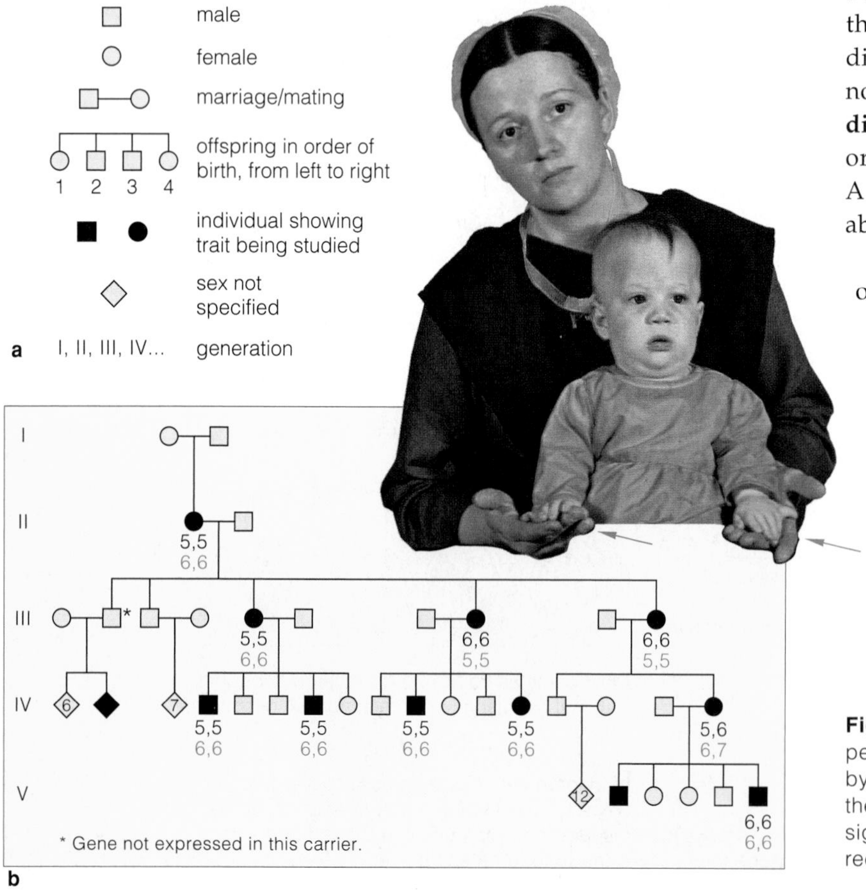

male
female
marriage/mating
offspring in order of birth, from left to right
1 2 3 4
individual showing trait being studied
sex not specified
a I, II, III, IV... generation

I
II 5,5 6,6
III 5,5 6,6 | 6,6 5,5 | 6,6 5,5
IV ⬦6 ⬦7 5,5 6,6 | 5,5 6,6 | 5,5 6,6 | 5,5 6,6 | 5,6 6,7
V ⬦2 6,6 6,6

* Gene not expressed in this carrier.
b

Figure 11.7 (**a**) Some standardized symbols used in pedigrees. (**b**) A pedigree for *polydactyly*, characterized by extra fingers, toes, or both. *Black* numerals signify the number of fingers on each hand; *blue* numerals signify the number of toes on each foot. This condition recurs as one symptom of Ellis–van Creveld syndrome.

Table 11.1   Examples of Human Genetic Disorders and Genetic Abnormalities

Disorder or Abnormality	Main Symptoms
Autosomal recessive inheritance	
Albinism	Absence of pigmentation
Blue offspring	Bright blue skin coloration
Cystic fibrosis	Excessive glandular secretions leading to tissue, organ damage
Ellis–van Creveld syndrome	Extra fingers, toes, short limbs
Fanconi anemia	Physical abnormalities, bone marrow failure
Galactosemia	Brain, liver, eye damage
Phenylketonuria (PKU)	Mental impairment
Sickle-cell anemia	Adverse pleiotropic effects on organs throughout body
Autosomal dominant inheritance	
Achondroplasia	One form of dwarfism
Camptodactyly	Rigid, bent fingers
Familial hypercholesterolemia	High cholesterol levels in blood; eventually clogged arteries
Huntington disease	Nervous system degenerates progressively, irreversibly
Marfan syndrome	Abnormal or no connective tissue
Polydactyly	Extra fingers, toes, or both
Progeria	Drastic premature aging
Neurofibromatosis	Tumors of nervous system, skin

Disorder or Abnormality	Main Symptoms
X-linked recessive inheritance	
Androgen insensitivity syndrome	XY individual but having some female traits; sterility
Color blindness	Inability to distinguish among some or all colors
Fragile X syndrome	Mental impairment
Hemophilia	Impaired blood-clotting ability
Muscular dystrophies	Progressive loss of muscle function
X-linked anhidrotic dysplasia	Mosaic skin (patches with or without sweat glands); other effects
Changes in chromosome number	
Down syndrome	Mental impairment; heart defects
Turner syndrome	Sterility; abnormal ovaries, abnormal sexual traits
Klinefelter syndrome	Sterility; mild mental impairment
XXX syndrome	Minimal abnormalities
XYY condition	Mild mental impairment or no effect
Changes in chromosome structure	
Chronic myelogenous leukemia (CML)	Overproduction of white blood cells in bone marrow; organ malfunctions
Cri-du-chat syndrome	Mental impairment; abnormally shaped larynx

Alleles that give rise to severe genetic disorders are rare in populations, because they put their bearers at risk. Why don't they disappear? Rare mutations introduce new copies of the alleles into populations. Also, in heterozygotes, a normal allele is paired with a harmful one and may cover its functions, in which case the harmful allele can be transmitted to offspring.

With these qualifications in mind, we turn next to examples of chromosomal inheritance patterns in the human population. Figure 11.8 is an early introduction to one of these examples—an autosomal dominant disorder called Huntington disease.

Pedigree analysis often reveals simple Mendelian inheritance patterns. From such patterns, specialists infer the probability that offspring will inherit certain alleles.

A genetic abnormality is a rare or less common version of a heritable trait. A genetic disorder is a heritable condition that results in mild to severe medical problems.

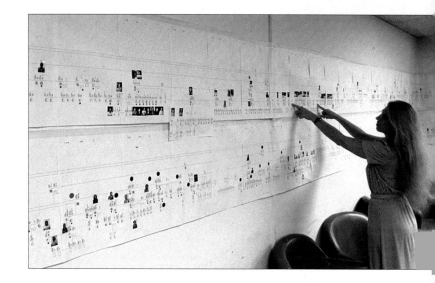

Figure 11.8 Pedigree for *Huntington disease*, a progressive degeneration of the nervous system. Researcher Nancy Wexler and her team constructed this extended family tree for nearly 10,000 Venezuelans. Their analysis of unaffected and affected individuals revealed that a dominant allele on human chromosome 4 is the culprit. Wexler has a special interest in the disease; it runs in her family.

11.5 Examples of Human Inheritance Patterns

Some human phenotypes arise from a dominant or recessive allele on an autosome or X chromosome that is inherited in simple Mendelian patterns.

AUTOSOMAL DOMINANT INHERITANCE

Figure 11.9*a* shows a typical inheritance pattern for an autosomal dominant allele. If one of the parents is heterozygous and the other homozygous, any child of theirs has a 50 percent chance of being heterozygous. The trait usually appears in every generation because the allele is expressed even in heterozygotes.

Achondroplasia is a classic example. This autosomal dominant disorder affects approximately 1 in 10,000 people. The homozygous dominants often die before birth, but heterozygotes can still reproduce. Skeletal cartilage does not form properly in achondroplasiacs. Adults have abnormally short arms and legs relative to other body parts. They are about 4 feet, 4 inches tall, as in Figure 11.9*a*. The dominant allele often has no other phenotypic effects.

In *Huntington disease*, the nervous system slowly deteriorates, and involuntary muscle action becomes more frequent. Symptoms may not start until past age thirty; those affected die in their forties or fifties. Many unknowingly transmit the gene to children, before the onset of symptoms. The mutation causing the disorder changes a protein necessary for normal development of brain cells. It is an *expansion* mutation, which ends up as multiple repeats in the same DNA segment. The repeats disrupt gene function.

A few dominant alleles that cause severe problems persist in populations because expression of the allele may not interfere with reproduction, or affected people reproduce before the symptoms become severe. Rarely, spontaneous mutations reintroduce some of them.

AUTOSOMAL RECESSIVE INHERITANCE

For some traits, inheritance patterns reveal clues that point to a recessive allele on an autosome. First, if both parents are heterozygous, any child of theirs will have a 50 percent chance of being heterozygous and a 25 percent chance of being homozygous recessive, as in Figure 11.9*b*. Second, if they are both homozygous recessive, any child of theirs will be, also.

About 1 in 100,000 newborns is homozygous for a recessive allele that causes *galactosemia*. They do not have working copies of one of the enzymes that digest lactose, so a reaction intermediate builds up to toxic levels. Normally, lactose is converted to glucose and galactose, then glucose–1–phosphate (which is broken down by glycolysis or converted to glycogen). The conversion is blocked in galactosemics (Figure 11.10).

High galactose levels can be detected in urine. The excess causes malnutrition, diarrhea, vomiting, and damage to the eyes, liver, and brain. When untreated, galactosemics typically die early. If they are quickly placed on a restricted diet excluding dairy products, they grow up symptom-free.

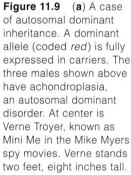

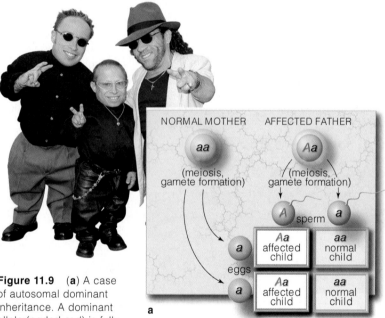

Figure 11.9 (**a**) A case of autosomal dominant inheritance. A dominant allele (coded *red*) is fully expressed in carriers. The three males shown above have achondroplasia, an autosomal dominant disorder. At center is Verne Troyer, known as Mini Me in the Mike Myers spy movies. Verne stands two feet, eight inches tall.

(**b**) An autosomal recessive pattern. In this case, both parents are heterozygous carriers of the recessive allele (coded *red*).

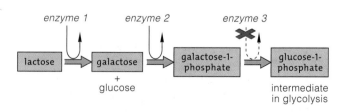

Figure 11.10 Blocked metabolic pathway in galactosemics.

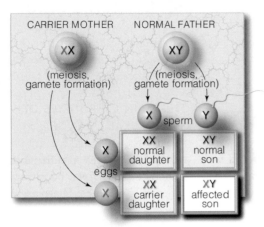

Figure 11.11 One pattern for X-linked recessive inheritance. In this case, the mother carries a recessive allele on one of her X chromosomes (*red*).

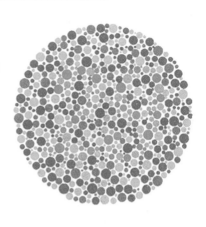

Figure 11.12 One of many standardized tests that can reveal color blindness. If you cannot see the red "29" inside this circle, then you may have some form of red–green color blindness.

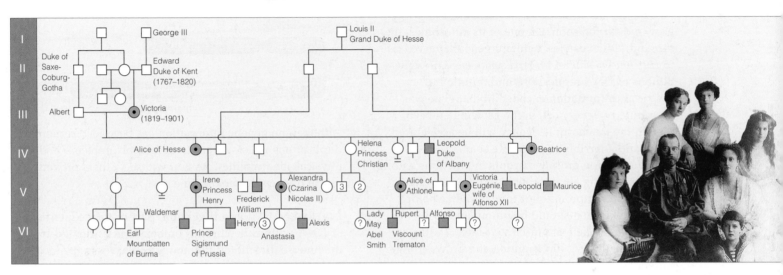

Figure 11.13 Partial pedigree for Queen Victoria's descendants, including carriers and affected males who inherited the X-linked allele for hemophilia A. At one time, the recessive allele was present in eighteen of Victoria's sixty-nine descendants, who sometimes intermarried. Of the Russian royal family members shown, the mother was a carrier; Crown Prince Alexis was hemophilic.

X-LINKED INHERITANCE

An X-linked gene is found only on the X chromosome. In X-linked genetic disorders, females are not affected as often as males, because a dominant allele on their other X chromosome can mask a recessive one (Figure 11.11). A son cannot inherit a X-linked allele from his father, but a daughter can. When she does, each of her sons has a 50 percent chance of inheriting it.

Color blindness is an inability to distinguish among some or all colors. It results from several common recessive disorders associated with X-linked genes. Mutant forms of the genes change the light-absorbing capacity of sensory receptors inside the eyes.

Normally, humans can detect differences among 150 colors. A person who is red–green color blind sees fewer than 25 colors; some or all of the receptors that respond to visible light of red and green wavelengths are weakened or absent. Others confuse red and green colors or see shades of gray instead of green. Tests can identify affected people (Figure 11.12).

The trait is more common in men, but heterozygous women also show symptoms. Can you explain why?

Hemophilia A, a blood-clotting disorder, is one case of X-linked recessive inheritance. Normally, a clotting mechanism quickly stops bleeding from minor injuries. Some clotting proteins are products of genes on the X chromosome. Bleeding is prolonged in males with one of these mutant X-linked genes. About 1 in 7,000 males is affected. In heterozygous females, clotting time is close to normal.

The frequency of hemophilia A was high in royal families of nineteenth-century Europe, in which close relatives often married (Figure 11.13).

Genetic analyses of family pedigrees have revealed simple Mendelian inheritance patterns for certain traits, as well as for many genetic disorders that arise from expression of alleles on an autosome or X chromosome.

11.6 Too Young, Too Old

FOCUS ON HEALTH

Sometimes textbook examples of the human condition seem a bit abstract, so take a moment to think about two boys who were too young to be old.

Imagine being ten years old with a mind trapped in a body that is getting a bit more shriveled, more frail—*old*—every day. You are barely tall enough to peer over the top of the kitchen counter; you weigh less than thirty-five pounds. Already you are bald and have a crinkled nose. Maybe you have a few more years to live. Would you, like Mickey Hayes and Fransie Geringer, still be able to laugh?

Of every 8 million newborn humans, one will grow old far too soon. On one of its autosomes, that rare individual carries a mutant gene that gives rise to *Hutchinson–Gilford progeria syndrome*. Through billions of DNA replications and mitotic cell divisions, information encoded in that gene was distributed to every cell in the growing embryo, then in the newborn. Its legacy will be accelerated aging and a terribly reduced life span.

The mutation grossly disrupts interactions among genes that bring about growth and development. Observable symptoms start to materialize before age two. Skin that should be plump and resilient starts to thin. Skeletal muscles weaken. Tissues in limb bones that should lengthen and grow stronger soften. Hair loss is pronounced; premature baldness is inevitable (Figure 11.14). There are no documented cases of progeria running in families, so we suspect it arises from spontaneous mutations. Probably the mutated gene is dominant over a normal allele on the homologous chromosome.

Most progeriacs expect to die in their early teens, from strokes or heart attacks. These final insults are brought on by a hardening of the wall of arteries, a condition typical of advanced age. When Mickey turned eighteen, he was the oldest living progeriac. Fransie was seventeen when he died.

Figure 11.14
Two boys who met at a gathering of progeriacs at Disneyland, California, when they were not yet ten years old.

11.7 Altered Chromosomes

Rarely, chromosome structure changes spontaneously or by exposure to chemicals or irradiation. Some changes can be detected. Many have severe or lethal outcomes.

THE MAIN CATEGORIES OF STRUCTURAL CHANGE

DUPLICATION Even normal chromosomes have gene sequences that have been repeated several to many thousands of times. These are **duplications**:

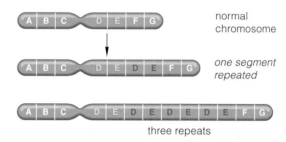

normal chromosome

one segment repeated

three repeats

Although no genetic information has been lost, certain duplications cause a variety of neural problems and physical abnormalities. As you will see, others proved useful over evolutionary time.

INVERSION With an **inversion**, part of the sequence of DNA within the chromosome becomes oriented in the reverse direction, with no molecular loss:

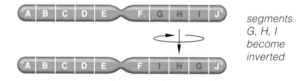

segments G, H, I become inverted

An inversion is not a problem if it does not disrupt a crucial gene region. But it mispairs during meiosis, so it can lead to chromosome deletions in gametes. Some people don't even know they have an inverted chromosome region until they have kids.

DELETION Whether it happens as a consequence of inversion or of an attack by an environmental agent, a **deletion** is the loss of a portion of a chromosome:

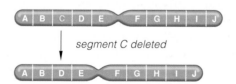

segment C deleted

In mammals, most deletions cause serious disorders, or are lethal. Why? Missing or incomplete genes disrupt the body's program of growth, development, and maintenance activities. For example, one deletion

---

from human chromosome 5 results in an abnormally shaped larynx and mental impairment. When affected infants cry, they produce sounds like a cat's meow. Hence the name of the disorder, *cri-du-chat*, which means cat-cry in French. Sounds become normal later on. Figure 11.15 shows an affected boy.

TRANSLOCATION   In **translocation**, a broken part of a chromosome is attached to a different chromosome. Most translocations are reciprocal; both chromosomes exchange broken parts:

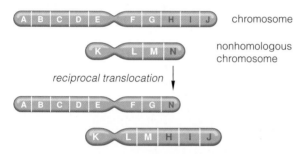

If the chromosome's genetic information does not get garbled, translocations may not pose a threat to the individual or its offspring. However, translocations can cause severe problems, including some sarcomas, lymphomas, myelomas, and leukemias. One notorious reciprocal translocation results in the Philadelphia chromosome, which is named after the city in which it was discovered. It is a killer (Figure 11.16).

DOES CHROMOSOME STRUCTURE EVOLVE?

Alterations in the structure of chromosomes generally are not good and tend to be selected against. Even so, over evolutionary time, many alterations with neutral effects became built into the DNA of all species.

We can expect that some of the duplications turned out to be adaptive. Perhaps some copies continued to specify an unaltered gene product even as others underwent modification. Think back on hemoglobin's polypeptide chains (Section 3.6). In humans and other primates, several globin genes are strikingly similar. They may have evolved as an outcome of duplications, mutations, and transpositions of the same gene. With small structural differences, the different globins have slightly different capacities to bind and then transport oxygen under a range of cellular conditions.

In addition, alterations in chromosome structure may have contributed to differences among closely related organisms, such as apes and humans. Consider this: Eighteen of the twenty-three pairs of human chromosomes are almost identical with chimpanzee

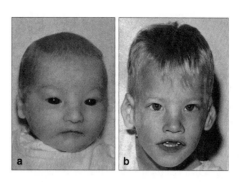

Figure 11.15 (**a**) Male infant who developed cri-du-chat syndrome. His ears are low on the side of the head relative to the eyes. (**b**) Same boy, four years later. By this age, affected humans stop making mewing sounds typical of the syndrome.

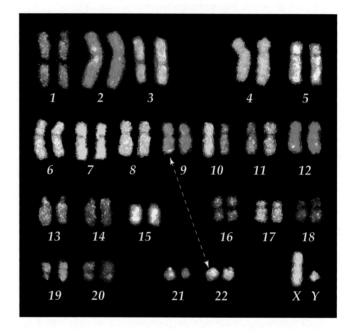

Figure 11.16 A reciprocal translocation, as revealed by spectral karyotyping. The Philadelphia chromosome is longer than its normal counterpart, human chromosome 9.

By chance, chromosomes 9 and 22 broke in a stem cell in bone marrow. Each broken part was reattached on the wrong one. At the broken end of chromosome 9, a gene with a role in cell division fused with the control region of a gene at chromosome 22's broken end. Overexpression of the mutant gene leads to uncontrolled divisions of white blood cells. A type of cancer, chronic myelogenous leukemia (CML), is the outcome.

and gorilla chromosomes. The other five chromosomes differ only at inverted and translocated regions.

On rare occasions, a segment of a chromosome may become duplicated, inverted, moved to a new location, or deleted.

Most chromosome changes are harmful or lethal. Others have been conserved over evolutionary time; they confer adaptive advantages or have had neutral effects.

11.8 Changes in the Chromosome Number

Occasionally, abnormal events occur before or during cell division, and gametes and new individuals end up with the wrong chromosome number. Consequences range from minor to lethal physical changes.

In **aneuploidy**, cells usually have one extra or one less chromosome. Autosomal aneuploidy is usually fatal for humans and is linked to most miscarriages. In **polyploidy**, cells have three or more of each type of chromosome. Half of all species of flowering plants, some insects, fishes, and other animals are polyploid.

Nearly all changes in chromosome number arise through **nondisjunction**, whereby one or more pairs of chromosomes don't separate as they should during mitosis or meiosis. Figure 11.17 shows an example.

The chromosome number also may change during fertilization. Suppose a normal gamete fuses by chance with an $n + 1$ gamete, with one extra chromosome. The new individual will be trisomic ($2n + 1$), with three of one type of chromosome and two of every other type. If an $n - 1$ gamete fuses with a normal n gamete, the new individual will be monosomic ($2n - 1$). Mitotic divisions perpetuate the mistake when the embryo is growing in size and developing.

AUTOSOMAL CHANGE AND DOWN SYNDROME

A few trisomics are born alive, but only trisomy 21 individuals reach adulthood. A newborn with three chromosomes 21 will develop *Down syndrome*. This autosomal disorder is the most frequent type of altered chromosome number in humans; it occurs once in every 800 to 1,000 births. It affects more than 350,000 people in the United States. Figure 11.17*b* shows a karyotype for a trisomic 21 female. About 95 percent of all cases arise through nondisjunction at meiosis.

Affected individuals have upward-slanting eyes, a fold of skin that starts at the inner corner of each eye, a deep crease across each palm and foot sole, one (not two) horizontal furrows on their fifth fingers, and somewhat flattened facial features. Not all of these symptoms develop in every individual.

That said, trisomic 21 individuals have moderate to severe mental impairment and heart defects. Their skeleton develops abnormally, so older children have shorter body parts, loose joints, and misaligned hip, finger, and toe bones. Muscles and reflexes are weak. Speech and other motor skills develop slowly. With medical care, they live fifty-five years, on average.

The incidence of nondisjunction rises as mothers become older (Figure 11.18). It may originate with the father, but less often. Trisomy 21 is one of hundreds

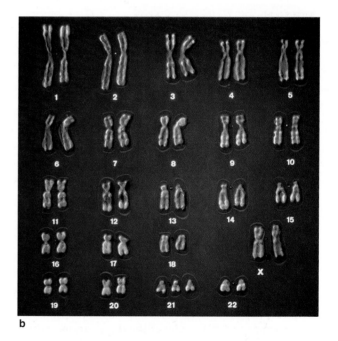

b

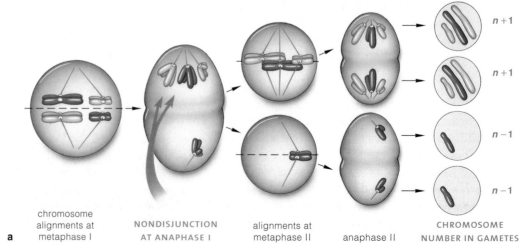

Figure 11.17 (**a**) One example of how nondisjunction arises. Of the two pairs of homologous chromosomes shown here, one fails to separate during anaphase I of meiosis. The chromosome number is altered in the gametes that form after meiosis.

(**b**) An actual case of nondisjunction. This karyotype reveals the trisomic 21 condition of a human female.

a   chromosome alignments at metaphase I   **NONDISJUNCTION AT ANAPHASE I**   alignments at metaphase II   anaphase II   **CHROMOSOME NUMBER IN GAMETES**

$n + 1$
$n + 1$
$n - 1$
$n - 1$

of conditions that can be detected through prenatal diagnosis (Section 11.9). With early special training and medical intervention, individuals still can take part in normal activities. As a group, they tend to be cheerful and sociable.

CHANGES IN THE SEX CHROMOSOME NUMBER

Nondisjunction also causes most of the alterations in the number of X and Y chromosomes. The frequency of such changes is 1 in 400 live births. Most often they lead to difficulties in learning and motor skills, such as speech, although problems can be so subtle that the underlying cause is not even diagnosed.

FEMALE SEX CHROMOSOME ABNORMALITIES *Turner syndrome* individuals have an X chromosome and no corresponding X or Y chromosome (XO). About 1 in 2,500 to 10,000 newborn girls are XO. Nondisjunction originating with the father accounts for 75 percent of the cases. Yet cases are few, compared to other sex chromosome abnormalities. At least 98 percent of XO embryos may spontaneously abort early in pregnancy.

Despite the near lethality, XO survivors are not as disadvantaged as other aneuploids. On average, they are only four feet, eight inches high, but they are well proportioned (Figure 11.19). Most can't make enough sex hormones; they don't have functional ovaries. This affects development of secondary sexual traits, such as breast enlargement. A few eggs form in ovaries but are destroyed by the time these girls are two years old.

Another example: A few females inherit three, four, or five X chromosomes. The *XXX syndrome* occurs at a frequency of about 1 in 1,000 live births. Adults are fertile. Except for slight learning difficulties, most fall within the normal range of social behavior.

MALE SEX CHROMOSOME ABNORMALITIES About one of every 500 to 2,000 males inherits one Y and two or more X chromosomes, mainly through nondisjunction. Most have an XXY mosaic genotype. About 67 percent of those affected inherited the extra chromosome from their mother.

The resulting *Klinefelter syndrome* develops during puberty. XXY males tend to be overweight and tall. The testes and the prostate gland usually are smaller than average. Many XXY males are within the normal range of intelligence, although some have short-term memory loss and learning disabilities. They make less testosterone and more estrogen than normal males, with feminizing effects. Sperm counts are low. Hair is sparse, the voice is pitched high, and the breasts are a

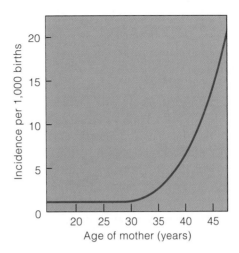

Figure 11.18 Relationship between the frequency of Down syndrome and mother's age at childbirth. The data are from a study of 1,119 affected children. The risk of having a trisomic 21 baby rises with the mother's age. This may seem odd, because about 80 percent of trisomic 21 individuals are born to women not yet 35 years old. However, these women are in the age categories with the highest fertility rates, and they simply have more babies.

bit enlarged. Testosterone injections starting at puberty can reverse the feminized traits.

About 1 in 500 to 1,000 males has one X and two Y chromosomes, an *XYY condition*. They tend to be taller than average, with mild mental impairment, but most are phenotypically normal. XYY males were once thought to be genetically predisposed to a life of crime. This misguided view was based on a sampling error—too few cases among narrowly selected groups, such as prison inmates. The same researchers gathered the karyotypes *and* personal histories. Fanning the stereotype was a report that a mass murderer of young nurses was XYY. He wasn't.

In 1976 a Danish geneticist reported on a study of 4,139 tall males, all twenty-six years old, who had reported to their draft board. Besides giving results of physical examinations and intelligence tests, those draft records held clues to their social and economic status, education, and criminal convictions, if any. Twelve of the males were XYY, which meant there were more than 4,000 males in the control group. The only finding was that mentally impaired, tall males who engage in criminal activity are just more likely to get caught—irrespective of karyotype.

The majority of XXY, XXX, and XYY children may not even be properly diagnosed. Some are dismissed unfairly as being underachievers.

Figure 11.19 One young girl with Turner syndrome.

Nondisjunction in germ cells, gametes, or early embryonic cells changes the number of autosomes or the number of sex chromosomes. The change affects development and the resulting phenotypes.

Nondisjunction at meiosis causes most sex chromosome abnormalities, which typically lead to subtle difficulties with learning, and speech and other motor skills.

11.9 Prospects in Human Genetics

With the arrival of their newborn, parents typically ask, "Is our baby normal?" Quite naturally, they want their baby to be free of genetic disorders, and most babies are. What are the options when they are not?

BIOETHICAL QUESTIONS

Humans do not view diseases and genetic disorders the same way. We attack diseases with antibiotics, surgery, and other tactics. But how do we attack a heritable "enemy" that can be transmitted to our own offspring?

Should we institute regional, national, or global programs to identify people who may carry harmful alleles? Should they be told that they are "defective" and might bestow some disorder on their children? Who decides which alleles are bad? Should society bear the cost of treating all genetic disorders of all individuals, before and after birth? If so, should society also have a say in whether an embryo that bears harmful alleles will be born at all, or aborted? An **abortion** is the expulsion of a pre-term embryo or fetus from the uterus.

As you most likely have learned by now, such questions are the tip of an ethical iceberg.

SOME OF THE OPTIONS

GENETIC SCREENING Through large-scale screening programs, affected individuals or carriers of some harmful allele can be detected early enough to start preventive measures before symptoms develop. For instance, most hospitals in the United States routinely screen newborns for PKU, described next, so we now see fewer individuals with symptoms of the disorder.

PHENOTYPIC TREATMENTS The symptoms of a number of genetic disorders can be minimized or alleviated by surgery, drugs, hormone replacement therapy, or in some cases by controlling diet.

For instance, dietary control works for individuals affected by *phenylketonuria*, or PKU. In this case, a homozygous recessive mutation impairs an enzyme that converts the amino acid phenylalanine to tyrosine. Phenylalanine builds up and is diverted into other pathways. Compounds that impair brain function form as a result. Affected people can lead relatively normal lives by restricting phenylalanine intake. For example, they can avoid soft drinks and other food products sweetened with aspartame, a compound that contains phenylalanine.

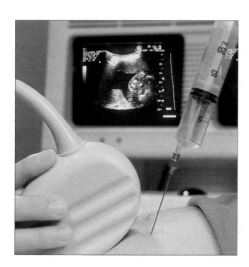

Figure 11.20 Amniocentesis, a prenatal diagnostic tool.

A pregnant woman's doctor holds an ultrasound emitter against her abdomen while drawing a sample of amniotic fluid into a syringe. He monitors the path of the needle with an ultrasound screen, in the background. Then he directs the needle into the amniotic sac that holds the developing fetus and withdraws twenty milliliters or so of amniotic fluid. The fluid contains fetal cells and wastes that can be analyzed for genetic disorders.

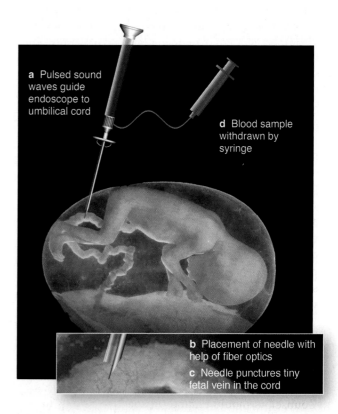

a Pulsed sound waves guide endoscope to umbilical cord

d Blood sample withdrawn by syringe

b Placement of needle with help of fiber optics

c Needle punctures tiny fetal vein in the cord

Figure 11.21 Fetoscopy for prenatal diagnosis.

PRENATAL DIAGNOSIS Methods of *prenatal diagnosis* are used to determine the sex of embryos or fetuses and to screen for more than 100 genetic abnormalities. *Prenatal* means before birth. *Embryo* is a term that applies until eight weeks after fertilization, after which the term *fetus* is appropriate.

Suppose a forty-five-year-old woman is pregnant and worries about Down syndrome. Between 8 and 12 weeks after conception, such women often request *amniocentesis* (Figure 11.20). A tiny sample of fluid inside the amnion, a membranous sac enclosing the fetus, is withdrawn. Some cells shed by the fetus are suspended in the sample. The cells are analyzed for many genetic disorders, such as Down syndrome, sickle-cell anemia, and cystic fibrosis.

Chorionic villi sampling (CVS) is another procedure. A clinician withdraws a few cells from the chorion, a membranous sac that encloses the amnion and helps form the placenta. Unlike amniocentesis, CVS can yield results as early as eight weeks into pregnancy.

A developing fetus can be seen with an endoscope, a fiber-optic device. During *fetoscopy*, pulsed sound waves are used to scan the uterus and locate parts of the fetus, umbilical cord, or placenta (Figure 11.21). A sample of fetal blood can be drawn, so fetoscopy also is useful to diagnose blood cell disorders such as sickle-cell anemia and hemophilia.

There are risks to a fetus associated with all three procedures, including punctures or infection. Also, if the amnion does not reseal itself fast, too much fluid can leak out and endanger the fetus. Amniocentesis raises the risk of miscarriage by 1 to 2 percent. With CVS, placental development may be compromised, and 0.3 percent of newborns will have missing or underdeveloped fingers and toes. Fetoscopy raises the risk of a miscarriage by 2 to 10 percent.

GENETIC COUNSELING Parents-to-be can seek *genetic counseling* to compare risks of diagnostic procedures against the risk that their child will be affected by a severe genetic disorder. But they also should be told about the small overall risk of 3 percent that *any* child might have some kind of birth disorder. And they should also consider whether the risk becomes greater with increased age of the potential mother or father.

Suppose a first child or close relative has a severe disorder. Genetic counseling may involve diagnosis of parental genotypes, pedigrees, and genetic testing for known disorders. Using this information, geneticists can predict the risk for disorders in future children. Counselors should remind prospective parents that the same risk usually applies to each pregnancy.

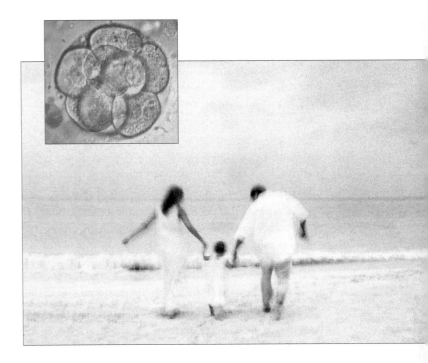

Figure 11.22 Eight-cell and multicelled stages of human development.

REGARDING ABORTION What happens after prenatal diagnosis reveals a serious problem? Do prospective parents opt for an induced abortion? We can only say here that they must weigh awareness of the severity of the disorder against their ethical and religious beliefs. Worse, they must play out their personal tragedy on a larger stage dominated by a nationwide battle between highly vocal "pro-life" and "pro-choice" factions. We return to this topic in Section 38.12.

PREIMPLANTATION DIAGNOSIS This procedure relies on **in vitro fertilization**. Sperm and eggs taken from prospective parents are mixed in a sterile culture medium. One or more eggs may be fertilized. If so, within forty-eight hours, mitotic cell divisions may convert it into a ball of eight cells (Figure 11.22 and Section 38.12). According to one view, the tiny, free-floating ball is a *pre*-pregnancy stage. Like unfertilized eggs discarded monthly from a woman, it has not attached to the uterus. All of its cells have the same genes; all are not yet committed to being specialized for any organ. Doctors take one of the undifferentiated cells and analyze its genes. If it has no detectable genetic defects, the ball is inserted into the uterus.

Some couples at risk of passing on cystic fibrosis, muscular dystrophy, or other genetic disorders have opted for the procedure. Many of the resulting "*test-tube*" *babies* have been born in good health.

Summary

Section 11.1 Human somatic cells are diploid (2*n*), with twenty-three pairs of homologous chromosomes. One is a pairing of sex chromosomes—XX in females, XY in males. All other chromosomes are autosomes, which are the same in both sexes. Crossing over in mitosis produces new combinations of alleles.

Section 11.2 Karyotyping is a diagnostic tool that makes a preparation of an individual's metaphase chromosomes and arranges them by their defining features, such as centromere location, length, and shape.

Section 11.3 The theory of independent assortment does not explain all gene combinations, because pairs of homologous chromosomes swap segments by crossing over during prophase I of meiosis. This frequent and expected event invites genetic recombination, or new combinations of alleles in chromosomes. The farther apart two genes are on the same chromosome, the more likely they will undergo crossing over.

Section 11.4 Geneticists often use pedigrees, or charts of genetic connections in a lineage over time, to estimate probabilities that offspring will inherit a given trait.

Sections 11.5, 11.6 Dominant or recessive alleles on either an autosome or X chromosome can be tracked when they are inherited in simple Mendelian patterns.

Section 11.7 On rare occasions, a chromosome's structure changes. A segment is deleted, inverted, moved to a new location (translocated), or duplicated. Most alterations are harmful or lethal. However, many have accumulated in the chromosomes of all species over evolutionary time. Either they had neutral effects or they later proved to be useful.

Section 11.8 The parental chromosome number can change, as by nondisjunction during meiosis. Aneuploids have one extra or one less chromosome; most autosomal aneuploids die before birth. About half of all flowering plants and some insects, fishes, and other animals are polyploid (three or more of each type of chromosome). More often, changes in number cause genetic disorders.

Section 11.9 Phenotypic treatments, genetic screening, genetic counseling, prenatal diagnosis, and preimplantation diagnosis are some options available for potential parents at risk of having children who will develop a genetic disorder.

Self-Quiz
Answers in Appendix III

1. The probability of a crossover occurring between two genes on the same chromosome is _____ .
   a. unrelated to the distance between them
   b. increased if they are close together
   c. increased if they are far apart

2. Genes on the same chromosome are _____ .
   a. linked   c. homologous   e. all of the
   b. identical alleles d. autosomes   above

3. Chromosome structure can be altered by a _____ .
   a. deletion   c. inversion   e. all of the
   b. duplication   d. translocation   above

4. A recognized set of symptoms that characterize a specific disorder is a _____ .
   a. syndrome   b. disease   c. pedigree

5. Most genes for human traits are located on _____ .
   a. the X chromosome   c. autosomes
   b. the Y chromosome   d. dominant chromosomes

6. Nondisjunction at meiosis can result in _____ .
   a. karyotyping   c. duplications
   b. crossing over   d. aneuploidy

7. Turner syndrome (XO) is an example of _____ .
   a. dominance   c. aneuploidy
   b. polyploidy   d. gene linkage

8. Match the chromosome terms appropriately.
   _____ crossing over   a. number and defining
   _____ deletion   features of an individual's
   _____ nondisjunction   metaphase chromosomes
   _____ translocation   b. segment of a chromosome
   _____ karyotype   moves to a nonhomologous
   _____ linkage group   chromosome
                          c. disrupts gene linkages
                          d. one outcome: gametes with
                             wrong chromosome number
                          e. a chromosome segment lost
                          f. all genes on a chromosome

Genetics Problems
Answers in Appendix IV

1. Human females are XX and males are XY.
   a. Does a male inherit the X from his mother or father?
   b. With respect to X-linked alleles, how many different types of gametes can a male produce?
   c. If a female is homozygous for an X-linked allele, how many types of gametes can she produce with respect to that allele?
   d. If a female is heterozygous for an X-linked allele, how many types of gametes might she produce with respect to that allele?

2. Marfan syndrome follows a pattern of autosomal dominant inheritance. What is the chance that any child will inherit the dominant allele if one parent does not carry the allele and the other is heterozygous for it?

3. Somatic cells of individuals with Down syndrome usually have an extra chromosome 21; they contain forty-seven chromosomes.
   a. At which stages of meiosis I and II could a mistake alter the chromosome number?
   b. A few individuals have forty-six chromosomes, including two normal-appearing chromosomes 21 and a longer-than-normal chromosome 14. Speculate on how this chromosome abnormality may have arisen.

4. Much of what we know about human genetics comes from studies of experimental organisms. For example, the embryologist Thomas Morgan discovered a genetic basis for a relationship between sex determination and some nonsexual traits in *Drosophila melanogaster*. This fruit fly

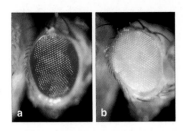

Figure 11.23 The common fruit fly *Drosophila melanogaster*, with (**a**) wild-type red eyes and (**b**) white eyes. (**c**) One experimental search for a *Drosophila* sex-linked gene.

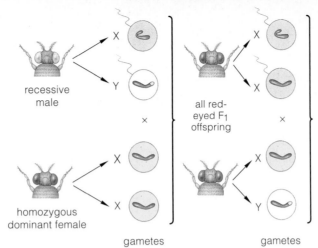

recessive male

homozygous dominant female

gametes

all red-eyed F₁ offspring

gametes

1/2 1/4♂ 1/4♀ 1/4♂ 1/4♀ 1/2

White-eyed males show up in F₂ generation.

can live in small bottles on agar, cornmeal, molasses, and yeast. A female lays hundreds of eggs in a few days and offspring reproduce in less than two weeks. In a single year, Morgan was able to follow traits through nearly thirty generations of thousands of flies.

At first all the flies were wild-type for eye color; they had red eyes. Then mutation gave rise to a recessive allele for eye color, and a white-eyed male turned up. Morgan established true-breeding strains of white-eyed males and females for *reciprocal crosses*. In the first of such paired crosses, one parent displays the trait of interest. In the second cross, the other parent displays it.

Morgan let white-eyed males mate with homozygous red-eyed females. All F₁ offspring had red eyes, and some F₂ males had white eyes (Figure 11.23). Then Morgan mated true-breeding red-eyed males with white-eyed females. Half the F₁ offspring were red-eyed females, and half were white-eyed males. Also, of the F₂ offspring, 1/4 were red-eyed females, 1/4 white-eyed females, 1/4 red-eyed males, and 1/4 white-eyed males.

Test results pointed to a relationship between an eye-color gene and sex determination. Was the locus on a sex chromosome? Which one? Before answering, think about male and female sex chromosome pairings, and how a dominant allele can mask a recessive one.

5. Does the phenotype indicated by red circles and squares in this pedigree show a Mendelian inheritance pattern that's autosomal dominant, autosomal recessive, or X-linked?

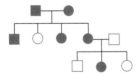

6. One of the *muscular dystrophies*, a category of genetic disorders, is due to a recessive X-linked allele. Usually, symptoms start in childhood. Gradual, progressive loss of muscle function leads to death, usually by age twenty or so. Unlike color blindness, the disorder is nearly always restricted to males. Suggest why.

7. In the human population, mutation of two genes on the X chromosome causes two types of X-linked hemophilia (A and B). In a few cases, a woman is heterozygous for both mutant alleles (one on each of the X chromosomes). All of her sons should have either hemophilia A or B.

However, on very rare occasions, one of these women gives birth to a son who does not have hemophilia, and his one X chromosome does not have either mutant allele. Explain how such an X chromosome could arise.

IMPACTS, ISSUES   *Goodbye, Dolly*

In 1997, geneticist Ian Wilmut made headlines when he coaxed part of a specialized cell from an adult sheep into becoming part of the first cell of an embryo. His team had been removing the nucleus from unfertilized eggs and slipping a nucleus from a specialized cell of an adult animal into them. Of hundreds of modified eggs, one developed into a whole animal.

The cloned lamb, named Dolly, grew up (Figure 12.1). In time she gave birth to six lambs of her own. Since then, researchers all over the world have cloned other kinds of mammals, including mice, cows, pigs, rabbits, a mule, and cats.

Wilmut and Dolly were back in the limelight in early 2002 with bad news. By age five, Dolly had become fat and arthritic. Sheep usually don't get old-age symptoms until they are about ten years old. In 2003, Dolly developed a progressive lung infection and was put to sleep.

Did Dolly develop health problems simply because she was a clone? Earlier studies of her telomeres had raised suspicions. Telomeres are short segments that cap the ends of chromosomes and stabilize them. They get shorter and shorter as an animal ages. When Dolly was only two years old, her telomeres were as short as those of a six-year-old sheep—the exact age of the animal from which she had been cloned.

Cloning mammals is difficult. Not many nuclear transfers are successful. Most individuals that develop from modified eggs die before birth or shortly afterward.

Figure 12.1   (a) Where the molecular revolution started—James Watson and Francis Crick posing in 1953 by their newly unveiled structural model of DNA, the molecule of inheritance in all living cells. (b) The now-deceased Dolly. She helped awaken society to the implications of where the molecular revolution is taking us.

the big picture

DNA's Function   Early experiments with viruses and bacteria revealed that DNA is the hereditary material in living things. Biochemical analysis helped show that DNA has two strands, helically coiled in a precise pattern.

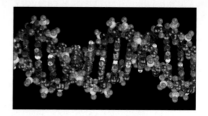

DNA's Structure   In all living things, the structure of DNA arises from base pairing between adenosine and thymine, guanine and cytosine. The sequence of bases along its two strands is unique for each species. It is the foundation for life's diversity.

It took almost seven hundred attempts to get one live clone of a guar, a wild ox on the endangered species list. Less than two days after his foster mother gave birth, he died from complications following an infection.

Surviving clones typically have health problems. Like Dolly, many become unusually overweight as they age. Other clones are exceptionally large from birth or have some enlarged organs. Cloned mice develop lung and liver problems, and almost all die prematurely. Cloned pigs have heart problems, they limp, and one never did develop a tail or, worse still, an anus.

Physically moving a nucleus from one cell to another is just part of the challenge. Most genes in an adult cell are inactive. They have to be reprogrammed or switched on in controlled ways in an unfertilized egg. So far, not all genes in clones are being properly activated.

Some people want to put a stop to cloning complex animals, saying the risk of bringing defective ones into the world troubles them deeply. Others want research to continue because the potential benefits are enormous. However, nearly all agree that cloning humans would be an outrage.

Think about these issues as you read through the rest of the chapters in this unit of the book. They deal with how cells replicate and repair their DNA, how genes are expressed, and what happens when things go wrong. They also invite you to reflect on how researchers are programming these molecular events in previously unimaginable ways.

 How Would You Vote?

Animal cloning experiments often produce abnormal animals, but cloning research may also result in new drugs and organ replacements for human patients. Should animal cloning be banned? See the Media Menu for details, then vote online.

How DNA Is Replicated   During the DNA replication process, the two strands of a double-stranded DNA molecule unwind from each other. Each serves as the template for assembly of a new strand with a complementary base sequence.

Reprogramming DNA   With recent advances in nuclear transfer techniques, researchers have been able to reprogram the DNA of specialized cells to make exact genetic replicas, or clones, of adult mammals.

12.1 The Hunt for Fame, Fortune, and DNA

With this chapter, we turn to investigations that led to our understanding of DNA. The chapter is more than a march through details of DNA's structure and function. It also reveals how ideas are generated in science.

EARLY AND PUZZLING CLUES

In the 1800s, Johann Miescher was collecting cells from the pus of open wounds and sperm cells from a fish. Such cells have little cytoplasm, which makes it easier to isolate their nuclear material. Miescher, a physician, wanted to identify the composition of the nucleus. In time, he isolated an acidic compound that had a bit of phosphorus. He had discovered what became known as **deoxyribonucleic acid**, or **DNA**.

Now fast-forward to 1928. An army medical officer, Frederick Griffith, wanted to develop a vaccine against the bacterium *Streptococcus pneumoniae*, a major cause of pneumonia. He did not succeed, but he isolated and cultured two strains that unexpectedly shed light on mechanisms of heredity. Colonies of one strain had a rough surface appearance; colonies of the other strain appeared smooth. Griffith designated the strains *R* and *S*. He then used them in a series of four experiments, as shown in Figure 12.2.

First, he injected mice with live *R* cells. The mice did not develop pneumonia. *The R strain was harmless.*

Second, he injected other mice with live *S* cells. The mice died. Blood samples from them teemed with live *S* cells. *The S strain was pathogenic; it caused the disease.*

Third, he killed *S* cells by exposing them to high temperature. *Mice injected with dead S cells did not die.*

Fourth, he mixed live *R* cells with heat-killed *S* cells. He injected them into mice. The mice died—*and blood samples drawn from them teemed with live S cells!*

What went on in the fourth experiment? Maybe heat-killed *S* cells in the mix weren't really dead. But if that were so, then the mice injected with just the heat-killed *S* cells in experiment 3 would have died. Or maybe the harmless *R* cells had mutated into a killer strain. But if that were so, then mice injected with just *R* cells in experiment 1 would have died.

The simplest explanation was this: *Heat had killed the S cells but did not destroy their hereditary material—including the part that specified "how to cause infection."* Somehow, that material had been transferred from the dead *S* cells into living *R* cells, which put it to use.

After later tests, it was clear that the transformation was permanently heritable. Even after a few hundred generations, *S* cell descendants were still infectious.

What was the hereditary material that caused the transformation? Scientists started looking in earnest, but most were thinking "proteins." Because heritable traits are diverse, they assumed the molecules of inheritance had to be structurally diverse, too. Proteins, they said, could be built from unlimited mixes of twenty kinds of amino acids. Other molecules just seemed too simple.

But Griffith's results intrigued Oswald Avery, who went on to transform the harmless bacterial cells with extracts of killed pathogens. When he added protein-digesting enzymes to the extracts, bacterial cells were still transformed. However, when he added an enzyme that digests DNA but not protein to the extracts, the cells were *not* transformed. DNA was looking good.

CONFIRMATION OF DNA FUNCTION

By the 1950s, molecular detectives were using viruses for experiments. **Bacteriophages**, which infect certain bacteria, were the viruses of choice. These infectious particles contain information on how to build new virus particles. At some point after they infect a host cell, viral enzymes take over its metabolic machinery. And then the machinery starts synthesizing substances necessary to make more virus particles.

As researchers knew, some bacteriophages consist only of DNA and a protein coat. Also, micrographs revealed that the coat remains on the *outer surface* of infected cells. Were the viruses injecting only hereditary material into cells? If so, was the material protein, DNA, or both? Figure 12.3 outlines just two of many experiments that pointed to DNA.

① Mice injected with live cells of harmless strain *R*

② Mice injected with live cells of killer strain *S*

③ Mice injected with heat-killed *S* cells

④ Mice injected with live *R* cells plus heat-killed *S* cells

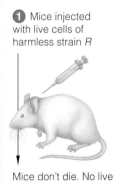
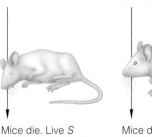
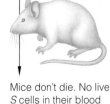
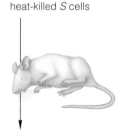

Mice don't die. No live *R* cells in their blood

Mice die. Live *S* cells in their blood

Mice don't die. No live *S* cells in their blood

Mice die. Live *S* cells in their blood

Figure 12.2 Summary of results of Fred Griffith's experiments with *Streptococcus pneumoniae* and laboratory mice.

Read Me First!
and watch the narrated animation on
the Hershey–Chase experiments

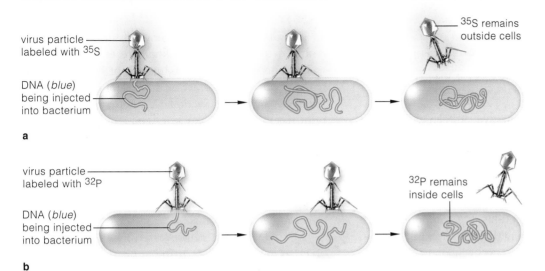

virus particle labeled with ^{35}S

DNA (*blue*) being injected into bacterium

^{35}S remains outside cells

a

virus particle labeled with ^{32}P

DNA (*blue*) being injected into bacterium

^{32}P remains inside cells

b

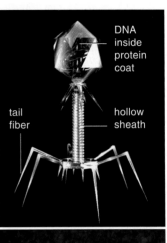

DNA inside protein coat

tail fiber

hollow sheath

micrograph of virus particles injecting DNA into an *E. coli* cell

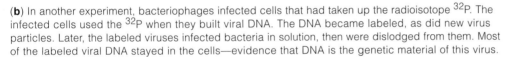

Figure 12.3 Example of the landmark experiments that tested whether genetic material resides in bacteriophage DNA, proteins, or both. As Alfred Hershey and Martha Chase knew, sulfur (S) but not phosphorus (P) is present in proteins, and phosphorus but not sulfur is present in DNA.

(**a**) In one experiment, bacterial cells were grown on a culture medium with a tracer, the radioisotope ^{35}S. The cells used the ^{35}S when they built proteins. Bacteriophages infected the labeled cells, which started making viral proteins. So the proteins, and new virus particles, became labeled with the ^{35}S. The labeled virus particles infected a new batch of unlabeled cells. The mixture was whirred in a kitchen blender. Whirring dislodged the viral protein coats from infected cells. Chemical analysis revealed the presence of labeled protein in the solution but only traces of it inside the cells.

(**b**) In another experiment, bacteriophages infected cells that had taken up the radioisotope ^{32}P. The infected cells used the ^{32}P when they built viral DNA. The DNA became labeled, as did new virus particles. Later, the labeled viruses infected bacteria in solution, then were dislodged from them. Most of the labeled viral DNA stayed in the cells—evidence that DNA is the genetic material of this virus.

Then Linus Pauling did something no one had done before. With his training in biochemistry, a talent for model building, and a dose of intuition, he deduced the structure of a protein—collagen. His discovery was electrifying. If someone could pry open the secrets of proteins, then why not DNA? And if DNA's structural details were deduced, wouldn't they hold clues to how it functions? *Someone could go down in history as having discovered the secret of life!*

ENTER WATSON AND CRICK

Having a shot at fame and fortune quickens the pulse of men and women in any profession, and scientists are no exception. However, science is a community effort. Individuals share not only what they find but also what they do not understand. Even if an experiment does not yield an expected result, it may turn up something that others can use or raise questions others can answer.

And so scientists all over the world started sifting through all the clues. Among them were James Watson,

a postdoctoral student from Indiana University, and Francis Crick, a researcher at Cambridge University. They spent hours arguing over everything they read about DNA's size, shape, and bonding requirements. They fiddled with cardboard cutouts and badgered chemists to help them identify possible bonds they may have overlooked. They built models from thin bits of metal connected with suitably angled "bonds" of wire.

In 1953, they built a model that fit all the pertinent biochemical rules and insights they had gleaned from other sources. They had discovered DNA's structure. As you will see, the structure's breathtaking simplicity helped Crick answer another enormous riddle—*how life can show unity at the molecular level and still give rise to spectacular diversity at the level of whole organisms.*

DNA functions as the cell's treasurehouse of inheritance. Its molecular structure encodes the information required to reproduce parental traits in offspring.

12.2 The Discovery of DNA's Structure

Long before the bacteriophage studies were under way, biochemists knew that DNA contains only four kinds of nucleotides that are the building blocks of nucleic acids. But how were the nucleotides arranged in DNA?

DNA'S BUILDING BLOCKS

Each **nucleotide** consists of a five-carbon sugar (which, in DNA, is deoxyribose), a phosphate group, and one of the following nitrogen-containing bases:

adenine	guanine	thymine	cytosine
A	G	T	C

In all four types of nucleotides, the component parts are organized the same way (Figure 12.4). But **T** and **C** are pyrimidines, with a carbon backbone arranged as a single ring. **A** and **G** are purines, which are larger, bulkier molecules; they have two carbon rings.

By 1949, the biochemist Erwin Chargaff had shared with the scientific community two crucial insights into the composition of DNA. First, the amount of adenine relative to guanine differs from one species to the next. Second, the amounts of thymine and adenine in a DNA molecule are exactly the same, and so are the amounts of cytosine and guanine. We may show this as **A = T** and **G = C**. The symmetrical proportions of the four kinds of nucleotides had to mean something. Was this a tantalizing clue to how the nucleotides are arranged in the DNA molecule?

The first convincing evidence of that arrangement emerged from Maurice Wilkins's research laboratory in England. Rosalind Franklin, one of his colleagues, made good **x-ray diffraction images** of DNA. (Maybe for reasons given in Section 12.3, her contribution has only recently been acknowledged.) X-ray diffraction images are made after directing a beam of x-rays at a molecule, which scatters the x-rays in a pattern that can be captured on film. The pattern consists only of dots and streaks; in itself, it is not the structure of the molecule. Researchers use it to calculate the positions of the molecule's atoms.

Also, DNA must be processed first. A suspension of DNA molecules has to be spun rapidly, spooled onto a rod, and gently pulled into gossamer fibers, like cotton candy. When dry, the fibers twist and turn into two forms, which makes x-ray diffraction images too complicated to decipher. Wet fibers have only one.

Franklin was the first to make a spectacularly clear x-ray diffraction image of wet DNA fibers, as Figure 12.5 shows. She used it to calculate that a molecule of DNA is long and thin, with a 2-nanometer diameter. And she calculated that some molecular configuration is repeated every 0.34 nanometer along its length, and another every 3.4 nanometers.

Figure 12.5 Rosalind Franklin's superb x-ray diffraction image of DNA fibers.

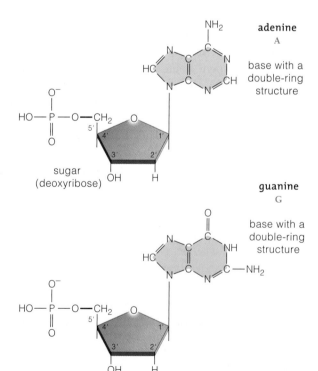

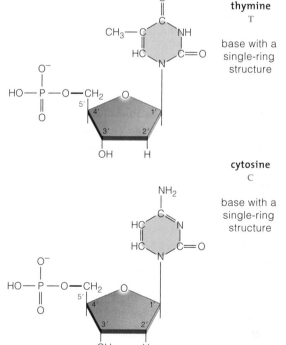

Figure 12.4 All of the chromosomes in a cell contain DNA. What does DNA contain? Four kinds of nucleotides: A, G, T, and C.

Could the sequence of DNA's nucleotide bases be twisting up in a repeating pattern, a bit like a circular stairway? Certainly Pauling thought so. After all, he discovered a helical shape in collagen. Like everyone else—including Wilkins, Watson, and Crick—he was thinking "helix." Watson later wrote, "We thought, why not try it on DNA? We were worried that *Pauling* would say, why not try it on DNA? Certainly he was a very clever man. He was a hero of mine. But we beat him at his own game. I still can't figure out why."

Pauling, it turned out, made a big chemical mistake. His model had all the negatively charged phosphate groups inside the DNA helix instead of outside. If they were that close together, they would repel each other too much to be stable.

PATTERNS OF BASE PAIRING

Franklin filed away the image of wet fibers, and then Watson and Crick took the lead. They perceived that DNA must consist of two strands of nucleotides, held together at their bases by hydrogen bonds (Figure 12.6). Such bonds form when the two strands run in opposing directions and twist to form a double helix. Two kinds of base pairings form along the molecule's length: A—T and G—C.

The bonding pattern accommodates variation in the order of bases. For instance, a stretch of DNA from a rose, a human, or any other organism might be:

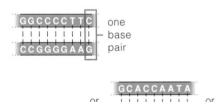

All DNA molecules show the same bonding pattern, but each species has a number of unique DNA base sequences. *This molecular constancy and variation among species is the foundation for the unity and diversity of life.*

Intriguingly, computer simulations show that if you want to pack a string into the least space, coil it into a helix. Was a space-saving advantage a factor in the molecular evolution of the DNA double helix? Maybe.

The pattern of base pairing between the two strands in DNA is constant for all species—A with T, and G with C. However, each species has a number of unique sequences of base pairs along the length of their DNA molecules.

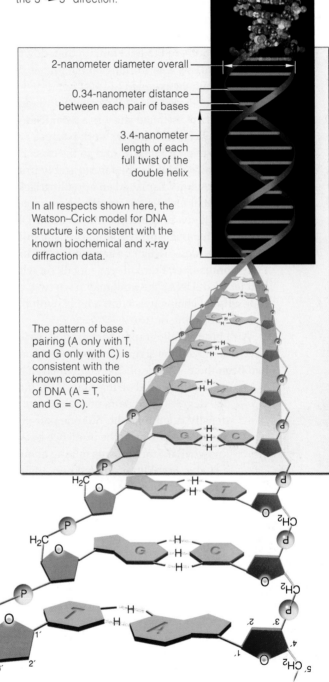

Figure 12.6 Composite of different models for a DNA double helix. The two sugar–phosphate backbones run in *opposing* directions. Think of the sugar units (deoxyribose) of one strand as being upside down.

By comparing the numerals used to identify each carbon atom of the deoxyribose molecule (1′, 2′, 3′, and so on), you see that one strand runs in the 5′→3′ direction and the other runs in the 3′→5′ direction.

2-nanometer diameter overall

0.34-nanometer distance between each pair of bases

3.4-nanometer length of each full twist of the double helix

In all respects shown here, the Watson–Crick model for DNA structure is consistent with the known biochemical and x-ray diffraction data.

The pattern of base pairing (A only with T, and G only with C) is consistent with the known composition of DNA (A = T, and G = C).

12.3 Rosalind's Story

Watson and Crick got the attention of the world, in part by using Rosalind Franklin's data. She got cancer, most likely because of her intensive work with x-rays.

When Rosalind Franklin started at King's Laboratory of Cambridge University, she already had impressive credentials. She developed a refined x-ray diffraction method while studying the structure of coal. She took a new mathematical approach to interpreting x-ray diffraction images and, like Pauling, had built three-dimensional molecular models. At Cambridge, she was asked to create and run a state-of-the-art x-ray crystallography laboratory. Her assignment was to investigate the structure of DNA.

No one bothered to tell Franklin that, down the hall, Maurice Wilkins was working on the puzzle. Even the graduate student assigned to assist her didn't mention it. No one bothered to tell Wilkins about Franklin's assignment; he assumed she was a technician hired to do his x-ray crystallography work because he didn't know how to do it himself. And so the clash began. To Franklin, Wilkins seemed inexplicably prickly. To Wilkins, Franklin displayed an appalling lack of the deference that technicians usually show researchers.

Wilkins had a prized cache of crystalline DNA fibers —each with parallel arrays of hundreds of millions of DNA molecules—which he gave to his "technician." Five months later, Franklin gave a talk on what she had learned. DNA, she said, may have two, three, or four parallel chains twisted in a helix, with phosphate groups projecting outward.

With his crystallography background, Crick would have recognized the significance of her report—*if* he had been there. (A *pair* of chains oriented in opposing directions would be the same even if flipped 180 degrees. Two pairs of chains? No. DNA's density ruled that out. But one pair of chains? Yes!) Watson was in the audience but didn't know what Franklin was talking about.

Later, Franklin produced her outstanding x-ray diffraction image of wet DNA fibers. It fairly screamed *Helix!* She also worked out DNA's length and diameter. But she had been working with dry fibers for a long time and didn't dwell on her new data. Wilkins did.

In 1953, he let Watson see that image and reminded him of what Franklin had reported more than a year before. When Watson and Crick did focus on her data, they had the final bit of information they needed to build a DNA model—one with two helically twisted chains running in opposing directions.

Figure 12.7 Portrait of Rosalind Franklin arriving at Cambridge in style, from Paris.

12.4 DNA Replication and Repair

The discovery of DNA structure was a turning point in studies of inheritance. Crick understood at once how cells duplicate their DNA before they divide.

Until Watson and Crick presented their model, no one could explain **DNA replication**, or how the molecule of inheritance is duplicated before a cell divides.

Enzymes easily break the hydrogen bonds between the two nucleotide strands of a DNA molecule. When enzymes and other proteins act on the molecule, one strand unwinds from the other and exposes stretches of its nucleotide bases. Cells contain stockpiles of free nucleotides that can pair with the exposed bases.

Each parent strand stays intact, and a companion strand gets assembled on each one according to this base-pairing rule: A to T, and G to C. As soon as a stretch of a new, partner strand forms on a stretch of the parent strand, the two twist together into a double helix. Because the parent DNA strand is conserved during the replication process, half of every double-stranded DNA molecule is "old" and half is "new." Figures 12.8 and 12.9 describe this process, which we call *semiconservative* replication.

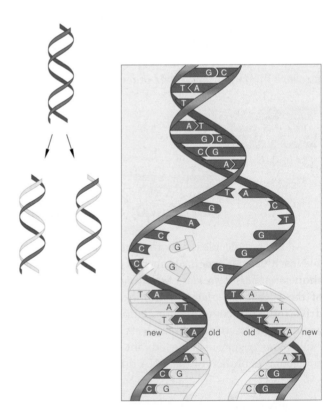

Figure 12.8 A simple picture of the semiconservative nature of DNA replication. The original two-stranded DNA molecule is coded *blue*. Each parent strand remains intact. One new strand (*gold*) is assembled on each of the parent strands.

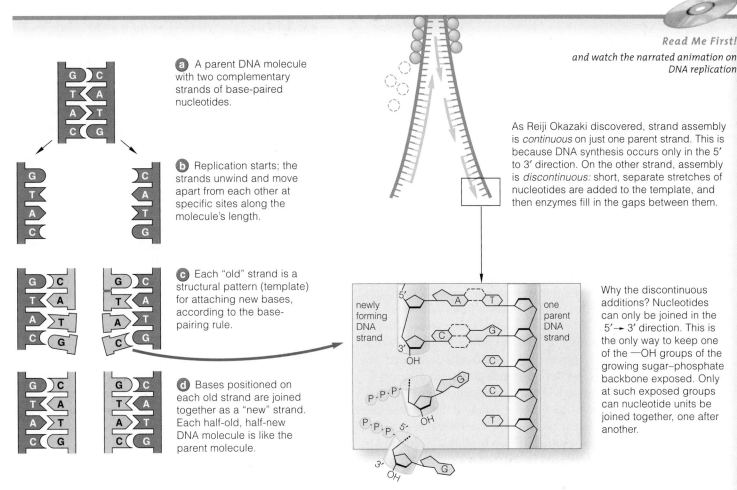

Read Me First!
and watch the narrated animation on DNA replication

a A parent DNA molecule with two complementary strands of base-paired nucleotides.

b Replication starts; the strands unwind and move apart from each other at specific sites along the molecule's length.

c Each "old" strand is a structural pattern (template) for attaching new bases, according to the base-pairing rule.

d Bases positioned on each old strand are joined together as a "new" strand. Each half-old, half-new DNA molecule is like the parent molecule.

As Reiji Okazaki discovered, strand assembly is *continuous* on just one parent strand. This is because DNA synthesis occurs only in the 5' to 3' direction. On the other strand, assembly is *discontinuous:* short, separate stretches of nucleotides are added to the template, and then enzymes fill in the gaps between them.

Why the discontinuous additions? Nucleotides can only be joined in the 5'→ 3' direction. This is the only way to keep one of the —OH groups of the growing sugar–phosphate backbone exposed. Only at such exposed groups can nucleotide units be joined together, one after another.

Figure 12.9 A closer look at DNA replication.

DNA replication uses a team of molecular workers. In response to cellular signals, replication enzymes become active along the length of the DNA molecule. Along with other proteins, some enzymes unwind the strands in both directions and prevent them from rewinding. Enzyme action jump-starts the unwinding but is not required to unzip hydrogen bonds between the strands; hydrogen bonds are individually weak.

Now **DNA polymerases**, a class of enzymes, attach short stretches of free nucleotides to unwound parts of the parent template. Free nucleotides themselves drive the strand assembly. Each has three phosphate groups. A DNA polymerase splits off two, releasing energy that drives the attachments.

DNA ligases fill in the tiny gaps between the new short stretches and form one continuous strand. Then enzymes wind up the template and complementary strands together, forming a DNA double helix.

Sometimes a molecule of DNA breaks. Sometimes it is replicated incorrectly so that it does not exactly match the parent molecule; it acquired mismatched bases or has missing or extra segments. DNA repair processes minimize such damage. Ligases can fix the breaks, and specialized DNA polymerases can correct the mismatched base pairs or replace mutated ones.

The repair processes confer survival advantage on cells. Why? Mistakes in DNA can result in the altered or diminished function of encoded proteins and thus disrupt how cells operate. This is what happens with genetic disorders. Also, a broken strand of DNA may block replication and cause a cell to commit suicide by issuing signals for its own death.

DNA is replicated prior to cell division. Enzymes unwind its two strands. Each strand remains intact throughout the process—it is conserved—and enzymes assemble a new, complementary strand on each one.

Mistakes happen. Repair systems fix mismatched base pairs and help maintain the integrity of genetic information. They also bypass breaks, which helps keep replication from shutting down.

12.5 Reprogramming DNA To Clone Mammals

*Knowledge of DNA structure and function opened up
exciting, and troubling, research avenues—including
cloning adult mammals from little more than DNA
and a cell stripped of its nucleus.*

Geneticists started out cloning some embryos from
in vitro fertilization. Briefly, a sperm fertilizes an egg
in a petri dish. Mitotic divisions produce two cells,
then four, then eight. The eight-cell stage is gently
split into two- or four-cell clusters that are implanted
in surrogate mothers. There they grow and develop
into genetically identical animals; they are clones.

Splitting such early stages, or *artificial twinning*,
gives us clones that are identical to one another but
not to sexually reproducing parents; they have genes
from both parents. Such clones must grow up before
researchers can find out whether genes for a desired
maternal or paternal trait were inherited.

Using a differentiated cell is faster, because the
desired genotype is already known. You may wonder
what "differentiated" means. All cells descended from
a fertilized egg have the same DNA, but different
lineages start making unique selections from it during
development. The selections commit them to becoming
liver cells, blood cells, or other specialists in structure,
composition, and function in the adult (Section 14.3).

A differentiated cell must be tricked into rewinding
the clock. *Its DNA must be reprogrammed into starting over
again and directing the development of a whole individual.*
Nuclear transfer is one way to trick it. The nucleus
of a differentiated cell from an animal to be cloned
replaces an unfertilized egg's nucleus (Figure 12.10).
Chemicals or electric shocks may induce the cell to
divide. If all goes well, a cluster of embryonic cells
forms and can be implanted in a surrogate mother.

In Dolly's case, the nucleus came from a cell in a
sheep's udder. Nuclei from cumulus cells were used
to clone mice and CC, the first cloned cat. Cumulus
cells surround immature eggs in mammalian ovaries.
Genetic tests confirmed that CC (short for *Carbon
Copy*) is a clone, even though her coat patterning
differs from that of the genetic donor (Figure 12.10).
Here is visible evidence that environmental factors
(in this case, in the uterus) can alter gene expression.

Variations in gene expression are less obvious but
more of a problem in other clones. About 4 percent of
all the genes tested in cloned mice were expressed at
abnormal levels. Gene expression also was disturbed
in cloned mice that had received genetic material from
cells of entirely different tissues. Does this mean that
nuclear transfer procedures invite defects? Probably.

Abnormal gene expression in clones isn't surprising.
Genes switch on and off during normal development.
Researchers are not yet rewinding the clock to cover
all of the ticks—minutes or hours—between nuclear
transfer and the first cell divisions.

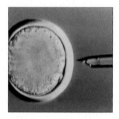 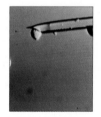  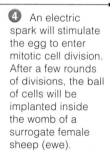 

1 A microneedle is about to remove the nucleus from an unfertilized sheep egg (center).

2 The microneedle has now emptied the sheep egg of its own nucleus, which held the DNA.

3 DNA from a donor cell is about to be deposited in the enucleated egg.

4 An electric spark will stimulate the egg to enter mitotic cell division. After a few rounds of divisions, the ball of cells will be implanted inside the womb of a surrogate female sheep (ewe).

the first cloned sheep

Figure 12.10 Steps in the nuclear transfer process that led to Dolly, and a gallery of famous firsts in the brave new world of mammalian cloning.

the first cloned mice

the first cloned pigs

CC (*left*), and her genetic donor, Rainbow.

Summary

Section 12.1 Experimental tests that used bacteria and bacteriophages offered the first solid evidence that DNA is the hereditary material in living organisms.

Sections 12.2, 12.3 DNA consists only of nucleotides, each with a five-carbon sugar (deoxyribose), a phosphate group, and one of four kinds of nitrogen-containing bases: adenine, thymine, guanine, or cytosine.

A DNA molecule consists of two nucleotide strands twisted together into a double helix. Bases of one strand hydrogen-bond with bases of the other.

Bases of the two DNA strands pair in a constant way. Adenine pairs with thymine (**A–T**), and guanine with cytosine (**G–C**). Which base follows another along a strand varies among species. The DNA of each species incorporates some number of unique stretches of base pairs that set it apart from the DNA of all other species.

Section 12.4 In DNA replication, enzymes unwind the two strands of a double helix and assemble a new strand of complementary sequence on each parent strand. Two double-stranded DNA molecules result. One strand of each molecule is old (is conserved); the other is new.

During replication, repair systems fix base-pairing mistakes and mutated bases. They also repair breaks in DNA strands that could shut down replication. DNA ligase and special DNA polymerases are involved.

Section 12.5 Embryo splitting and nuclear transfers are two methods that produce clones, or individuals that have identical DNA. Clones can show phenotypic differences if they are exposed to different factors that affect gene expression during development.

Self-Quiz   *Answers in Appendix III*

1. Which is *not* a nucleotide base in DNA?
   a. adenine   c. uracil   e. cytosine
   b. guanine   d. thymine   f. All are in DNA.

2. What are the base-pairing rules for DNA?
   a. A–G, T–C   c. A–U, C–G
   b. A–C, T–G   d. A–T, G–C

3. One species' DNA differs from others in its _____ .
   a. sugars   c. base sequence
   b. phosphates   d. all of the above

4. When DNA replication begins, _____ .
   a. the two DNA strands unwind from each other
   b. the two DNA strands condense for base transfers
   c. two DNA molecules bond
   d. old strands move to find new strands

5. DNA replication requires _____ .
   a. free nucleotides   c. many enzymes
   b. new hydrogen bonds   d. all of the above

6. Cell differentiation involves _____ .
   a. cloning   c. selective gene expression
   b. nuclear transfers   d. both b and c

Critical Thinking

1. Matthew Meselson and Frank Stahl's experiments supported a semiconservative model of DNA replication. These researchers obtained "heavy" DNA by growing *Escherichia coli* in a medium enriched with ^{15}N, a heavy isotope of nitrogen. They also prepared "light" DNA by growing *E. coli* in the presence of ^{14}N, the more common isotope. An available technique helped them identify which replicated molecules were heavy, light, or hybrid (one heavy strand and one light). Use pencils of two colors, one for heavy strands and one for light. Starting with a DNA molecule having two heavy strands, arrange them to show how daughter molecules would form after replication in a ^{14}N-containing medium. Show the four DNA molecules that would form if daughter molecules are replicated a second time in the ^{14}N medium.

2. Mutations, permanent changes in DNA base sequences, are the original source of genetic variation and the raw material of evolution. Yet how can mutations accumulate, given that cells have repair systems that fix structurally altered or discontinuous DNA strands during replication?

Media Menu

Student CD-ROM

Impacts, Issues Video
   Goodbye, Dolly
Big Picture Animation
   DNA structure and function
Read-Me-First Animation
   Hershey–Chase experiments
   DNA replication
Other Animations and Interactions
   Griffith's experimental transformation of bacteria
   DNA double helix
   Cloning by nuclear transfer

InfoTrac

- Beyond the Double Helix: Francis Crick. *Time*, February 2003.
- Combing Chromosomes. *American Scientist*, May 2002.
- Jumpstarting DNA Repair. *Environmental Health Perspectives*, December 2002.
- Ma's Eyes, Not Her Ways: Clones Can Vary in Behavioral—and Physical—Traits. *Scientific American*, April 2003.

Web Sites

- Dolan DNA Learning Center: www.dnalc.org
- DNA Structure: molvis.sdsc.edu/dna
- Nobel e-Museum: www.nobel.se/medicine/educational
- Roslin Institute: www.roslin.ac.uk

How Would You Vote?

Mammalian cloning using adult cells is a difficult process and often produces abnormal individuals. Many researchers argue that continued experimentation will allow them to refine methods and develop new drugs and organs for transplants. Some activists argue that cloning animals from adult cells should be banned. Should this cloning research continue?

IMPACTS, ISSUES *Ricin and Your Ribosomes*

In 2003, police acting on an intelligence tip stormed a London apartment, where they collected castor oil beans (Figure 13.1) and laboratory glassware. They arrested several young men and reminded the world of ricin's potential as a biochemical weapon.

Ricin is a protein product of the castor oil plant (*Ricinus communis*). A dose the size of a grain of salt can kill you; only plutonium and botulism toxin are more deadly. Researchers knew about it as long ago as 1888. Later, when Germany unleashed mustard gas against allied troops during World War I, the United States and England feverishly investigated whether ricin, too, could be used as a weapon. Both countries shelved the research when the war ended.

Fast-forward to 1969. Georgi Markov, a Bulgarian writer, defected to the West at the height of the Cold War.

Figure 13.1 Castor oil plant seeds, source of the ribosome-busting ricin.

As he strolled down a London street, an assassin used a modified umbrella to poke a tiny ball laced with ricin into one of his legs. Markov died in agony three days later.

Ricin is on stage once again. Traces of ricin showed up in hastily abandoned Afghanistan caves in 2001 and on a Chechen fighter killed in Moscow in 2003. In early 2004, traces turned up in a United States Senate mailroom, in a State Department building, and in an envelope addressed to the White House.

Each year, a lot of ricin-rich wastes form during castor oil production. The entire castor oil plant is poisonous, but ricin is most concentrated in seeds. How does ricin exert its deadly effects? It inactivates ribosomes, the cell's protein-building machinery.

Ricin is a protein. One of its two polypeptide chains, shown in the filmstrip, helps ricin insert itself into cells. The other chain, an enzyme, wrecks part of the ribosome where amino acids are joined together. It yanks adenine subunits from an RNA molecule that is a crucial part of the ribosome. The ribosome's three-dimensional shape unravels, protein synthesis stops, and cells spiral toward death. So does the individual; there is no antidote.

It's possible to get on with your life without knowing what a ribosome is or what it does. It also is possible to recognize that protein synthesis is not a topic invented to torture biology students. It is something worth knowing about and appreciating for how it keeps us alive—and for appreciating anti-terrorism researchers who are working to keep us that way.

the big picture

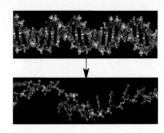

Making the Transcripts It takes two steps to get from DNA's protein-building information to a new protein molecule. In the first step, a strand of mRNA is transcribed from a gene region, a sequence of nucleotide bases in an unwound part of a DNA molecule.

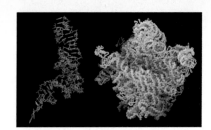

Readers of the Genetic Code Every three ribonucleotide bases along the length of an mRNA transcript is a "word" corresponding to a particular amino acid. Two other classes of RNAs recognize a range of these base triplets, which represent a genetic code.

So start with what you know about DNA, the book of protein-building information in cells. The alphabet used to write the book is simple enough—just A, T, G, and C, for the nucleotide bases adenine, thymine, guanine, and cytosine. But how do you get from an alphabet to a protein? The answer starts with the order, or sequence, of those four nucleotide bases in a DNA molecule.

As you already know, the two strands unwind from each other entirely when a cell is replicating its DNA. At other times, however, cells selectively unwind the two strands in certain regions and thereby expose the base sequences we call genes. Most of the genes encode information on building particular proteins.

You'll see from this chapter that it takes two steps, transcription and translation, to do something with the information in a gene. In all eukaryotic cells, the first step proceeds in the nucleus. A newly exposed DNA base sequence functions as a structural pattern, or a template, for making a strand of ribonucleic acid (RNA) from the cell's pool of free nucleotides.

The RNA then moves into the cytoplasm, where it is translated. In this second step of protein synthesis, the RNA guides the assembly of amino acids into a new polypeptide chain. The new chains become folded into the three-dimensional shapes of specific proteins.

In short, DNA guides the synthesis of RNA, then RNA guides the synthesis of proteins:

$$DNA \xrightarrow{\text{transcription}} RNA \xrightarrow{\text{translation}} PROTEIN$$

How Would You Vote?

Ricin is difficult to disperse through the air and is unlikely to be used in a large-scale terrorist attack. However, ricin powder did turn up in a Senate office building. Scientists are working to develop a vaccine against ricin. If mass immunizations were to be offered, would you sign up to be vaccinated? See the Media Menu for details, then vote online.

Translating the Transcripts In the second step of protein synthesis, tRNAs and rRNAs interact to translate the mRNA transcript of a gene region into a polypeptide chain. The chain grows as one of the rRNA components of ribosomes catalyzes the bonding between amino acids.

Mutations and Proteins Mutations change the genetic code words in the messages that specify particular proteins. When the protein is an essential part of cell architecture or metabolism, we can expect the outcome to be an abnormal cell.

13.1 How Is RNA Transcribed From DNA?

*In **transcription**, the first step in protein synthesis, the base sequence in an unwound DNA region becomes a template for assembling a strand of ribonucleic acid, or RNA.*

It takes three classes of RNA molecules to synthesize proteins. Most genes are transcribed into **messenger RNA**, or **mRNA**—the only kind that carries *protein-building* instructions. Other genes are transcribed into **ribosomal RNA**, or **rRNA**, a component of ribosomes.

A ribosome is a large molecular structure upon which polypeptide chains are assembled. Transcription of still other genes yields **transfer RNA**, or **tRNA**, which can deliver amino acids one at a time to a ribosome.

THE NATURE OF TRANSCRIPTION

An RNA molecule is almost but not quite like a single strand of DNA. It has four kinds of ribonucleotides, each with the five-carbon sugar ribose, a phosphate group, and a base. Three bases—adenine, cytosine, and guanine—are the same as those in DNA. In RNA, however, the fourth base is **uracil**, not thymine. Like thymine, uracil can pair with adenine. This means a new RNA strand can be built according to the same base-pairing rules as DNA (Figure 13.2).

Transcription *differs* from DNA replication in three respects. Part of a DNA strand, not the whole molecule, is used as the template. The enzyme **RNA polymerase**, not DNA polymerase, adds ribonucleotides one at a time to the end of a growing strand of RNA. And transcription results in one free strand of RNA, not a hydrogen-bonded double helix.

The many coding regions in DNA are transcribed separately, and each has its own START and STOP signal. A **promoter** is one sequence of bases in DNA that signals the start of a gene. RNA synthesis gets going as soon as RNA polymerases and other proteins attach to it. Each polymerase moves along the DNA strand, joining one ribonucleotide after another on

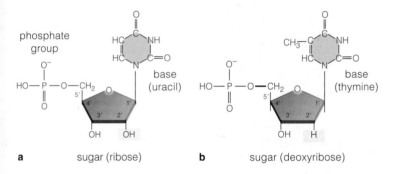

phosphate group

base (uracil)

a   sugar (ribose)

base (thymine)

b   sugar (deoxyribose)

Figure 13.2 (**a**) Uracil, one of four ribonucleotides in RNA. The other three—adenine, guanine, and cytosine—differ only in their bases. Compare uracil to (**b**) thymine, a DNA nucleotide. (**c**) Base pairing of DNA with RNA at transcription, compared to base pairing during DNA replication.

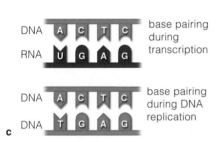

DNA   A C T C   base pairing during transcription
RNA   U G A G

DNA   A C T C   base pairing during DNA replication
DNA   T G A G

c

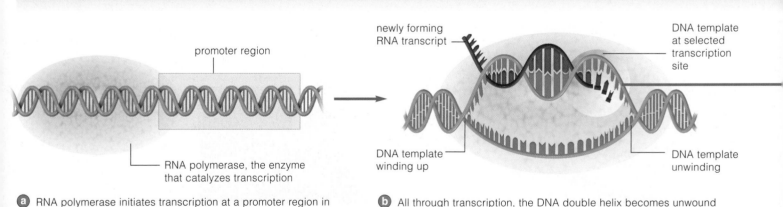

promoter region

RNA polymerase, the enzyme that catalyzes transcription

newly forming RNA transcript

DNA template at selected transcription site

DNA template winding up

DNA template unwinding

a RNA polymerase initiates transcription at a promoter region in DNA. It recognizes a base sequence located next to the promoter as a template. It will link the nucleotides adenine, cytosine, guanine, and uracil into a strand of RNA, in the order specified by DNA.

b All through transcription, the DNA double helix becomes unwound in front of the RNA polymerase. Short lengths of the newly forming RNA strand briefly wind up with its DNA template strand. New stretches of RNA unwind from the template (and the two DNA strands wind up again).

Figure 13.3 Gene transcription. By this process, an RNA molecule is assembled on a DNA template. (**a**) Gene region of DNA. The base sequence along one of DNA's two strands (not both) is used as the template. (**b–d**) Transcribing that region results in a molecule of RNA.

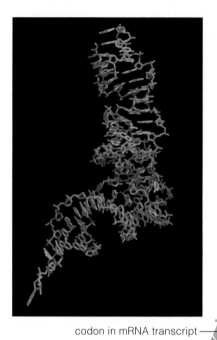

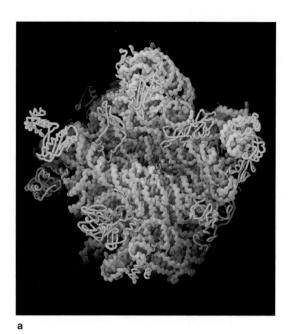

Figure 13.8 (**a**) Ribbon model for the large subunit of a bacterial ribosome. It has two rRNA molecules (*gray*) and thirty-one structural proteins (*gold*), which stabilize the structure. At one end of a tunnel through the large subunit, rRNA catalyzes polypeptide chain assembly. This is an ancient, highly conserved structure. Its role is so vital that the corresponding subunit of the eukaryotic ribosome, which is larger, may be similar in structure and function. (**b**) Model for the small and large subunits of a eukaryotic ribosome.

a

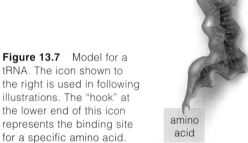

codon in mRNA transcript

anticodon in tRNA

Figure 13.7 Model for a tRNA. The icon shown to the right is used in following illustrations. The "hook" at the lower end of this icon represents the binding site for a specific amino acid.

amino acid

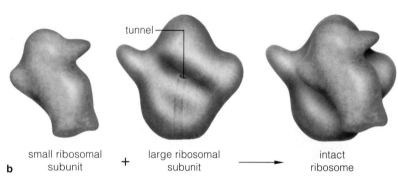

tunnel

small ribosomal subunit + large ribosomal subunit → intact ribosome

b

THE OTHER RNAs

In the cytoplasm of all cells are pools of free amino acids and tRNA molecules. Each tRNA has a molecular "hook," an attachment site for an amino acid. It has an **anticodon**, a ribonucleotide base triplet that can pair with an mRNA codon (Figure 13.7). When tRNAs bind to mRNA on a ribosome, their amino acid cargo will become automatically positioned in the order that the codons specify.

There are sixty-four codons but not as many kinds of tRNAs. How do tRNAs match up with more than one type of codon? According to base-pairing rules, adenine pairs with uracil, and cytosine with guanine. However, in codon–anticodon interactions, these rules can loosen for the third base in a codon. This freedom in codon–anticodon pairing at a base is known as the "wobble effect."

To give one example, AUU, AUC, and AUA specify isoleucine. All three codons can base-pair with one type of tRNA that hooks on to isoleucine.

Again, interactions between the tRNAs and mRNA take place at ribosomes. A ribosome has two subunits (Figure 13.8). They are built from rRNA and structural proteins in the nucleus, then shipped separately to the cytoplasm. There, a large and small subunit converge into an intact, functional ribosome only when mRNA is to be translated.

The genetic code is a set of sixty-four codons, which are ribonucleotide bases in mRNA that are read in sets of three. Different amino acids are specified by different codons.

Only mRNA carries DNA's protein-building instructions from the nucleus into the cytoplasm.

tRNAs deliver amino acids to ribosomes. Their anticodons base-pair with codons in the order specified by mRNA.

Polypeptide chains are built on ribosomes, each consisting of a large and small subunit made of rRNA and proteins.

13.3 Translating mRNA Into Protein

DNA's hereditary information must be stored intact, safely, in one place. Think of mRNA transcripts as intermediaries that deliver messages from DNA to ribosomes, which translate them into the polypeptide chains of proteins.

Translation has three stages: initiation, elongation, and termination. *Initiation* requires an initiator tRNA, the only one that can start translation. It binds to a small ribosomal subunit. Then mRNA's START codon, AUG, joins with that tRNA's anticodon. A large ribosomal subunit now joins with the small one (Figure 13.9*a–c*). Together, the ribosome, mRNA, and initiator tRNA are an initiation complex. The next stage can begin.

In *elongation*, a polypeptide chain is synthesized as the mRNA passes between the two ribosomal subunits,

like a thread passing through the eye of a needle. tRNA molecules move amino acids to the ribosome, where they bind to the mRNA in the order specified by its codons. Part of an rRNA molecule at the center of the large ribosomal subunit functions as an enzyme. It catalyzes peptide bond formation between the amino acids (Figure 13.9*d–f*).

Figure 13.9*g* shows how one peptide bond forms between the most recently attached amino acid and the next one brought to the ribosome. Here, you might look once more at Section 3.5, which includes a step-by-step description of peptide bond formation during protein synthesis.

During the last stage of translation, *termination*, the ribosome reaches the mRNA's STOP codon. No tRNA

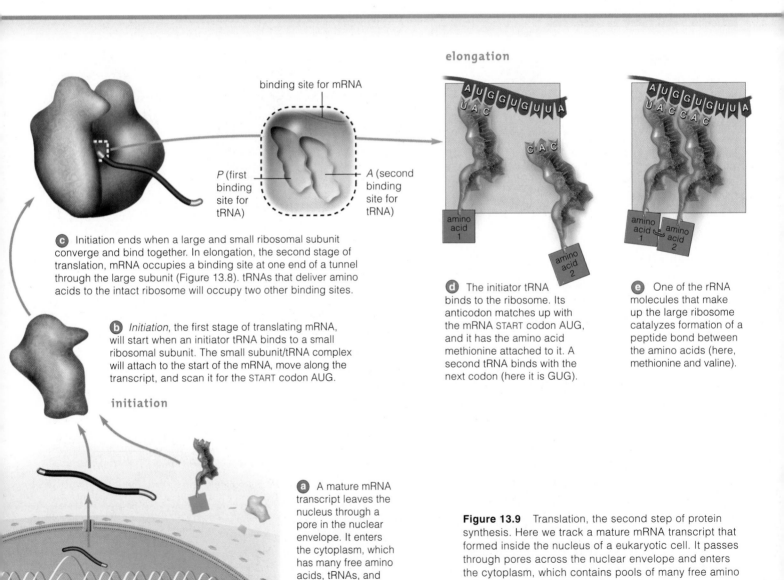

elongation

binding site for mRNA

P (first binding site for tRNA)

A (second binding site for tRNA)

c Initiation ends when a large and small ribosomal subunit converge and bind together. In elongation, the second stage of translation, mRNA occupies a binding site at one end of a tunnel through the large subunit (Figure 13.8). tRNAs that deliver amino acids to the intact ribosome will occupy two other binding sites.

b *Initiation*, the first stage of translating mRNA, will start when an initiator tRNA binds to a small ribosomal subunit. The small subunit/tRNA complex will attach to the start of the mRNA, move along the transcript, and scan it for the START codon AUG.

initiation

amino acid 1

amino acid 2

d The initiator tRNA binds to the ribosome. Its anticodon matches up with the mRNA START codon AUG, and it has the amino acid methionine attached to it. A second tRNA binds with the next codon (here it is GUG).

amino acid 1 amino acid 2

e One of the rRNA molecules that make up the large ribosome catalyzes formation of a peptide bond between the amino acids (here, methionine and valine).

a A mature mRNA transcript leaves the nucleus through a pore in the nuclear envelope. It enters the cytoplasm, which has many free amino acids, tRNAs, and ribosomal subunits.

Figure 13.9 Translation, the second step of protein synthesis. Here we track a mature mRNA transcript that formed inside the nucleus of a eukaryotic cell. It passes through pores across the nuclear envelope and enters the cytoplasm, which contains pools of many free amino acids, tRNAs, and ribosomal subunits.

has a corresponding anticodon. Proteins called release factors bind to the ribosome. Binding triggers enzyme activity that detaches the mRNA *and* the polypeptide chain from the ribosome (Figure 13.9i–k).

Unfertilized eggs and other cells that rapidly make many copies of different proteins usually stockpile mRNA transcripts in their cytoplasm. In cells that are quickly using or secreting proteins, you often observe many clusters of ribosomes (polysomes) on an mRNA transcript, all translating it at the same time.

Many newly formed polypeptide chains carry out their functions in the cytoplasm. Many others have a shipping label, a special sequence of amino acids. The label lets them enter the ribosome-studded, flattened sacs of rough ER (Section 4.7). In the organelles of the

endomembrane system, the chains will take on final form before shipment to their ultimate destinations as structural or functional proteins.

> Translation is initiated when a small ribosomal subunit and an initiator tRNA arrive at an mRNA transcript's START codon, and then a large ribosomal subunit binds to them.
>
> tRNAs deliver amino acids to a ribosome in the order dictated by the linear sequence of mRNA codons. A polypeptide chain lengthens as peptide bonds form between the amino acids.
>
> Translation ends when a STOP codon triggers events that cause the polypeptide chain and the mRNA to detach from the ribosome.

Read Me First!
and watch the narrated animation on translation

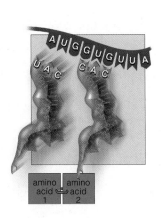

f The first tRNA is released, and the ribosome moves to the next codon position.

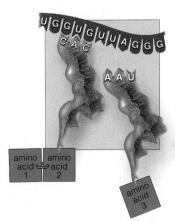

g A third tRNA binds with the next codon (here it is UUA). The ribosome catalyzes peptide bond formation between amino acids 2 and 3.

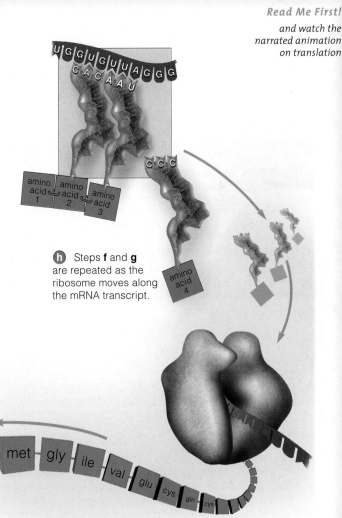

h Steps **f** and **g** are repeated as the ribosome moves along the mRNA transcript.

termination

i A STOP codon moves into the area where the chain is being built. It is the signal to release the mRNA transcript from the ribosome.

j The new polypeptide chain is released from the ribosome. It is free to join the pool of proteins in the cytoplasm or to enter rough ER of the endomembrane system.

k The two ribosomal subunits now separate, also.

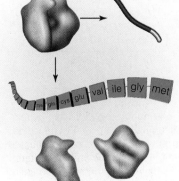
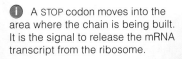
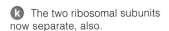

13.4 Mutated Genes and Their Protein Products

When a cell taps its genetic code, it is making proteins with precise structural and functional roles that keep it alive. If something changes a gene, the protein that it encodes may change. If the protein has an essential role, we can expect the outcome to be an abnormal cell.

Gene sequences can change. Sometimes one base gets substituted for another in the nucleotide sequence. At other times, an extra base is inserted or one is lost. Such small-scale changes in the nucleotide sequence of a DNA molecule are **gene mutations**.

There is some leeway here, because more than one codon specifies the same amino acid. If UCU were changed to UCC, for example, it probably would not have dire effects, because both codons specify serine. However, many mutations give rise to proteins that function in altered ways or not at all. Repercussions are sometimes harmful or lethal.

COMMON MUTATIONS

In gene mutations called **base-pair substitutions**, one base is copied incorrectly during DNA replication. Its outcome? A protein may incorporate the wrong amino acid, or its synthesis may have been cut off too soon. In the example in Figure 13.10b, adenine *replaced* one thymine in a gene for beta hemoglobin. The mutant gene's product has a single amino acid substitution that causes sickle-cell disease (Section 3.6).

Figure 13.10c shows a different gene mutation, one in which a single base—thymine—was *deleted*. Again, DNA polymerases read base sequences in blocks of three. A deletion is one of the *frameshift* mutations; it shifts the "three-bases-at-a-time" reading frame. An altered mRNA is transcribed from the mutant gene, so an altered protein is the result.

Frameshift mutations fall in the broader categories of **insertions** and **deletions**. One or more base pairs become inserted into DNA or are deleted from it.

Other mutations arise from transposable elements, or **transposons**, that can jump around in the genome. Geneticist Barbara McClintock found that these DNA segments or copies of them move spontaneously to a new location in a chromosome or even to a different chromosome. When transposons land in a gene, they alter the timing or duration of its activity, or block it entirely. Their unpredictability can give rise to odd variations in traits. Figure 13.11 gives an example.

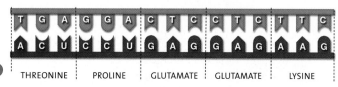

part of DNA template

mRNA transcribed from DNA

THREONINE   PROLINE   GLUTAMATE   GLUTAMATE   LYSINE   resulting amino acid sequence

(a)

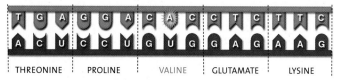

base substitution in DNA

altered mRNA

THREONINE   PROLINE   VALINE   GLUTAMATE   LYSINE   altered amino acid sequence

(b)

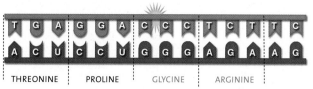

deletion in DNA

altered mRNA

THREONINE   PROLINE   GLYCINE   ARGININE   altered amino acid sequence

(c)

Figure 13.10 Gene mutation. (**a**) Part of the gene, the mRNA, and the resulting amino acid sequence of the hemoglobin beta chain. (**b**) A base substitution in DNA replaces a thymine with an adenine. When the altered mRNA transcript is translated, valine replaces glutamate as the sixth amino acid of the new polypeptide chain. Sickle-cell anemia is the eventual outcome.

(**c**) Deletion of the same thymine would be a frameshift mutation. The reading frame for the rest of the mRNA shifts, a different protein product forms, and it causes thalassemia, a different type of red blood cell disorder.

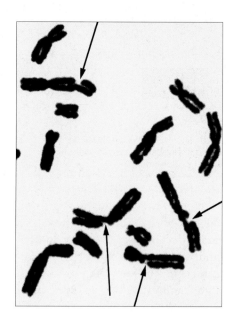

Figure 13.12 Chromosomes from a human cell exposed to gamma rays, a form of ionizing radiation. We can expect such broken pieces (*arrows*) to be lost in interphase, when DNA is being replicated. The extent of chromosome damage in an exposed cell typically depends on how much radiation it absorbed.

Figure 13.11 Barbara McClintock, who won a Nobel Prize for her research. She proved that transposons slip into and out of different locations in DNA. The curiously nonuniform coloration of kernels in strains of Indian corn (*Zea mays*) sent her on the road to discovery.

Several genes govern pigment formation and deposition in corn kernels, which are a type of seed. Mutations in one or more of these genes produce yellow, white, red, orange, blue, and purple kernels. However, as McClintock realized, *unstable* mutations can cause streaks or spots in *individual* kernels.

All of a corn plant's cells have the same pigment-encoding genes. But a transposon invaded a pigment-encoding gene before the plant started growing from a fertilized egg. While a kernel's tissues were forming, its cells couldn't make pigment. But the same transposon jumped back out of the pigment-encoding gene in some of its cells. Descendants of *those* cells could make pigment. The streaks and spots in individual kernels are evidence of those cell lineages.

HOW DO MUTATIONS ARISE?

Many mutations happen spontaneously while DNA is being replicated. This is not surprising, given the swift pace of replication (about twenty bases per second in humans and a thousand bases per second in certain bacteria). DNA polymerases can repair most of the mistakes (Section 12.4). Sometimes, however, they go on assembling a new strand right over an error. The bypass can result in a mutated DNA molecule.

Not all mutations are spontaneous. A number arise after DNA is exposed to mutation-causing agents. For instance, x-rays and similar high-energy wavelengths of **ionizing radiation** break chromosomes into pieces (Figure 13.12). Such radiation also indirectly damages DNA because it penetrates living tissue, leaving in its wake a potentially destructive trail of free radicals. Because of this, doctors and dentists use the lowest possible doses of x-rays in order to minimize damage to their patients' DNA.

Nonionizing radiation boosts electrons to a higher energy level. DNA absorbs one form, ultraviolet (UV) radiation. Two types of nucleotides in DNA, cytosine and thymine, are most vulnerable to excitation that can change base-pairing properties. For example, UV light can induce two adjacent thymine bases to bond and become a bulky dimer. At least seven gene products interact as a DNA repair mechanism to remove this error, which is a thymine dimer. Thymine dimers form in skin cells after exposure of unprotected skin to sunlight.

When they are not repaired, thymine dimers cause DNA polymerase to make additional errors during the next cycle of replication. They are the source of mutations that lead to certain cancers.

Natural and synthetic chemicals accelerate the rates of spontaneous mutations. **Alkylating agents** are one example. They transfer charged methyl or ethyl groups to reactive sites in DNA. At these sites, DNA is more vulnerable to base-pair changes that invite mutation. Cancer-causing agents in cigarette smoke and many substances exert their effects by alkylating DNA.

THE PROOF IS IN THE PROTEIN

When a mutation arises in a somatic cell, its good or bad effects do not endure, because it cannot be passed on to offspring. When a mutation arises in a germ cell or a gamete, however, it may enter the evolutionary arena. It also may do so if it arises during asexual reproduction. Either way, *a protein product of a heritable mutation will have harmful, neutral, or beneficial effects on the individual's ability to function in the prevailing environment.* The effects of uncountable mutations in millions of species have had spectacular evolutionary consequences. And that is a topic of later chapters.

A gene mutation is a change involving one or more bases in the nucleotide sequence of DNA. The most common types are base-pair substitutions, insertions, and deletions.

Exposure to harmful radiation and chemicals in the environment can cause mutations in DNA.

A protein specified by a mutated gene may have harmful, neutral, or beneficial effects on the ability of an individual to function in the environment.

Summary

Section 13.1 Transcription and translation are two steps of a process leading from genes to proteins.

$$\text{DNA} \xrightarrow{\textit{transcription}} \text{RNA} \xrightarrow{\textit{translation}} \text{PROTEIN}$$

In eukaryotic cells, transcription occurs in the nucleus (Figure 13.13). DNA's two strands unwind from each other at a selected region. RNA polymerases use the exposed DNA bases as a template on which an RNA molecule is built from free ribonucleotides (adenine, guanine, cytosine, and uracil). The mRNA transcript becomes modified before it leaves the nucleus.

Section 13.2 In translation, three types of RNAs interact to build polypeptide chains. Messenger RNA (mRNA) carries DNA's transcribed protein-building information from the nucleus to the cytoplasm. Its genetic message is written in codons, or sets of three nucleotides along an mRNA strand that specify an amino acid. There are sixty-four codons, a few of which act as START or STOP signals for translation. Ribosomes consist of ribosomal RNA (rRNA) and proteins that stabilize it. Transfer RNA (tRNA) molecules bind free amino acids in the cytoplasm and deliver them to ribosomes during protein synthesis. Different tRNAs bind different amino acids.

Section 13.3 During translation, amino acids are joined in the order specified by codons in mRNA.

Translation proceeds through three stages. In initiation, ribosomal subunits, an initiator tRNA, and an mRNA join to form an initiation complex. In elongation, tRNAs deliver amino acids to ribosomes, which synthesize a polypeptide chain from them. Part of the rRNA in the ribosomes catalyzes peptide bond formation between the amino acids. At termination, a STOP codon and other factors trigger the release of the mRNA and the new polypeptide chain, and they make the ribosome's subunits separate from each other.

Section 13.4 Gene mutations are heritable, small-scale changes in the base sequence of DNA. Major types are base-pair substitutions, insertions, and deletions. Many arise spontaneously as DNA is being replicated. Some occur when transposons jump around in a gene or after DNA is exposed to ionizing radiation or to chemicals in the environment. Mutations may cause changes in protein structure, protein function, or both.

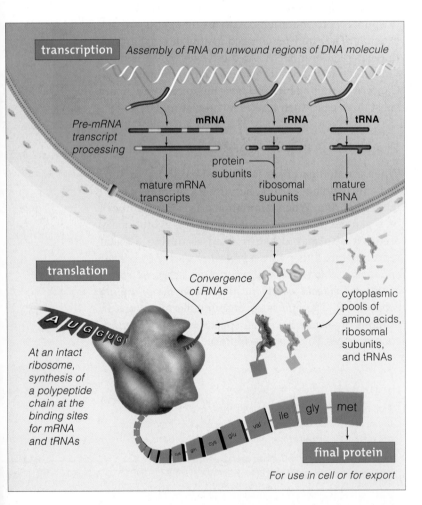

Figure 13.13 Summary of protein synthesis in eukaryotes. DNA is transcribed into RNA in the nucleus. RNA is translated in the cytoplasm. Prokaryotic cells don't have a nucleus; transcription and translation proceed in their cytoplasm.

Self-Quiz

Answers in Appendix III

1. DNA contains many different genes that are transcribed into different _____ .
   - a. proteins
   - b. mRNAs only
   - c. mRNAs, tRNAs, rRNAs
   - d. all of the above

2. An RNA molecule is typically _____ .
   - a. a double helix
   - b. single-stranded
   - c. double-stranded
   - d. triple-stranded

3. An mRNA molecule is synthesized by _____ .
   - a. replication
   - b. duplication
   - c. transcription
   - d. translation

4. Each codon specifies a (an) _____ .
   - a. protein
   - b. polypeptide
   - c. amino acid
   - d. mRNA

5. Anticodons pair with _____ .
   - a. mRNA codons
   - b. DNA codons
   - c. RNA anticodons
   - d. amino acids

6. Match the terms with the most suitable description.
   - _____ alkylating agent
   - _____ chain elongation
   - _____ exons
   - _____ genetic code
   - _____ anticodon
   - _____ introns
   - _____ codon

   - a. parts of mature mRNA transcript
   - b. base triplet for amino acid
   - c. second stage of translation
   - d. base triplet; pairs with codon
   - e. one environmental agent that induces mutation in DNA
   - f. set of 64 codons in mRNA
   - g. the parts removed from a pre-mRNA transcript before translation

Critical Thinking

1. *Antisense drugs* may help us fight cancer and viral diseases, including SARS. They are short mRNA strands that are complementary to the mRNAs associated with these illnesses. Speculate on how these drugs work.

2. A DNA polymerase made an error while a crucial gene region of DNA was being replicated. DNA repair enzymes didn't detect or repair the damage. Here is the part of the DNA strand that contains the error:

...AATTCCGACTCCTATGG
...TTAAGGTTGAGGATACC

After the DNA molecule is replicated, two daughter cells form. One daughter cell is carrying the mutation and the other cell is normal. Develop a hypothesis to explain this observation.

3. *Neurofibromatosis* is a human autosomal dominant disorder caused by mutations in the *NF1* gene. It is characterized by the formation of soft, fibrous tumors in the peripheral nervous system and skin as well as abnormalities in muscles, bones, and internal organs (Figure 13.14).

Because the gene is dominant, an affected child usually has an affected parent. Yet in 1991, scientists reported on a boy who had neurofibromatosis whose parents did not. When they examined both copies of his *NF1* gene, they found the copy he had inherited from his father contained a transposon. Neither the father nor the mother had a transposon in any of the copies of their own *NF1* genes. Explain the cause of neurofibromatosis in the boy and how it arose.

4. Cigarette smoke is mostly carbon dioxide, nitrogen, and oxygen. The rest contains at least fifty-five different chemicals that have been identified as carcinogenic, or cancer-causing, by the International Agency for Research on Cancer (IARC). When these carcinogens enter the bloodstream, enzymes convert them to a series of chemical intermediates in an attempt to make them easier to excrete. Some of the intermediates bind irreversibly to DNA. Speculate on one mechanism by which smoking causes cancer.

5. Using the data in Figure 13.6, translate the following mRNA segment into an amino acid sequence:

5'-GGUUUCUUCAAGAGA-3'

6. The termination of DNA transcription by prokaryotic RNA polymerases depends in some cases on the structure of the newly forming RNA transcript. The terminal end of an mRNA chain often folds back on itself and makes a hairpin-looped structure like the one shown to the right.

Why do you suppose a "stem-loop" structure such as this one causes RNA polymerases to stop transcription when they reach it?

```
                C
             U—C
             G—C
             A—U
             C—G
             C—G
             G—C
             C—G
             C—G
...CCCACAG—CAUUUUU...
```

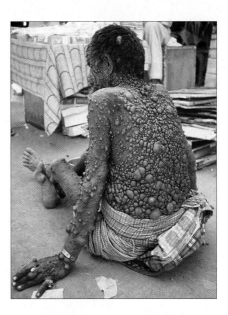

Figure 13.14 Soft skin tumors on a person with neurofibromatosis, an autosomal dominant disorder.

Media Menu

Student CD-ROM

Impacts, Issues Video
  Ricin and Your Ribosomes
Big Picture Animation
  Protein synthesis and its control
Read-Me-First Animation
  Transcription
  Translation
Other Animations and Interactions
  Modification of a messenger RNA
  The genetic code
  A base-pair substitution

InfoTrac

- UCLA Molecular Biologists Unravel Mysteries of "Factory of Life." *Ascribe Higher Education News Service*, March 2002.
- Killing the Messenger: Turning Off RNA Could Thwart Cancer and AIDS. *Scientific American*, August 2002.
- Study: "Jumping Genes" Create Ripples in the Genome—and Perhaps Species' Evolution. *Ascribe Higher Education News Service*, August 2002.

Web Sites

- DNA-RNA-Protein: www.nobel.se/medicine/educational/dna/
- Bringing RNA into View: gslc.genetics.utah.edu/units/rna/
- What Makes a Firefly Glow?: gslc.genetics.utah.edu/units/basics/firefly

How Would You Vote?

Scientists in Texas produced a vaccine that protects mice against ricin. Vaccination involves injection of a nonfunctional form of ricin; the active site of its catalytic chain has been altered. The vaccine still has to be tested in humans. Assuming it turns out to be safe, would you support a mass immunization program for the public?

IMPACTS, ISSUES *Between You and Eternity*

You are in college, your whole life ahead of you. Your risk of developing cancer is as remote as old age, an abstract statistic that is easy to forget.

"There is a moment when everything changes—when the width of two fingers can suddenly be the total distance between you and eternity." Robin Shoulla wrote those words after being diagnosed with breast cancer. She was only seventeen. At an age when most young women are thinking about school, parties, and potential careers, Robin was dealing with a radical mastectomy, pleading with her oncologist not to use her jugular vein for chemotherapy, wondering if she would survive through the next year (Figure 14.1).

Robin became an annual statistic—one of 10,000 or so females and males under age forty who develop breast cancer. About 180,000 new cases are diagnosed each year in the United States population at large.

Cancers are as diverse as their underlying causes, but several gene mutations predispose individuals to developing certain kinds. Either the mutant genes are inherited or they mutate spontaneously in individuals after being assaulted by environmental agents, such as toxic chemicals and ultraviolet radiation.

One gene on chromosome 17 encodes *Her2*, a type of membrane receptor. *Her2* is part of a control pathway that governs the cell cycle—that is, when and how often cells divide. It also is one of the **proto-oncogenes**. When mutated or overexpressed, such genes help bring about cancerous transformations. Cells of about

organized clusters of normal cells

loose, irregular clusters of cancer cells

Figure 14.1 Breast cancer. (**a**) Infiltrating ductal carcinoma cells form irregular clusters in breast tissue. (**b**) Robin Shoulla. Diagnostic tests revealed the presence of such cells in her body.

the big picture

Types of Control Mechanisms Whether and how a gene is expressed depends on regulatory proteins that interact with DNA, RNA, proteins, and one another. It also depends on the attachment and detachment of certain functional groups to the DNA.

Gene Control in Prokaryotes Being tiny single cells and fast reproducers, prokaryotic cells make rapid responses to short-term changes in nutrient availability and other aspects of the environment. They compensate for the changes by quickly adjusting gene transcription rates.

25 percent of breast cancer patients have too many *Her2* receptors or extra copies of the gene itself. They divide too fast, and abnormal masses of cells result.

Proteins encoded by two different genes, *BRCA1* and *BRCA2*, are among the tumor suppressors that help keep benign or cancerous cell masses from forming. The filmstrip shows part of one of the proteins, which are crucial for DNA repair processes. When *BRCA1* or *BRCA2* is mutated, a cell's capacity to fix breaks in DNA or correct replication errors is compromised. Diverse mutations are free to accumulate throughout the DNA, and such an accumulation leads to cancer.

BRCA1 and *BRCA2* are known as *breast cancer genes*, because cancerous breast cells often hold mutated versions of them. A female in which a *BRCA* gene has mutated in one of three especially dangerous ways has about an 80 percent chance of developing breast cancer before reaching seventy.

Robin Shoulla survived. She may never know which mutation caused her cancer. Thirteen years later, she has what she calls a normal life—a career, husband, children. Her goal is to grow very old with grey hair and spreading hips, smiling.

Robin's story invites you to enter the world of **gene controls**, the molecular mechanisms that govern when and how fast specific genes will be transcribed and translated, and whether gene products will be switched on or silenced. You will be returning to the impact of such controls in many chapters throughout the book.

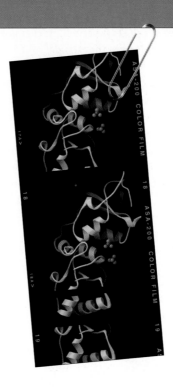

 How Would You Vote?

Some females at high risk of developing breast cancer opt for prophylactic mastectomy, the surgical removal of one or more breasts even before cancer develops. Many of them would never have developed cancer. Should the surgery be restricted to cancer treatment? See the Media Menu for details, then vote online.

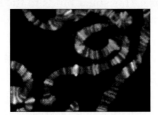

Gene Control in Eukaryotes Like prokaryotes, eukaryotic cells control short-term shifts in diet and activity. Unlike prokaryotes, they also control a long-term program of development, which is based largely on selective gene expression and cell differentiation.

Researching Gene Controls In complex, multicelled eukaryotes, cascades of gene controls guide development of a single fertilized egg into a complete individual with a predictable body plan. A century of research with the common fruit fly has yielded clues about how these controls work.

14.1 Some Control Mechanisms

When, how, and to what extent any gene is expressed depends on the type of cell, its functions, its chemical environment, and signals from the outside.

Diverse mechanisms control gene expression through interactions with DNA, RNA, and new polypeptide chains or the final proteins. Some respond to rising or falling concentrations of specific substances in a cell. Others respond to external signaling molecules.

Control agents include **regulatory proteins** that intervene before, during, or after gene transcription or translation. They include signaling molecules such as hormones, which initiate changes in cell activities when they dock at suitable receptors.

With **negative control**, regulatory proteins slow or stop gene action; with **positive control**, they promote or enhance it. Some DNA base sequences that don't encode proteins are sites of transcriptional control. A **promoter** is a common type of noncoding sequence that marks where to start transcription. **Enhancers** are binding sites for some activator proteins.

Chemical modification offers more control. With methylation, for example, methyl groups ($-CH_3$) get attached to specific regions of newly replicated DNA and prevent access to them. Many heavily methylated genes are activated when the groups are stripped off. Attachment of acetyl groups to histones that organize DNA also exerts control (Section 8.1 and Figure 14.2).

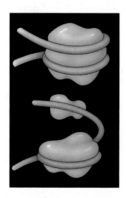

Figure 14.2 How loosening of the DNA–histone packaging in chromosomes may expose genes for transcription. Attachment of an acetyl group to a histone makes it loosen its grip on the DNA that is wound around it. Enzymes that are associated with transcription attach or detach acetyl groups.

You'll read about major signaling mechanisms later. Here, we will sample the events they set in motion.

Gene expression is controlled by regulatory proteins that interact with one another, with control elements built into the DNA, with RNA, and with newly synthesized proteins.

Control also is exerted through chemical modifications that inactivate or activate specific gene regions or the histones that organize the DNA.

14.2 Prokaryotic Gene Control

Think about the dot of the letter "i." About a thousand bacterial cells would stretch side by side across the dot—and each depends as much on gene controls as you do!

Prokaryotic cells grow and divide fast when nutrients are plentiful and other conditions also favor growth. At such times, controls promote the rapid synthesis of enzymes for nutrient absorption and other growth-related metabolic events. Genes that specify enzymes for a metabolic pathway often occur as a linear set in the DNA. And they all may be transcribed together, in a single RNA strand.

NEGATIVE CONTROL OF THE LACTOSE OPERON

With this bit of background, consider an example of how one kind of prokaryote responds to the presence or absence of lactose. *Escherichia coli* lives in the gut of mammals, where it dines on nutrients traveling past. Milk typically nourishes mammalian infants. It does not contain glucose, the sugar of choice for *E. coli*. It does contain lactose, a different sugar.

After being weaned, infants of most species drink little (if any) milk. Even so, *E. coli* cells can still use lactose if and when it shows up in the gut. They can activate a set of three genes for lactose-metabolizing enzymes. A promoter precedes all three genes in *E. coli* DNA, and operators flank it. An **operator** is a binding site for a repressor, a regulatory protein that stops transcription. Such an arrangement, in which a promoter and a set of operators control more than one bacterial gene, is called an **operon** (Figure 14.3).

In the absence of lactose, a repressor molecule binds to a set of operators. Binding causes the DNA region that contains the promoter to twist into a loop, as in Figure 14.3*b*. RNA polymerase, the workhorse that transcribes genes, can't bind to a looped-up promoter. So operon genes aren't used when they aren't required.

When lactose *is* in the gut, *E. coli* converts some of it to allolactose. This sugar binds to the repressor and changes its molecular shape. The altered repressor can't bind to operators. The looped DNA unwinds and RNA polymerase transcribes the genes, so lactose-degrading enzymes are produced when required.

POSITIVE CONTROL OF THE LACTOSE OPERON

E. coli cells pay far more attention to glucose than to lactose. They transcribe genes for its breakdown faster, and continuously. Even when lactose is in the gut, the lactose operon is not used much—unless there is no glucose. Such conditions call for an **activator** protein

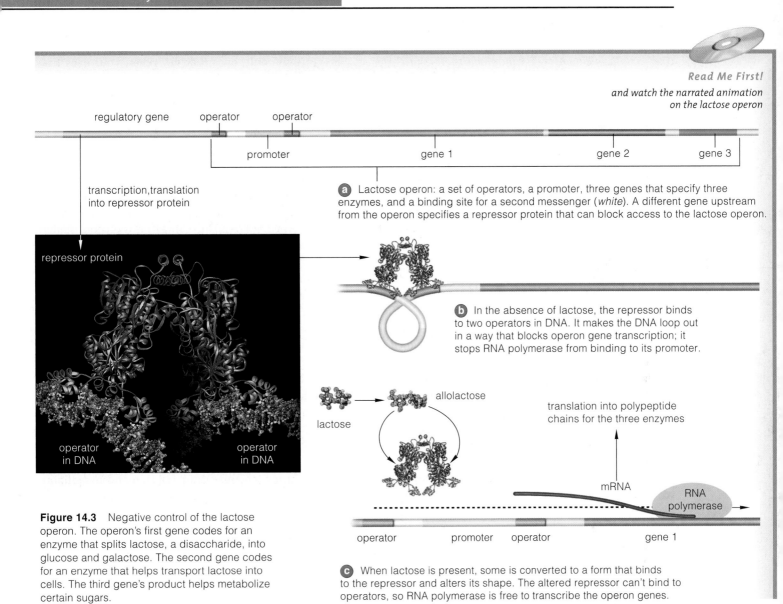

Read Me First!
and watch the narrated animation
on the lactose operon

regulatory gene   operator   operator

promoter   gene 1   gene 2   gene 3

transcription,translation
into repressor protein

a Lactose operon: a set of operators, a promoter, three genes that specify three enzymes, and a binding site for a second messenger (*white*). A different gene upstream from the operon specifies a repressor protein that can block access to the lactose operon.

repressor protein

b In the absence of lactose, the repressor binds to two operators in DNA. It makes the DNA loop out in a way that blocks operon gene transcription; it stops RNA polymerase from binding to its promoter.

operator in DNA   operator in DNA

allolactose

lactose

translation into polypeptide chains for the three enzymes

mRNA

RNA polymerase

operator   promoter   operator   gene 1

Figure 14.3 Negative control of the lactose operon. The operon's first gene codes for an enzyme that splits lactose, a disaccharide, into glucose and galactose. The second gene codes for an enzyme that helps transport lactose into cells. The third gene's product helps metabolize certain sugars.

c When lactose is present, some is converted to a form that binds to the repressor and alters its shape. The altered repressor can't bind to operators, so RNA polymerase is free to transcribe the operon genes.

known as CAP (short for catabolite activator protein). This activator exerts positive control over the lactose operon by making a promoter far more inviting to RNA polymerase. But CAP can't issue the invitation until it is bound to a chemical messenger called cAMP (cyclic adenosine monophosphate). When cAMP and this activator join together and bind to the promoter, they make it far easier for RNA polymerase to start transcribing genes.

When glucose is plentiful, ATP forms by glycolysis, but synthesis of an enzyme necessary to make cAMP is blocked. Blocking is lifted when glucose is scarce and lactose becomes available. cAMP accumulates, CAP–cAMP complexes form, and the lactose operon genes are transcribed. The gene products allow lactose to be used as an alternative energy source.

Unlike cells of *E. coli*, many of us develop *lactose intolerance*. Cells making up the lining of our small intestine make and then secrete lactase into the gut. As many people age, however, concentrations of this lactose-digesting enzyme decline. Lactose accumulates and ends up in the large intestine (colon), where it promotes population explosions of resident bacteria. As the bacteria digest the lactose, a gaseous metabolic product accumulates, distends the colon, and causes pain. Short fatty acid chains released by the bacteria also lead to diarrhea, which can be severe.

Transcription rates of bacterial genes for nutrient-digesting enzymes are quickly adjusted downward and upward by control systems that respond to nutrient availability.

14.3 Eukaryotic Gene Control

Like bacteria, eukaryotic cells control short-term shifts in diet and in levels of activity. If those cells happen to be among hundreds or trillions of cells in a multicelled organism, long-term controls also enter the picture. They orchestrate gene interactions during development.

SAME GENES, DIFFERENT CELL LINEAGES

Later in the book, you will be reading about how you and other complex organisms developed from a single cell. For now, tentatively accept this premise: All cells of your body started out life with the same genes, because every one arose by mitotic cell divisions from the same fertilized egg. And they all transcribe many of the same genes, because they are alike in most aspects of structure and basic housekeeping activities.

In other ways, however, *nearly all of your body cells became specialized in composition, structure, and function.* This process of **cell differentiation** occurs during the development of all multicelled organisms. Differences arise among cells that use different subsets of genes. Specialized tissues and organs are the result.

For example, nearly all of your cells continually transcribe genes for the enzymes of glycolysis. Only immature red blood cells can transcribe the genes for hemoglobin. Your liver cells transcribe genes required to make enzymes that neutralize certain toxins, but they are the only ones that do. When your eyes first formed, certain cells accessed the genes necessary for synthesizing crystallin. No other cells can activate the genes for this protein, which helps make transparent fibers of the lens in each eye.

WHEN CONTROLS COME INTO PLAY

Ultimately, gene expression is all about controlling the amounts and kinds of proteins present in a cell in any specified interval. Just imagine the coordination that goes into making, stockpiling, using, exporting, and degrading thousands of types of proteins in the same moment of cellular time.

Most genes in complex, multicelled organisms are switched off, either permanently or part of the time. Expression of the rest is adjusted up and down. Why? Cells continually deliver and secrete substances into tissue fluids—the body's internal environment—and withdraw substances from it. Inputs and outputs cause slight shifts in the concentrations of nutrients, signaling molecules, metabolic products, and other solutes. Homeostasis is maintained as cells respond to these changes by adjusting gene expression.

Controls over gene expression work at certain stages before, during, and after transcription and translation. Figure 14.4 introduces the main control points.

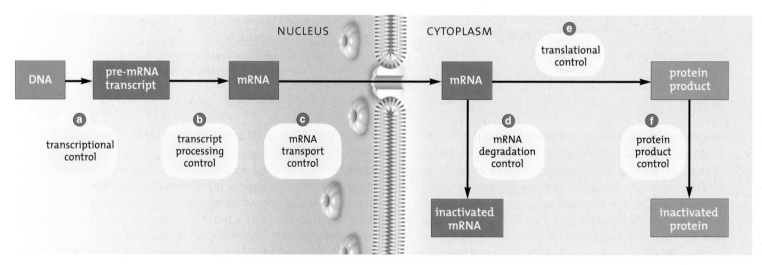

a Chemical modification of DNA restricts access to genes. Genes can be duplicated or rearranged.

b Pre-mRNA spliced in alternative ways can lead to different forms of a protein. Other modifications affect whether a transcript reaches the cytoplasm.

c Transport protein binding determines whether an mRNA becomes delivered to the correct region of cytoplasm for local translation.

d How long an mRNA lasts depends on the proteins that are attached to it and the length of its poly-A tail.

e Translation can be blocked. mRNA cannot attach to a ribosome when proteins bind to it. Initiation factors can be inactivated.

f Processing of new polypeptides may activate or disable them. Control here indirectly affects other activities.

Figure 14.4 Controls that influence whether, when, and how a eukaryotic gene will be expressed.

Figure 14.5 Polytene chromosomes. To sustain their rapid growth rate, *Drosophila* (fruit fly) larvae eat continuously and use a lot of saliva. Giant chromosomes in their salivary gland cells are produced by repeated mitotic DNA replication without cell division. Each strand contains many copies of the same chromosome, aligned side-by-side.

An insect hormone, ecdysone, serves as a regulatory protein; it promotes gene transcription. In response to the hormonal signal, these chromosomes loosen, and they puff out in the regions where genes are being transcribed. Puffs are largest and most diffuse where transcription is most intense.

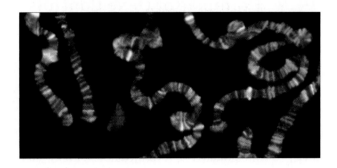

CONTROLS BEFORE TRANSCRIPTION Remember how many histones and other proteins organize the DNA in a eukaryotic chromosome (Section 8.1)? They affect whether RNA polymerase can access genes and start transcription. Methyl, acetyl, and other functional groups attached to the DNA also can block access to genes. In diploid cells, either the maternal or paternal allele at a gene locus may get methylated, which can block the maternal or paternal influence on a trait.

Also before transcription, some controls trigger the duplication or rearrangement of gene sequences. In immature amphibian eggs and gland cells of certain insect larvae, chromosomes are copied repeatedly in an undividing cell. These multiple DNA replications produce *polytene* chromosomes that have hundreds or thousands of side-by-side gene copies (Figure 14.5).

CONTROL OF TRANSCRIPT PROCESSING After genes are transcribed, several mechanisms control what the cell does with the RNA. Transcript processing steps dictate whether, when, and how pre-mRNA becomes translated (Section 13.1). For instance, in different kinds of muscle cells, enzymes remove different parts of the pre-RNA transcript for troponin, a contractile protein. After the remaining exons are spliced together, their protein-building message is unique in one tiny region. In each cell type, the resulting protein works in a distinctive way, which helps account for subtle variations in how different kinds of muscles function.

The nuclear membrane is a barrier between a new mRNA and the cellular machinery that can translate it. Only after the mRNA binds to certain proteins will nuclear pore complexes let it cross to the cytoplasm.

Once in the cytoplasm, an mRNA is guided about according to base sequences in its untranslated ends, which are like zip codes. A transport protein bound to a zip code region delivers the mRNA to a particular area of the cell, where it will be translated or stored. In immature eggs, uneven distribution of "maternal messages" and their protein products determines the head-to-tail polarity of the future developing embryo. Control over mRNA localization occurs in the form of

binding proteins that attach to the zip code region. These delay or block delivery of an mRNA.

Some transcripts are shelved when the cytoplasm has too many Y-box proteins. When phosphorylated, these proteins bind and help stabilize an mRNA, but if too many of them become attached they block its translation. Thus, phosphorylation of Y-box proteins is a control point for mRNA inactivation. The mRNA stored in unfertilized eggs is bound to Y-box proteins.

CONTROLS AT TRANSLATION The greatest range of controls over eukaryotic gene expression operates at translation. This process depends on the coordinated participation of many kinds of molecules, including ribosomal subunits and a host of initiation factors. Each kind of molecule is regulated independently of the other kinds.

The stability of mRNA transcripts is also a control point. The more stable a given transcript is, the more proteins can be produced from it. Enzymes typically start digesting mRNA within minutes, nibbling away at its poly-A tail (Section 13.1). How fast they do the deed depends on the tail's length, on base sequences in untranslated regions and other sequences in the coding region, and on attached proteins.

CONTROLS AFTER TRANSLATION Lastly, control over gene expression is exerted when the protein products are modified, as when phosphate groups are attached to Y-box proteins. Diverse controls activate, inhibit, and stabilize enzymes and other molecules used in protein synthesis. A case in point is allosteric control of tryptophan synthesis, as Section 5.4 describes.

Cell differentiation arises when diverse populations of cells activate or suppress genes in selective, unique ways.

In the cells of complex, multicelled species, gene expression is controlled by mechanisms that govern events before, during, and after transcription and translation.

Most controls over gene expression occur at translation.

14.4 Examples of Gene Controls

Cells rarely use more than 5 to 10 percent of their genes at a given time; controls silence most of them. Which genes are active depends on the type of organism, the stage of growth and development it's passing through, and the controls operating at that stage.

The preceding section introduced you to an important idea. All differentiated cells in a complex, multicelled body use most of their genes in much the same way, but each type also uses a fraction of those genes in a unique, selective way. **Selective gene expression** has made each kind distinctive in one or more aspects of their structure, composition, and function. Here we consider two examples of the controls that guide their selections during embryonic development.

HOMEOTIC GENES AND BODY PLANS

Whether a particular gene gets transcribed depends in part on the action of regulatory proteins, which can bind with promoters, enhancers, or one another. For example, **homeotic genes** are a class of master genes in most eukaryotic organisms. They are transcribed in specific locations in the developing embryo, so their products form in local tissue regions. By interacting with one another and with other control elements, homeotic genes guide formation of organs and limbs by turning on other genes in precise areas, according to a basic body plan.

Homeotic genes were discovered through mutations that cause cells in a *Drosophila* embryo to develop into a body part that belongs somewhere else. For instance, the *antennapedia* gene is supposed to be transcribed where a thorax, complete with legs, should form. In all other regions, cells normally don't transcribe this gene. But Figure 14.6a shows what happens when a mutation allows the gene to be wrongly transcribed in the body region destined to become a head.

Do animals alone have homeotic genes? No. In corn plants, for instance, a different homeotic gene guides the formation of all leaf veins in straight, parallel lines. If the gene mutates, the veins will twist.

Homeotic genes code for regulatory proteins that include a "homeodomain," a sequence of about sixty amino acids. This sequence binds to control elements in promoters and enhancers (Figure 14.6b). More than 100 homeotic genes have been identified in diverse eukaryotes—and the same mechanisms control their transcription. Many of the genes are interchangeable among species as evolutionarily distant as yeasts and humans, so we can expect that they evolved in the most ancient eukaryotic cells. Their protein products often differ only in *conservative* substitutions. In other words, one amino acid has replaced another, but it has similar chemical properties.

X CHROMOSOME INACTIVATION

Diploid cells of female humans and female calico cats have two X chromosomes. One is in threadlike form. The other stays scrunched up, even during interphase. This scrunching is a programmed shutdown of all but about three dozen genes on *one* of two homologous X chromosomes. The shutdown is called **X chromosome inactivation**, and it happens in female embryos of all placental mammals and their marsupial relatives.

Figure 14.7a shows one condensed X chromosome in the nucleus of a cell at interphase. We also call this condensed structural form a Barr body (after Murray Barr, who first identified it).

One X chromosome gets inactivated when embryos are still a tiny ball of cells. In placental mammals, the shutdown is random, in that *either* chromosome could become condensed. The maternal X chromosome may be inactivated in one cell; the paternal or the maternal X chromosome may be inactivated in a cell next to it.

Figure 14.6 (**a**) Experimental evidence of controls over where body parts develop. In *Drosophila* larvae, activation of genes in one group of cells normally results in antennae on the head. A mutation that affects *antennapedia* gene transcription puts legs on the head. This is one of the genes controlled by regulatory proteins that have homeodomains. (**b**) Stick model for the binding of a homeodomain sequence to a transcriptional control site in DNA.

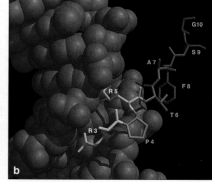

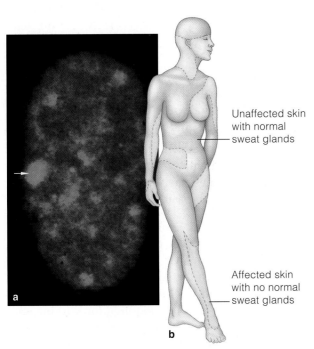

Figure 14.7 (**a**) In the somatic cell nucleus of a human female, a condensed X chromosome, also called a Barr body (*arrow*). The X chromosome in cells of human males is not condensed this way. (**b**) A mosaic tissue effect that shows up in anhidrotic ectodermal dysplasia.

Unaffected skin with normal sweat glands

Affected skin with no normal sweat glands

Figure 14.8 Why is this female cat "calico"? In her body cells, one of her two X chromosomes has a dominant allele for the brownish-black pigment melanin. Expression of the allele on her other X chromosome results in orange fur. When this cat was an embryo, one X chromosome was inactivated at random in each cell that had formed by then.

Patches of different colors reflect which allele was inactivated in cells that formed a given tissue region. White patches are an outcome of an interaction that involves a different gene, the product of which blocks melanin synthesis.

Once that random molecular decision is made in a cell, all of that cell's descendants make the exact same decision as they go on dividing to form tissues. What is the outcome? *A fully developed female has patches of tissue where genes of the maternal X chromosome are being expressed, and patches of tissue where genes of the paternal X chromosome are being expressed.* She has become a "mosaic" for X chromosome expression!

When alleles on two homologous X chromosomes are not identical, differences may occur among patches of tissues throughout the body. Mosaic tissues can be observed in human females who are heterozygous for a rare recessive allele that causes an absence of sweat glands. Sweat glands formed in only parts of their skin. Where the glands are absent, the recessive allele is on the X chromosome that was not shut down. This mosaic effect is one symptom of *anhidrotic ectodermal dysplasia* (Figure 14.7b), a heritable disorder that is characterized by abnormalities in the skin and in the structures derived from it, including teeth, hair, nails, and sweat glands.

A different mosaic tissue effect shows up in female calico cats, of the sort shown in Figure 14.8. These cats are heterozygous for a certain coat color allele on their X chromosomes.

The shutdown isn't an accident of evolution; it has an important function. In mammals, recall, males have one X and one Y chromosome. This means the females have twice as many X chromosome genes. Inactivating one of their X chromosomes balances gene expression between the sexes. The normal development of female embryos depends on this type of control mechanism, which is called **dosage compensation**.

How, in a single nucleus, does one X chromosome get shut down while the other does not? Several molecules participate, including histone methylases and an X chromosome gene called *XIST*. The *XIST* product, a large RNA molecule, binds chromosomal DNA like a gene-masking paint. Although the *XIST* gene is found on both X chromosomes, only one of them expresses it. As it does, it gets fully painted with RNA, and so its genes become inactivated. The other X chromosome does not express *XIST*, and does not become painted. Only the genes on this chromosome remain active and may be transcribed. Why only one of the two X chromosomes expresses *XIST* is not yet fully understood.

Controls over when, how, and to what extent a gene is expressed depend on the type of cell and its functions, on the cell's chemical environment, and on signals for change. Homeotic gene expression and dosage compensation are examples of control mechanisms in eukaryotic cells.

14.5 There's a Fly in My Research

Structural patterns emerge as the embryos of animals and plants develop, and they are both beautiful and fascinating. Researchers have correlated those patterns with the expression of specific genes at particular times, in particular tissues, for diverse organisms.

DROSOPHILA!

For about a hundred years, *Drosophila melanogaster* has been the fly of choice for laboratory experiments. It costs almost nothing to feed and house this tiny fruit fly. *D. melanogaster* reproduces fast in bottles, it has a short life cycle, and disposing of spent bodies after an experiment is a snap. Thanks to automated gene sequencing, we now know how its 13,601 genes are distributed among its four pairs of chromosomes.

Studies of *Drosophila* at the anatomical, cytological, biochemical, and genetic levels continue to reveal much about gene controls over how animal embryos develop. They also yield insights into the evolutionary connections among groups of animals.

CLUES TO GENE CONTROLS

Over the past ten years, *Drosophila* researchers have made remarkable discoveries about how embryos develop, especially through **knockout experiments**. In such experiments, individual genes are deleted from wild-type experimental organisms. Differences between the engineered and wild-type organisms, either morphological or behavioral, are clues to the function of the missing gene.

Knockout experiments have identified many hundreds of *Drosophila* genes, which tend to be named after what happens when they are missing. Many turned out to be homeotic genes. For instance, *eyeless* is a control gene expressed in fruit fly embryos. In its absence, no eyes form. Other named genes include *dunce* (a regulatory protein required for learning and memory), *wingless*, *wrinkled*, *tinman* (necessary for heart development), *minibrain*, and *groucho* (which, among other things, prevents overproduction of whisker bristles). Figures 14.9 and 14.10 show a small sampling of mutant flies.

More ambitious *Drosophila* experiments with deleted genes yield intriguing information about the controls over development. By adding special promoters to a gene, researchers can control its expression with external cues, such as temperature. They also can delete genes from one part of the *Drosophila* genome and insert them into another. This molecular sleight-of-hand with the *eyeless* gene demonstrated that its expression can induce an eye to form not only on the fly's head, but also on the legs, wings, and antennae (Figure 14.10).

Astonishingly, the *eyeless* gene has counterparts in humans (a gene named *Aniridia*), mice (*Pax-6*), and squids (also *Pax-6*). Humans who have no

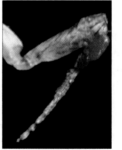 

Figure 14.9 A few *Drosophila* mutants. (**a**) Wild-type (normal) fruit fly. The photograph above it can give you an idea of a fruit fly's size relative to the surface of a peach. (**b**) Yellow miniature. (**c**) Curly wings. (**d**) Vestigial wings.

Figure 14.10 Two more *Drosophila* mutations. *Left*, an eye that formed on a fruit fly leg. *Right*, a fruit fly with a double thorax, the outcome of a homeobox gene mutation.

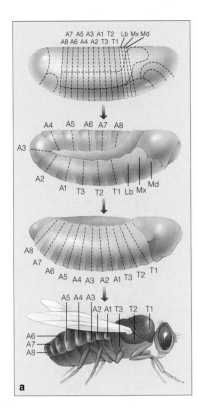

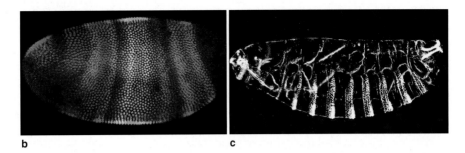

b   c

Figure 14.11 Genes and *Drosophila*'s segmented body plan. (**a**) Fate map for the surface of a *Drosophila* zygote. Such maps indicate where each differentiated cell type in the adult originated. The pattern starts with the polar distribution of maternal mRNA and proteins in the unfertilized egg. This polarity dictates the future body axis. A series of segments will develop along this axis. Genes specify whether legs, wings, eyes, or some other body parts will develop on a particular segment.

Briefly, here's how it happens: Maternal gene products prompt expression of gap genes. Different gap genes become activated in regions of the embryo with higher or lower concentrations of different maternal gene products. Gap gene products influence each other's expression as well. They form a primitive spatial map.

Depending where they occur relative to the concentrations of gap gene products, embryonic cells express different pair-rule genes. Products of pair-rule genes accumulate in seven transverse stripes that mark the onset of segmentation (**b**). They activate other genes, the products of which divide the body into units (**c**). These interactions influence the expression of homeotic genes, which collectively govern the identity of each segment.

functional *Aniridia* genes have eyes without irises. *Aniridia* or *Pax-6* inserted into an *eyeless* mutant fly has the same effect as the *eyeless* gene—it induces eye formation wherever it is expressed. Here is evidence that animals as evolutionarily distant as insects, cephalopods, and mammals are connected by a shared ancestor.

GENES AND PATTERNS IN DEVELOPMENT

Different cells become organized in different ways in a new embryo. They divide, differentiate, and live or die; they migrate or stick to cells of the same type in tissues. Descendant cells fill in the details in orderly patterns, in keeping with a master body plan.

Such master plans consist of genes expressed in certain places at certain times during development. The regional and temporal gene expression generates a three-dimensional map of many overlapping proteins, most of which are transcription factors.

As an embryo develops, certain proteins induce undifferentiated cells to develop into different body tissues, depending on where the cells start out on the map. One example is the development of segments in *Drosophila* embryos (Figure 14.11).

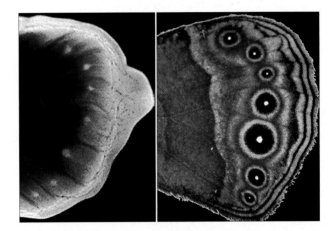

Figure 14.12 *Left*, seven spots in the embryonic wing of a moth larva identify the presence of a gene product that will induce the formation of seven "eyespots" in the wing of the adult (*right*).

Pattern formation is the name for the emergence of embryonic tissues and organs in predictable patterns, in places where we expect them to be. Figures 14.11 and 14.12 are graphic examples. In Section 38.5, you will be taking a closer look at the controlled gene interactions that fill in details of the body plan.

Summary

Section 14.1 Whether, when, and how a gene gets expressed depends on controls over transcription and translation, and on modifications to protein products. Regulatory proteins (e.g., activators and inhibitors of transcription) and hormones are examples of control agents. These controls interact with one another, with control elements built into DNA molecules, with RNA, and with gene products.

With negative control mechanisms, regulatory proteins slow or curtail gene activity. With positive control mechanisms, they promote gene activity.

Section 14.2 Like all cells, prokaryotes respond quickly to short-term shifts in nutrients and other environmental conditions. Most of their gene control mechanisms adjust transcription rates in response to nutrient availability. Bacterial operon systems are examples of prokaryotic gene regulation.

Section 14.3 All cells of complex multicelled eukaryotes inherit the same genes, but each cell type selectively activates or suppresses a fraction of the genes in ways that lead to one or more unique aspects of structure, composition, and function.

At any time, most genes in a eukaryotic cell are shut off, unused. Those that the cell uses for housekeeping purposes, ongoing metabolic functions, are switched on all the time, at low levels. Expression of the other genes is adjustable. When control mechanisms come into play depends on cell type, prevailing chemical conditions, and signals from other cell types that can change a target cell's activities.

Gene expression within a cell changes in response to external conditions and is subject to long-term controls over growth and development. Eukaryotic cells control gene expression at key points, including transcription, RNA processing, RNA transport, mRNA degradation, translation, and protein activity. Translation is the major control point for most eukaryotic genes because so many participating molecules are regulated.

Section 14.4 Selective gene expression is the basis of cell differentiation during growth and development. It gives rise to cells that differ from one another in structure and function.

Complex eukaryotic body plans are influenced by homeotic genes, the master genes that control the emergence of the basic body plan during development.

X-chromosome inactivation is an example of dosage compensation, a control mechanism that maintains a crucial balance of gene expression between the sexes.

Section 14.5 Experiments with *Drosophila* identified a host of control genes. In embryo development, spatial maps of regulatory proteins guide the formation of tissues and organs in expected patterns.

Self-Quiz   *Answers in Appendix III*

1. The expression of a given gene depends on the _____ .
   a. type of cell and its functions c. environmental signals
   b. chemical conditions   d. all of the above

2. Hormones may _____ gene transcription in target cells.
   a. promote   c. participate in
   b. inhibit   d. both a and b

3. Eukaryotic genes guide _____ .
   a. fast short-term activities   c. development
   b. overall growth   d. all of the above

4. Gene expression adjusts in response to changing _____ .
   a. nutrient availability   c. signals from other cells
   b. solute concentrations   d. all of the above

5. Cell differentiation _____ .
   a. occurs in all complex multicelled organisms
   b. requires unique genes in different cells
   c. involves selective gene expression
   d. both a and c
   e. all of the above

6. Regulatory proteins interact with _____ .
   a. DNA   c. gene products
   b. RNA   d. all of the above

7. An operon typically governs _____ .
   a. bacterial genes   c. genes of all types
   b. eukaryotic genes   d. DNA replication

8. In prokaryotic cells but not eukaryotic cells, a(n) _____ is a type of base sequence that precedes genes of an operon.
   a. lactose molecule   c. operator
   b. promoter   d. both b and c

9. A nucleotide sequence that signals the start of a gene is a(n) _____ .
   a. promoter   b. operator   c. enhancer   d. activator

10. Eukaryotic cells in complex organisms regulate gene expression by controlling different processes in _____ .
    a. transcription   e. mRNA degradation
    b. RNA processing   f. protein activity
    c. translation   g. a and d
    d. RNA transport   h. all of the above

11. X chromosome inactivation _____ .
    a. is dosage compensation   c. makes calico cats
    b. balances gene expression d. both a and d

12. Homeotic genes _____ .
    a. are part of a bacterial operon
    b. control eukaryotic body plans
    c. control X chromosome inactivation
    d. both a and c

13. A cell with a Barr body is _____ .
    a. prokaryotic   c. from a female mammal
    b. from a male mammal   d. infected by the Barr virus

14. Match the terms with the most suitable description.
    _____ homeotic gene   a. binding site for repressor
    _____ operator   b. specialization during
    _____ proto-oncogene   development
    _____ differentiation c. inactivated X chromosome
    _____ Barr body   d. can cause cancer
                           e. body plan development

Critical Thinking

1. Distinguish between:
   a. repressor protein and activator protein
   b. promoter and operator

2. Define three types of gene controls. Do they work for both prokaryotic and eukaryotic cells?

3. Unlike most rodents, guinea pigs are well developed at the time of birth. Within a few days, they can eat grass, vegetables, and other plant material. Suppose a breeder decides to separate baby guinea pigs from their mothers after three weeks. He wants to keep the males and females in different cages. However, he has trouble identifying the sex of young guinea pigs. Suggest how a microscope can help him identify their sex.

4. A plant, a fungus, and an animal consist of diverse cell types. How might this diversity arise, given that body cells in each of these organisms inherit the same set of genetic instructions? As part of your answer, define cell differentiation and the general way that selective gene expression brings it about.

5. In what fundamental way do negative and positive controls of transcription differ? Is the effect of one or the other form of control (or both) reversible?

6. If all cells in your body start out life with the same inherited information on how to build proteins, then what caused the differences between a red blood cell and a white one? Between a white blood cell and a nerve cell?

7. *Duchenne muscular dystrophy*, a genetic disorder, affects boys almost exclusively. Early in childhood, muscles begin to atrophy (waste away) in affected individuals, who typically die in their teens or early twenties.

   Muscle biopsies of a few women who carry an allele that is associated with the disorder identified some body regions of atrophied muscle tissue. They also showed that muscles adjacent to a region of atrophy were normal or even larger and more chemically active, as if to compensate for the weakness of the adjoining region.

   Form a hypothesis about the genetic basis of Duchenne muscular dystrophy that includes an explanation of why it might appear in some body regions but not others.

8. The closer a mammalian species is to humans in its genetic makeup, the more useful information it yields in laboratory studies of the mechanisms of cancer. Do you support the use of any mammal for cancer research? Why or why not?

9. Geraldo isolated an *E. coli* strain in which a mutation has hampered the capacity of CAP to bind to a region of the lactose operon, as it would do normally. How will this mutation affect transcription of the lactose operon when the *E. coli* cells are exposed to the following conditions? Briefly state your answers:
   a. Lactose and glucose are both available.
   b. Lactose is available but glucose is not.
   c. Both lactose and glucose are absent.

10. Calico cats are almost always female. A male calico cat is usually sterile. Briefly explain why.

11. The *Drosophila* embryo in Figure 14.13 displays a repeating pattern of gene expression. Reflect on Figure 14.11, then think about the gene product that made the red rings. What type of gene specified this product?

Figure 14.13 *Drosophila* zygote. The fluorescent rings are evidence that a gene is being expressed in certain regions.

Media Menu

Student CD-ROM

Impacts, Issues Video
  Between You and Eternity
Big Picture Animation
  Regulating and researching gene expression
Read-Me-First Animation
  The lactose operon
Other Animations and Interactions
  X chromosome inactivation in a calico cat

InfoTrac

- How Hibernators Might One Day Solve Medical Problems. *The Lancet*, October 2001.
- Face Shift: How Sleeping Sickness Parasites Evade Human Defenses. *Scientific American*, May 2002.
- Researchers Discover DNA Packaging in Living Cells Is Dynamic. *Ascribe Higher Education News Service*, January 2003.
- Silence of the Xs. *Science News*, August 2001.

Web Sites

- The lac Repressor: www.rcsb.org/pdb/molecules/pdb39_1.html
- Genomes in Flux: opbs.okstate.edu/~melcher/MG/MGW3/MG3.html
- Mutant Fruit Flies: www.exploratorium.edu/exhibits/mutant_flies

How Would You Vote?

Women and men with particular gene mutations are far more susceptible to developing breast cancer than people who do not carry those mutations. Prophylactic mastectomy reduces their risk by the surgical removal of one or both breasts before cancer can develop. Statistically, most of the people who opt for prophylactic mastectomy would never have developed cancer in the first place. Should mastectomy be restricted to people who have already developed cancer?

IMPACTS, ISSUES   *Golden Rice or Frankenfood?*

Not too long ago, the World Health Organization made a conservative estimate that 124 million children around the world show vitamin A deficiencies. These children may become permanently blind and develop other disorders. Researchers began working on a solution. They transferred three genes into rice plants. The genes directed the plants to make beta-carotene, a yellow pigment that is a precursor for vitamin A. Eating just 300 grams per day of the new "golden rice" might be enough to prevent vitamin A deficiency.

No one wants children to suffer or die. But many people oppose the idea of genetically modified foods, including golden rice. Possibly they are unaware of the history of agrarian societies. It isn't as if our ancestors were twiddling their green thumbs. For thousands of years, their artificial selection practices coaxed new plants and new breeds of cattle, cats, dogs, and birds from wild ancestral stocks. Meatier turkeys, seedless watermelons, big juicy corn kernels from puny hard ones—the list goes on (Figure 15.1).

And we're newcomers at this! During the 3.8 billion years before we even made our entrance, nature busily conducted uncountable numbers of genetic experiments by way of mutation, crossing over, and gene transfers

Figure 15.1 Snapshots from our food spectrum: Too little food in Ethiopia and lots of Indonesian rice plants. *Above*, an artificial selection success story—a big kernel from a modern strain of corn next to tiny kernels of an ancestral corn species discovered in a prehistoric cave in Mexico.

the big picture

The Genome Project   The discovery of the structure of DNA in 1953 sparked intense interest in creating technologies to manipulate that structure. Fifty years later, the entire sequence of bases in the human genome was completed.

Tools of the Trade   Scientists use DNA technologies to cut, identify, isolate, clone, copy, sequence, compare, and manipulate the DNA of any organism they wish to study. They put these technologies to practical use in genetic engineering.

between species. These processes introduced changes in the molecular messages of inheritance, and today we see their outcomes in the sweep of life's diversity.

Maybe the unsettling thing about the more recent human-directed changes is that the pace has picked up, hugely. We're getting pretty good at tinkering with the genetics of many organisms. We do this for pure research and for useful, practical applications.

Some say we must never alter the DNA of anything. The concern is that we as a species simply do not have the wisdom to bring about genetic changes without causing irreparable harm. One is reminded of our very human tendency to leap before we look.

And yet, we dream of the impossible. Something about the human experience gave us a capacity to imagine wings of our own making, and that capacity carried us to the frontiers of space. Someone else dreamed of turning plain rice into more nutritious food that might keep some children from going blind.

Many economic questions also remain unanswered. For example, will the patents on golden rice translate into higher production costs for the rural farmers of developing countries that urgently need the rice? Will transfer of beta-carotene genes disrupt a rice plant's messages of inheritance in some unexpected way?

The questions confronting you are these: Should we be more cautious, believing the risk takers may go too far? What do we stand to lose if risks are not taken?

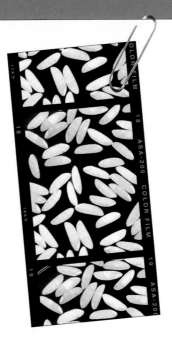

 How Would You Vote?

Nutritional labeling is required on all packaged food in the United States, but genetically modified food products may be sold without labeling. Should food distributors be required to label all products made from genetically modified plants or livestock? See the Media Menu for details, then vote online.

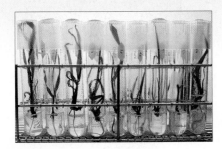

Genetic Engineering Normal or modified genes are being inserted into individual organisms both for research and practical applications. Genetically modified organisms help farmers produce food more efficiently. They are also a source of biomaterials and pharmacologic products.

Bioethics The human genome has been sequenced, and the findings are being used for gene therapy and other applications. Many ethical and social issues remain unresolved as objections to the use of genetic engineering continue.

15.1 Tinkering With the Molecules of Life

In this unit, you started with cell division mechanisms that allow parents to pass on DNA to new generations. You moved to the chromosomal and molecular basis of inheritance, then on to gene controls that guide life's continuity. The sequence parallels the history of genetics. And now, you have arrived at the point where geneticists hold molecular keys to the kingdom of inheritance.

EMERGENCE OF MOLECULAR BIOLOGY

In 1953, James Watson and Francis Crick unveiled their model of the DNA double helix and ignited a global blaze of optimism about genetic research. The very book of life seemed to open up for scrutiny. In reality, it dangled just beyond reach. Major scientific breakthroughs are seldom accompanied by the simultaneous discovery of the tools necessary to study them. New methods of DNA research had to be invented before that book could become readable.

In 1972, Paul Berg and his associates were the first to make **recombinant DNA**. They fused fragments of DNA from one species into the genetic material from a different species, which they had grown in the laboratory. Their new recombinant DNA technique allowed them to isolate and replicate manageable subsets of DNA from any organism they wanted to study. The science of molecular biology was born, and suddenly everybody was worried about it.

Although researchers knew that DNA was not toxic, they could not predict with absolute certainty what would happen every time they fused genetic material from different organisms. Would they create new super-pathogens by accident? Could DNA from normally harmless organisms be fused to create a new form of life? What if their creation escaped into the environment and transformed other organisms?

In a remarkably quick and responsible display of self-regulation, scientists reached a consensus on safety guidelines for DNA research. Adopted at once by the National Institutes of Health (NIH), the guidelines listed laboratory procedural precautions. They covered the design and use of host organisms that could survive only under the narrow range of conditions that occur in the laboratory. Researchers stopped using the DNA from pathogenic or toxic organisms for recombination experiments until proper containment facilities were developed.

A golden age of recombinant DNA research soon followed. The emphasis had shifted from DNA's chemical and physical properties to its specific molecular structure. In 1977, Allan Maxam, Walter Gilbert, and Fred Sanger developed a method for determining the nucleotide sequence of cloned DNA fragments. The tools for reading the book of life, opened more than twenty years before, were now available for everyone to use.

DNA sequencing was cool, a visually rewarding, data-rich technique that entranced more than a few scientists. Unbelievable amounts of sequence data accumulated, from unbelievably diverse organisms. Computer technology at the time was advancing simultaneously, but it was barely keeping pace with

Figure 15.2 A few bases of the human genome—and a few of the supercomputers used to sequence it—at Celera Genomics in Maryland.

the tremendous demand for sequence data analysis and storage. In 1982, the NIH provided three million dollars to fund the first large-scale DNA database in the United States, one accessible to the public.

THE HUMAN GENOME PROJECT

Around 1986, everyone seemed to be arguing about sequencing the human genome. A **genome** is all the DNA in a haploid number of chromosomes. Many scientists insisted that the benefits for medicine and pure research would be incalculable. Others said the mapping would divert funding from other studies that had greater urgency as well as more likelihood of success.

At the time, sequencing three billion bases was a daunting and seemingly impossible task. With the techniques available at the time, it would have taken a worldwide consortium at least fifty years just to identify the sequence, even before deciphering what it meant. But techniques were getting better every year, and more bases were being sequenced and analyzed in less time. Automated (robotic) sequencing had just been invented, as had PCR, the polymerase chain reaction. Although both techniques were still cumbersome, expensive, and far from standardized, many sensed their potential for molecular biology.

Sequencing was still laborious. Waiting for faster methods seemed to be the most efficient means of sequencing the human genome, but exactly when was the technology going to be fast *enough*? Who would decide?

It was during this heated debate in 1987 that several independent organizations launched their own versions of the Human Genome Project. Among them was a company started by Walter Gilbert. He declared that his company would not only sequence the human genome, it would also patent the genome.

In early 1988, the NIH effectively annexed the entire Human Genome Project by hiring Watson as its head and providing researchers with 200 million dollars per year. A consortium formed between the NIH and other institutions working on different versions of the project.

Watson set aside 3 percent of the funding to study ethical and social issues arising from the research. He resigned in 1992 because of a disagreement with the NIH about patenting partial gene sequences. Francis Collins replaced him in 1993.

Amid ongoing squabbles over patent issues, the bulk of genome project sequencing in the United States continued at the NIH until 1998, when the

Figure 15.3 Everyone pitches in. The Dalai Lama prepares mouse DNA for sequencing during his 2003 visit to Whitehead Institute/MIT Center for Genome Research in Cambridge, Massachusetts.

scientist Craig Venter started Celera Genomics (Figure 15.2). Venter declared that *his* new company would be the first to complete the genome sequence. His challenge prompted the United States government to move its sequencing efforts into high gear.

Sequencing of the human genome was officially completed in 2003—fifty years after the discovery of DNA structure. About 99 percent of the coding regions in human DNA have been deciphered with a high degree of accuracy. A number of other genomes also have been fully sequenced (Figure 15.3).

What do we do with this vast amount of data? The next step is to investigate questions about precisely what that sequence means—where the genes are, where they are not, what the control mechanisms are and how they operate.

Recently, more than 21,000 human genes were identified. This doesn't mean we know what all those genes encode; it only means we know they are definitely genes. One of the many interesting discoveries is that the first intron and the last exon of most gene sequences are longer than the others. They may actually be part of an as yet undiscovered transcriptional control mechanism.

15.2 A Molecular Toolkit

Analysis of genes starts with manipulation of DNA. With molecular tools, researchers can cut DNA from different sources, then splice the fragments together.

THE SCISSORS: RESTRICTION ENZYMES

In 1970, Hamilton Smith and his colleagues were studying viral infection of *Haemophilus influenzae*, a species of bacteria. The bacteria protected themselves from infection by cutting up the invading viral DNA before it inserted itself into the bacterial chromosome.

Smith isolated one of the bacterial enzymes that was cutting up the viral DNA, the first known **restriction enzyme**. In time, several hundred strains of bacteria and a few eukaryotic cells yielded thousands more. Each restriction enzyme cuts double-stranded DNA at a specific base sequence between four and eight base pairs in length. Most of these recognition sites contain the same nucleotide sequence on both strands of the DNA. For instance, GAATTC is recognized on both strands and cut by the enzyme EcoRI.

Many restriction enzymes make staggered cuts that put a single-stranded "tail" on DNA fragments. Such cuts have a "sticky" end—a single-stranded tail. That tail can base-pair with a tail of another DNA molecule cut by the same enzyme, because the sticky ends of both fragments will match up (Figure 15.4a).

Tiny nicks remain when the fragments base-pair. A different enzyme, **DNA ligase**, seals the nicks, which results in a recombinant DNA molecule (Figure 15.4b). Recombinant DNA can consist of base sequences from different organisms of the same or different species.

CLONING VECTORS

Bacterial cells, recall, have only one chromosome—a circular DNA molecule. But many also have plasmids. A **plasmid** is a small circle of extra DNA with just a few genes (inset, *left*). It gets replicated right along with the bacterial chromosome. Bacteria normally can live without plasmids. Even so, some plasmid genes are useful, as when they confer resistance to antibiotics.

Under favorable conditions, bacteria divide often, so huge populations of genetically identical cells form swiftly. Before each division, replication enzymes copy both the chromosomal DNA *and* the plasmid DNA, in some cases repeatedly. This gave researchers an idea. Why not try to insert a fragment of foreign DNA into a plasmid and see if a bacterial cell replicates it?

A modified plasmid that accepts foreign DNA and slips into a host bacteria, yeast, or some other cell is a **cloning vector**. Cloning vectors usually have multiple cloning sites, which are several unique restriction enzyme sequences clustered in one part of the vector. As you'll see later, the vector also has genes that help researchers identify which cells it slips into, such as genes for antibiotic resistance (Figure 15.5).

A cell that takes up a cloning vector may found a huge population of descendant cells, each containing an identical copy of the vector and the foreign DNA inserted into it. Collectively, all of the identical cells hold many "cloned" copies of the foreign DNA.

Such DNA cloning is a tool that helps researchers amplify and harvest unlimited amounts of particular DNA fragments for their studies (Figure 15.6).

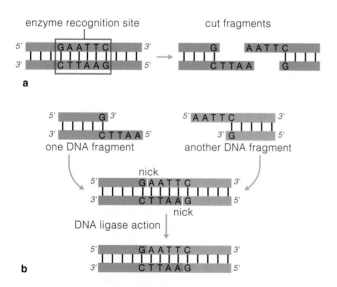

Figure 15.4 (**a**) Formation of restriction fragments and (**b**) splicing fragments into a recombinant DNA molecule.

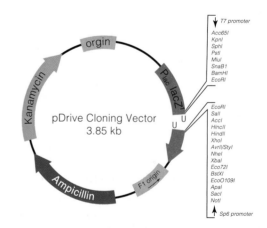

Figure 15.5 A commercially available cloning vector, with its useful restriction enzyme sites listed at right. This vector includes antibiotic resistance genes (*blue*) and the bacterial *lacZ* gene (*red*). These genes help researchers identify cells that take up recombinant molecules.

Read Me First!
*and watch the narrated animation
on DNA recombination*

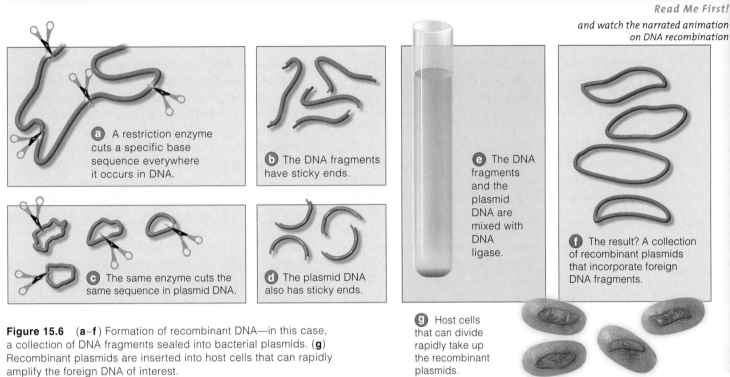

a A restriction enzyme cuts a specific base sequence everywhere it occurs in DNA.

b The DNA fragments have sticky ends.

c The same enzyme cuts the same sequence in plasmid DNA.

d The plasmid DNA also has sticky ends.

e The DNA fragments and the plasmid DNA are mixed with DNA ligase.

f The result? A collection of recombinant plasmids that incorporate foreign DNA fragments.

g Host cells that can divide rapidly take up the recombinant plasmids.

Figure 15.6 (**a–f**) Formation of recombinant DNA—in this case, a collection of DNA fragments sealed into bacterial plasmids. (**g**) Recombinant plasmids are inserted into host cells that can rapidly amplify the foreign DNA of interest.

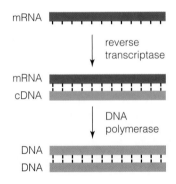

Figure 15.7 How to make cDNA. Reverse transcriptase catalyzes the assembly of a single DNA strand on an mRNA template, forming an mRNA–cDNA hybrid molecule. Next, DNA polymerase replaces the mRNA with another DNA strand. The result is double-stranded DNA.

cDNA CLONING

Chromosomal DNA usually contains introns (Section 13.1). Sometimes it's impossible to tell whether a gene sequence is part of an intron or exon or to pinpoint where it starts and ends. A researcher investigating gene products or gene expression focuses on mRNA, because the introns have already been snipped out of it. All that's left is coding sequence and some small signal sequences. Any time a gene is being expressed, mRNA is being transcribed, so cells that are actually using a gene will also contain the mRNA it encodes.

Restriction enzymes do not cut RNA, so mRNA cannot be cloned until it has been translated first into DNA. Replication enzymes isolated from viruses or bacteria can be used to translate the mRNA *in vitro*, or inside a test tube. **Reverse transcriptase** is a viral enzyme that uses the mRNA as a template. Using free nucleotides, it assembles a single strand of **cDNA**, or *complementary* DNA, on the template (Figure 15.7). A hybrid molecule is the outcome; one strand of mRNA and one strand of cDNA are base-paired together.

DNA polymerase added to the mix strips the RNA from the hybrid molecule as it copies the first strand of cDNA into a second strand. The result is a double-stranded DNA copy of the original mRNA. And that copy may be used for cloning.

Molecular biologists manipulate DNA and RNA. Restriction enzymes cut DNA from organisms of the same or different species, and ligases glue the fragments into plasmids.

A recombinant plasmid is a cloning vector; it can slip into bacteria, yeast, or other cells that divide rapidly. Host cells make multiple, identical copies of the foreign DNA.

Reverse transcriptase uses mRNA as a template to make cDNA.

15.3 Haystacks to Needles

Any genome consists of thousands of genes. E. coli has 4,279; humans have about 30,000. To study or modify any one of those genes, researchers must first find it among all others in the genome, and it's like searching for a needle in a haystack. Once found, it must be copied many times to make enough material for experiments.

ISOLATING GENES

Each **gene library** is a collection of bacterial cells that house different cloned fragments of DNA. We call the cloned fragments of an entire genome a *genomic* library. By contrast, a *cDNA library* is derived from mRNA.

A particular gene of interest must be isolated from millions of other genes. Clones containing that gene are mixed up in a library with thousands or millions of others that do not. A **probe**, a short stretch of DNA labeled with a radioisotope (or sometimes a pigment), may be used to find a one-in-a-million clone. Probes distinguish one DNA sequence from all of the others in a library of clones or any other collection of mixed DNA. A radiolabeled probe base-pairs with DNA in the gene region of interest, then researchers can find it with devices that detect radiation. Such base-pairing between DNA (or RNA) from more than one source is known as **nucleic acid hybridization**.

How do researchers make a suitable probe? If they already know the desired gene sequence, they can use it to design and build an oligomer (a short stretch of nucleotides). Or they can use DNA from a closely related gene as a probe even if it isn't an exact match.

Figure 15.8 shows steps of one probe hybridization technique. Bacterial cells containing a gene library are spread apart on the surface of a solid growth medium, usually enriched agar, in a petri dish. Individual cells undergo repeated divisions, which form large clusters, or colonies, of genetically identical bacterial cells.

Press a piece of nylon or nitrocellulose paper on top of the petri dish and some of the cells from each colony will stick to it, mirroring the distribution of all colonies on the dish. Soaking the paper in an alkaline solution ruptures the cells, which releases their DNA. The solution also denatures the DNA, separating it into single strands that stick to the paper in the spots

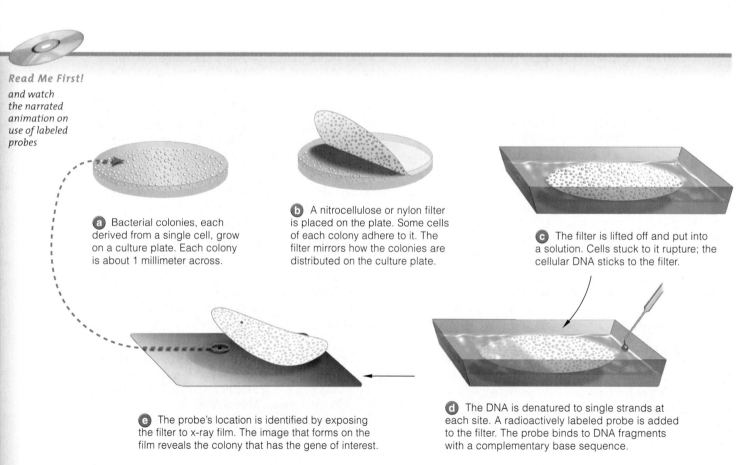

Read Me First!
and watch the narrated animation on use of labeled probes

a Bacterial colonies, each derived from a single cell, grow on a culture plate. Each colony is about 1 millimeter across.

b A nitrocellulose or nylon filter is placed on the plate. Some cells of each colony adhere to it. The filter mirrors how the colonies are distributed on the culture plate.

c The filter is lifted off and put into a solution. Cells stuck to it rupture; the cellular DNA sticks to the filter.

e The probe's location is identified by exposing the filter to x-ray film. The image that forms on the film reveals the colony that has the gene of interest.

d The DNA is denatured to single strands at each site. A radioactively labeled probe is added to the filter. The probe binds to DNA fragments with a complementary base sequence.

Figure 15.8 Use of a radioactive probe to identify a bacterial colony that contains a targeted gene.

Read Me First!
and watch the narrated
animation on PCR

where the colonies were. When the probe is washed over the paper, it hybridizes with, or sticks to, only the DNA that has the target sequence. The hybridized probe makes a radioactive spot that can be detected with x-ray film. The position of the spot on the film reflects the position of the original colony on the petri dish. Cells from that colony alone are cultured to isolate the cloned gene of interest.

PCR

Researchers may replicate a gene, or part of it, with **PCR** (Polymerase Chain Reaction). PCR uses primers and a heat-tolerant polymerase for a hot–cold cycled reaction that replicates targeted DNA fragments. And it can replicate them by a billionfold. This technique can transform one needle in a haystack, that one-in-a-million DNA fragment, into a huge stack of needles with a little hay in it.

Figure 15.9 shows the reaction steps. **Primers** are synthetic nucleotide oligomers, usually between ten and thirty bases long. They are designed to base-pair with specific nucleotide sequences on either end of the fragment of interest. In a PCR reaction, researchers mix primers, DNA polymerase, nucleotides, and the DNA, which will act as a template for replication. Then the researchers expose the mixture to repeated cycles of high and low temperatures. The two strands of a DNA double helix separate into single strands at high temperature. When the mixture is cooled, some of the primers will hybridize with the DNA template.

The elevated temperatures required to separate DNA strands destroy typical DNA polymerases. But the heat-tolerant DNA polymerase employed for PCR reactions is from *Thermus aquaticus*, a bacterium that lives in superheated water springs (Chapter 19). Like all DNA polymerases, it recognizes primers bound to DNA as places to initiate synthesis.

Synthesis proceeds along the DNA template until the temperature cycles up and the DNA strands are separated again. When the temperature cycles down, primers rehybridize, and the reactions start all over. With each round of temperature cycling, the number of copies of targeted DNA can double. PCR quickly and exponentially amplifies even a tiny bit of DNA.

Probes may be used to help identify one particular gene among many in gene libraries.

The polymerase chain reaction (PCR) is a method of rapidly and exponentially amplifying DNA samples of interest.

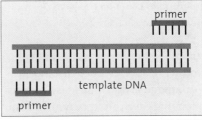

a Primers, free nucleotides, and DNA template are mixed with heat-tolerant DNA polymerase.

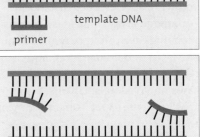

b When the mixture is heated, the DNA denatures. When it is cooled, some primers hydrogen-bond to the DNA template.

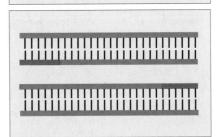

c *Taq* polymerase uses the primers to initiate synthesis, copying the DNA template. The first round of PCR is completed.

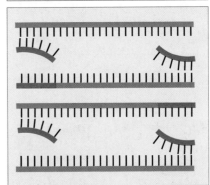

d The mixture is heated again. This denatures all the DNA into single strands. When the mixture is cooled, some of the primers hydrogen-bond to the DNA.

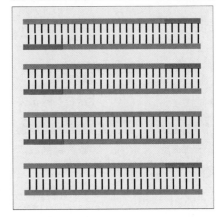

e *Taq* polymerase uses the primers to initiate synthesis, copying the DNA. The second round of PCR is complete. Each successive round of synthesis can double the number of DNA molecules.

Figure 15.9 Two rounds of the polymerase chain reaction, or PCR. A bacterium, *Thermus aquaticus*, is the source of the *Taq* polymerase. Thirty or more cycles of PCR may yield a billionfold increase in the number of starting DNA template molecules.

15.4 First Just Fingerprints, Now DNA Fingerprints

Except for identical twins, no two people have exactly the same base sequence in their DNA. Scientists can distinguish one person from another on the basis of differences in those sequences.

Each human has a unique set of fingerprints. Like all other sexually reproducing species, each also has a **DNA fingerprint**—a unique array of DNA sequences inherited in a Mendelian pattern from parents. More than 99 percent of the DNA is the same in all humans, but the other 1 percent is unique to each individual. These unique stretches of DNA are sprinkled through the human genome as **tandem repeats**—many copies of the same short DNA sequences, positioned one after the other along the length of a chromosome.

For example, one person's DNA might contain four repeats of the bases TTTTC in a certain location. Another person's DNA might have them repeated fifteen times in the same location. One person might have five repeats of CGG, and another might have fifty. Such repetitive sequences slip spontaneously into the DNA during replication, and their numbers grow or shrink over time. The mutation rate is high in these regions.

DNA fingerprinting reveals differences in the tandem repeats among individuals. A restriction enzyme cuts their genomic DNA into an assortment of fragments. The sizes of those fragments are unique to the individual. They reveal genetic differences between individuals, and they can be detected as RFLPs (restriction fragment length polymorphisms).

The differences show up with **gel electrophoresis**. In this technique, an electric field pulls a sample of DNA fragments through a slab of a semisolid matrix, such as an agar gel. Fragments of different sizes migrate through the matrix at different rates. Larger molecules are hindered by the matrix more than smaller ones, much as elephants are slower than tigers at slipping between trees in a dense forest. In short, gel electrophoresis separates the fragments of DNA according to their length. After a time, the different fragments separate into distinct bands.

A banding pattern of genomic DNA fragments is the DNA fingerprint unique to the individual. It is identical only between identical twins. Otherwise, the odds of two people sharing an identical DNA fingerprint are one in three trillion.

PCR can also be used to amplify tandem-repeat regions. Differences in the size of the resulting amplified DNA fragments are again detected with gel electrophoresis. A few drops of blood, semen, or cells from a hair follicle at a crime scene or on a suspect's clothing yield enough DNA to amplify with PCR, and then generate a fingerprint.

DNA fingerprints help forensic scientists identify criminals, victims, and innocent suspects. Figure 15.10 shows some tandem repeat RFLPs that were separated by gel electrophoresis. Those samples of DNA had been taken from seven people and from a bloodstain left at a crime scene. One of the DNA fingerprints matched.

Defense attorneys initially challenged the use of DNA fingerprinting as evidence in court. Today, however, the procedure has been firmly established as accurate and unambiguous. DNA fingerprinting is routinely submitted as evidence in disputes over paternity, and it is being widely used to convict the guilty and exonerate the innocent. To date, such evidence has already helped release 143 innocent people from prison.

DNA fingerprint analysis also has confirmed that human bones exhumed from a shallow pit in Siberia belonged to five individuals of the Russian imperial family, all shot to death in secrecy in 1918. It also was used to identify the remains of those who died in the World Trade Center on September 11, 2001.

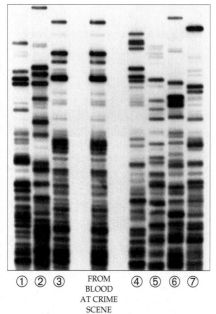

① ② ③ FROM BLOOD AT CRIME SCENE ④ ⑤ ⑥ ⑦

Figure 15.10 Damning comparison of the DNA fingerprints from a bloodstain left behind at a crime scene and from blood samples of seven suspects (the circled numbers). Can you point out which of the seven is a match?

15.5 Automated DNA Sequencing

Sequencing reveals the order of nucleotides in DNA. This technique uses DNA polymerase to partially replicate a DNA template. In current research labs, manual methods have been replaced largely by automated techniques.

Automated DNA sequencing can reveal the sequence of a stretch of cloned or PCR-amplified DNA in just a few hours. Researchers use four standard nucleotides (T, C, A, and G). They also use four modified versions, which we represent as T*, C*, A*, and G*. Each of the four types of modified nucleotide has become labeled with a pigment that will fluoresce in a particular color when it passes through a laser beam.

Researchers mix all eight kinds of nucleotides with a single-stranded DNA template, a primer, and DNA polymerase. The polymerase uses the primer to copy the template DNA into new strands of DNA. One by one, it adds nucleotides in the order dictated by the sequence of the DNA template.

Each time, the polymerase randomly attaches one of the standard *or* one of the modified nucleotides to the DNA template. When one of the modified nucleotides becomes covalently bonded to the newly forming DNA strand, it stops further synthesis of that strand. After enough time passes, there will be some new strands that stop at each base in the DNA template sequence.

Eventually the mixture holds millions of copies of DNA fragments, all fluorescent-tagged. The fragments are now separated by gel electrophoresis, which is part of an automated sequencer. Shortest fragments migrate fastest and reach the end of the block of gel first; the longest fragment is last. Fragments of the same length migrate through the gel at the same speed, and they form observable bands (Figure 15.11*a*).

Each fragment passes through a laser beam, and the modified nucleotide attached to its tail end makes it fluoresce a certain color. The sequencer detects and records the fluorescent colors as the fragments pass through the end of the gel. Because each color codes for a particular nucleotide, the order of colored bands is the DNA sequence. The machine itself assembles the sequence data.

Figure 15.11*b* shows partial results from a run through an automated DNA sequencer. Each peak in the tracing represents the detection of one fluorescent color as the fragments reached the end of the gel. The sequence is shown beneath the graph line.

With automated DNA sequencing, the order of nucleotides in a DNA fragment that has been cloned or amplified can be determined rapidly.

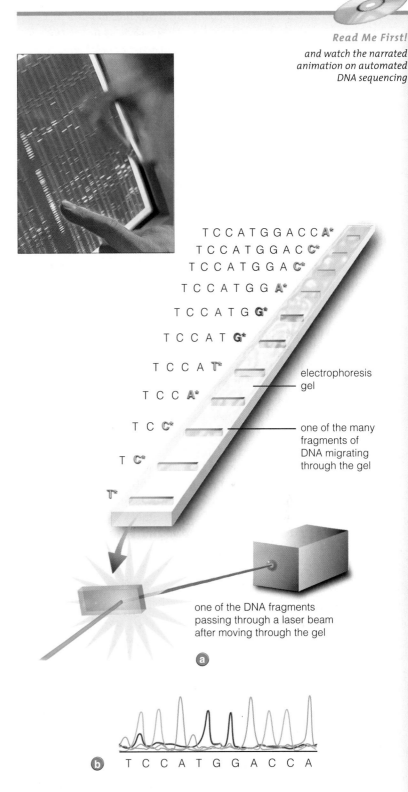

Read Me First!
and watch the narrated animation on automated DNA sequencing

electrophoresis gel

one of the many fragments of DNA migrating through the gel

one of the DNA fragments passing through a laser beam after moving through the gel

(a)

(b) T C C A T G G A C C A

Figure 15.11 Automated DNA sequencing. (**a**) DNA fragments are synthesized using a template and fluorescent nucleotides. The bands are separated by gel electrophoresis. (**b**) The order of the fluorescent bands that appear in the gel is detected by the automated sequencer, and indicates the template DNA sequence. Today, researchers use sequence databases that are accessible globally via the Internet.

15.6 Practical Genetics

Even the tiniest living organisms are able to make complex organic compounds. Researchers harness this ability for practical purposes in genetic engineering.

DESIGNER PLANTS

As crop production expands to keep pace with human population growth, it puts unavoidable pressure on ecosystems everywhere. Irrigation leaves mineral and salt residues in soils. Tilled soil erodes, taking topsoil with it. Runoff clogs rivers, and fertilizer in it causes algae to grow so much that fish suffocate. Pesticides harm humans, other animals, and beneficial insects.

Pressured to produce more food at lower cost and with less damage to the environment, some farmers are turning to genetically engineered crop plants.

Genetic engineering is the process of changing the genetic makeup of an organism, often with intent to alter one or more aspects of phenotype. Researchers may accomplish this by transferring a gene from one species into another species, or by modifying a gene and inserting it into an organism of the same species.

Cotton plants with a built-in insecticide gene kill only the insects that eat it, so farmers that grow them don't have to use as many pesticides. Genetically modified wheat has double yields per acre. Certain transgenic tomato plants survive in salty soils that wither other plants; they also absorb and store excess salt in their leaves, thus purifying saline soil for future crops. *Transgenic* simply refers to an organism into which DNA from another species has been inserted, as in Figures 15.12 and 15.13.

a　　　　　　　　　　b

Figure 15.12 Transgenic plants. (**a**) Cotton plant (*left*), and cotton plant with a gene for herbicide resistance (*right*). Both were sprayed with weed killer. (**b**) Genetically engineered aspen seedlings in which lignin biosynthesis has been partially blocked. Unmodified seedling is on the left.

The cotton plants in Figure 15.12*a* were genetically engineered for resistance to a relatively short-lived herbicide. Spraying fields with this herbicide will kill all weeds but not the engineered cotton plants. The practice means farmers can use fewer and less toxic chemicals. They also don't have to till the soil as much to control weeds, so there is less river-clogging runoff.

Aspen tree seedlings in which a lignin biosynthesis pathway has been modified still make lignin, but not as much—and root, stem, and leaf growth are greatly enhanced (Figure 15.12*b*). Wood from lignin-deficient trees makes it easier to manufacture paper and clean-burning fuels such as ethanol.

Read Me First!

and watch the narrated animation on gene transfer

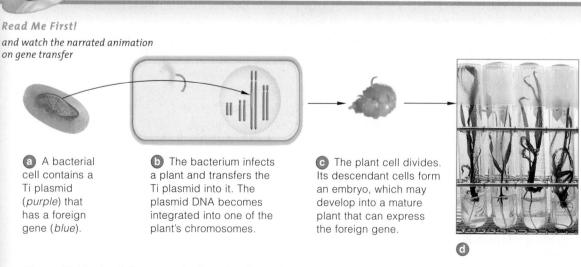

a A bacterial cell contains a Ti plasmid (*purple*) that has a foreign gene (*blue*).

b The bacterium infects a plant and transfers the Ti plasmid into it. The plasmid DNA becomes integrated into one of the plant's chromosomes.

c The plant cell divides. Its descendant cells form an embryo, which may develop into a mature plant that can express the foreign gene.

d

e Example of a young plant with a fluorescent gene product.

Figure 15.13 (**a–d**) Gene transfer from *Agrobacterium tumefaciens* to a plant cell using a Ti plasmid. (**e**) A transgenic plant expressing a firefly gene for the enzyme luciferase.

Figure 15.14 Two genetically modified animals: (**a**) Mira, a goat transgenic for human antithrombin III, an anticlotting factor. (**b**) This transgenic mouse has been engineered to produce green fluorescent protein (GFP).

(**c**) A featherless chicken breed developed by traditional cross-breeding methods in Israel. They thrive in desert environments where cooling systems are not an option. Chicken farmers in the United States have lost millions of feathered chickens at a time when temperatures skyrocketed.

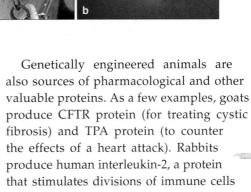

Engineering plant cells starts with vectors that can carry genes into plant cells. *Agrobacterium tumefaciens* is a bacterial species that infects eudicots, including beans, peas, potatoes, and other vital crops. Its plasmid genes cause tumor formation on these plants; hence the name Ti plasmid (*Tumor-inducing*). The Ti plasmid is used as a vector for transferring new or modified genes into plants.

Researchers excise the tumor-inducing genes, then insert a desired gene into the plasmid (Figure 15.13). Some plant cells cultured with the modified plasmid take it up. Whole plants may be regenerated.

Modified *A. tumefaciens* bacteria deliver genes into monocots that also are food sources, including wheat, corn, and rice. Researchers can also transfer genes into plants by way of electric shocks, chemicals, or blasts of microscopic particles coated with DNA.

BARNYARD BIOTECH

The first mammals enlisted for experiments in genetic engineering were laboratory mice. Transgenic mice appeared on the research scene in 1982 when scientists built a plasmid containing a gene for rat somatotropin (also known as growth hormone). They injected the recombinant DNA into fertilized mouse eggs, which were subsequently implanted into female mice. One-third of the resulting offspring grew much larger than their littermates—the rat gene had become integrated into their DNA and was being expressed.

Transgenic animals are now used routinely for medical research. The function and regulation of many gene products have been discovered using "knockout mice," in which targeted genes are inactivated. Defects in the resulting mice give clues about the gene. Strains of mice engineered to be susceptible to human diseases allow researchers to study both the diseases and their cures without experimenting on humans.

Genetically engineered animals are also sources of pharmacological and other valuable proteins. As a few examples, goats produce CFTR protein (for treating cystic fibrosis) and TPA protein (to counter the effects of a heart attack). Rabbits produce human interleukin-2, a protein that stimulates divisions of immune cells (T-lymphocytes). Cattle, too, may soon be producing human collagen that can be used to repair cartilage, bone, and skin. Goats make spider silk protein that might be used to make bullet-proof vests, medical supplies, and space equipment. Other goats make human antithrombin, used to treat people with blood clotting disorders (Figure 15.14*a*).

Genetic engineering has also given us dairy goats with healthier milk, pigs whose manure is easier on the environment, freeze-resistant salmon, extra-hefty sheep, low-fat pigs, mad cow disease-resistant cows, and even allergen-free cats.

Tinkering with the genetics of animals for the sake of human convenience does raise some serious ethical issues, particularly because failed experiments can have gruesome results. However, is transgenic animal research simply an extension of thousands of years of acceptable barnyard breeding practices (Figure 15.14*c*)? The techniques have changed, but not the intent. Like our ancestors, we continue to have a vested interest in improving our livestock.

Transgenic plants help farmers grow crops more efficiently and with less impact on the environment.

Transgenic animals are widely used in medical research. Some are sources of medically valued proteins and other biomaterials. Food animals are being altered to be more nutritious, disease resistant, or easier to raise.

15.7 Weighing the Benefits and Risks

We as a society continue to work our way through the ethical implications of DNA research even while we are applying the new techniques to medicine, industry, agriculture, and environmental remediation.

WHO GETS WELL?

More than 15,500 genetic disorders affect between 3 and 5 percent of all newborns, and they cause 20 to 30 percent of all infant deaths per year. They account for about 50 percent of the mentally impaired and nearly 25 percent of all hospital admissions.

Rhys Evans (Figure 15.15*a*) was born with a severe immune deficiency known as SCID-X1, which stems from mutations in gene *IL2RG*. Children affected by this disorder can live only in germ-free isolation tents, because they cannot fight infections.

In 1998, a virus was used to insert nonmutated copies of *IL2RG* into stem cells taken from the bone marrow of eleven boys with SCID-X1. *Stem* cells are still "uncommitted" and have the potential to differentiate into other types, including white blood cells of the immune system. Each child's modified stem cells were infused back into his bone marrow. Months afterward, ten of the children left their isolation tents for good. Their immune systems had been repaired by the gene therapy. Since then, many other SCID-X1 patients, including Rhys Evans, have been cured in other gene therapy trials.

In 2002, two children from the initial experiment in 1998 developed leukemia. Their illness surprised researchers, who had anticipated that any cancer related to the therapy would be extremely rare. An overproduction of white blood cells (T-lymphocytes) caused the leukemia in both children. The very gene targeted for repair work— *IL2RG*—may be the problem, particularly when combined with the viral vector used in the gene therapy. No other children in any gene therapy experiments for SCID-X1 have developed leukemia. Even so, our understanding of the human genome clearly lags behind our ability to modify it.

WHO GETS ENHANCED?

Modifying the human genome has profound ethical implications even beyond the unexpected risks. To many of us, human gene therapy to correct genetic disorders seems like a socially acceptable goal. Now take this idea one step further. Is it acceptable to change some genes of a normal human in order to alter or enhance traits?

Through gene transfers, researchers have already engineered strains of mice with enhanced memory and learning abilities. Maybe their work heralds help for Alzheimer's disease patients, perhaps even for those who just want more brain power.

The idea of being able to select desirable human traits is referred to as *eugenic engineering*. Yet who decides which forms of a trait are the most desirable? Realistically, cures for many severe but rare genetic disorders will not be pursued because the payback for research is not financially attractive. Eugenics, however, might turn a profit. Just how much would potential parents pay to engineer tall or blue-eyed or fair-skinned children? Would it be okay to engineer

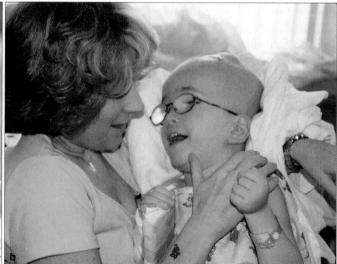

Figure 15.15 Experimental gene therapy patients. (**a**) Rhys Evans was born with a gene that causes SCID-X1. His immune system never developed in a way that could fight infections. A gene transfer freed him from life in a germ-free isolation tent. (**b**) Max Randell smiles at his mother after receiving gene therapy in 2001 for Canavan's disease. This is a degenerative and fatal disease of the central nervous system. At the time of this writing, Max is alive and doing well.

"superhumans" who have breathtaking strength or intelligence? How about an injection that would help you lose extra weight, and keep it off permanently? The borderline between interesting and abhorrent is not the same for everyone.

In a survey conducted not long ago in the United States, more than 40 percent of those interviewed said it would be fine to use gene therapy to make smarter and better looking babies. In one poll of British parents, 18 percent were willing to use genetic enhancement to prevent their children from being aggressive, and 10 percent were willing to use it to keep them from growing up to be homosexual.

KNOCKOUT CELLS AND ORGAN FACTORIES

Each year, about 75,000 people are on waiting lists for an organ transplant, but human donors are in short supply. There is talk of harvesting organs from pigs (Figure 15.16), because pig organs function very much like ours do. Transferring an organ from one species into another is called **xenotransplantation**.

The human immune system battles anything that it recognizes as "nonself." It rejects a pig organ at once. A certain sugar molecule occurs on the plasma membrane of cells that make up a pig organ's blood vessels. Antibodies circulating in human blood latch on to that sugar quickly and doom the transplant. Within a few hours, cascading reactions lead to massive coagulation inside the organ's blood vessels, and failure is swift. Drugs can suppress this immune response, but there's a serious side effect: the drugs make organ recipients vulnerable to infections.

Pig DNA contains two copies of *Ggta1*, the gene for alpha-1,3-galactosyltransferase. This enzyme catalyzes a key step in biosynthesis of alpha-1,3-galactose, the pig sugar that human antibodies recognize. Researchers succeeded in knocking out both copies of the *Ggta1* gene in transgenic piglets. Without the gene, the pigs lack alpha-1,3-galactose. If one of their organs or tissues is transplanted, the human immune system might not recognize it. The tissues and organs from such animals could benefit millions of people, including those who suffer from diabetes or Parkinson's disease.

Critics of xenotransplantation are concerned that, among other things, pig–human transplants would invite pig viruses to cross species and infect humans, perhaps catastrophically. Their concerns are not unfounded. In 1918, an influenza pandemic killed twenty million people worldwide. It originated with a swine flu virus—in pigs.

Figure 15.16 Inquisitive transgenic pig at the Virginia Tech Swine Research facility.

REGARDING "FRANKENFOOD"

Genetically engineered food crops are widespread in the United States. At least 45 percent of cotton crops, 38 percent of soybean crops, and 25 percent of corn crops are now engineered to withstand weedkillers or to make their own pesticides. For years, modified corn and soybeans have been used in tofu, breakfast cereals, soy sauce, vegetable oils, beer, and soft drinks. They are fed to farm animals. Engineered crop plants hold down food production costs, reduce dependence on pesticides and herbicides, and enhance crop yields. Food plants are being designed for flavor, nutritional value, and extended shelf life.

In Europe especially, public resistance to modified food runs high. Besides arguing that modified foods might be toxic and have lower nutritional value, many people worry that designer plants might cross-pollinate wild plants and produce "superweeds."

The chorus of critics in Europe may provoke a trade war with the United States. The outcome is not small potatoes, so to speak. In 1998, the value of American agricultural exports was about 50 billion dollars. Restrictions will profoundly impact agriculture in the United States, and inevitably the impact will trickle down to what you eat and how much you pay for it.

All of which invites you to read scientific research and form your own opinions. The alternative is to be swayed by media hype (the term "Frankenfood," for instance), or by potentially biased reports from other groups that might have a different agenda (such as chemical pesticide manufacturers).

15.8 Brave New World

The structural and comparative analysis of genomes is yielding information about evolutionary trends as well as potential therapies for genetic diseases.

GENOMICS

Research into genomes of humans and other species has converged into a new research field—**genomics**. The *structural* genomics branch deals with the actual mapping and sequencing of genomes of individuals. The *comparative* genomics branch is concerned with finding evolutionary relationships among groups of organisms. Comparative genomics researchers analyze similarities and differences among genomes.

Comparative genomics has practical applications as well as potential for research. The basic premise is that the genomes of all existing organisms are derived from common ancestors. For instance, pathogens share some conserved genes with human hosts even though the lineages diverged long ago. Shared gene sequences, how they are organized, and where they differ may hold clues to where our immune defenses against pathogens are strongest or the most vulnerable.

Genomics has potential for **human gene therapy**—the transfer of one or more normal or modified genes into a person's body cells to correct a genetic defect or boost resistance to disease. However, even though the human genome is fully sequenced, it is not easy to manipulate within the context of a living individual.

Experimenters employ stripped-down viruses as vectors that inject genes into human cells. Some gene therapies deliver modified cells into a patient's tissue. In many cases, therapies make a patient's symptoms subside even when the modified cells are producing just a small amount of a required protein.

However, no one can yet predict where virus-injected genes will end up in a person's chromosomes. The danger is that the insertion will disrupt other genes, particularly those controlling cell division and growth. One-for-one gene swaps with recombination methods are possible but still experimental.

DNA CHIPS

Analysis of genomes is now advancing at a stunning pace. Researchers pinpoint which genes are silent and which are being expressed with the use of **DNA chips**. These are microarrays of thousands of gene sequences representing an entire genome—all stamped onto a glass plate about the size of a smallish business card.

A fluorescent labeled cDNA probe is made using mRNA, say, from cells of a cancer patient. Only the

Figure 15.17 Complete yeast genome array on a DNA chip that is about 19 millimeters (3/4 inch) across. Green spots pinpoint the genes that are active during fermentation. Red spots pinpoint the ones used during aerobic respiration. Yellow spots indicate genes active during both pathways.

genes expressed at the time the cells are harvested will be making mRNA, so they alone will make up the resulting probe population. The labeled probe is then incubated with a chip made from genomic DNA. Wherever the probe binds with complementary base sequences on the chip, there will be a spot that glows under fluorescent light. Analysis of which spots on the chip are glowing reveals which of the thousands of genes inside the cells are active and which are not.

DNA chips are being used to compare different gene expression patterns between cells. Examples are yeasts grown in the presence and absence of oxygen, and different types of cells from the same multicelled individual. RNA from one set of cells is transformed into green fluorescent cDNA, and RNA from the other set into red fluorescent cDNA. The cDNAs are mixed and incubated with a genomic DNA chip. Green or red fluorescence indicates expression of genes in the different cell types. Yellow is a mixture of both red and green, and it indicates that both genes were being expressed at the same time in a cell (Figure 15.17).

In genomics, new techniques such as DNA chips allow researchers to rapidly evaluate and compare genome-spanning expression patterns.

Summary

Section 15.1 Discovery of DNA's double helical structure sparked interest in deciphering its genetic messages. A global race to complete the sequence of the human genome spurred rapid development of new techniques to study and manipulate DNA. The entire human genome has been sequenced and is now being analyzed. Genomes of other organisms have been sequenced as well.

Section 15.2 Recombinant DNA technology uses restriction enzymes that cut DNA into fragments. The fragments may be spliced into cloning vectors by using DNA ligase. Recombinant plasmids are taken up by rapidly dividing cells, such as bacteria, to make multiple, identical copies of the foreign DNA. Reverse transcriptase copies mRNA into cDNA for cloning.

Section 15.3 A gene library is a mixed collection of cells that have taken up cloned DNA. A particular gene can be isolated from a library by using a probe, a short stretch of DNA that can base-pair with the gene and that is traceable with a radioactive or pigment label. Probes help researchers identify one particular clone among millions of others. Base-pairing between nucleotide sequences from different sources is called nucleic acid hybridization.

The polymerase chain reaction (PCR) is a way to rapidly copy particular pieces of DNA. A sample of a DNA template is mixed with nucleotides, primers, and a heat-resistant DNA polymerase. Each round of PCR proceeds through a series of temperature changes that amplifies the number of DNA molecules exponentially.

Section 15.4 Tandem repeats are multiple copies of a short DNA sequence that follow one another along a chromosome. The number and distribution of tandem repeats, unique in each person, can be revealed by gel electrophoresis; they form a DNA fingerprint.

Section 15.5 Automated DNA sequencing rapidly reveals the order of nucleotides in DNA fragments. As DNA polymerase is copying a template DNA, progressively longer fragments stop growing when one of four different fluorescent nucleotides becomes attached. Electrophoresis separates the resulting labeled fragments of DNA into bands according to length. The order of the colored bands as they migrate through the gel reflects which fluorescent base was added to the end of each fragment, and so indicates the template DNA base sequence.

Section 15.6 Genetic engineering is the directed modification of the genetic makeup of an organism, often with intent to modify its phenotype. Researchers insert normal or modified genes from one organism into another of the same or different species. Gene therapies also reinsert altered genes into individuals.

Genetically engineered bacteria produce medically valued proteins. Transgenic crop plants help farmers produce food more efficiently. Genetic engineering of animals allows commercial production of human proteins, as well as research into genetic disorders.

Section 15.7 Human gene therapy and modification of animals for xenotransplantation are examples of developing technologies. As with any new technology, potential benefits must be weighed against potential risks, including ecological and social repercussions.

Section 15.8 Genomics, the study of human and other genomes, is shedding light on evolutionary relationships and has practical uses. Human gene therapy transfers normal or modified genes into body cells to correct genetic defects. Gene chips are used to compare patterns of gene expression.

Self-Quiz   Answers in Appendix III

1. _____ is the transfer of normal genes into body cells to correct a genetic defect.
   a. Reverse transcription   c. PCR
   b. Nucleic acid hybridization   d. Gene therapy

2. DNA is cut at specific sites by _____ .
   a. DNA polymerase   c. restriction enzymes
   b. DNA probes   d. reverse transcriptase

3. Fill in the blank: A _____ is a small circle of bacterial DNA that is not part of the bacterial chromosome.

4. By reverse transcription, _____ is assembled on a(n) _____ template.
   a. mRNA; DNA   c. DNA; ribosomes
   b. cDNA; mRNA   d. protein; mRNA

5. PCR stands for _____ .
   a. polymerase chain reaction
   b. polyploid chromosome restrictions
   c. polygraphed criminal rating
   d. politically correct research

6. By gel electrophoresis, fragments of DNA can be separated according to _____ .
   a. sequence   b. length   c. species

7. Automated DNA sequencing relies on _____ .
   a. supplies of standard and labeled nucleotides
   b. primers and DNA polymerases
   c. gel electrophoresis and a laser beam
   d. all of the above

8. _____ can be used to insert genes into human cells.
   a. PCR   c. Xenotransplantation
   b. Modified viruses   d. DNA microarrays

9. Match the terms with the most suitable description.
   ____ DNA fingerprint   a. selecting "desirable" traits
   ____ Ti plasmid   b. mutations, crossovers
   ____ nature's genetic   c. used in some gene transfers
        experiments   d. a person's unique collection
   ____ nucleic acid   of tandem repeats
        hybridization   e. base pairing of nucleotide
   ____ eugenic   sequences from different
        engineering   DNA or RNA sources

Figure 15.18 (**a**) ANDi, the first transgenic primate; his cells incorporate a jellyfish gene for bioluminescence. (**b**) The same gene was transferred into these zebrafish.

Media Menu

How Would You Vote?

The United States is the world's leading producer and consumer of genetically modified organisms. Some people are uneasy about genetic engineering and would like to avoid products based on this technology. Should food that contains genetically modified plants or livestock be clearly identified on product labels?

Critical Thinking

1. What if it were possible to create life in test tubes? This is the question behind recent attempts to model and eventually create *minimal organisms*, which we define as living cells having the smallest set of genes required to survive and reproduce.

Craig Venter and Claire Fraser recently found that *Mycoplasma genitalium*, a bacterium that has 517 genes (and 2,209 transposons), is a good candidate for genetic research. By disabling its genes one at a time in the laboratory, they discovered that it may have only 265–350 essential protein-coding genes.

What if those genes were to be synthesized one at a time and inserted into an engineered cell consisting only of a plasma membrane and cytoplasm? Would the cell come to life? The possibility that it might prompted Venter and Fraser to seek advice from a panel of bioethicists and theologians. No one on the panel objected to synthetic life research. They felt that much good might come of it, provided scientists didn't claim to have found "the secret of life." The 10 December 1999 issue of *Science* includes an essay from the panel and an article on *M. genitalium* research. Read both, then write down your thoughts about creating life in a test tube.

2. Lunardi's Market put out a bin of tomatoes having vine-ripened redness, flavor, and texture. A sign identified them as genetically engineered produce. Most shoppers selected unmodified tomatoes in the adjacent bin even though those tomatoes were pale pink, mealy-textured, and tasteless. Which tomatoes would you pick? Why?

3. The sequence of the human genome has been completed, and knowledge about a number of the newly discovered genes is already being used to detect genetic disorders. Many women have refused to take advantage of genetic screening for a gene that is associated with the development of breast cancer.

Should medical records about people participating in genetic research and in genetic clinical services be made readily available to insurance companies, potential employers, and others? If not, how can such information be protected?

4. Scientists at Oregon Health Sciences University produced Tetra, the first primate clone. They also made the first transgenic primate by inserting a jellyfish gene into a fertilized egg of a rhesus monkey. (The gene encodes a bioluminescent protein that fluoresces green.) The egg was implanted in a surrogate monkey's uterus, where it developed into a male that was named ANDi (Figure 15.18).

The long-term goal of this gene transfer project is not to make glowing-green monkeys. It is the transfer of human genes into the primates whose genomes are most like ours. Transgenic primates could be studied to gain insight into genetic disorders, which might lead to the development of cures for those who are affected and vaccines for those at risk.

However, something more controversial is at stake. Will the time come when foreign genes can be inserted into human embryos? Would it be ethical to transfer a chimpanzee or monkey gene into a human embryo to cure a genetic defect? Or to bestow immunity against a potentially fatal disease such as AIDS?

BIOLOGICAL PRINCIPLES AND THE HUMAN IMPERATIVE

Molecules, single cells, tissues, organs, organ systems, multicelled organisms, populations, communities, ecosystems, and the biosphere. These are architectural systems of life, assembled in increasingly complex ways over the past 3.8 billion years. We are latecomers to this immense biological building program. Yet within the relatively short span of 10,000 years, our activities have been changing the character of the land, ocean, and atmosphere, even the genetic character of species.

It would be presumptuous to think that we alone have had profound impact on the world of life. As long ago as the Proterozoic, photosynthetic organisms were irrevocably changing the course of biological evolution by enriching the atmosphere with oxygen. During the past as well as the present, competitive adaptations led to the rise of some groups, whose dominance assured the decline of others. Change is nothing new. What *is* new is the capacity of one species to comprehend what might be going on.

We now have the population size, technology, and cultural inclination to use up energy and modify the environment at rapid rates. Where will this end? Will feedback controls operate as they do, for instance, when population growth exceeds carrying capacity? In other words, will negative feedback controls come into play and keep things from getting too far out of hand?

Feedback control will not be enough, for it operates after deviation. Our patterns of resource consumption and population growth are founded on an illusion of unlimited resources and a forgiving environment. A prolonged, global shortage of food or the passing of a critical threshold for the global climate can come too fast to be corrected; in which case the impact of the deviation may be too great to be reversed.

What about feedforward mechanisms, which might serve as early warning systems? For example, when sensory receptors near the surface of skin detect a drop in outside air temperature, each sends messages to the nervous system. That system responds by triggering mechanisms that raise the body's core temperature before the body itself becomes dangerously chilled.

Extrapolating from this, if we develop feedforward control mechanisms, would it not be possible to start corrective measures before we do too much harm?

Feedforward controls alone will not work, for they operate after change is under way. Think of the DEW line—the Distant Early Warning system. It is like a vast sensory receptor for detecting missiles launched against North America. By the time it does what it is supposed to, it may be too late to stop widespread destruction.

It would be naive to assume we can ever reverse who we are at this point in evolutionary time, to de-evolve ourselves culturally and biologically into becoming less complex in the hope of averting disaster. Yet there is reason to believe we can avert disaster by using a third kind of control mechanism—a capacity to anticipate events even before they happen. We are not locked into responding only after irreversible change has begun. We have the capacity to anticipate the future—it is the essence of our visions of utopia and hell. *We all have the capacity to adapt to a future that we can partly shape.*

For instance, we can stop trying to "beat nature" and learn to work with it. Individually and collectively, we can work to develop long-term policies that take into account biotic and abiotic limits on population growth. Far from being a surrender, this would be one of the most intelligent behaviors of which we are capable.

Having a capacity to adapt and using it are not the same thing. We have already put the world of life on dangerous ground because we have not yet mobilized ourselves as a species to work toward self-control.

Our survival depends on predicting possible futures. It depends on preserving, restoring, and constructing ecosystems that fit with our definition of basic human values and available biological models. Human values can change; our expectations can and must be adapted to biological reality. *For the principles of energy flow and resource utilization, which govern the survival of all systems of life, do not change.* It is our biological and cultural imperative that we come to terms with these principles, and ask ourselves what our long-term contribution will be to the world of life.

Appendix I. Classification System

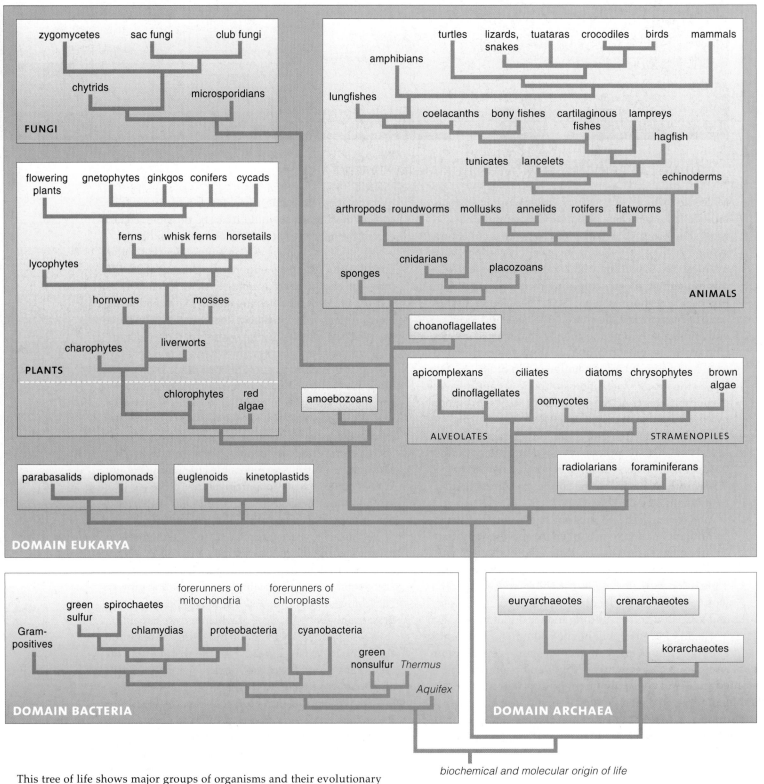

This tree of life shows major groups of organisms and their evolutionary connections. Each set of organisms (taxon) has living representatives. Each branch point represents the last common ancestor of the set above it. Small boxes within domains Archaea and Eukarya highlight taxa that are currently being recognized as the equivalent of kingdoms in earlier classification systems. This tree is based on morphological, genetic, and molecular comparisons of the most important groups. It is a work in progress and subject to refinements as more information comes in.

DOMAIN OF BACTERIA

KINGDOM BACTERIA Gram-negative and Gram-positive prokaryotic cells. Collectively, great metabolic diversity; photosynthetic autotrophs, chemosynthetic autotrophs, and heterotrophs.

PHYLUM FIRMICUTES Typically Gram-positive, thick wall. Heterotrophs. *Bacillus, Staphylococcus, Streptococcus, Clostridium, Actinomycetes.*

PHYLUM GRACILICUTES Typically Gram-negative, thin wall. Autotrophs (photosynthetic and chemosynthetic) and heterotrophs. *Anabaena* and other cyanobacteria. *Escherichia, Pseudomonas, Neisseria, Myxococcus.*

PHYLUM TENERICUTES Gram-negative, wall absent. Heterotrophs (saprobes, pathogens). *Mycoplasma.*

DOMAIN OF ARCHAEBACTERIA (ARCHAEA)

KINGDOM ARCHAEBACTERIA Methanogens, extreme halophiles, extreme thermophiles. Evolutionarily closer to eukaryotic cells than to eubacteria. All strict anaerobes living in habitats as harsh as those that probably prevailed on the early Earth. Compared with other prokaryotic cells, all archaebacteria have a distinctive cell wall and unique membrane lipids, ribosomes, and RNA sequences. *Methanobacterium, Halobacterium, Sulfolobus.*

Table A   Representative Bacteria and Archaea Grouped on the Basis of Numerical Taxonomy

Some Major Groups	Main Habitats	Characteristics	Representatives
BACTERIA			
Photoautotrophs:			
Cyanobacteria, green sulfur bacteria, and purple sulfur bacteria	Mostly lakes, ponds; some marine, terrestrial habitats	Photosynthetic; use sunlight energy, carbon dioxide; cyanobacteria use oxygen-producing noncyclic pathway; some also use cyclic route	*Anabaena, Spirulina, Rhodopseudomonas,*
Photoheterotrophs:			
Purple nonsulfur and green nonsulfur bacteria	Anaerobic, organically rich muddy soils, and sediments of aquatic habitats	Use sunlight energy; organic compounds as electron donors; some purple nonsulfur may also grow chemotrophically	*Rhodospirillum, Chlorobium*
Chemoautotrophs:			
Nitrifying, sulfur-oxidizing, and iron-oxidizing bacteria	Soil; freshwater, marine habitats	Use carbon dioxide, inorganic compounds as electron donors; influence crop yields, cycling of nutrients in ecosystems	*Nitrosomonas, Nitrobacter, Thiobacillus*
Chemoheterotrophs:			
Spirochetes	Aquatic habitats; parasites of animals	Helically coiled, motile; free-living and parasitic species; some major pathogens	*Spirochaeta, Treponema*
Gram-negative aerobic rods and cocci	Soil, aquatic habitats; parasites of animals, plants	Some major pathogens; some fix nitrogen (e.g., *Rhizobium*)	*Pseudomonas, Neisseria, Rhizobium, Agrobacterium*
Gram-negative facultative anaerobic rods	Soil, plants, animal gut	Many major pathogens; one bioluminescent (*Photobacterium*)	*Salmonella, Escherichia, Proteus, Photobacterium*
Rickettsias and chlamydias	Host cells of animals	Intracellular parasites; many pathogens	*Rickettsia, Chlamydia*
Myxobacteria	Decaying organic material; bark of living trees	Gliding, rod-shaped; aggregation and collective migration of cells	*Myxococcus*
Gram-positive cocci	Soil; skin and mucous membranes of animals	Some major pathogens	*Staphylococcus, Streptococcus*
Endospore-forming rods and cocci	Soil; animal gut	Some major pathogens	*Bacillus, Clostridium*
Gram-positive nonsporulating rods	Fermenting plant, animal material; gut, vaginal tract	Some important in dairy industry, others major contaminators of milk, cheese	*Lactobacillus, Listeria*
Actinomycetes	Soil; some aquatic habitats	Include anaerobes and strict aerobes; major producers of antibiotics	*Actinomyces, Streptomyces*
ARCHAEA			
Methanogens	Anaerobic sediments of lakes, swamps; animal gut	Chemosynthetic; methane producers; used in sewage treatment facilities	*Methanobacterium*
Extreme halophiles	Brines (extremely salty water)	Heterotrophic; also, unique photosynthetic pigments (bacteriorhodopsin) form in some	*Halobacterium*
Extreme thermophiles	Acidic soil, hot springs, hydrothermal vents	Heterotrophic or chemosynthetic; use inorganic substances as electron donors	*Sulfolobus, Thermoplasma*

DOMAIN OF EUKARYOTES (EUKARYA)

KINGDOM "PROTISTA"
Diverse single-celled, colonial, and multicelled eukaryotic species. Existing types are unlike prokaryotes and most like the earliest forms of eukaryotes. Autotrophs, heterotrophs, or both. Reproduce sexually and asexually (by meiosis, mitosis, or both). Not a monophyletic group. The kingdom may soon be split into multiple kingdoms, and some of its groups (chlorophytes and charophytes) are classified by some botanists as plants.

PHYLUM "MASTIGOPHORA" Flagellated protozoans. Free-living heterotrophs; many are internal parasites. They have one to several flagella. A non-monophyletic grouping of ancient lineages, including the diplomonads, parabasalids, and kinetoplastids. *Trypanosoma, Trichomonas, Giardia.*

PHYLUM EUGLENOPHYTA Euglenoids. Mostly heterotrophs, some photoautotrophs, some both depending on conditions. Most with one short, one long flagellum. Pigmented (red, green) or colorless. Related to kinetoplastids. *Euglena.*

PHYLUM SARCODINA Amoeboid protozoans. Heterotrophs, free-living or endosymbionts, some pathogens. Soft-bodied, with or without shell, pseudopods. Rhizopods (naked amoebas, foraminiferans), actinopods (radiolarians, heliozoans). *Amoeba, Entamoeba.*

ALVEOLATES

PHYLUM CILIOPHORA Ciliated protozoans. Heterotrophs, predators or symbionts, some parasitic. All have cilia. Free-living, sessile, or motile. *Paramecium.*

PHYLUM APICOMPLEXA Heterotrophs, sporozoite-forming parasites. Complex structures at head end. Most familiar types known as sporozoans. *Cryptosporidium, Plasmodium, Toxoplasma.*

PHYLUM PYRRHOPHYTA Dinoflagellates. Photosynthetic, mostly, but some heterotrophs. *Noctiluca, Karenia brevis.*

STRAMENOPILES

PHYLUM OOMYCOTA Water molds. Heterotrophs. Decomposers, some parasites. *Saprolegnia, Phytophthora, Plasmopara.*

PHYLUM CHRYSOPHYTA Golden algae, yellow-green algae, diatoms, coccolithophores. Photosynthetic. Some flagellated. *Mischococcus, Synura, Vaucheria.*

PHYLUM PHAEOPHYTA Brown algae. Photosynthetic, nearly all endemic to temperate or marine waters. *Macrocystis, Laminaria, Sargassum, Postelsia.*

GROUPS CLOSELY RELATED TO PLANTS

PHYLUM RHODOPHYTA Red algae. Mostly photosynthetic, some parasitic. Nearly all marine, some in freshwater habitats. *Porphyra, Antithamion.*

PHYLUM CHLOROPHYTA Green algae. Mostly photosynthetic, some parasitic. Most freshwater, some marine or terrestrial. *Chlamydomonas, Spirogyra, Ulva, Volvox, Codium, Halimeda.*

PHYLUM CHAROPHYTA Closest relatives of plants. Desmids, stoneworts. *Micrasterias, Chara.*

GROUPS OF SLIME MOLDS

PHYLUM MYXOMYCOTA Plasmodial slime molds. Heterotrophs. A multinucleated mass (the plasmodium) arises by mitosis without cell division, feeds and migrates as a unit, then forms spore-bearing structures. *Physarum.*

PHYLUM ACRASIOMYCOTA Cellular slime molds. Heterotrophs; free-living, phagocytic amoeboid cells aggregate into a mass that migrate as a unit, then form spore-bearing structures. *Dictyostelium.*

FUNGI
Nearly all multicelled eukaryotic species with chitin-containing cell walls. Heterotrophs, mostly saprobic decomposers, some parasites. Nutrition based upon extracellular digestion of organic matter and absorption of nutrients by individual cells. Multicelled species form absorptive mycelia within substrates and structures that produce asexual spores (and sometimes sexual spores).

PHYLUM CHYTRIDIOMYCOTA Chytrids. Primarily aquatic; saprobic decomposers or parasites that produce flagellated spores. *Chytridium.*

PHYLUM ZYGOMYCOTA Zygomycetes. Producers of zygospores (zygotes inside thick wall) by way of sexual reproduction. Bread molds, related forms. *Rhizopus, Philobolus.*

PHYLUM ASCOMYCOTA Ascomycetes. Sac fungi. Sac-shaped cells form sexual spores (ascospores). Most yeasts and molds, morels, truffles. *Saccharomycetes, Morchella, Neurospora, Sarcoscypha, Claviceps, Ophiostoma, Candida, Aspergillus, Penicillium.*

PHYLUM BASIDIOMYCOTA Basidiomycetes. Club fungi. Most diverse group. Produce basidiospores inside club-shaped structures. Mushrooms, shelf fungi, stinkhorns. *Agaricus, Amanita, Craterellus, Gymnophilus, Puccinia, Ustilago.*

"IMPERFECT FUNGI" Sexual spores absent or undetected. The group has no formal taxonomic status. If better understood, a given species might be grouped with sac fungi or club fungi. *Arthobotrys, Histoplasma, Microsporum, Verticillium.*

"LICHENS" Mutualistic interactions between fungal species and a cyanobacterium, green alga, or both. *Lobaria, Usnea.*

KINGDOM PLANTAE
Multicelled eukaryotes. Nearly all photosynthetic autotrophs with chlorophylls *a* and *b*. Some parasitic. Nonvascular and vascular species, generally with well-developed root and shoot systems. Nearly all adapted to survive on land; a few in aquatic habitats. Sexual reproduction predominant with spore-forming chambers and embryos in life cycle; also asexual reproduction by vegetative propagation and other mechanisms.

PHYLUM "BRYOPHYTA" Bryophytes; mosses, liverworts, hornworts. Not a monophyletic group. Seedless, nonvascular, haploid dominance, sperm are flagellated; require water for fertilization. *Marchantia, Polytrichum, Sphagnum.*

SEEDLESS VASCULAR PLANTS

Diploid sporophyte dominates, flagellated sperm require water for fertilization.

PHYLUM "RHYNIOPHYTA" Earliest known vascular plants; muddy habitats. A polyphyletic group, some are primitive lycophytes. Extinct. *Cooksonia, Rhynia.*

PHYLUM LYCOPHYTA Lycophytes, club mosses. Small single-veined leaves, branching rhizomes. *Lepidodendron* (extinct), *Lycopodium, Selaginella.*

PHYLUM SPHENOPHYTA Horsetails. Reduced scalelike leaves. Some stems photosynthetic, others nonphotosynthetic, spore-producing. *Calamites* (extinct), *Equisetum.*

PHYLUM PTEROPHYTA Ferns. Large leaves, usually with sori. Largest group of seedless vascular plants (12,000 species), mainly tropical, temperate habitats. *Pteris, Trichomanes, Cyathea* (tree ferns), *Polystichum.*

PHYLUM PSILOPHYTA Whisk ferns. No obvious roots, leaves on sporophyte, very reduced. *Psilotum.*

PHYLUM "PROGYMNOSPERMOPHYTA" The progymnosperms. Ancestral to early seed-bearing plants; extinct. *Archaeopteris.*

SEED-BEARING VASCULAR PLANTS

PHYLUM "PTERIDOSPERMOPHYTA" Seed ferns. Fernlike gymnosperms; extinct. *Medullosa.*

PHYLUM CYCADOPHYTA Cycads. Group of gymnosperms (vascular, bear "naked" seeds). Tropical, subtropical. Compound leaves, simple cones on male and female plants. Plants usually palm-like. *Zamia, Cycas.*

PHYLUM GINKGOPHYTA Ginkgo (maidenhair tree). Type of gymnosperm. Seeds with fleshy outer layer. *Ginkgo.*

PHYLUM GNETOPHYTA Gnetophytes. Only gymnosperms with vessels in xylem and double fertilization (but endosperm does not form). *Ephedra, Welwitchia, Gnetum.*

PHYLUM CONIFEROPHYTA Conifers. Most common and familiar gymnosperms. Generally cone-bearing species with needle-like or scale-like leaves.

    Family Pinaceae. Pines (*Pinus*), firs (*Abies*), spruces (*Picea*), hemlock (*Tsuga*), larches (*Larix*), true cedars (*Cedrus*).

    Family Cupressaceae. Junipers (*Juniperus*), Cypresses (*Cupressus*), Bald cypress (*Taxodium*), redwood (*Sequoia*), bigtree (*Sequoiadendron*), dawn redwood (*Metasequoia*).

    Family Taxaceae. Yews. *Taxus.*

PHYLUM ANTHOPHYTA Angiosperms (the flowering plants). Largest, most diverse group of vascular seed-bearing plants. Only organisms that produce flowers, fruits. Some families from several representative orders are listed:

BASAL FAMILIES

Family Amborellaceae. *Amborella.*
Family Nymphaeaceae. Water lilies.
Family Illiciaceae. Star anise.

MAGNOLIIDS

Family Magnoliaceae. Magnolias.
Family Lauraceae. Cinnamon, sassafras, avocados.
Family Piperaceae. Black pepper, white pepper.

EUDICOTS

Family Papaveraceae. Poppies.
Family Cactaceae. Cacti.
Family Euphorbiaceae. Spurges, poinsettia.
Family Salicaceae. Willows, poplars.
Family Fabaceae. Peas, beans, lupines, mesquite.
Family Rosaceae. Roses, apples, almonds, strawberries.
Family Moraceae. Figs, mulberries.
Family Cucurbitaceae. Squashes, melons, cucumbers.
Family Fagaceae. Oaks, chestnuts, beeches.
Family Brassicaceae. Mustards, cabbages, radishes.
Family Malvaceae. Mallows, okra, cotton, hibiscus, cocoa.
Family Sapindaceae. Soapberry, litchi, maples.
Family Ericaceae. Heaths, blueberries, azaleas.
Family Rubiaceae. Coffee.
Family Lamiaceae. Mints.
Family Solanaceae. Potatoes, eggplant, petunias.
Family Apiaceae. Parsleys, carrots, poison hemlock.
Family Asteraceae. Composites. Chrysanthemums, sunflowers, lettuces, dandelions.

MONOCOTS

Family Araceae. Anthuriums, calla lily, philodendrons.
Family Liliaceae. Lilies, tulips.
Family Alliaceae. Onions, garlic.
Family Iridaceae. Irises, gladioli, crocuses.
Family Orchidaceae. Orchids.
Family Arecaceae. Date palms, coconut palms.
Family Bromeliaceae. Bromeliads, pineapples.
Family Cyperaceae. Sedges.
Family Poaceae. Grasses, bamboos, corn, wheat, sugarcane.
Family Zingiberaceae. Gingers.

KINGDOM ANIMALIA
Multicelled eukaryotes, nearly all with tissues, organs, and organ systems; show motility during at least part of their life cycle; embryos develop through a series of stages. Diverse heterotrophs, predators (herbivores, carnivores, omnivores), parasites, detritivores. Reproduce sexually and, in many species, asexually as well.

PHYLUM PORIFERA Sponges. No symmetry, tissues. *Euplectella.*

PHYLUM PLACOZOA Marine. Simplest known animal. Two cell layers, no mouth, no organs. *Trichoplax.*

PHYLUM CNIDARIA Radial symmetry, tissues, nematocysts.
  Class Hydrozoa. Hydrozoans. *Hydra, Obelia, Physalia, Prya.*
  Class Scyphozoa. Jellyfishes. *Aurelia.*
  Class Anthozoa. Sea anemones, corals. *Telesto.*

PHYLUM MESOZOA Ciliated, wormlike parasites, about the same level of complexity as *Trichoplax.*

PHYLUM PLATYHELMINTHES Flatworms. Bilateral, cephalized; simplest animals with organ systems. Saclike gut.
  Class Turbellaria. Triclads (planarians), polyclads. *Dugesia.*
  Class Trematoda. Flukes. *Clonorchis, Schistosoma.*
  Class Cestoda. Tapeworms. *Diphyllobothrium, Taenia.*

PHYLUM ROTIFERA Rotifers. *Asplancha, Philodina.*

PHYLUM NEMERTEA Ribbon worms. *Tubulanus.*

PHYLUM MOLLUSCA Mollusks.

  Class Polyplacophora. Chitons. *Cryptochiton, Tonicella.*

  Class Gastropoda. Snails (periwinkles, whelks, limpets, abalones, cowries, conches, nudibranchs, tree snails, garden snails), sea slugs, land slugs. *Aplysia, Ariolimax, Cypraea, Haliotis, Helix, Liguus, Limax, Littorina, Patella.*

  Class Bivalvia. Clams, mussels, scallops, cockles, oysters, shipworms. *Ensis, Chlamys, Mytelus, Patinopectin.*

  Class Cephalopoda. Squids, octopuses, cuttlefish, nautiluses. *Dosidiscus, Loligo, Nautilus, Octopus, Sepia.*

PHYLUM BRYOZOA Bryozoans (moss animals).

PHYLUM BRACHIOPODA Lampshells.

PHYLUM ANNELIDA Segmented worms.

  Class Polychaeta. Mostly marine worms. *Eunice, Neanthes.*

  Class Oligochaeta. Mostly freshwater and terrestrial worms, many marine. *Lumbricus* (earthworms), *Tubifex.*

  Class Hirudinea. Leeches. *Hirudo, Placobdella.*

PHYLUM NEMATODA Roundworms. *Ascaris, Caenorhabditis elegans, Necator* (hookworms), *Trichinella.*

PHYLUM TARDIGRADA Water bears.

PHYLUM ONYCHOPHORA Onychophorans. *Peripatus.*

PHYLUM ARTHROPODA

  Subphylum Trilobita. Trilobites; extinct.

  Subphylum Chelicerata. Chelicerates. Horseshoe crabs, spiders, scorpions, ticks, mites.

  Subphylum Crustacea. Shrimps, crayfishes, lobsters, crabs, barnacles, copepods, isopods (sowbugs).

  Subphylum Uniramia.

    Superclass Myriapoda. Centipedes, millipedes.

    Superclass Insecta.

      Order Ephemeroptera. Mayflies.
      Order Odonata. Dragonflies, damselflies.
      Order Orthoptera. Grasshoppers, crickets, katydids.
      Order Dermaptera. Earwigs.
      Order Blattodea. Cockroaches.

Order Mantodea. Mantids.
Order Isoptera. Termites.
Order Mallophaga. Biting lice.
Order Anoplura. Sucking lice.
Order Hemiptera. Cicadas, aphids, leafhoppers, spittlebugs, bugs.
Order Coleoptera. Beetles.
Order Diptera. Flies.
Order Mecoptera. Scorpion flies. *Harpobittacus.*
Order Siphonaptera. Fleas.
Order Lepidoptera. Butterflies, moths.
Order Hymenoptera. Wasps, bees, ants.
Order Neuroptera. Lacewings, antlions.

PHYLUM ECHINODERMATA   Echinoderms.

Class Asteroidea. Sea stars. *Asterias.*
Class Ophiuroidea. Brittle stars.
Class Echinoidea. Sea urchins, heart urchins, sand dollars.
Class Holothuroidea. Sea cucumbers.
Class Crinoidea. Feather stars, sea lilies.
Class Concentricycloidea. Sea daisies.

PHYLUM HEMICHORDATA   Acorn worms.

PHYLUM CHORDATA   Chordates.

Subphylum Urochordata. Tunicates, related forms.

Subphylum Cephalochordata. Lancelets.

CRANIATES

Superclass "Agnatha." Jawless fishes, including ostracoderms (extinct).

Class Myxini. Hagfishes.

Class Cephalaspidomorphi. Lampreys.

Subphylum Vertebrata. Jawed vertebrates.

Class "Placodermi." Jawed, heavily armored fishes; extinct.

Class Chondrichthyes. Cartilaginous fishes. (sharks, rays, skates, chimaeras).

Class "Osteichthyes." Bony fishes. Not monophyletic.

Subclass Dipnoi. Lungfishes.

Subclass Crossopterygii. Coelacanths, related forms.

Subclass Actinopterygii. Ray-finned fishes.

Order Acipenseriformes. Sturgeons, paddlefishes.
Order Salmoniformes. Salmon, trout.
Order Atheriniformes. Killifishes, guppies.
Order Gasterosteiformes. Seahorses.
Order Perciformes. Perches, wrasses, barracudas, tunas, freshwater bass, mackerels.
Order Lophiiformes. Angler fishes.

TETRAPODS (A subgroup of craniates)

Class Amphibia. Amphibians.
Order Caudata. Salamanders.
Order Anura. Frogs, toads.
Order Apoda. Apodans (caecilians).

AMNIOTES (A subgroup of tetrapods)

Class "Reptilia." Skin with scales, embryo protected and nutritionally supported by extraembryonic membranes.
Subclass Anapsida. Turtles, tortoises.
Subclass Lepidosaura. *Sphenodon,* lizards, snakes.
Subclass Archosaura. Dinosaurs (extinct), crocodiles, alligators.

Class Aves. Birds. In some of the more recent classification systems, dinosaurs, crocodilians, and birds are grouped in the same category, the archosaurs.
Order Struthioniformes. Ostriches.
Order Sphenisciformes. Penguins.
Order Procellariiformes. Albatrosses, petrels.
Order Ciconiiformes. Herons, bitterns, storks, flamingoes.
Order Anseriformes. Swans, geese, ducks.
Order Falconiformes. Eagles, hawks, vultures, falcons.
Order Galliformes. Ptarmigan, turkeys, domestic fowl.
Order Columbiformes. Pigeons, doves.
Order Strigiformes. Owls.
Order Apodiformes. Swifts, hummingbirds.
Order Passeriformes. Sparrows, jays, finches, crows, robins, starlings, wrens.
Order Piciformes. Woodpeckers, toucans.
Order Psittaciformes. Parrots, cockatoos, macaws.

Class Mammalia. Skin with hair; young nourished by milk-secreting glands of adult.

Subclass Prototheria. Egg-laying mammals (monotremes; duckbilled platypus, spiny anteaters).

Subclass Metatheria. Pouched mammals or marsupials (opossums, kangaroos, wombats, Tasmanian devil).

Subclass Eutheria. Placental mammals.

Order Edentata. Anteaters, tree sloths, armadillos.
Order Insectivora. Tree shrews, moles, hedgehogs.
Order Chiroptera. Bats.
Order Scandentia. Insectivorous tree shrews.
Order Primates.

Suborder Strepsirhini (prosimians). Lemurs, lorises.
Suborder Haplorhini (tarsioids and anthropoids).

Infraorder Tarsiiformes. Tarsiers.
Infraorder Platyrrhini (New World monkeys).

Family Cebidae. Spider monkeys, howler monkeys, capuchin.

Infraorder Catarrhini (Old World monkeys and hominoids).

Superfamily Cercopithecoidea. Baboons, macaques, langurs.

Superfamily Hominoidea. Apes and humans.

Family Hylobatidae. Gibbon.

Family "Pongidae." Chimpanzees, gorillas, orangutans.

Family Hominidae. Existing and extinct human species (*Homo*) and humanlike species, including the australopiths.

Order Lagomorpha. Rabbits, hares, pikas.
Order Rodentia. Most gnawing animals (squirrels, rats, mice, guinea pigs, porcupines, beavers, etc.).
Order Carnivora. Carnivores.

Suborder Feloidea. Cats, mongooses, hyenas.
Suborder Canoidea. Dogs, weasels, skunks, otters, raccoons, pandas, bears.

Order Pinnipedia. Seals, walruses, sea lions.
Order Proboscidea. Elephants; mammoths (extinct).
Order Sirenia. Sea cows (manatees, dugongs).
Order Perissodactyla. Odd-toed ungulates (horses, tapirs, rhinos).
Order Tubulidentata. African aardvarks.
Order Artiodactyla. Even-toed ungulates (camels, deer, bison, sheep, goats, antelopes, giraffes, etc.).
Order Cetacea. Whales, porpoises.

Appendix II. Units of Measure

Metric-English Conversions

Length

English		Metric
inch	=	2.54 centimeters
foot	=	0.30 meter
yard	=	0.91 meter
mile (5,280 feet)	=	1.61 kilometer

To convert	multiply by	to obtain
inches	2.54	centimeters
feet	30.00	centimeters
centimeters	0.39	inches
millimeters	0.039	inches

Weight

English		Metric
grain	=	64.80 milligrams
ounce	=	28.35 grams
pound	=	453.60 grams
ton (short) (2,000 pounds)	=	0.91 metric ton

To convert	multiply by	to obtain
ounces	28.3	grams
pounds	453.6	grams
pounds	0.45	kilograms
grams	0.035	ounces
kilograms	2.2	pounds

Volume

English		Metric
cubic inch	=	16.39 cubic centimeters
cubic foot	=	0.03 cubic meter
cubic yard	=	0.765 cubic meters
ounce	=	0.03 liter
pint	=	0.47 liter
quart	=	0.95 liter
gallon	=	3.79 liters

To convert	multiply by	to obtain
fluid ounces	30.00	milliliters
quart	0.95	liters
milliliters	0.03	fluid ounces
liters	1.06	quarts

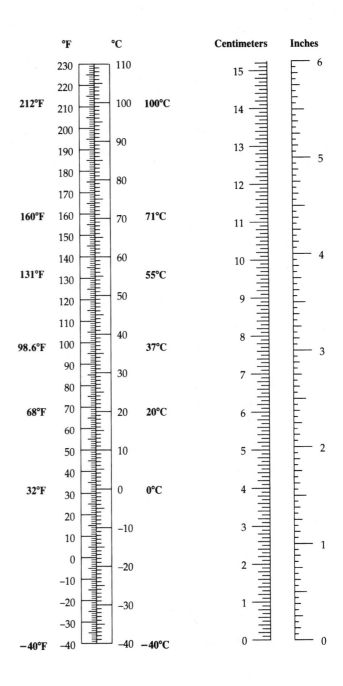

Italicized numbers refer to relevant section numbers

CHAPTER 1

1.	cell	1.1
2.	Metabolism	1.2
3.	Homeostasis	1.2
4.	adaptive	1.4
5.	mutation	1.4
6.	domains	1.3
7.	a	1.2
8.	d	1.2, 1.4
9.	d	1.4
10.	a	1.6
11.	c	1.4
	e	1.4
	d	1.5
	b	1.5
	a	1.5

CHAPTER 2

1.	F; hydrogen atoms have no neutrons	2.1
2.	b	2.1
3.	d	2.2
4.	c	2.4
5.	a	2.4
6.	f	2.5
7.	f	2.6
8.	acid, base	2.6
9.	c	2.6
10.	e	Impacts, Issues
	d	2.6
	b	2.4
	c	2.5
	a	2.1

CHAPTER 3

1.	See table 3.1	
2.	d	3.1
3.	c	3.1
4.	f	3.3
5.	b	3.4
6.	d	3.4
7.	e	3.4
8.	d	3.5, 3.7
9.	d	3.5
10.	d	3.7
11.	b	3.7
12.	c	3.5
	e	3.7
	b	3.4
	d	3.7
	a	3.3

CHAPTER 4

1.	c	4.3
2.	See Figs. 4.19, 4.20	
3.	d	4.5
4.	d	4.11
5.	False; many cells have a wall	4.11
6.	c	4.1
7.	e	4.8
	d	4.8
	a	4.1, 4.4
	b	4.7
	c	4.7

CHAPTER 5

1.	c	5.1
2.	b	5.2
3.	d	5.3
4.	a	5.7
5.	d	5.5
6.	b	5.5
7.	d	5.8
8.	d	5.5
9.	c	5.2
	g	5.6
	a	5.2
	d	5.2
	e	5.2
	b	5.2
	f	5.1

CHAPTER 6

1.	carbon dioxide; sunlight	Impacts, Issues
2.	a	6.2, 6.3
3.	b	6.2, 6.5
4.	c	6.3
5.	c	6.2, 6.5
6.	b	6.5
7.	c	6.5
	a	6.3, 6.4
	b	6.5

CHAPTER 7

1.	d	7.1
2.	c	7.1, 7.2
3.	b	7.3
4.	c	7.4
5.	See Fig. 7.3	
6.	c	7.5
7.	b	7.5
8.	d	7.6
9.	b	7.2
	c	7.5
	a	7.3
	d	7.4

CHAPTER 8

1.	d	8.1
2.	b	8.1
3.	c	8.1
4.	d	8.2
5.	a	8.2
6.	c	8.2
7.	a	8.3
8.	b	8.2
9.	d	8.3
	b	8.3
	c	8.3
	a	8.3

CHAPTER 9

1.	c	9.2
2.	b	9.2
3.	a	9.2
4.	d	9.1, 9.5
5.	d	9.2, 9.4
6.	b	9.2
7.	d	9.2
8.	c	9.3
9.	d	9.3
10.	d	9.2
	a	9.1
	c	9.3
	b	9.2

CHAPTER 10

1.	a	10.1
2.	b	10.1, 10.2
3.	a	10.1, 10.6
4.	b	10.1, 10.2
5.	c	10.2
6.	a	10.2, 10.4
7.	d	10.3
8.	b	10.3
	d	10.2
	a	10.1
	c	10.1

CHAPTER 11

1.	c	11.1, 11.3
2.	a	11.3
3.	e	11.7
4.	a	11.4
5.	c	11.1
6.	d	11.8
7.	c	11.8
8.	c	11.3
	e	11.7
	d	11.4
	b	11.7
	a	11.2
	f	11.3

CHAPTER 12

1.	c	12.2
2.	d	12.2
3.	c	12.2
4.	a	12.4
5.	d	12.4
6.	c	12.5

CHAPTER 13

1.	c	13.1
2.	b	13.1
3.	c	13.1
4.	c	13.2
5.	a	13.2
6.	e	13.4
	c	13.3
	a	13.1
	f	13.2
	d	13.2
	g	13.1
	b	13.2

CHAPTER 14

1.	d	14.1, 14.3
2.	d	14.1
3.	d	14.3, 14.5
4.	d	14.3
5.	d	14.3
6.	d	14.1, 14.2, 14.3
7.	a	14.2
8.	d	14.2
9.	a	14.1, 14.2, 14.3
10.	h	14.3
11.	d	14.3
12.	b	14.4
13.	c	14.4
14.	e	14.4, 14.5
	a	14.2
	d	Impacts, Issues
	b	14.3
	c	14.4

CHAPTER 15

1.	d	15.7
2.	c	15.2
3.	plasmid	15.2
4.	b	15.2
5.	a	15.3
6.	b	15.4
7.	d	15.5
8.	b	15.7, 15.8
9.	d	15.4
	c	15.6
	b	Impacts, Issues
	e	15.3
	a	15.7

CHAPTER 16

1.	populations	16.5
2.	d	Impacts, Issues
3.	a	16.5
4.	c	16.3
5.	b	16.7
6.	c	16.8
7.	b	16.11
8.	c	16.11
	d	16.3
	a	16.5
	b	16.10

CHAPTER 17

1.	a	17.4
2.	d	17.7
3.	c	17.10
4.	c	17.11
5.	c	17.5
6.	d	17.7
7.	d	17.11
8.	c	17.11
9.	d	17.11
10.	See Fig. 17.31	
11.	e	17.11
	a	17.1
	f	17.1
	c	17.4
	b	17.11
	d	17.4
	g	17.10

CHAPTER 18

1.	c	18.1
2.	c	18.2
3.	c	18.3
4.	b	18.4
5.	f	18.1
	c	18.2
	d	18.2
	a	18.3
	b	18.4
	e	18.4

CHAPTER 19

1.	Left, head (top), sheath (middle), tail fiber (bottom). Right: capsid (left), envelope (right)	19.4
2.	d	19.1
3.	c	19.3
4.	c	19.1
5.	c	19.2
6.	d	19.2
7.	b	19.2
8.	d	19.2
9.	b	19.4
10.	false	19.4
11.	d	19.4
12.	d	19.1
13.	d	19.3
	e	19.2
	b	19.4
	f	19.1
	c	19.3
	g	19.4
	a	19.5

CHAPTER 20

1.	b	20.2
2.	d	20.2
3.	b	20.3
4.	b	20.5
5.	d	20.5
6.	d	20.4
7.	a	20.6
8.	c	20.7
9.	a	20.8
10.	c	20.9
11.	c	20.9
12.	b	20.2
	e	20.2
	f	20.5
	i	20.3
	h	20.5
	j	20.7
	d	20.5
	a	20.10
	c	20.12
	g	20.12

CHAPTER 21

1.	a	21.3
2.	c	21.5
3.	b	21.2
4.	c	21.3
5.	a	21.3
6.	b	21.5
7.	c	21.6
	e	21.1
	g	21.3
	h	21.5
	f	21.2
	a	21.1
	b	21.1
	d	21.7

CHAPTER 22

1.	d	22.1
2.	a	22.1
3.	a	22.4
4.	a	22.5
5.	b	22.12
6.	c	22.5, 22.6
7.	b	22.1, 22.13
8.	b	22.13
9.	i	22.2
	c	22.3
	h	22.4
	b	22.5
	a	22.8
	f	22.6
	d	22.9
	e	22.7
	g	22.13

CHAPTER 23

1.	b	23.1
2.	a	23.2
3.	d	23.3, 23.4
4.	c	23.6
5.	f	23.6, 23.7
6.	a	23.7
7.	c	23.8
8.	f	23.2, 23.6 23.9, 23.11
9.	c	23.12
10.	g	23.3
	a	23.4
	e	23.7
	b	23.8
	c	23.9
	f	23.9
	d	23.12

CHAPTER 24

1.	a	24.1
2.	c	24.1
3.	d	24.2
4.	d	24.5
5.	b	24.4
	c	24.1
	a	24.5
	d	24.3

CHAPTER 25

1.	Left; right	25.1
2.	a	25.1
3.	d	25.1
4.	Eudicot; monocot; see Fig. 25.4	
5.	c	25.2
6.	c	25.2
7.	b	25.2
8.	b	25.1, 25.2
9.	See Fig. 25.21	
10.	d	25.6
11.	b	25.3
	d	25.6
	e	25.2
	c	25.2
	f	25.4
	a	25.6

CHAPTER 26

1.	e	26.1
2.	c	26.3
3.	b	26.2
4.	b	26.2
5.	c	26.3
6.	d	26.3
7.	a	26.4
8.	d	26.4
9.	c	26.4
	g	26.1
	e	26.5
	b	26.2
	d	26.3
	a	26.3
	f	26.5

CHAPTER 27

1.	a	27.1
2.	c	27.3
3.	b	27.2
4.	c	27.3
5.	c	27.4
6.	e	27.6
7.	c	27.6
8.	c	27.9
9.	e	27.8
	f	27.9
	b	27.2
	c	27.2, 27.3
	d	27.1
	a	27.10

CHAPTER 28

1.	a	28.1
2.	c	28.1
3.	a	28.1
4.	b	28.2
5.	b	28.2
6.	c	28.2
7.	c	28.3
8.	d	28.3
9.	d	28.4
10.	b	28.1
	g	28.1
	a	28.2
	c	28.6
	d	28.3
	f	28.2
	e	28.1

CHAPTER 29

1.	a	29.1
2.	c	29.1
3.	d	29.2
4.	a	29.3
5.	d	29.1
6.	c	29.6
7.	b	29.6
8.	b	29.7
9.	a	29.7
10.	b	29.8
11.	e	29.4
	d	29.3
	f	29.8
	b	29.7
	g	29.8
	a	29.7
	c	29.7

CHAPTER 30

1.	c	30.1
2.	c	30.2
3.	e	30.1, 30.3
4.	a	30.2
5.	b	30.4
6.	b	30.5
7.	d	30.7
	g	30.5
	f	30.6
	a	30.5
	c	30.7
	e	30.3
	b	30.4

CHAPTER 31

1.	f	31.1
2.	b	31.3
3.	See Figs. 31.4, 31.5	31.3
4.	a	31.3
5.	e	31.4, 31.5
6.	b	31.5
7.	b	31.4
8.	d	31.5
9.	d	31.4
	f	31.4
	c	31.5
	e	31.5
	a	31.6
	b	31.5

CHAPTER 32

1.	d	32.1
2.	b	32.4
3.	d	32.5
4.	b	32.3
5.	b	32.4
6.	d	32.4
7.	e	32.2
	f	32.6
	g	32.6
	h	32.2
	a	32.4
	c	32.2
	b	32.1
	i	32.4
	d	32.6

CHAPTER 33

1.	c	33.1
2.	b	33.1
3.	d	33.2
4.	b	33.4
5.	d	33.2
6.	b	33.6
7.	c	33.6
8.	a	33.7
9.	c	33.7
10.	d	33.10
11.	f	33.8
	a	33.10
	e	33.2
	g	33.6
	b	33.6
	c	33.7
	d	33.5
12.	See Fig. 33.11	33.6
13.	See Fig. 33.17	33.7

CHAPTER 34

1.	e	34.1
2.	c	34.3
3.	d	34.4
4.	d	34.4, 34.5
5.	e	34.3
6.	e	34.6
7.	a	34.6
8.	b	34.7
9.	c	34.3
	b	34.6
	a	34.1
	e	34.5
	d	34.9

CHAPTER 35

1.	a	35.1
2.	d	35.1
3.	c	35.2
4.	a	35.4
5.	c	35.5, 35.7
6.	d	35.6
7.	a	35.6
8.	a	35.7
9.	d	35.5
	h	35.5
	f	35.5, 35.7
	e	35.1
	g	35.5
	c	35.5
	b	35.5
	a	35.5

CHAPTER 36

1.	d	36.1
2.	b	36.3
3.	c	36.4
4.	b	36.3, 36.4
5.	a	36.4
6.	c	36.6
7.	b	36.8
8.	f	36.3
	b	36.6
	a	36.3
	d	36.4
	e	36.3
	c	36.3

CHAPTER 37

1.	c	37.1
2.	b	37.2
3.	d	37.3
4.	b	37.3
5.	a	37.3
6.	c	37.2
	a	37.2
	b	37.2
	e	37.2
	d	37.3
7.	d	37.7
8.	a	37.7
9.	b	37.6
	a	37.6
	d	37.6
	c	37.6
	e	37.6

CHAPTER 38

1.	d	38.1
2.	c	38.2, 38.3
3.	c	38.2, 38.4
4.	c	38.5
5.	d	38.7
6.	c	38.9
7.	c	38.9
8.	c	38.14
9.	a	38.14
10.	e	38.13
11.	c	38.2
	d	38.2, 38.11
	a	38.2, 38.3
	b	38.2, 38.15
	f	38.2, 38.4
	e	38.2, 38.4
12.	c	38.6
	h	38.8
	a	38.16
	g	38.8, 38.19
	d	38.9, 38.10
	e	38.8, 38.11
	b	38.6, 38.7
	f	38.8

CHAPTER 39

1.	f	39.1
2.	a	39.3
3.	a	39.3
4.	d	39.4
5.	d	39.5
6.	c	39.7
7.	c	39.4
	d	39.3
	a	39.3
	e	39.4
	b	39.4

CHAPTER 40

1.	d	40.1
2.	d	40.1
3.	d	40.3
4.	b	40.4
5.	d	40.6
6.	d	40.8
7.	e	40.11
8.	b	40.12
9.	c	40.9
	d	40.11
	a	40.8
	e	40.8
	b	40.9
	g	40.12
	f	40.13

CHAPTER 41

1.	d	41.1
2.	d	41.1
3.	d	41.4
4.	d	41.3
5.	a	41.7
6.	b	41.8
7.	d	41.11
8.	c	41.10, 41.11
9.	a	41.10
10.	d	41.1
	a	41.1
	c	41.1
	b	41.1

CHAPTER 42

1.	d	42.1
2.	c	42.2
3.	d	42.3
4.	a	42.3
5.	c	42.2
6.	e	42.4
7.	d	42.4, 42.8
8.	c	42.5
9.	d	42.9, 42.10
10.	d	42.7
	h	42.5
	e	42.5
	c	42.5
	b	42.10
	g	42.6
	a	42.6
	f	42.12

CHAPTER 43

1.	a	43.3
2.	d	43.1
3.	d	43.6
4.	a	43.3
5.	d	43.7
6.	c	43.7
7.	c	43.1
	d	43.3
	b	43.1, 43.2
	a	43.2
	e	43.4

Appendix IV. Answers to Genetics Problems

CHAPTER 10

1. a. Both parents are heterozygotes (*Aa*). Their children may be albino (*aa*) or unaffected (*AA* or *Aa*).

b. All are homozygous recessive (*aa*).

c. Homozygous recessive (*aa*) father, and heterozygous (*Aa*) mother. The albino child is *aa*, the unaffected children *Aa*.

2. a. *AB* **c.** *Ab, ab*
b. *AB, aB* **d.** *AB, Ab, aB, ab*

3. a. All offspring will be *AaBB*.

b. 1/4 *AABB* (25% each genotype)
1/4 *AABb*
1/4 *AaBB*
1/4 *AaBb*

c. 1/4 *AaBb* (25% each genotype)
1/4 *Aabb*
1/4 *aaBb*
1/4 *aabb*

d. 1/16 *AABB* (6.25%)
1/8 *AaBB* (12.5%)
1/16 *aaBB* (6.25%)
1/8 *AABb* (12.5%)
1/4 *AaBb* (25%)
1/8 *aaBb* (12.5%)
1/16 *AAbb* (6.25%)
1/8 *Aabb* (12.5%)
1/16 *aabb* (6.25%)

4. A mating of two M^L cats yields 1/4 MM, 1/2 M^LM, and 1/4 $M^L M^L$. Because $M^L M^L$ is lethal, the probability that any one kitten among the survivors will be heterozygous is 2/3.

5. Yellow is recessive. Because F_1 plants have a green phenotype and must be heterozygous, green must be dominant over the recessive yellow.

6. a. *ABC*

b. *ABc, aBc*

c. *ABC, aBc, ABc, aBc*

d. *ABC, aBC, AbC, abC, ABc, aBc, Abc, abc*

7. Because all F_1 plants of this dihybrid cross had to be heterozygous for both genes, then 1/4 (25%) of the F_2 plants will be heterozygous for both genes.

8. a. The mother must be heterozygous $I^A i$. The male with type B blood could have fathered the child if he were heterozygous $I^B i$.

b. Genotype alone cannot prove the accused male is the father. Even if he happens to be heterozygous, *any* male who carries the *i* allele could be the father, including those heterozygous for type A blood ($I^A i$) or type B blood ($I^B i$) and those with type O blood (*ii*).

9. A mating between a mouse from a true-breeding, white-furred strain and a mouse from a true-breeding, brown-furred strain would provide you with the most direct evidence.

Because true-breeding strains of organisms typically are homozygous for a trait being studied, all F_1 offspring from this mating should be heterozygous. Record the phenotype of each F_1 mouse, then let them mate with one another. Assuming only one gene locus is involved, these are possible outcomes for the F_2 offspring:

a. All F_1 mice are brown, and their F_2 offspring segregate:
3 brown : 1 white.
Conclusion: Brown is dominant to white.

b. All F_1 mice are white, and their F_2 offspring segregate:
3 white : 1 brown.
Conclusion: White is dominant to brown.

c. All F_1 mice are tan, and the F_2 offspring segregate:
1 brown : 2 tan : 1 white.
Conclusion: The alleles at this locus show incomplete dominance.

10. You cannot guarantee that the puppies will not develop the disorder without more information about Dandelion's genotype. You could do so only if she is a heterozygous carrier, if the male is free of the alleles, and if the alleles are recessive.

11. Fred could use a testcross to find out if his pet's genotype is *WW* or *Ww*. He can let his black guinea pig mate with a white guinea pig having the genotype *ww*.

If any F_1 offspring are white, then the genotype of his pet is *Ww*. If the two guinea pig parents are allowed to mate repeatedly and all the offspring of the matings are black, then there is a high probability that his pet guinea pig is *WW*.

(If, say, ten offspring are all black, then the probability that the male is *WW* is about 99.9 percent. The greater the number of offspring, the more confident Fred can be of his conclusion.)

12. a. 1/2 red, 1/2 pink

b. All pink

c. 1/4 red, 1/2 pink, 1/4 white

d. 1/2 pink, 1/2 white

13. 9/16 walnut comb
3/16 rose comb
3/16 pea comb
1/16 single comb

14. Because both parents are heterozygotes (Hb^AHb^S), the following are the probabilities for each child:

a. 1/4 Hb^SHb^S

b. 1/4 Hb^AHb^A

c. 1/2 Hb^AHb^S

CHAPTER 11

1. a. Human males (XY) inherit their X chromosome from their mother.

b. A male can produce two kinds of gametes. Half carry an X chromosome and half carry a Y chromosome. All the gametes that carry the X chromosome carry the same X-linked allele.

c. A female homozygous for an X-linked allele produces only one kind of gamete.

d. Half of the gametes of a female who is heterozygous for an X-linked allele carry one of the two alleles at that locus; the other half carry its partner allele for that locus.

2. If only one parent is heterozygous for the autosomal dominant allele, the chance of a child inheriting that allele is 50 percent.

3. a. Nondisjunction can occur at anaphase I or anaphase II of meiosis.

b. As a result of translocation, chromosome 21 may get attached to the end of chromosome 14. The new individual's chromosome number would still be 46, but its somatic cells would have the translocated chromosome 21 in addition to two normal chromosomes 21.

4. Because females (XX) could be white-eyed, the recessive allele had to be on one of their X chromosomes. What if white-eyed males (XY) had the recessive allele on their X chromosome and their Y chromosome had no corresponding eye-color allele? In that case, they would have white eyes. They would have no dominant allele to mask the effect of the recessive one.

5. Because the phenotype appeared in every generation shown in the diagram, this must be a pattern of autosomal dominant inheritance.

However, if a son bears the allele for the disorder on his X chromosome, then it will be expressed. He will develop the disorder, and most likely he will not father children because of his early death.

6. A daughter could develop this muscular dystrophy only if she were to inherit two X-linked recessive alleles—one from each parent. Males who carry the allele are unlikely to father children because they develop the disorder and die an early death.

7. In the mother, a crossover between the two genes at meiosis generates an X chromosome that carries neither mutant allele.

Appendix V. Closer Look at Some Major Metabolic Pathways

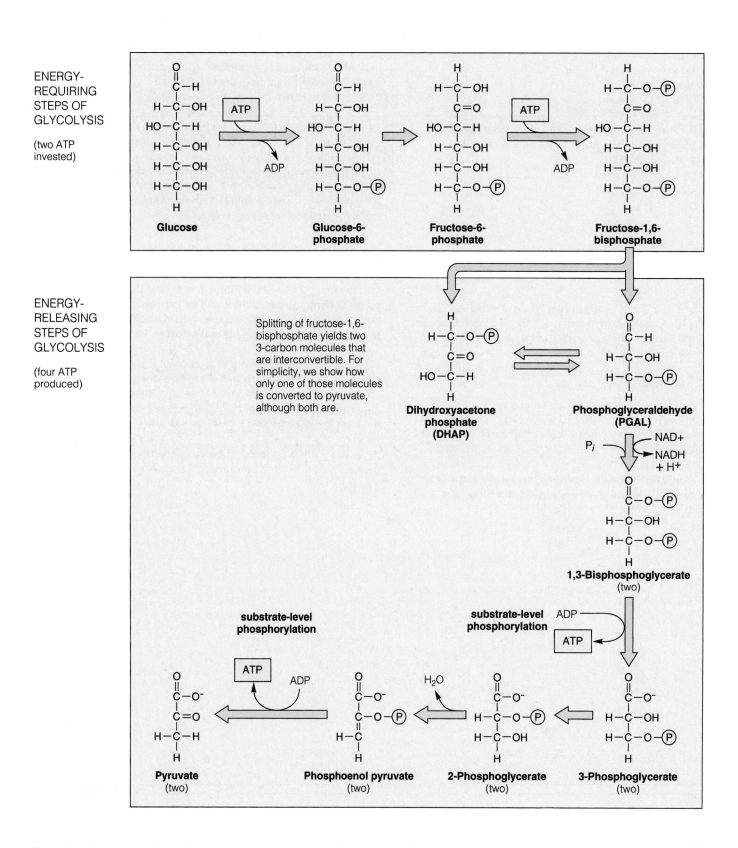

Figure A Glycolysis, ending with two 3-carbon pyruvate molecules for each 6-carbon glucose molecule entering the reactions. The *net* energy yield is two ATP molecules (two invested, four produced).

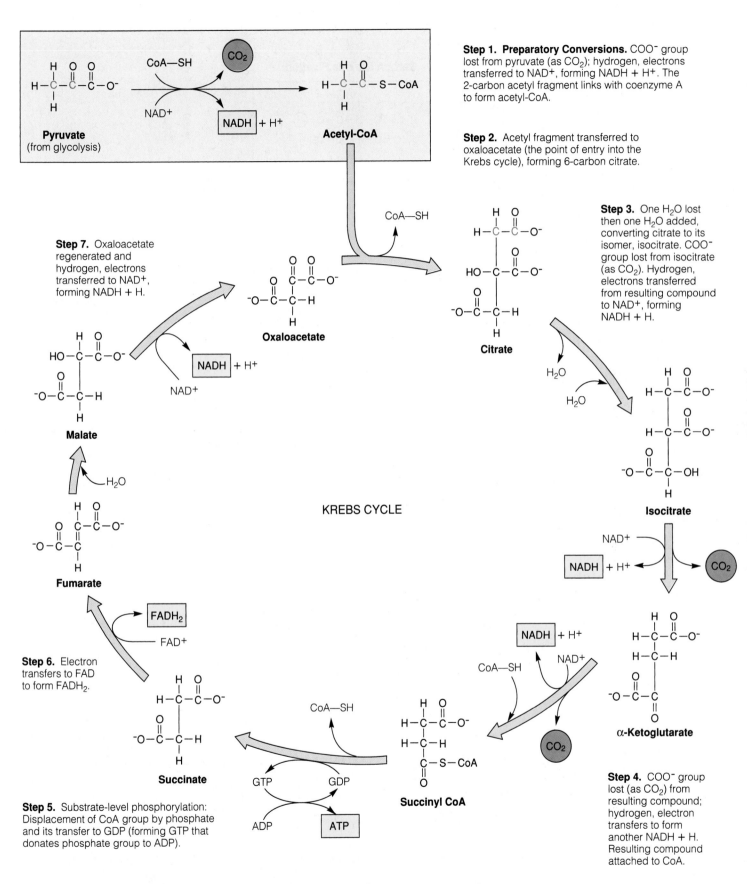

Step 1. Preparatory Conversions. COO$^-$ group lost from pyruvate (as CO_2); hydrogen, electrons transferred to NAD$^+$, forming NADH + H$^+$. The 2-carbon acetyl fragment links with coenzyme A to form acetyl-CoA.

Step 2. Acetyl fragment transferred to oxaloacetate (the point of entry into the Krebs cycle), forming 6-carbon citrate.

Step 3. One H_2O lost then one H_2O added, converting citrate to its isomer, isocitrate. COO$^-$ group lost from isocitrate (as CO_2). Hydrogen, electrons transferred from resulting compound to NAD$^+$, forming NADH + H.

Step 7. Oxaloacetate regenerated and hydrogen, electrons transferred to NAD$^+$, forming NADH + H.

Step 6. Electron transfers to FAD to form FADH$_2$.

Step 5. Substrate-level phosphorylation: Displacement of CoA group by phosphate and its transfer to GDP (forming GTP that donates phosphate group to ADP).

Step 4. COO$^-$ group lost (as CO_2) from resulting compound; hydrogen, electron transfers to form another NADH + H. Resulting compound attached to CoA.

KREBS CYCLE

Figure B Krebs cycle, also known as the citric acid cycle. *Red* identifies carbon atoms entering the cyclic pathway (by way of acetyl-CoA) and leaving (by way of carbon dioxide). These cyclic reactions run twice for each glucose molecule that has been degraded to two pyruvate molecules.

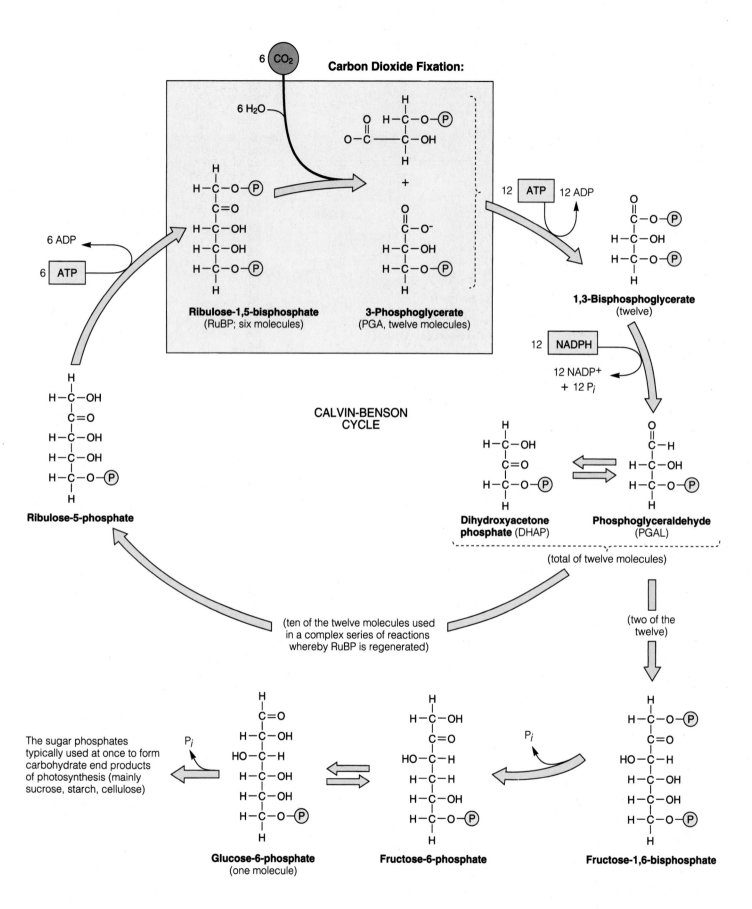

Figure C   Calvin–Benson cycle of the light-independent reactions of photosynthesis.

Appendix VI. The Amino Acids

Neutral, nonpolar side group

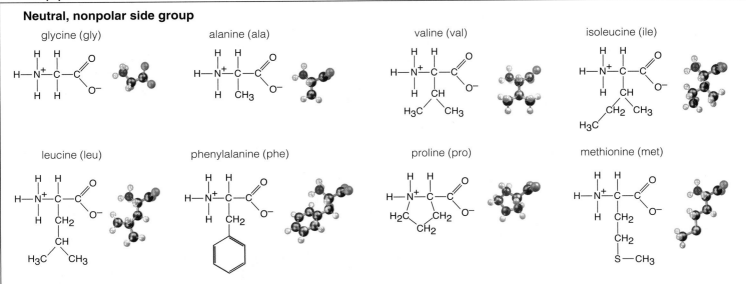

glycine (gly)

alanine (ala)

valine (val)

isoleucine (ile)

leucine (leu)

phenylalanine (phe)

proline (pro)

methionine (met)

Neutral, polar side group

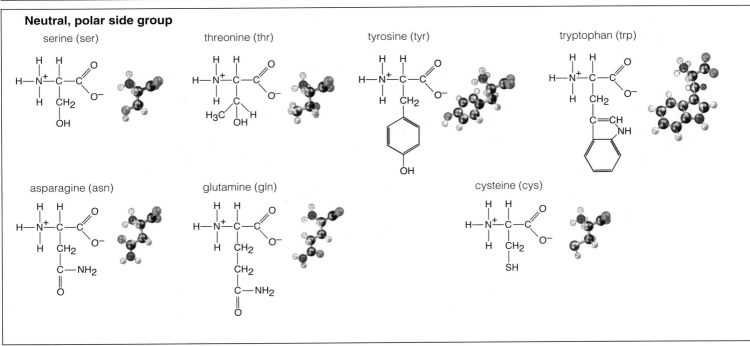

serine (ser)

threonine (thr)

tyrosine (tyr)

tryptophan (trp)

asparagine (asn)

glutamine (gln)

cysteine (cys)

Acidic side group

aspartic acid (asp)

glutamic acid (glu)

Basic side group

lysine (lys)

arginine (arg)

histidine (his)

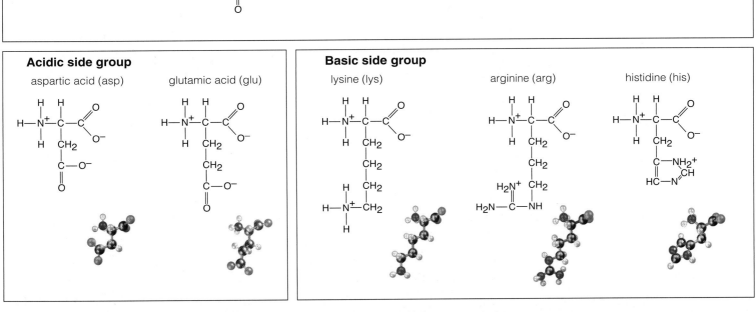

Appendix VII. Periodic Table of the Elements

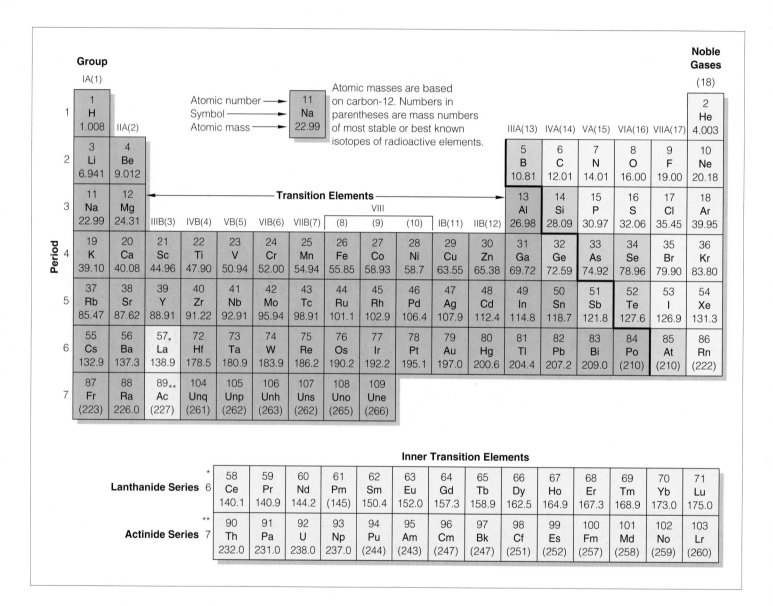

Group

IA(1)

Atomic number ⟶ 11
Symbol ⟶ Na
Atomic mass ⟶ 22.99

Atomic masses are based on carbon-12. Numbers in parentheses are mass numbers of most stable or best known isotopes of radioactive elements.

Noble Gases
(18)

Transition Elements

Period

1																	

Period 1: 1 H 1.008 — IIA(2) — 2 He 4.003

Period 2: 3 Li 6.941 | 4 Be 9.012 — IIIA(13) 5 B 10.81 | IVA(14) 6 C 12.01 | VA(15) 7 N 14.01 | VIA(16) 8 O 16.00 | VIIA(17) 9 F 19.00 | 10 Ne 20.18

Period 3: 11 Na 22.99 | 12 Mg 24.31 — 13 Al 26.98 | 14 Si 28.09 | 15 P 30.97 | 16 S 32.06 | 17 Cl 35.45 | 18 Ar 39.95

IIIB(3) | IVB(4) | VB(5) | VIB(6) | VIIB(7) | VIII (8) (9) (10) | IB(11) | IIB(12)

Period 4: 19 K 39.10 | 20 Ca 40.08 | 21 Sc 44.96 | 22 Ti 47.90 | 23 V 50.94 | 24 Cr 52.00 | 25 Mn 54.94 | 26 Fe 55.85 | 27 Co 58.93 | 28 Ni 58.7 | 29 Cu 63.55 | 30 Zn 65.38 | 31 Ga 69.72 | 32 Ge 72.59 | 33 As 74.92 | 34 Se 78.96 | 35 Br 79.90 | 36 Kr 83.80

Period 5: 37 Rb 85.47 | 38 Sr 87.62 | 39 Y 88.91 | 40 Zr 91.22 | 41 Nb 92.91 | 42 Mo 95.94 | 43 Tc 98.91 | 44 Ru 101.1 | 45 Rh 102.9 | 46 Pd 106.4 | 47 Ag 107.9 | 48 Cd 112.4 | 49 In 114.8 | 50 Sn 118.7 | 51 Sb 121.8 | 52 Te 127.6 | 53 I 126.9 | 54 Xe 131.3

Period 6: 55 Cs 132.9 | 56 Ba 137.3 | 57* La 138.9 | 72 Hf 178.5 | 73 Ta 180.9 | 74 W 183.9 | 75 Re 186.2 | 76 Os 190.2 | 77 Ir 192.2 | 78 Pt 195.1 | 79 Au 197.0 | 80 Hg 200.6 | 81 Tl 204.4 | 82 Pb 207.2 | 83 Bi 209.0 | 84 Po (210) | 85 At (210) | 86 Rn (222)

Period 7: 87 Fr (223) | 88 Ra 226.0 | 89** Ac (227) | 104 Unq (261) | 105 Unp (262) | 106 Unh (263) | 107 Uns (262) | 108 Uno (265) | 109 Une (266)

Inner Transition Elements

Lanthanide Series 6 *
| 58 Ce 140.1 | 59 Pr 140.9 | 60 Nd 144.2 | 61 Pm (145) | 62 Sm 150.4 | 63 Eu 152.0 | 64 Gd 157.3 | 65 Tb 158.9 | 66 Dy 162.5 | 67 Ho 164.9 | 68 Er 167.3 | 69 Tm 168.9 | 70 Yb 173.0 | 71 Lu 175.0 |

Actinide Series 7 **
| 90 Th 232.0 | 91 Pa 231.0 | 92 U 238.0 | 93 Np 237.0 | 94 Pu (244) | 95 Am (243) | 96 Cm (247) | 97 Bk (247) | 98 Cf (251) | 99 Es (252) | 100 Fm (257) | 101 Md (258) | 102 No (259) | 103 Lr (260) |

Appendix VIII. Annotations to A Journal Article

This journal article reports on the movements of a female wolf during the summer of 2002 in northwestern Canada. It also reports on a scientific process of inquiry, observation and interpretation to learn where, how and why the wolf traveled as she did. In some ways, this article reflects the story of "how to do science" told in section 1.5 of this textbook. These notes are intended to help you read and understand how scientists work and how they report on their work.

(1) ARCTIC

(2) VOL. 57, NO. 2 (JUNE 2004) P. 196–203

(3) Long Foraging Movement of a Denning Tundra Wolf

(4) Paul F. Frame,[1,2] David S. Hik,[1] H. Dean Cluff,[3] and Paul C. Paquet[4]

(5) (Received 3 September 2003; accepted in revised form 16 January 2004)

(6) ABSTRACT. Wolves (*Canis lupus*) on the Canadian barrens are intimately linked to migrating herds of barren-ground caribou (*Rangifer tarandus*). We deployed a Global Positioning System (GPS) radio collar on an adult female wolf to record her movements in response to changing caribou densities near her den during summer. This wolf and two other females were observed nursing a group of 11 pups. She traveled a minimum of 341 km during a 14-day excursion. The straight-line distance from the den to the farthest location was 103 km, and the overall minimum rate of travel was 3.1 km/h. The distance between the wolf and the radio-collared caribou decreased from 242 km one week before the excursion to 8 km four days into the excursion. We discuss several possible explanations for the long foraging bout.

(7) *Key words:* wolf, GPS tracking, movements, *Canis lupus*, foraging, caribou, Northwest Territories

(8) RÉSUMÉ. Les loups (*Canis lupus*) dans la toundra canadienne sont étroitement liés aux hardes de caribous des toundras (*Rangifer tarandus*). On a équipé une louve adulte d'un collier émetteur muni d'un système de positionnement mondial (GPS) afin d'enregistrer ses déplacements en réponse au changement de densité du caribou près de sa tanière durant l'été. On a observé cette louve ainsi que deux autres en train d'allaiter un groupe de 11 louveteaux. Elle a parcouru un minimum de 341 km durant une sortie de 14 jours. La distance en ligne droite de la tanière à l'endroit le plus éloigné était de 103 km, et la vitesse minimum durant tout le voyage était de 3,1 km/h. La distance entre la louve et le caribou muni du collier émetteur a diminué de 242 km une semaine avant la sortie à 8 km quatre jours après la sortie. On commente diverses explications possibles pour ce long épisode de recherche de nourriture.

Mots clés: loup, repérage GPS, déplacements, *Canis lupus*, recherche de nourriture, caribou, Territoires du Nord-Ouest

Traduit pour la revue *Arctic* par Nésida Loyer.

(9) Introduction

Wolves (*Canis lupus*) that den on the central barrens of mainland Canada follow the seasonal movements of their main prey, migratory barren-ground caribou (*Rangifer tarandus*) (Kuyt, 1962; Kelsall, 1968; Walton et al., 2001). However, most wolves do not den near caribou calving grounds, but select sites farther south, closer to the tree line (Heard and Williams, 1992). Most caribou migrate beyond primary wolf denning areas by mid-June and do not return until mid-to-late July (Heard et al., 1996; Gunn et al., 2001). Conse-quently, caribou density near dens is low for part of the summer.

During this period of spatial separation from the main caribou herds, wolves must either search near the homesite for scarce caribou or alternative prey (or both), travel to where prey are abundant, or use a combination of these strategies. **(10)**

Walton et al. (2001) postulated that the travel of tundra wolves outside their normal summer ranges is a response to low caribou availability rather than a pre-dispersal exploration like that observed in terri torial wolves (Fritts and Mech, 1981; Messier, 1985). The authors postulated this because most such travel was directed toward caribou calving grounds. We report details of such a long-distance excursion by a breeding female tundra wolf wearing a GPS radio collar. We discuss the relationship of the excursion to movements of satellite-collared caribou (Gunn et al., 2001), supporting the hypothesis that tundra wolves make directional, rapid, long-distance movements in response to seasonal prey availability. **(11)**

[1] Department of Biological Sciences, University of Alberta, Edmonton, Alberta T6G 2E9, Canada
[2] Corresponding author: pframe@ualberta.ca
[3] Department of Resources, Wildlife, and Economic Development, North Slave Region, Government of the Northwest Territories, P.O. Box 2668, 3803 Bretzlaff Dr., Yellowknife, Northwest Territories X1A 2P9, Canada; Dean_Cluff@gov.nt.ca
[4] Faculty of Environmental Design, University of Calgary, Calgary, Alberta T2N 1N4, Canada; current address: P.O. Box 150, Meacham, Saskatchewan S0K 2V0, Canada

196

---

1 Title of the journal, which reports on science taking place in Arctic regions.

2 Volume number, issue number and date of the journal, and page numbers of the article.

3 Title of the article: a concise but specific description of the subject of study—one episode of long-range travel by a wolf hunting for food on the Arctic tundra.

4 Authors of the article: scientists working at the institutions listed in the footnotes below. Note #2 indicates that P. F. Frame is the *corresponding author*—the person to contact with questions or comments. His email address is provided.

5 Date on which a draft of the article was received by the journal editor, followed by date one which a revised draft was accepted for publication. Between these dates, the article was reviewed and critiqued by other scientists, a process called peer review. The authors revised the article to make it clearer, according to those reviews.

6 ABSTRACT: A brief description of the study containing all basic elements of this report. First sentence summarizes the *background* material. Second sentence encapsulates the *methods* used. The rest of the paragraph sums up the *results*. Authors introduce the main *subject* of the study—a female wolf (#388) with pups in a den—and refer to later *discussion* of possible explanations for her behavior.

7 Key words are listed to help researchers using computer databases. Searching the databases using these key words will yield a list of studies related to this one.

8 RÉSUMÉ: The French translation of the abstract and key words. Many researchers in this field are French Canadian. Some journals provide such translations in French or in other languages.

9 INTRODUCTION: Gives the background for this wolf study. This paragraph tells of known or suspected wolf behavior that is important for this study. Note that (a) major species mentioned are always accompanied by scientific names, and (b) statements of fact or *postulations* (claims or assumptions about what is likely to be true) are followed by references to studies that established those facts or supported the postulations.

10 This paragraph focuses directly on the wolf behaviors that were studied here.

11 This paragraph starts with a statement of the *hypothesis* being tested, one that originated in other studies and is supported by this one. The hypothesis is restated more succinctly in the last sentence of this paragraph. This is the *inquiry* part of the scientific process—asking questions and suggesting possible answers.

12 This map shows the study area and depicts wolf and caribou locations and movements during one summer. Some of this information is explained below.

13 STUDY AREA: This section sets the stage for the study, locating it precisely with latitude and longitude coordinates and describing the area (illustrated by the map in Figure 1).

14 Here begins the story of how prey (caribou) and predators (wolves) interact on the tundra. Authors describe movements of these nomadic animals throughout the year.

15 We focus on the denning season (summer) and learn how wolves locate their dens and travel according to the movements of caribou herds.

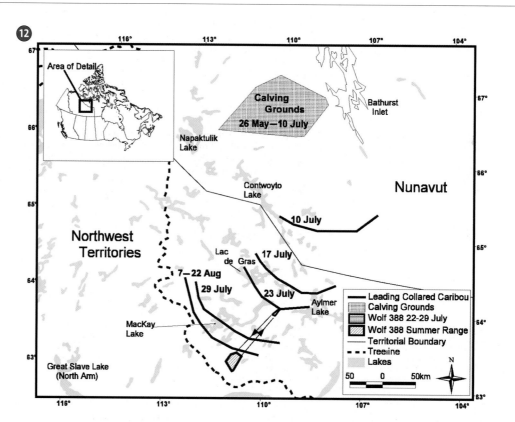

Figure 1. Map showing the movements of satellite radio-collared caribou with respect to female wolf 388's summer range and long foraging movement, in summer 2002.

13 Study Area

Our study took place in the northern boreal forest–low Arctic tundra transition zone (63° 30′ N, 110° 00′ W; Figure 1; Timoney et al., 1992). Permafrost in the area changes from discontinuous to continuous (Harris, 1986). Patches of spruce (*Picea mariana, P. glauca*) occur in the southern portion and give way to open tundra to the northeast. Eskers, kames, and other glacial deposits are scattered throughout the study area. Standing water and exposed bedrock are characteristic of the area.

14 *Details of the Caribou-Wolf System*

The Bathurst caribou herd uses this study area. Most caribou cows have begun migrating by late April, reaching calving grounds by June (Gunn et al., 2001;

Figure 1). Calving peaks by 15 June (Gunn et al., 2001), and calves begin to travel with the herd by one week of age (Kelsall, 1968). The movement patterns of bulls are less known, but bulls frequent areas near calving grounds by mid-June (Heard et al., 1996; Gunn et al., 2001). In summer, Bathurst caribou cows generally travel south from their calving grounds and then, parallel to the tree line, to the northwest. The rut usually takes place at the tree line in October (Gunn et al., 2001). The winter range of the Bathurst herd varies among years, ranging through the taiga and along the tree line from south of Great Bear Lake to southeast of Great Slave Lake. Some caribou spend the winter on the tundra (Gunn et al., 2001; Thorpe et al., 2001).

In winter, wolves that prey on Bathurst caribou do **15** not behave territorially. Instead, they follow the herd throughout its winter range (Walton et al., 2001; Musiani, 2003). However, during denning (May–

Table 1. Daily distances from wolf 388 and the den to the nearest radio-collared caribou during a long excursion in summer 2002.

Date (2002)	Mean distance from caribou to wolf (km)	Daily distance from closest caribou to den
12 July	242	241
13 July	210	209
14 July	200	199
15 July	186	180
16 July	163	162
17 July	151	148
18 July	144	137
19 July[1]	126	124
20 July	103	130
21 July	73	130
22 July	40	110
23 July[2]	9	104
29 July[3]	16	43
30 July	32	43
31 July	28	44
1 August	29	46
2 August[4]	54	52
3 August	53	53
4 August	74	74
5 August	75	75
6 August	74	75
7 August	72	75
8 August	76	75
9 August	79	79

[1] Excursion starts.
[2] Wolf closest to collared caribou.
[3] Previous five days' caribou locations not available.
[4] Excursion ends.

August, parturition late May to mid-June), wolf movements are limited by the need to return food to the den. To maximize access to migrating caribou, many wolves select den sites closer to the tree line than to caribou calving grounds (Heard and Williams, 1992). Because of caribou movement patterns, tundra denning wolves are separated from the main caribou herds by several hundred kilometers at some time during summer (Williams, 1990:19; Figure 1; Table 1).

16 Muskoxen do not occur in the study area (Fournier and Gunn, 1998), and there are few moose there (H.D. Cluff, pers. obs.). Therefore, alternative prey for wolves includes waterfowl, other ground-nesting birds, their eggs, rodents, and hares (Kuyt, 1972; Williams, 1990:16; H.D. Cluff and P.F. Frame, unpubl. data). During 56 hours of den observations, we saw no ground squirrels or hares, only birds. It appears that the abundance of alternative prey was relatively low in 2002.

17 Methods

Wolf Monitoring

18 We captured female wolf 388 near her den on 22 June 2002, using a helicopter net-gun (Walton et al., 2001). She was fitted with a releasable GPS radio collar (Merrill et al., 1998) programmed to acquire locations at 30-

minute intervals. The collar was electronically released (e.g., Mech and Gese, 1992) on 20 August 2002. From 27 June to 3 July 2002, we observed 388's den with a 78 mm spotting scope at a distance of 390 m.

Caribou Monitoring

In spring of 2002, ten female caribou were captured by helicopter net-gun and fitted with satellite radio collars, bringing the total number of collared Bathurst cows to 19. Eight of these spent the summer of 2002 south of Queen Maud Gulf, well east of normal Bathurst caribou range. Therefore, we used 11 caribou for this analysis. The collars provided one location per day during our study, except for five days from 24 to 28 July. Locations of satellite collars were obtained from Service Argos, Inc. (Landover, Maryland).

Data Analysis

Location data were analyzed by ArcView GIS software (Environmental Systems Research Institute Inc., Redlands, California). We calculated the average distance from the nearest collared caribou to the wolf and the den for each day of the study. **19**

Wolf foraging bouts were calculated from the time 388 exited a buffer zone (500 m radius around the den) until she re-entered it. We considered her to be traveling when two consecutive locations were spatially separated by more than 100 m. Minimum distance traveled was the sum of distances between each location and the next during the excursion.

We compared pre- and post-excursion data using Analysis of Variance (ANOVA; Zar, 1999). We first tested for homogeneity of variances with Levene's test (Brown and Forsythe, 1974). No transformations of these data were required.

Results **20**

Wolf Monitoring

Pre-Excursion Period: Wolf 388 was lactating when captured on 22 June. We observed her and two other females nursing a group of 11 pups between 27 June and 3 July. During our observations, the pack consisted of at least four adults (3 females and 1 male) and 11 pups. On 30 June, three pups were moved to a location 310 m from the other eight and cared for by an uncollared female. The male was not seen at the den after the evening of 30 June. **21**

Before the excursion, telemetry indicated 18 foraging bouts. The mean distance traveled during these bouts was 25.29 km (± 4.5 SE, range 3.1–82.5 km). Mean greatest distance from the den on foraging

16 Other variables are considered—prey other than caribou and their relative abundance in 2002.

17 METHODS: There is no one scientific method. Procedures for each and every study must be explained carefully.

18 Authors explain when and how they tracked caribou and wolves, including tools used and the exact procedures followed.

19 This important subsection explains what data were calculated (average distance ...) and how, including the software used and where it came from. (The calculations are listed in Table 1.) Note that the behavior measured (traveling) is carefully defined.

20 RESULTS: The heart of the report and the *observation* part of the scientific process. This section is organized parallel to the Methods section.

21 This subsection is broken down by periods of observation. Pre-excursion period covers the time between 388's capture and the start of her long-distance travel. The investigators used visual observations as well as telemetry (measurements taken using the global positioning system (GPS)) to gather data. They looked at how 388 cared for her pups, interacted with other adults, and moved about the den area.

22 The key in the lower right-hand corner of the map shows areas (shaded) within which the wolves and caribou moved, and the dotted trail of 388 during her excursion. From the results depicted on this map, the investigators tried to determine when and where 388 might have encountered caribou and how their locations affected her traveling behavior.

23 The wolf's excursion (her long trip away from the den area) is the focus of this study. These paragraphs present detailed measurements of daily movements during her two-week trip—how far she traveled, how far she was from collared caribou, her time spent traveling and resting, and her rate of speed. Authors use the phrase "minimum distance traveled" to acknowledge they couldn't track every step but were measuring samples of her movements. They knew that she went at least as far as they measured. This shows how scientists try to be exact when reporting results. Results of this study are depicted graphically in the map in Figure 2.

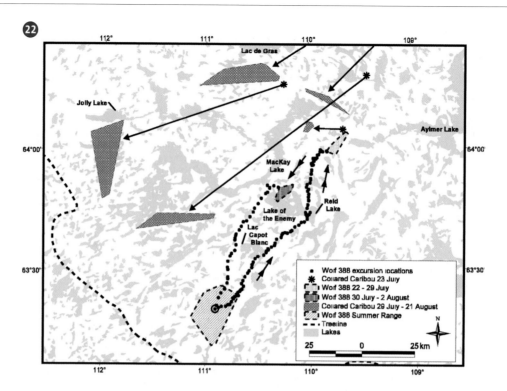

Figure 2. Details of a long foraging movement by female wolf 388 between 19 July and 2 August 2002. Also shown are locations and movements of three satellite radio-collared caribou from 23 July to 21 August 2002. On 23 July, the wolf was 8 km from a collared caribou. The farthest point from the den (103 km distant) was recorded on 27 July. Arrows indicate direction of travel.

bouts was 7.1 km (± 0.9 SE, range 1.7–17.0 km). The average duration of foraging bouts for the period was 20.9 h (± 4.5 SE, range 1–71 h).

The average daily distance between the wolf and the nearest collared caribou decreased from 242 km on 12 July, one week before the excursion period, to 126 km on 19 July, the day the excursion began (Table 1).

23 **Excursion Period:** On 19 July at 2203, after spending 14 h at the den, 388 began moving to the northeast and did not return for 336 h (14 d; Figure 2). Whether she traveled alone or with other wolves is unknown. During the excursion, 476 (71%) of 672 possible locations were recorded. The wolf crossed the southeast end of Lac Capot Blanc on a small land bridge, where she paused for 4.5 h after traveling for 19.5 h (37.5

km). Following this rest, she traveled for 9 h (26.3 km) onto a peninsula in Reid Lake, where she spent 2 h before backtracking and stopping for 8 h just off the peninsula. Her next period of travel lasted 16.5 h (32.7 km), terminating in a pause of 9.5 h just 3.8 km from a concentration of locations at the far end of her excursion, where we presume she encountered caribou. The mean duration of these three movement periods was 15.7 h (± 2.5 SE), and that of the pauses, 7.3 h (± 1.5). The wolf required 72.5 h (3.0 d) to travel a minimum of 95 km from her den to this area near caribou (Figure 2). She remained there (35.5 km2) for 151.5 h (6.3 d) and then moved south to Lake of the Enemy, where she stayed (31.9 km^2) for 74 h (3.1 d) before returning to her den. Her greatest distance from the den, 103 km, was recorded 174.5 h (7.3 d) after the excursion

Foraging Movement of A Tundra Wolf **199**

began, at 0433 on 27 July. She was 8 km from a collared caribou on 23 July, four days after the excursion began (Table 1).

The return trip began at 0403 on 2 August, 318 h (13.2 d) after leaving the den. She followed a relatively direct path for 18 h back to the den, a distance of 75 km.

The minimum distance traveled during the excursion was 339 km. The estimated overall minimum travel rate was 3.1 km/h, 2.6 km/h away from the den and 4.2 km/h on the return trip.

24 **Post-Excursion Period:** We saw three pups when recovering the collar on 20 August, but others may have been hiding in vegetation.

Telemetry recorded 13 foraging bouts in the post-excursion period. The mean distance traveled during these bouts was 18.3 km (+ 2.7 SE, range 1.2–47.7 km), and mean greatest distance from the den was 7.1 km (+ 0.7 SE, range 1.1–11.0 km). The mean duration of these post-excursion foraging bouts was 10.9 h (+ 2.4 SE, range 1–33 h).

When 388 reached her den on 2 August, the distance to the nearest collared caribou was 54 km. On 9 August, one week after she returned, the distance was 79 km (Table 1).

Pre- and Post-Excursion Comparison

25 We found no differences in the mean distance of foraging bouts before and after the excursion period ($F = 1.5$, $df = 1$, 29, $p = 0.24$). Likewise, the mean greatest distance from the den was similar pre- and post-excursion ($F = 0.004$, $df = 1$, 29, $p = 0.95$). However, the mean duration of 388's foraging bouts decreased by 10.0 h after her long excursion ($F = 3.1$, $df = 1$, 29, $p = 0.09$).

26 *Caribou Monitoring*

Summer Movements: On 10 July, 5 of 11 collared caribou were dispersed over a distance of 10 km, 140 km south of their calving grounds (Figure 1). On the same day, three caribou were still on the calving grounds, two were between the calving grounds and the leaders, and one was missing. One week later (17 July), the leading radio-collared cows were 100 km farther south (Figure 1). Two were within 5 km of each other in front of the rest, who were more dispersed. All radio-collared cows had left the calving grounds by this time. On 23 July, the leading radio-collared caribou had moved 35 km farther south, and all of them were more widely dispersed. The two cows closest to the leader were 26 km and 33 km away, with 37 km between them. On the next location (29 July), the most southerly caribou were 60 km

farther south. All of the caribou were now in the areas where they remained for the duration of the study (Figure 2).

A Minimum Convex Polygon (Mohr and Stumpf, 1966) around all caribou locations acquired during the study encompassed 85 119 km².

Relative to the Wolf Den: The distance from the **27** nearest collared caribou to the den decreased from 241 km one week before the excursion to 124 km the day it began. The nearest a collared caribou came to the den was 43 km away, on 29 and 30 July. During the study, four collared caribou were located within 100 km of the den. Each of these four was closest to the wolf on at least one day during the period reported.

28 Discussion

Prey Abundance

Caribou are the single most important prey of tundra **29** wolves (Clark, 1971; Kuyt, 1972; Stephenson and James, 1982; Williams, 1990). Caribou range over vast areas, and for part of the summer, they are scarce or absent in wolf home ranges (Heard et al., 1996). Both the long distance between radio-collared caribou and the den the week before the excursion and the increased time spent foraging by wolf 388 indicate that caribou availability near the den was low. Observations of the pups' being left alone for up to 18 h, presumably while adults were searching for food, provide additional support for low caribou availability locally. Mean foraging bout duration decreased by 10.0 h after the excursion, when collared caribou were closer to the den, suggesting an increase in caribou availability nearby.

Foraging Excursion

One aspect of central place foraging theory (CPFT) **30** deals with the optimality of returning different-sized food loads from varying distances to dependents at a central place (i.e., the den) (Orians and Pearson, 1979). Carlson (1985) tested CPFT and found that the predator usually consumed prey captured far from the central place, while feeding prey captured nearby to dependants. Wolf 388 spent 7.2 days in one area near caribou before moving to a location 23 km back towards the den, where she spent an additional 3.1 days, likely hunting caribou. She began her return trip from this closer location, traveling directly to the den. While away, she may have made one or more successful kills and spent time meeting her own energetic needs before returning to the den. Alternatively, it may have taken several attempts to make a kill,

24 Post-excursion measurements of 388's movements were made to compare with those of the pre-excursion period. In order to compare, scientists often use *means*, or averages, of a series of measurements—mean distances, mean duration, etc.

25 In the comparison, authors used statistical calculations (F and df) to determine that the differences between pre- and post-excursion measurements were *statistically insignificant*, or close enough to be considered essentially the same or similar.

26 As with wolf 388, the investigators measured the movements of caribou during the study period. The areas within which the caribou moved are shown in Figure 2 by shaded polygons mentioned in the second paragraph of this subsection.

27 This subsection summarizes how distances separating predators and prey varied during the study period.

28 DISCUSSION: This section is the *interpretation* part of the scientific process.

29 This subsection reviews observations from other studies and suggests that this study fits with patterns of those observations.

30 Authors discuss a prevailing *theory* (CBFT) which might explain why a wolf would travel far to meet her own energy needs while taking food caught closer to the den back to her pups. The results of this study seem to fit that pattern.

31 Here our authors note other possible explanations for wolves' excursions presented by other investigators, but this study does not seem to support those ideas.

32 Authors discuss possible reasons for why 388 traveled directly to where caribou were located. They take what they learned from earlier studies and apply it to this case, suggesting that the lay of the land played a role. Note that their description paints a clear picture of the landscape.

33 Authors suggest that 388 may have learned in traveling during previous summers where the caribou were. The last two sentences suggest ideas for future studies.

34 Or maybe 388 followed the scent of the caribou. Authors acknowledge difficulties of proving this, but they suggest another area where future studies might be done.

35 Authors suggest that results of this study support previous studies about how fast wolves travel to and from the den. In the last sentence, they speculate on how these observed patterns would fit into the theory of evolution.

36 Authors also speculate on the fate of 388's pups while she was traveling. This leads to . . .

which she then fed on before beginning her return trip. We do not know if she returned food to the pups, but such behavior would be supported by CPFT.

31 Other workers have reported wolves' making long round trips and referred to them as "extraterritorial" or "pre-dispersal" forays (Fritts and Mech, 1981; Messier, 1985; Ballard et al., 1997; Merrill and Mech, 2000). These movements are most often made by young wolves (1–3 years old), in areas where annual territories are maintained and prey are relatively sedentary (Fritts and Mech, 1981; Messier, 1985). The long excursion of 388 differs in that tundra wolves do not maintain annual territories (Walton et al., 2001), and the main prey migrate over vast areas (Gunn et al., 2001).

Another difference between 388's excursion and those reported earlier is that she is a mature, breeding female. No study of territorial wolves has reported reproductive adults making extraterritorial movements in summer (Fritts and Mech, 1981; Messier, 1985; Ballard et al., 1997; Merrill and Mech, 2001). However, Walton et al. (2001) also report that breeding female tundra wolves made excursions.

Direction of Movement

32 Possible explanations for the relatively direct route 388 took to the caribou include landscape influence and experience. Considering the timing of 388's trip and the locations of caribou, had the wolf moved northwest, she might have missed the caribou entirely, or the encounter might have been delayed.

A reasonable possibility is that the land directed 388's route. The barrens are crisscrossed with trails worn into the tundra over centuries by hundreds of thousands of caribou and other animals (Kelsall, 1968; Thorpe et al., 2001). At river crossings, lakes, or narrow peninsulas, trails converge and funnel towards and away from caribou calving grounds and summer range. Wolves use trails for travel (Paquet et al., 1996; Mech and Boitani, 2003; P. Frame, pers. observation). Thus, the landscape may direct an animal's movements and lead it to where cues, such as the odor of caribou on the wind or scent marks of other wolves, may lead it to caribou.

33 Another possibility is that 388 knew where to find caribou in summer. Sexually immature tundra wolves sometimes follow caribou to calving grounds (D. Heard, unpubl. data). Possibly, 388 had made such journeys in previous years and killed caribou. If this were the case, then in times of local prey scarcity she might travel to areas where she had hunted successfully before. Continued monitoring of tundra wolves may answer questions about how their food needs are met in times of low caribou abundance near dens.

Caribou often form large groups while moving **34** south to the tree line (Kelsall, 1968). After a large aggregation of caribou moves through an area, its scent can linger for weeks (Thorpe et al., 2001:104). It is conceivable that 388 detected caribou scent on the wind, which was blowing from the northeast on 19–21 July (Environment Canada, 2003), at the same time her excursion began. Many factors, such as odor strength and wind direction and strength, make systematic study of scent detection in wolves difficult under field conditions (Harrington and Asa, 2003). However, humans are able to smell odors such as forest fires or oil refineries more than 100 km away. The olfactory capabilities of dogs, which are similar to wolves, are thought to be 100 to 1 million times that of humans (Harrington and Asa, 2003). Therefore, it is reasonable to think that under the right wind conditions, the scent of many caribou traveling together could be detected by wolves from great distances, thus triggering a long foraging bout.

Rate of Travel

Mech (1994) reported the rate of travel of Arctic **35** wolves on barren ground was 8.7 km/h during regular travel and 10.0 km/h when returning to the den, a difference of 1.3 km/h. These rates are based on direct observation and exclude periods when wolves moved slowly or not at all. Our calculated travel rates are assumed to include periods of slow movement or no movement. However, the pattern we report is similar to that reported by Mech (1994), in that homeward travel was faster than regular travel by 1.6 km/h. The faster rate on return may be explained by the need to return food to the den. Pup survival can increase with the number of adults in a pack available to deliver food to pups (Harrington et al., 1983). Therefore, an increased rate of travel on homeward trips could improve a wolf's reproductive fitness by getting food to pups more quickly.

Fate of 388's Pups

Wolf 388 was caring for pups during den observa- **36** tions. The pups were estimated to be six weeks old, and were seen ranging as far as 800 m from the den. They received some regurgitated food from two of the females, but were unattended for long periods. The excursion started 16 days after our observations, and it is improbable that the pups could have traveled the distance that 388 moved. If the pups died, this would have removed parental responsibility, allowing the long movement.

Our observations and the locations of radio-collared caribou indicate that prey became scarce in the area of the den as summer progressed. Wolf 388 may have abandoned her pups to seek food for herself. However, she returned to the den after the excursion, where she was seen near pups. In fact, she foraged in a similar pattern before and after the excursion, suggesting that she again was providing for pups after her return to the den.

(37) A more likely possibility is that one or both of the other lactating females cared for the pups during 388's absence. The three females at this den were not seen with the pups at the same time. However, two weeks earlier, at a different den, we observed three females cooperatively caring for a group of six pups. At that den, the three lactating females were observed providing food for each other and trading places while nursing pups. Such a situation at the den of 388 could have created conditions that allowed one or more of the lactating females to range far from the den for a period, returning to her parental duties afterwards. However, the pups would have been weaned by eight weeks of age (Packard et al., 1992), so nonlactating adults could also have cared for them, as often happens in wolf packs (Packard et al., 1992; Mech et al., 1999).

Cooperative rearing of multiple litters by a pack could create opportunities for long-distance foraging movements by some reproductive wolves during summer periods of local food scarcity. We have recorded multiple lactating females at one or more tundra wolf dens per year since 1997. This reproductive strategy may be an adaptation to temporally and **(38)** spatially unpredictable food resources. All of these possibilities require further study, but emphasize both the adaptability of wolves living on the barrens and their dependence on caribou.

Long-range wolf movement in response to caribou **(39)** availability has been suggested by other researchers (Kuyt, 1972; Walton et al., 2001) and traditional ecological knowledge (Thorpe et al., 2001). Our report demonstrates the rapid and extreme response of wolves to caribou distribution and movements in summer. Increased human activity on the tundra (mining, road building, pipelines, ecotourism) may influence caribou movement patterns and change the interactions between wolves and caribou in the region. Continued monitoring of both species will help us to assess whether the association is being affected adversely by anthropogenic change.

(40) Acknowledgements

This research was supported by the Department of Resources, Wildlife, and Economic Development, Government of the Northwest Territories; the Department of Biological Sciences at the University of Alberta; the Natural Sciences and Engineering Research Council of Canada; the Department of Indian and Northern Affairs Canada; the Canadian Circumpolar Institute; and DeBeers Canada, Ltd. Lorna Ruechel assisted with den observations. A. Gunn provided caribou location data. We thank Dave Mech for the use of GPS collars. M. Nelson, A. Gunn, and three anonymous reviewers made helpful comments on earlier drafts of the manuscript. This work was done under Wildlife Research Permit – WL002948 issued by the Government of the Northwest Territories, Department of Resources, Wildlife, and Economic Development.

(41) References

BALLARD, W.B., AYRES, L.A., KRAUSMAN, P.R., REED, D.J., and FANCY, S.G. 1997. Ecology of wolves in relation to a migratory caribou herd in northwest Alaska. Wildlife Monographs 135. 47 p.

BROWN, M.B., and FORSYTHE, A.B. 1974. Robust tests for the equality of variances. Journal of the American Statistical Association 69:364–367.

CARLSON, A. 1985. Central place foraging in the red-backed shrike (*Lanius collurio* L.): Allocation of prey between forager and sedentary consumer. Animal Behaviour 33:664–666.

CLARK, K.R.F. 1971. Food habits and behavior of the tundra wolf on central Baffin Island. Ph.D. Thesis, University of Toronto, Ontario, Canada.

ENVIRONMENT CANADA. 2003. National climate data information archive. Available online: http://www.climate.weatheroffice.ec.gc.ca/Welcome_e.html

FOURNIER, B., and GUNN, A. 1998. Musk ox numbers and distribution in the NWT, 1997. File Report No. 121. Yellowknife: Department of Resources, Wildlife, and Economic Development, Government of the Northwest Territories. 55 p.

FRITTS, S.H., and MECH, L.D. 1981. Dynamics, movements, and feeding ecology of a newly protected wolf population in northwestern Minnesota. Wildlife Monographs 80. 79 p.

GUNN, A., DRAGON, J., and BOULANGER, J. 2001. Seasonal movements of satellite-collared caribou from the Bathurst herd. Final Report to the West Kitikmeot Slave Study Society, Yellowknife, NWT. 80 p. Available online: http://www.wkss.nt.ca/HTML/08_ProjectsReports/PDF/Seasonal MovementsFinal.pdf

HARRINGTON, F.H., and ASA, C.S. 2003. Wolf communication. In: Mech, L.D., and Boitani, L., eds. Wolves: Behavior, ecology, and conservation. Chicago: University of Chicago Press. 66–103.

HARRINGTON, F.H., MECH, L.D., and FRITTS, S.H. 1983. Pack size and wolf pup survival: Their relationship under varying ecological conditions. Behavioral Ecology and Sociobiology 13:19–26.

HARRIS, S.A. 1986. Permafrost distribution, zonation and stability along the eastern ranges of the cordillera of North America. Arctic 39(1):29–38.

HEARD, D.C., and WILLIAMS, T.M. 1992. Distribution of wolf dens on migratory caribou ranges in the Northwest

37 Discussion of cooperative rearing of pups and, in turn, to speculation on how this study and what is known about cooperative rearing might fit into the animal's strategies for survival of the species. Again, the authors approach the broader theory of evolution and how it might explain some of their results.

38 And again, they suggest that this study points to several areas where further study will shed some light.

39 In conclusion, the authors suggest that their study supports the hypothesis being tested here. And they touch on the implications of increased human activity on the tundra predicted by their results.

40 ACKNOWLEDGEMENTS: Authors note the support of institutions, companies and individuals. They thank their reviewers ad list permits under which their research was carried on.

41 REFERENCES: List of all studies cited in the report. This may seem tedious, but is a vitally important part of scientific reporting. It is a record of the sources of information on which this study is based. It provides readers with a wealth of resources for further reading on this topic. Much of it will form the foundation of future scientific studies like this one.

Territories, Canada. Canadian Journal of Zoology 70:1504–1510.

HEARD, D.C., WILLIAMS, T.M., and MELTON, D.A. 1996. The relationship between food intake and predation risk in migratory caribou and implication to caribou and wolf population dynamics. Rangifer Special Issue No. 2:37–44.

KELSALL, J.P. 1968. The migratory barren-ground caribou of Canada. Canadian Wildlife Service Monograph Series 3. Ottawa: Queen's Printer. 340 p.

KUYT, E. 1962. Movements of young wolves in the Northwest Territories of Canada. Journal of Mammalogy 43:270–271.

———. 1972. Food habits and ecology of wolves on barren-ground caribou range in the Northwest Territories. Canadian Wildlife Service Report Series 21. Ottawa: Information Canada. 36 p.

MECH, L.D. 1994. Regular and homeward travel speeds of Arctic wolves. Journal of Mammalogy 75:741–742.

MECH, L.D., and BOITANI, L. 2003. Wolf social ecology. In: Mech, L.D., and Boitani, L., eds. Wolves: Behavior, ecology, and conservation. Chicago: University of Chicago Press. 1–34.

MECH, L.D., and GESE, E.M. 1992. Field testing the Wildlink capture collar on wolves. Wildlife Society Bulletin 20:249–256.

MECH, L.D., WOLFE, P., and PACKARD, J.M. 1999. Regurgitative food transfer among wild wolves. Canadian Journal of Zoology 77:1192–1195.

MERRILL, S.B., and MECH, L.D. 2000. Details of extensive movements by Minnesota wolves (*Canis lupus*). American Midland Naturalist 144:428–433.

MERRILL, S.B., ADAMS, L.G., NELSON, M.E., and MECH, L.D. 1998. Testing releasable GPS radiocollars on wolves and white-tailed deer. Wildlife Society Bulletin 26:830–835.

MESSIER, F. 1985. Solitary living and extraterritorial movements of wolves in relation to social status and prey abundance. Canadian Journal of Zoology 63:239–245.

MOHR, C.O., and STUMPF, W.A. 1966. Comparison of methods for calculating areas of animal activity. Journal of Wildlife Management 30:293–304.

MUSIANI, M. 2003. Conservation biology and management of wolves and wolf-human conflicts in western North America. Ph.D. Thesis, University of Calgary, Calgary, Alberta, Canada.

ORIANS, G.H., and PEARSON, N.E. 1979. On the theory of central place foraging. In: Mitchell, R.D., and Stairs, G.F., eds. Analysis of ecological systems. Columbus: Ohio State University Press. 154–177.

PACKARD, J.M., MECH, L.D., and REAM, R.R. 1992. Weaning in an arctic wolf pack: Behavioral mechanisms. Canadian Journal of Zoology 70:1269–1275.

PAQUET, P.C., WIERZCHOWSKI, J., and CALLAGHAN, C. 1996. Summary report on the effects of human activity on gray wolves in the Bow River Valley, Banff National Park, Alberta. In: Green, J., Pacas, C., Bayley, S., and Cornwell, L., eds. A cumulative effects assessment and futures outlook for the Banff Bow Valley. Prepared for the Banff Bow Valley Study. Ottawa: Department of Canadian Heritage.

STEPHENSON, R.O., and JAMES, D. 1982. Wolf movements and food habits in northwest Alaska. In: Harrington, F.H., and Paquet, P.C., eds. Wolves of the world. New Jersey: Noyes Publications. 223–237.

THORPE, N., EYEGETOK, S., HAKONGAK, N., and QITIRMIUT ELDERS. 2001. The Tuktu and Nogak Project: A caribou chronicle. Final Report to the West Kitikmeot/Slave Study Society, Ikaluktuuttiak, NWT. 160 p.

TIMONEY, K.P., LA ROI, G.H., ZOLTAI, S.C., and ROBINSON, A.L. 1992. The high subarctic forest-tundra of northwestern Canada: Position, width, and vegetation gradients in relation to climate. Arctic 45(1):1–9.

WALTON, L.R., CLUFF, H.D., PAQUET, P.C., and RAMSAY, M.A. 2001. Movement patterns of barren-ground wolves in the central Canadian Arctic. Journal of Mammalogy 82:867–876.

WILLIAMS, T.M. 1990. Summer diet and behavior of wolves denning on barren-ground caribou range in the Northwest Territories, Canada. M.Sc. Thesis, University of Alberta, Edmonton, Alberta, Canada.

ZAR, J.H. 1999. Biostatistical analysis. 4th ed. New Jersey: Prentice Hall. 663 p.

Glossary

ABC model Idea that products of three groups of master genes direct a flower's development.

ABO blood typing Method of characterizing an individual's blood based on proteins (A, B, or their absence) at surface of red blood cells.

abortion Expulsion of a pre-term embryo or fetus from the uterus.

abscisic acid ABA. Plant hormone; induces bud and seed dormancy; makes stomata close.

abscission Dropping of leaves, flowers, fruits, or other parts from plants.

acclimatization Long-lasting physiological and behavioral adaptation to a new habitat.

acid Any dissolved substance that donates H+ to other solutes or to water molecules.

acid rain Falling of rain (or snow) rich in acidic sulfur and nitrogen oxides.

acid–base balance State in which extracellular fluid is not too acidic or too basic, an outcome of controls over the concentrations of dissolved ions.

actin Cytoskeletal protein; the main component of thin filaments in a sarcomere.

action potential Brief reversal in the resting membrane potential of an excitable cell.

activation energy Minimum amount of energy required to start a reaction; enzyme action lowers this energy barrier.

activator Regulatory protein that enhances a cell activity (e.g., gene transcription).

active transport Pumping of a specific solute across a membrane against its concentration gradient, through a transport protein's interior. Requires energy input.

acute inflammation Nonspecific defense response to tissue injury in animals. Signs include localized redness, heat, swelling, pain.

adaptation Any aspect of form, function, behavior, or development that improves an individual's capability of surviving and reproducing in a given environment.

adaptive behavior Behavior that contributes to the individual's reproductive success.

adaptive immunity Capacity of B cell and T cell populations to tailor their defenses against previously unencountered pathogens.

adaptive radiation Burst of diversification from a single lineage; gives rise to new species adapted to specific environmental niches.

adaptive zone Some way of life available to species physically and behaviorally able to live it (e.g., "catching flying insects at night").

adenine Nitrogen-containing base component of nucleic acids; also a nucleic acid containing an adenine base. Base-pairs with thymine in DNA or uracil in RNA.

ADH Antidiuretic hormone. Hypothalamic hormone that promotes water conservation.

adhering junction Structure that forms a site of adhesion between cells. Found in tissues subject to stretching or abrasion.

adipose tissue Connective tissue that specializes in fat storage.

adrenal cortex Outer portion of adrenal gland; secretes cortisol and aldosterone.

adrenal medulla Inner portion of adrenal gland; secretes epinephrine, norepinephrine.

aerobic respiration Oxygen-dependent pathway of ATP formation in which glucose is broken down to carbon dioxide and water in several steps, including glycolysis, the Krebs cycle, and electron transfer phosphorylation. Typical net yield: 36 ATP.

age structure Of a population, distribution of individuals among different age categories.

alcoholic fermentation Anaerobic ATP-forming pathway. NADH transfers electrons to acetaldehyde, forming ethanol. Reactions start with pyruvate from glycolysis and regenerate NAD$^+$. Net yield: 2 ATP.

aldosterone Adrenal cortex hormone; promotes sodium reabsorption in the kidney.

alkylating agent A substance that replaces a hydrogen with an alkyl (saturated organic) group in a biological molecule.

allantois Extraembryonic membrane that exchanges gases and stores metabolic wastes of embryos of reptiles, birds, some mammals. In humans, it forms urinary bladder, placental blood vessels.

allele One of two or more molecular forms of a gene that arise by mutation and specify slightly different versions of the same trait.

allergen Normally harmless substance that can provoke inflammation, excess mucus secretion, and often immune responses in susceptible people.

allergy Hypersensitivity to an allergen.

allopatric speciation Divergences end in speciation after a physical barrier that arises between populations of a species stops gene flow between them.

altruism Behavior that lowers an individual's chance of reproductive success but also helps others of its species.

alveolus, plural alveoli In bronchioles, a cup-shaped sac where gases are exchanged between blood and interstitial fluid.

amino acid Organic compound with an amino group (NH_2), a carboxylic acid group (COOH), and a side group bonded covalently to the same carbon atom. Subunit of proteins.

ammonification Of nitrogen cycle, process by which soil fungi and bacteria break down nitrogenous wastes and remains to ammonia compounds that plants may absorb.

amnion An extraembryonic membrane; encloses a fluid-filled sac in which amniote embryos develop.

amniote A tetrapod that produces amniote eggs. A reptile, bird, or mammal.

amoeboid protozoan Protist that forms pseudopods; some "naked," others "shelled" (e.g., amoeba, foraminiferan, radiolarian).

amphibian Vertebrate with four legs (or four-legged aquatic ancestor); its body plan and reproductive mode are somewhere between fishes and reptiles.

anagenesis Speciation pattern; changes occur within an unbranched line of descent.

analogous structures Similar body parts in distantly related lineages that arise as a result of similar environmental pressures.

anaphase Of mitosis, stage when sister chromatids of each chromosome move to opposite spindle poles. During anaphase I (meiosis), each duplicated chromosome and its homologue move to opposite poles. During anaphase II, sister chromatids of each chromosome move to opposite poles.

anemia Disorder resulting from deformed or insufficient quantity of red blood cells.

aneuploidy In cells, too many or too few chromosomes relative to the parental number.

angiosperm Flowering plant.

animal Multicelled, motile heterotroph that has embryonic stages and usually tissues, organs, and organ systems.

annelid Bilateral, highly segmented worm with well-developed organ systems (e.g., oligochaete, polychaete, leech).

anther Part of a stamen; pollen forms in it and is dispersed from it.

anthocyanin Red to blue photosynthetic accessory pigment.

antibiotic A natural or synthetic chemical agent that kills or inhibits growth of microorganisms, especially bacteria.

antibody Antigen-binding receptor made and secreted by B cells.

anticodon Series of three nucleotide bases in tRNA; can base-pair with an mRNA codon.

antigen A substance chemically recognized as nonself; triggers an immune response.

antigen-presenting cell Cell that can break down and display antigen attached to self markers on its surface (e.g., macrophage, dendritic cell, or B cell).

antioxidant Enzyme or cofactor that can help neutralize free radicals, which may otherwise damage DNA and other molecules of life.

aorta Main artery of systemic circulation.

apicomplexan One of a group of parasitic protists that has a unique device used in penetrating host cells.

apoptosis Programmed cell death.

appendix Narrow projection from the cecum.

archaea Evolutionarily distinct domain of prokaryotic organisms.

Archean Eon in which life arose (3.9–2.5 billion years ago).

archipelago An island chain some distance away from a continent.

area effect Idea that larger islands support more species than smaller ones at similar distances from sources of colonizer species.

arteriole Type of blood vessel between arteries and capillaries where control mechanisms govern the distribution of blood flow through the body.

artery Thick-walled, muscular, transport vessel; carries blood away from heart.

arthropod Invertebrate with exoskeleton, jointed appendages (e.g., crustacean, insect).

artificial selection Selection of traits among a population under contrived conditions.

asexual reproduction Any reproductive mode by which offspring arise from and inherit genes from just one parent.

atom Fundamental form of matter that has mass and takes up space, and cannot be broken apart by everyday means.

atomic number The number of protons in the nucleus of an atom; identifies an element.

ATP Adenosine triphosphate. Nucleotide made of adenine, ribose, and three phosphate groups; main energy carrier in cells.

ATP/ADP cycle Alternating formation of ATP and ADP through phosphate group transfers.

ATP synthase Membrane-bound active transport protein that acts as an enzyme of ATP formation.

australopith Type of early hominid; extinct.

autoimmune response An immune response of the body against its own normal cells.

autoimmunity Failure of self-recognition in which the immune system attacks normal body cells.

automated DNA sequencing Robotic method of determining the nucleotide sequence of a region of DNA. Uses gel electrophoresis and laser detection of fluorescent tracers.

autonomic nerve One of the nerves that carry signals to and from internal organs.

autonomic nervous system All nerves from central nervous system to smooth muscle, cardiac muscle, and glands of viscera.

autosome Any chromosome of a type that is the same in males and females of a species.

autotroph An organism that makes its own food using an environmental energy source and carbon from carbon dioxide.

auxin Plant hormone of apical meristems; induces stem lengthening and responses to gravity and light.

axon Neuron's signal-conducting zone.

B cell See B lymphocyte.

B lymphocyte White blood cell that secretes antibody molecules. Also called plasma cell.

bacteria The most widespread and diverse group of prokaryotic organisms.

bacterial conjugation Transfer of plasmid DNA from one prokaryotic cell to another.

bacteriophage A virus that infects bacteria.

balanced polymorphism Outcome of selection; two or more alleles for a trait are being maintained in a population over time.

bark All tissues external to the vascular cambium in older woody stems.

basal body An organelle that gives rise to cilia or flagella; resembles a centriole.

base Any substance that accepts hydrogen ions (H^+) when dissolved in water, thus forming hydroxyl ions (OH^-). Also, the nitrogen-containing component of a nucleic acid.

base-pair substitution Mutation in which one nucleotide is incorrectly substituted for another during DNA replication.

basophil Fast-acting white blood cell that secretes histamine during inflammation.

big bang Model for origin of universe in which all matter, energy, and time originated from a single point in a gigantic explosion.

bilateral symmetry Body plan with main axis from anterior to posterior, separated into right and left sides, and dorsal and ventral surfaces.

bile Liver secretion required for fat digestion.

biogeochemical cycle Movement of element from environmental reservoirs, through living things, then back to the environment.

biogeographic realm One of six vast land areas with distinctive species.

biogeography Study of the patterns of distribution of species.

biological clock Internal time-measuring mechanism; adjusts activities seasonally, daily, or both in response to environmental cues.

biological magnification Some substance becomes more concentrated in body tissues as it moves up through food chains.

biological species concept The definition of a species is based on its reproductive isolation.

biology The scientific study of life.

bioluminescence Production of fluorescent light by a living organism.

biomass Combined weight of all organisms at a given trophic level in an ecosystem.

biomass pyramid Diagram showing the dry weight of all organisms at each trophic level of an ecosystem.

biome A large land region characterized by dominant plant species and habitat conditions.

biosphere All regions of the Earth's waters, crust, and atmosphere where organisms live.

biotic potential The maximum rate of increase of a population under ideal conditions.

bipedalism Routinely walking upright.

bipolar mitotic spindle Dynamic array of microtubules that moves chromosomes in precise directions during mitosis or meiosis.

bird Only animal (besides some extinct related dinosaurs) that grows feathers.

blastocyst Early mammal development stage; two layers of cells surround a fluid-filled cavity.

blastomere One of the small, nucleated cells that form during cleavage of animal zygote.

blastula Early outcome of cleavage; one layer of blastomeres encloses a fluid-filled cavity.

blood Liquid connective tissue that has fluid and cellular components.

blood pressure Fluid pressure, generated by heart contractions, that circulates blood.

blood–brain barrier Mechanism that controls which solutes enter cerebrospinal fluid.

bone remodeling Ongoing mineral deposits and withdrawals from bone.

bone tissue Calcium-hardened connective tissue that composes the vertebrate skeleton.

bottleneck A sudden, drastic reduction in population size.

Bowman's capsule Part of a nephron; receives water and solutes being filtered from blood.

brain An integrating center that receives and processes sensory input and issues commands for responses by muscles and glands.

brain stem Most ancient nerve tissue in the vertebrate hindbrain, midbrain, and forebrain.

bronchiole One of the finely branched airways in the lung.

bronchus, plural **bronchi** Airway that branches from trachea and leads into lungs.

brown alga One of the stramenopiles; mostly marine, photosynthetic (e.g., kelp).

bryophyte A nonvascular land plant (e.g., moss, liverwort, hornwort).

bud Undeveloped shoot, consisting mostly of meristematic tissue.

buffer system A weak acid and the base that forms when it dissolves in water. The two work as a pair to counter slight shifts in pH.

bulk Of the vertebrate gut, the volume of undigested material in the small intestine that cannot be decreased by absorption.

bulk flow Mass movement of one or more substances in the same direction, in response to pressure, gravity, or another external force.

C3 plant Plant that makes three-carbon PGA in the first step of carbon fixation.

C4 plant Plant that makes four-carbon oxaloacetate in the first step of carbon fixation.

calcium pump Membrane-bound active transport protein specific for calcium ions.

Calvin–Benson cycle Light-independent cyclic reactions of photosynthesis. Forms sugars from CO_2 using ATP and NADPH.

CAM plant Plant that conserves water by opening stomata only at night, when it fixes carbon by repeated turns of the C4 pathway.

camouflage Coloration, patterning, or other aspects of form or behavior that make an individual blend with its surroundings.

cancer Malignant neoplasm; mass of cells that divide abnormally and can spread in the body.

capillary Smallest of the blood vessels; site of diffusion between blood and interstitial fluid.

capillary reabsorption Movement of fluid from interstitial fluid into capillaries.

capture–recapture method For population counts; collecting, marking, releasing, then recapturing representative animals.

carbon cycle Movement of carbon from the atmosphere, through food webs and ocean's waters and rocks, and back to atmosphere.

carbon fixation Autotrophic cell secures carbon atoms from the air and incorporates them into a stable organic compound.

cardiac cycle Sequence of muscle contraction and relaxation in a single heartbeat.

cardiac muscle Muscle of the heart wall.

cardiac pacemaker Sinoatrial (SA) node; a mass of self-excitatory cardiac muscle cells that set the rate for a normal heartbeat.

carotenoid Red to yellow accessory pigment.

carpel Female reproductive part of a flower.

carrying capacity The maximum number of individuals in a population (or species) that a given environment can sustain indefinitely.

cartilage A specialized connective tissue that is dense, pliable, yet resists compression.

cartilaginous fish Jawed fish with a skeleton of cartilage (e.g., shark, ray).

Casparian strip In roots; waxy, impermeable band in cell walls of endodermis or exodermis where water and mineral uptake is controlled.

catastrophism Idea that abrupt changes in the geologic or fossil record resulted from large scale disasters that were divinely invoked.

CD4 lymphocyte White blood cell having a receptor to which HIV may bind (e.g., T-cell).

cDNA DNA made from an mRNA transcript, using reverse transcriptase.

cell Smallest living unit, with a capacity to survive and reproduce on its own.

cell cortex Three-dimensional mesh of actin filaments and other proteins just under the plasma membrane.

cell count The number of cells of a given type in one microliter of blood.

cell cycle Series of events from one cell division to the next. Interphase, mitosis, and cytoplasmic division constitute one cycle.

cell differentiation Cell lineages become specialized in structure and function by selectively activating genes.

cell junction A site where adjoining cells interact physically, chemically, or both.

cell plate In a dividing plant cell, a disk-like structure that becomes a crosswall with new plasma membrane on both sides.

cell plate formation Mechanism of cytoplasmic division in plant cells.

cell theory Idea that all organisms consist of similar units of organization called cells.

cell wall A semirigid, permeable structure encloses the plasma membrane of many cells; helps cell retain its shape and resist rupturing.

central vacuole Fluid-filled storage organelle of a plant cell.

centriole Organelle that organizes formation and direction of cilia, flagella, and spindles.

centromere Constricted part of a chromosome to which spindle microtubules attach.

centrosome Cell region where microtubules are produced.

cephalization Evolutionary trend toward the concentration of sensory structures and nerve cells in a head.

cerebellum Hindbrain region; maintains balance and coordinates limb movements.

cerebrum Forebrain region that deals with olfactory input and motor responses. In mammals, offers complex level of integration.

charophyte Type of green alga; the closest living relatives of plants.

chemical bond A union between the electron structures of two or more atoms or ions.

chemical equilibrium The state at which the concentrations of reactants and products in a reversible chemical reaction remain constant.

chemical synapse Thin cleft between a presynaptic neuron and a postsynaptic cell. Neurotransmitter molecules diffuse across it.

chemoreceptor A sensory receptor which responds to chemical stimuli.

chemotaxin In animals, a chemical signal that attracts phagocytic white blood cells.

chlamydias A group of bacteria that are obligate intracellular parasites of vertebrates.

chlorophyll Primary photosynthetic pigment.

chlorophyte A member of the most diverse group of green algae.

chloroplast Organelle of photosynthesis in plants and many protists.

chordate Animal having a notochord, dorsal hollow nerve cord, pharynx, and gill slits in pharynx wall during at least part of life cycle.

chorion Extraembryonic membrane. In some mammals, becomes part of placenta.

chromatin All DNA molecules and associated proteins in a nucleus.

chromosome A coherent structure consisting of a DNA molecule and associated proteins.

chromosome number Sum of all chromosomes in a given type of cell.

chrysophyte A category of photosynthetic protists (e.g., golden algae).

ciliate Ciliated protozoan; type of protist that usually has profuse cilia at its surface.

cilium, plural **cilia** In some eukaryotic cells, a short motile structure or sensory structure.

circadian rhythm Biological activity repeated in cycles, each about twenty-four hours long.

circulatory system Organ system that moves substances to and from cells; can help stabilize body temperature and pH. In many animals, consists of a heart, blood vessels, and blood.

cladogenesis Speciation pattern; a lineage splits, and populations diverge genetically.

cladogram Evolutionary tree diagram; groups taxa on the basis of their shared derived traits.

classification system A way of organizing and retrieving information about species.

cleavage Early stage of animal development. Mitotic cell divisions divide a fertilized egg into many smaller, nucleated cells; original volume of egg cytoplasm does not increase.

climate Prevailing weather conditions in some region.

climax community Array of species that can, if habitat remains stable, persist indefinitely without being replaced by other species.

climax-pattern model Idea that more than one stable community can persist in the same region when environmental factors vary.

cloning vector DNA molecule that can accept foreign DNA and replicate in a host cell.

club fungus Fungus having club-shaped cells that produce and bear basidiospores.

cnidarian Radial invertebrate at the tissue level of organization; makes nematocysts.

coal Nonrenewable energy source formed over 280 million years ago from submerged, compacted plant remains.

codon Sequence of three bases in an mRNA strand that codes for an amino acid, or acts as a start or stop signal for translation.

coelom In most animals, a cavity between the gut and body wall that is lined with a tissue.

coenzyme Small molecule that participates in an enzymatic reaction, and is reversibly modified during the reaction (e.g., a vitamin).

coevolution Joint evolution of two interacting species, brought about by changes in selection pressures operating between the two.

cohesion The capacity to resist rupturing when placed under tension (stretched).

cohesion–tension theory Idea that evaporation from plants exerts tension in xylem, pulling cohesive columns of water upward from roots to leaves.

cohort A group of same-aged individuals, tracked throughout their life spans.

collecting duct Last tubular region of a kidney nephron.

collenchyma Simple plant tissue that imparts flexible support during primary growth.

colon Large intestine; concentrates undigested and unabsorbed material.

commensalism Interaction between species that benefits one and has no effect on other.

communication signal Information-laden cue directed by one member of a species to another; chemical, visual, acoustic, or tactile.

community All species living and interacting in some habitat.

companion cell Specialized parenchyma cell; helps load sugars into sieve tubes of phloem.

comparative morphology Scientific study of the body form and structures of major groups.

compartmentalization Defensive response by a woody plant; resin or toxins are secreted in response to injury or an attack.

competitive exclusion Idea that, when two species require exactly the same resources, competition will drive one or the other to extinction in a shared habitat.

complement system Plasma proteins that circulate in blood in inactive form; has roles in nonspecific defenses and immune responses.

compound Molecule consisting of two or more elements in unvarying proportions.

concentration gradient A difference in the number of molecules (or ions) of a substance between two adjoining regions.

condensation reaction Covalent bonding of two molecules into a larger molecule, often with the formation of water as a by-product.

conduction In temperature studies, exchange of heat between two touching objects owing to a thermal gradient between them.

cone Reproductive structure made of modified leaves (e.g., a cluster of ovule-bearing, woody scales of a pine tree).

cone cell Vertebrate photoreceptor; allows sharp daytime vision, color vision.

conifer Evergreen gymnosperm; tree or shrub with needlelike or scalelike leaves.

connective tissue Most abundant, pervasive animal tissue. Specialized types are cartilage, bone tissue, adipose tissue, and blood.

conservation biology Field devoted to surveying biological diversity, studying its origins, and attempting to maintain it.

consumer Heterotroph that obtains carbon and energy by feeding on other organisms.

continuous variation Of a population, a more or less continuous range of small differences in a given trait among its individuals.

control group A group used as a standard for comparison with an experimental group.

convection Movement of air or water next to an object aids conductive heat loss from it.

cork cambium A lateral meristem; replaces epidermis with cork on woody plant parts.

corpus luteum A glandular structure that forms from cells of a ruptured ovarian follicle; secretes progesterone and estrogen.

cortex A rindlike layer. In vascular plants, a ground tissue; supports parts and stores food.

cortisol Adrenal cortex hormone; roles in glucose regulation and stress responses.

cotyledon Seed leaf. Part of a plant embryo. Two form in eudicot seeds, one forms in monocot seeds.

countercurrent flow Movement of two fluids in opposite directions, as when water and blood flow in opposite directions in a fish gill.

covalent bond Sharing of one or more electrons between two atoms.

craniate Chordate having a brain inside a cranium. Includes living fishes, amphibians, reptiles, birds, and mammals.

creatine phosphate Energy source for muscle cells; transfers phosphate to ADP to form ATP.

crossing over At prophase I of meiosis, the reciprocal exchange of segments between two nonsister chromatids of a pair of homologous chromosomes; results in novel combinations of alleles.

culture Sum of behavior patterns of a social group, passed between generations by way of learning and symbolic behavior.

cuticle Body cover. Of plant surfaces, a layer of waxes and cutin. Of roundworms and annelids, a thin, flexible coat. Of arthropods, a lightweight exoskeleton hardened with protein and chitin.

cyanobacteria Bacteria that carry out noncyclic (oxygen-producing) photosynthesis.

cycad A gymnosperm that forms pollen- and seed-bearing structures on different plants; an ancient lineage that coexisted with dinosaurs.

cyst Resting structure; encloses certain small organisms or spores for part of the life cycle.

cytokine Signaling molecules of the immune system (e.g., interferons, interleukins).

cytokinin Plant hormone; stimulates cell division and leaf expansion, slows leaf aging.

cytoplasm All cell parts, particles, and semifluid substances between the plasma membrane and the nucleus (or nucleoid).

cytoplasmic localization Polar distribution of gene products in a cell. In an egg, determines body axis of the future embryo.

cytoskeleton Interconnected system of protein filaments that structurally supports, organizes, and moves a eukaryotic cell and its internal structures.

cytotoxic T cell T lymphocyte that touch-kills virus infected, cancerous, and other altered body cells with antigen bound to self markers.

day-neutral plant Plant that flowers when mature, rather than in response to daylength.

decomposer Fungal or bacterial heterotroph that obtains carbon and energy from remains, products, or wastes of organisms.

deforestation Removal of all trees from a large area.

deletion Loss of a chromosome segment. Also, a mutation involving the loss of one or more bases of a DNA molecule.

demographic transition model Explanation of the effects of industrialization on human population growth.

demographics A population's vital statistics (e.g., size, distribution, density, age structure).

denaturation The three-dimensional shape of a protein or some other complex molecule unravels as its hydrogen bonds are disrupted.

dendrite Short, slender extension from cell body of a neuron; a signal input zone.

dendritic cell Type of antigen-presenting white blood cell.

denitrification Conversion of nitrate or nitrite by certain soil bacteria to gaseous nitrogen (N_2) and nitrous oxide (N_2O).

dense, irregular connective tissue Animal tissue with fibroblasts, many asymmetrically positioned fibers in a ground substance. In skin, some capsules.

dense, regular connective tissue Animal tissue with rows of fibroblasts between bundles of fibers. In tendons, ligaments.

density-dependent control Factor that operates at high population density to slow birth rate and/or increase death rate (e.g., disease, competition).

density-independent factor Factor that impacts a population's birth rate or death rate regardless of density (e.g., fire or flood).

deoxyribonucleic acid See DNA.

derived trait A novel feature that arose in a species and is shared only by its descendants.

dermis Skin layer beneath the epidermis; consists mainly of dense connective tissue.

desalinization Removal of salt from seawater.

desertification Conversion of grassland or cropland to a desertlike condition.

detritivore Heterotroph that feeds on bits of decaying organic matter (e.g., an earthworm).

deuterostome Bilateral animal in which the first indentation in the embryo becomes the anus (e.g., echinoderms, chordates).

development Series of stages by which structurally and functionally distinct body parts emerge, in orderly patterns, in a new multicelled individual.

diaphragm Muscular partition between thoracic and abdominal cavities. Also, a contraceptive device inserted into the vagina to prevent sperm from entering uterus.

dicot Dicotyledon. Flowering plant having embryos with two cotyledons.

diffusion Net movement of like molecules or ions down their concentration gradient.

digestive system Body sac or tube, often with regions where food is ingested, digested, and absorbed, and where residues are eliminated.

dihybrid cross Intercross between two individuals, each heterozygous for two genes (e.g., *AaBb*).

dinoflagellate Single-celled, flagellated, cellulose-plated protist; most photosynthetic.

dinosaur One of a group of extinct reptiles that originated in the Triassic and dominated land environments for 140 million years.

diploid Presence of two of each type of chromosome (i.e., pairs of homologs) in a cell nucleus at interphase.

diploid number Total chromosome number in cells that have a pair of each type of chromosome characteristic of the species.

directional selection Mode of natural selection by which forms of a trait at one end of a range of phenotypic variation are favored and all others are selected against.

disaccharide A common oligosaccharide; two covalently bonded sugar monomers.

disease Illness caused by an infectious, dietary, or environmental factor.

disruptive selection Mode of natural selection by which forms at both ends of the range of phenotypic variation are favored and intermediate forms are selected against.

distal tubule Tubular part of nephron where water and sodium are selectively reabsorbed.

distance effect Idea that the farther away an island is from a source of potential colonizing species, the lower its species diversity will be.

DNA Deoxyribonucleic acid. Carries the primary hereditary information for all living organisms and many viruses.

DNA chip Microarray of DNA spots on a glass plate; used to study gene expression.

DNA fingerprint Unique cleavage pattern of an individual's DNA; also called restriction fragment length polymorphism (RFLP).

DNA ligase Repair enzyme that joins breaks in DNA molecule; connects new DNA fragments during replication.

DNA polymerase Enzyme that catalyzes replication and repair of DNA.

DNA replication Process by which a cell duplicates its DNA molecules before dividing.

dormancy A time of metabolic inactivity in spores, cysts, seeds, plants, and some animals.

dosage compensation Control mechanism that balances gene expression between the sexes, starting at early stages of development.

double fertilization Of flowering plants only, fusion of sperm and egg nuclei, plus fusion of another sperm nucleus with nuclei of a cell that gives rise to endosperm.

doubling time Length of time it takes a population to double in size.

downwelling Downward movement of water along a coast, from ocean surface to its depths.

duplication DNA sequence repeated several to many hundreds or thousands of times.

ecdysone Hormone of many insect life cycles; roles in metamorphosis, molting.

echinoderm Invertebrate with calcified spines and plates in the body wall. Radial with some bilateral features (e.g., sea stars, sea urchins).

ecology Study of how organisms interact with one another and with their environment.

ecoregion Broad land or ocean region defined by climate, geography, and producer species.

ecosystem An array of species and their physical environment.

ectoderm First-formed, outermost primary tissue layer of animal embryos; gives rise to nervous system tissues and integument's outer layer.

ectotherm Animal that maintains core temperature by absorbing environmental heat.

Ediacarian One of a group of soft-bodied animals that arose in the precambrian.

effector Muscle (or gland); helps bring about movement (or chemical change) in response to neural or endocrine signals.

effector cell Differentiated lymphocyte that, during immune responses, engages and destroys antigen-bearing agents.

egg Female gamete.

El Niño A recurring warm current that displaces cool, nutrient-rich water along South America's coast; has global effects.

electric gradient A difference in electric charge between adjoining regions.

electron Negatively charged unit of matter, with particle-like and wavelike properties; occupies an orbital around atomic nucleus.

electron transfer chain Array of membrane-bound enzymes and other molecules that accept and give up electrons in sequence; allows the release and capture of energy in small, useful increments.

electron transfer phosphorylation Last stage of aerobic respiration; electrons flow through mitochondrial electron transfer chains, to O_2. The flow sets up an electrochemical gradient that drives ATP formation.

element Material consisting of atoms all with the same atomic number.

embryonic induction Signaling molecules released from one embryonic tissue affect the development of an adjacent tissue.

emigration Individuals leave a population.

emulsification In the vertebrate gut, the coating of fat droplets with bile salts, so that the droplets become suspended in chyme.

endangered species An endemic (native) species that is highly vulnerable to extinction.

endocrine gland One of the ductless glands that secrete hormones into some body fluid.

endocrine system Integrative system of cells, tissues, and organs, functionally linked to the nervous system, that exerts control by way of its hormones and other chemical secretions.

endocytosis Cellular uptake of a substance; plasma membrane forms a vesicle around it.

endoderm Inner primary tissue layer of most animal embryos; source of inner gut lining and organs that are derived from it.

endometrium Inner lining of uterus.

endophytic fungi Fungi that live inside the bodies of plants.

endoplasmic reticulum ER. Organelle that starts at the nuclear envelope and extends through cytoplasm. Smooth ER assembles membrane lipids, breaks down fatty acids, and inactivates some toxins; Rough ER (has ribosomes on its cytoplasmic side) modifies new polypeptide chains.

endoskeleton Of chordates, the internal framework of cartilage and bone; works with skeletal muscle to support and move the body.

endosperm Triploid nutritive tissue in flowering plant seeds.

endospore Resistant resting structure that forms in some bacteria. It encloses the bacterial chromosome and some cytoplasm.

endosymbiosis One species spends its entire life inside another, in an interaction that benefits both.

endotherm Animal that can generate and maintain its body temperature using metabolic rate, body form and behavior.

energy Capacity to do work.

energy pyramid Diagram of an ecosystem's trophic structure; shows usable energy at each trophic level.

enhancer A small sequence in DNA that binds transcription regulating molecules.

ENSO El Niño Southern Oscillation. The eastward movement of warm surface waters of the western equatorial Pacific, displaces cold water off South America; has widespread climatic effects.

enzyme A type of protein (or, rarely, RNA) that accelerates a chemical reaction.

eosinophil White blood cell that acts against extracellular parasites, such as worms.

epidermis Outermost tissue layer; occurs in plants and all animals above the sponge level of organization.

epiglottis Flaplike structure between pharynx and larynx; its controlled positional changes direct air into trachea or food into esophagus.

epithelial tissue Animal tissue that covers external surfaces and lines internal cavities and tubes. One surface is free and the other rests on a basement membrane.

equilibrium model of island biogeography Model that predicts the number of species an island will support, based on island size and its distance from a source of colonists.

esophagus Muscular tube; in vertebrates it connects the pharynx and stomach.

essential amino acid Amino acid an animal cannot synthesize and must get from food.

essential fatty acid Fatty acid an animal cannot synthesize and must get from food.

estrogen Female sex hormone secreted by ovaries; helps oocytes mature, primes uterine lining for pregnancy, maintains secondary sexual traits, affects growth and development.

estuary Partly enclosed coast region where seawater mixes with fresh water and runoff from land, as from rivers.

ethylene Gaseous plant hormone; promotes fruit ripening and abscission of leaves, flowers, fruits.

eudicot True dicot; one of the flowering plants generally characterized by embryos with two cotyledons.

euglenoid Single-celled, flagellated protist of freshwater habitats; most are photosynthetic.

Eukarya Domain of eukaryotic cells; all protists, plants, fungi, and animals.

eutherian Placental mammal.

eutrophication Nutrient enrichment of a body of water (e.g., a lake or pond).

evaporation Process of conversion of a liquid to a gas; requires energy input.

evaporative heat loss Thermoregulation mechanism: cooling due to evaporation of water.

evolution, biological Genetic change in a line of descent. Outcome of microevolutionary events: gene mutation, natural selection, genetic drift, and gene flow.

evolutionary tree Diagram of evolutionary relationships; each branch signifies a separate line of descent from a common ancestor; each branch point a time of divergence.

exocrine gland Any gland that secretes products (e.g., milk) to a free epithelial surface, usually through ducts or tubes.

exocytosis Release of a vesicle's contents outside the cell surface when it fuses with and becomes part of the plasma membrane.

exodermis Cylindrical sheet of cells inside the root epidermis of most flowering plants; helps control uptake of water and solutes.

exon One of the base sequences of an mRNA transcript that eventually will be translated.

exoskeleton External skeleton (e.g., hardened arthropod cuticle).

exotic species A species that has left the community in which it evolved and become established elsewhere.

experimental group A group upon which an experiment is performed, and compared with a control group.

exponential growth, population An increase in population size by a fixed percentage of the whole in a given interval.

extinction Irrevocable loss of a species.

extracellular fluid Of most animals, all fluid not in cells; plasma (blood's liquid portion) plus interstitial fluid.

extreme halophile An archaean or other species of a notably salty habitat.

extreme thermophile An archaean or other species of a notably high-temperature habitat.

eye Sensory organ that incorporates a dense array of photoreceptors.

FAD Flavin adenine dinucleotide. Nucleotide coenzyme; transfers electrons and unbound protons (H^+) between reaction sites.

fat Type of lipid with a glycerol head attached to one, two, or three fatty acid tails.

fatty acid Organic compound with a backbone of up to 36 carbon atoms, and a carboxyl group at the end.

feedback inhibition Of cells, an activity causes a change in cellular conditions, and that change in turn causes the activity to slow down or stop.

fern A seedless vascular plant with fronds that often are divided into leaflets.

fertilization Fusion of a sperm nucleus and an egg nucleus, the result being a zygote.

fetus Stage of animal development; in humans, the start of the ninth week to birth.

fibrous root system The lateral branchings of adventitious roots that form on a young stem.

filter feeder Animal that filters food from a current of water directed through a body part (e.g., through a sea squirt's pharynx).

first law of thermodynamics The total amount of energy in the universe is constant; energy can be converted from one form to another, but cannot be created or destroyed.

fitness Degree of adaptation to an environment, as measured by relative genetic contribution to future generations.

fixation Only one kind of allele remains at a given locus in a population; all individuals have become homozygous for it. One outcome of genetic drift in small populations.

fixed action pattern Program of coordinated, stereotyped muscle activity that is completed independently of feedback from environment.

flagellated protozoan One of the most ancient heterotrophic protists; has one or more flagella.

flagellum, plural flagella A whip-like motile structure of many free-living eukaryotic cells.

flower Reproductive shoot of an angiosperm.

fluid mosaic model A cell membrane is fluid because of the motions and interactions of its component lipids and proteins.

food chain A linear flow of energy captured by primary producers (autotrophs) into ever higher trophic levels of an ecosystem.

food pyramid Charts showing proportions of different foods that compose a healthy diet.

food web Cross-connecting food chains.

fossil Recognizable, physical evidence of an organism that lived in the distant past.

fossilization Extremely slow transformation of an organism's remains to stony hardness as a result of pressure and chemical changes.

founder effect A form of bottlenecking. By chance, allele frequencies of a few individuals that establish a new population differ from the frequencies in the original population.

free radical Highly reactive molecule with at least one unpaired electron.

FSH Follicle-stimulating hormone. Produced and secreted by the anterior lobe of pituitary gland; has reproductive roles in both sexes.

functional group An atom or a group of atoms with characteristic properties that is covalently bonded to an organic compound's carbon backbone.

fungus, plural fungi Eukaryotic heterotroph that obtains nutrients by extracellular digestion and fabsorption; notable for prolific spore formation.

gametophyte Multicelled, gamete-producing body (haploid) that forms during life cycles of some algae and all plants.

ganglion plural ganglia Distinct cluster of cell bodies of neurons.

gap junction A channel through a complex of abutting membrane proteins of two cells; permits ions and small molecules to move rapidly between the cells.

gastric fluid Acidic mix of secretions (e.g., HCl, mucus) from the stomach's glandular epithelium.

gastrula Earliest developmental stage in which cells are arranged as two or three primary tissue layers.

gel electrophoresis Molecules that migrate through a gel matrix in response to an electric force become separated by size and charge.

gene Unit of information for a heritable trait in DNA, passed from parents to offspring.

gene control A molecular mechanism that governs if, when, or how a specific gene is used (transcribed or translated).

gene flow Physical flow of alleles into or out of a population by immigration or emigration.

gene library Mixed collection of host cells that contain cloned DNA fragments representing all or most of a genome.

gene locus A gene's chromosomal location.

gene mutation Small-scale change in the nucleotide sequence of a gene that can result in an altered protein product.

gene pool All the genes in a population.

genetic code The correspondence between triplets of nucleotides in DNA (then mRNA) and specific sequences of amino acids in a polypeptide chain; the basic language of protein synthesis in cells.

genetic disorder Heritable defect in one's genetic material; causes mild to severe medical problems.

genetic divergence Accumulation of differences in the gene pools of populations after something stops gene flow between them. Over time, if some of the differences promote reproductive isolation, speciation may follow.

genetic drift Random change in allele frequencies over time brought about by chance alone; its effect is greatest in small populations.

genetic engineering Manipulation of an organism's DNA, usually with the intent of altering at least one aspect of phenotype.

genome All the DNA in a haploid number of chromosomes for a given species.

genomics The study of genes and gene function in humans and other organisms.

genus A group of related species.

geographic dispersal Individuals move away from their home range and successfully establish themselves elsewhere.

geologic time scale Chronology of Earth history; major subdivisions correspond to mass extinctions.

germination Of seeds and spores, resumption of growth after dormancy, dispersal from the parent organism, or both.

gibberellin Plant hormone; stimulates stem lengthening, helps seeds and buds break dormancy, promotes flowering in some plants.

gill slit Opening in a thin-walled pharynx. Serves in food-trapping and respiration; jaws evolved from certain gill slit supports.

gills Type of respiratory organ that occurs in some invertebrates and most fishes.

ginkgo Deciduous gymnosperm of an ancient lineage that produces fleshy plum-sized fruits.

gland Secretory organ derived from epithelial tissue (e.g., sweat gland, thyroid gland).

global broiling hypothesis Idea that asteroid impact caused the K–T mass extinction by creating a colossal fireball, causing the global temperature to rise thousands of degrees.

global warming Long-term rise in the temperature of the Earth's lower atmosphere.

glomerular filtration Movement of water and small solutes out of glomerular capillaries and into the first part of the kidney tubule.

glycolysis Breakdown of glucose to two pyruvate molecules. First stage of aerobic respiration and fermentation.

gnetophyte Tropical tree, vine, or shrub of an ancient gymnosperm group.

GnRH Gonadotropin-releasing hormone; triggers hypothalamus to release LH and FSH.

Golgi body Organelle of endomembrane system; final modification of polypeptide chains into proteins, lipid assembly, and packaging of both in vesicles for secretion or for use inside cell.

Gondwana Paleozoic supercontinent that collided with other large land masses and formed Pangea.

Gram-positive bacteria One of the several bacterial groups having cell walls that are colored purple by Gram-staining procedure.

gravitropism In plants, directional growth of roots and shoots in response to gravity.

grazing food web Food web in which most energy from producers flows to herbivores, then to carnivores.

greenhouse effect Warming of the lower atmosphere as greenhouse gases reradiate heat energy back toward the Earth's surface.

groundwater Water in soil and aquifers.

growth Of multicelled species, increases in the number, size, and volume of cells. Of bacteria, increases in cell number.

growth and tissue specialization Stage of animal development when the body enlarges and organs assume their functions.

growth ring One of the alternating bands of early and late wood in a tree with extensive secondary growth.

gut Of animals, a sac or tube from which food is absorbed into the internal environment.

habitat Type of place where a species lives.

habitat loss Reduction of habitat for a species as a result of environmental destruction.

half-life The time it takes for half of a given quantity of atoms of a radioisotope to decay.

haploid number Total chromosome number in cells that have one of each type of chromosome characteristic of the species.

Hardy–Weinberg rule Allele frequencies will be stable over the generations if there is no mutation, the population is infinitely large and isolated from other populations of the same species, mating is random, and all individuals reproduce equally and randomly.

heart Muscular, pressure-generating pump that keeps blood flowing through the vessels of a circulatory system.

heartwood Dry core tissue of older stems and roots; functions in support and the storage of metabolic wastes.

helper T cell T lymphocyte that stimulates B cells and other T cells to divide in response to antigen recognition; critical component of all immune responses.

heme group Iron-containing functional group that reversibly binds oxygen.

hemoglobin Respiratory protein in red blood cells; consists of four polypeptide chains and four heme groups.

hemostasis Process that stops blood loss after injury by way of coagulation, vessel spasm, platelet plug formation, and other effects.

herbicide Natural or synthetic toxin that can kill plants or inhibit their growth.

heterotherm An endotherm that can lower metabolic rates; activities idle as it cuts energy cost of maintaining its core temperature.

heterotroph Organism unable to make its own organic compounds; feeds on autotrophs, other heterotrophs, or organic wastes.

heterozygous condition For a specified trait, having two different alleles at a locus.

higher taxa One of ever more inclusive groupings of species based on relatedness (e.g., phylum, kingdom, domain).

histamine Chemical released by mast cells during an immune response; contributes to inflammation and other symptoms of allergy.

homeostasis Maintenance of physical and chemical aspects of the internal environment within ranges suitable for cell activities.

homeotic gene One of a class of master genes; helps determine identity of body parts during embryonic development.

hominid A human or an extinct humanlike primate (e.g., an australopith).

hominoid Apes, humans, and their extinct recent ancestors.

homologous chromosome One of a pair of chromosomes, identical in size, shape, and gene sequence, each inherited from a different parent. Nonidentical sex chromosomes are also considered homologs.

homologous structure Similar body part that occurs in different species as a result of descent from a common ancestor.

homozygous dominant condition Having a pair of dominant alleles at a gene locus.

homozygous recessive condition Having a pair of recessive alleles at a gene locus.

hormone Chemical signaling molecule formed by one part of the body, acting upon another. In animals, a product of endocrine glands, endocrine cells, or neurons. In plants, a product of cells in primary shoots or roots.

horsetail Seedless vascular plant with tiny scale-like leaves, branching rhizomes, and silica-reinforced stems.

hot spot Habitat for a large number of species found nowhere else and facing extinction.

human Member of the genus *Homo*.

human gene therapy The transfer of normal or modified genes into a person to correct a genetic defect, or boost resistance to a disease.

humus Decomposing organic matter in soil.

hybrid Individual having a nonidentical pair of alleles for a trait being studied.

hydrogen bond An intermolecular interaction between a covalently bonded hydrogen atom and a different atom bearing a negative charge (e.g., oxygen, fluorine, or nitrogen).

hydrologic cycle Driven by solar energy, water evaporates from the ocean into the atmosphere, moves onto the land, then back to the ocean.

hydrolysis An enzymatic cleavage reaction in which a molecule is split, and the components of water (—OH and —H) become attached to each of the fragments.

hydrophilic substance Polar molecule (e.g., glucose) that easily dissolves in water.

hydrophobic substance Nonpolar molecule (e.g., oil) that resists dissolving in water.

hydrostatic pressure Pressure exerted by a volume of fluid against a wall, membrane, or some other structure that encloses it.

hydrostatic skeleton Of many soft-bodied invertebrates, a fluid-filled cavity or cell mass against which contractile cells act.

hypertonic solution Of two fluids, the one having the higher solute concentration.

hypha, plural **hyphae** Fungal filament with a chitin-reinforced wall; part of a mycelium.

hypothalamus Brain center of homeostatic control over the internal environment, viscera, and emotions; also produces some hormones.

hypothesis In science, a possible explanation of a phenomenon, one that has the potential to be proven false by experimental tests.

hypotonic solution Of two fluids, the one having the lower solute concentration.

immigration New individuals permanently move into an area.

immune system Body system that recognizes antigen and mounts attacks against specific threats. Adaptive in jawed vertebrates.

immunoglobulin One of the five classes of antibody proteins (e.g., IgG).

implantation In placental mammals, the burrowing of a blastocyst into the uterus wall.

imprinting Learning that occurs during a sensitive period for a young animal, triggered by exposure to a simple stimulus.

in vitro fertilization IVF. Combining sperm and eggs outside the body, as in a petri dish.

inbreeding Mating between close relatives.

inclusive fitness Genetic contribution made to the next generation by an individual and its close relatives.

independent assortment In meiosis, each homologous chromosome and its partner are assorted into different gametes independently of other pairs.

indicator species Any species that provides warning of changes in habitat and impending widespread loss of biodiversity.

induced-fit model An enzyme changes shape to fit a bound substrate, and the resulting tension destabilizes the substrate's bonds.

infection Invasion and multiplication of a pathogen in a host. Disease follows if defenses are not mobilized fast enough; the pathogen's activities interfere with normal body function.

inflammation See acute inflammation.

inhibitor A hypothalamic hormone that slows secretion by cells in a target gland.

insertion Mutation involving insertion of one to a few bases into a DNA strand. Also, a movable attachment of muscle to bone.

instinctive behavior Any behavior that an animal performs without having first learned it through experience.

integrator Control center (e.g., brain) for the animal body that receives, processes, and stores sensory input; issues commands for coordinated responses.

integumentary exchange Respiration across a thin, moist, and often vascularized surface layer of animal tissue.

intermediate filament Cytoskeletal element; mechanically strengthens some animal cells.

internal environment In animals, blood and interstitial fluid (extracellular fluid).

interneuron Neuron of brain or spinal cord.

interphase Cell cycle interval between nuclear divisions; a cell grows in mass and roughly doubles the number of cytoplasmic components. DNA replication occurs during the interphase that precedes mitosis.

interspecific competition Competition between members of different species.

interstitial fluid Extracellular fluid in the spaces between animal cells and tissues.

intron Noncoding gene sequence that is removed from a pre-mRNA before translation.

inversion Mutation in which a section of chromosome becomes oriented in reverse.

invertebral disk Cartilaginous flex point and shock absorber between vertebrae.

invertebrate An animal without a backbone.

ionic bond Interaction between ions held together by attraction of opposite charges.

ionizing radiation Radiation with enough energy to eject electrons from atoms.

isotonic solution A fluid having the same solute concentration as another fluid to which it is being compared.

isotopes Two or more forms of an element's atoms differing in the number of neutrons.

jaw Of chordates, a hinged pair of cartilaginous or bony feeding structures.

joint Area of contact between bones.

karyotype Preparation of an individual's metaphase chromosomes sorted by length, centromere location, and shape.

key innovation Change in body form or function that allows a lineage to exploit the environment in more efficient or novel ways.

keystone species A species that has a major role in shaping community structure.

kidney One of a pair of vertebrate organs that filter substances from blood and form urine.

kilocalorie A thousand calories of heat energy, the amount needed to raise the temperature of 1 kilogram of water by 1°C. Standard unit of measure for the energy content of foods.

knockout experiment Experiment in which, to study the function of a gene, an organism is engineered to lack its expression.

Krebs cycle The second stage of aerobic respiration in which pyruvate is broken down to carbon dioxide and water. Two ATP form. Occurs only in mitochondria.

K–T asteroid impact theory Idea that an asteroid impact caused a mass extinction at the Cretaceous–Tertiary boundary (65 million years ago).

La Niña Cool climatic event that occurs between El Niño episodes; has global effects.

labor Process by which a placental mammal gives birth.

lactate fermentation Anaerobic pathway of ATP formation. Pyruvate from glycolysis is converted to three-carbon lactate, and NAD^+ is regenerated. Net energy yield: 2 ATP.

lactation In mammals only, secretion of milk by mammary glands.

Langerhans cell Immune cell in skin; engulfs pathogens, alerts immune system to threats.

larva, plural **larvae** A sexually immature stage of many invertebrates.

larynx Tubular airway from the pharynx to lungs. Contains vocal cords in some animals.

lateral gene transfer Movement of genetic material between existing cells by conjugation or other processes.

leaching Loss of nutrients from soil as water percolates through it.

lethal mutation Mutation with drastic effects on phenotype; usually causes death.

LH Luteinizing hormone. Anterior pituitary hormone that has reproductive roles in males and females.

lichen Mutualistic interaction between a fungus and a photoautotroph.

life-history pattern Adaptations affecting life span, fertility, and age at first reproduction.

ligament Strap of dense connective tissue that bridges a joint and attaches to bones.

light-dependent reactions The first stage of photosynthesis. Sunlight energy is trapped and converted to chemical energy of ATP, NADPH, or both, depending on the pathway.

light-independent reactions Second stage of photosynthesis in which sugars are formed from CO_2 using ATP and NADPH. Also called the Calvin-Benson cycle.

limbic system Brain center that governs emotions and has roles in memory.

limiting factor Any essential resource that can halt population growth when supplies of it dwindle.

lineage An ancestor–descendant sequence of cells, populations, or species.

linkage group All genes on a chromosome.

lipid Nonpolar hydrocarbon; fats, oils, waxes, phospholipids, and sterols are lipids.

lipid bilayer Mainly phospholipids arranged tail-to-tail in two layers; structural basis of all cell membranes.

loam Soil with roughly the same proportions of sand, silt, and clay.

local signaling molecule A cell secretion that alters chemical conditions in nearby tissues.

logistic growth, population The size of a population increases slowly, then rapidly, then levels off as the carrying capacity is reached.

loop of Henle Hairpin-shaped, tubular part of a nephron that reabsorbs water and solutes.

loose connective tissue Animal tissue with fibers, fibroblasts loosely arrayed in semifluid ground substance.

lungs Internally moistened sacs specialized for gas exchange.

lycophyte Seedless vascular plant having leaves with a single vein (e.g., club moss).

lymph Fluid in vessels of lymphatic system.

lymph node Lymphoid organ packed with lymphocytes; filters lymph.

lymph vascular system Parts of lymphatic system; delivers excess tissue fluid, absorbed fats, and reclaimable solutes to blood.

lymphatic system Organ system that returns fluid and solutes from interstitial fluid to blood; also functions in body defense.

lysis Gross damage to a plasma membrane, cell wall, or both that lets the cytoplasm leak out and so causes cell death.

lysosome Organelle of intracellular digestion.

lysozyme Infection-fighting enzyme present in mucous membranes.

macroevolution Large-scale patterns, trends, and rates of change among higher taxa.

macrophage Phagocytic white blood cell with roles in nonspecific defense and immunity.

magnoliid One of the three flowering plant groups (e.g., magnolias, avocado trees).

marine snow Organic matter that drifts to ocean depths and supports food webs there.

marsupial Pouched mammal.

mass extinction Catastrophic event or phase in geologic time when entire families or other major groups are irrevocably lost.

mass number The sum of all protons and neutrons in an atom's nucleus.

mast cell Histamine-secreting white blood cell with roles in inflammation and allergies.

master gene A gene whose product has widespread effects on other genes.

mechanoreceptor Sensory cell or nearby cell that detects mechanical energy (e.g., a change in pressure).

medulla oblongata Hindbrain region with reflex centers that influence functions basic to survival (e.g., sleeping, breathing, coughing).

megaspore Haploid spore formed by meiosis in the ovary of a seed-bearing plant; one of its cellular descendants develops into an egg.

meiosis Only nuclear division process that halves the chromosome number of a parental cell, to the haploid number. Forms gametes in animals and spores in plants.

melanin Brownish-black pigment; protects human skin from ultraviolet radiation.

memory The capacity to store and retrieve information about past sensory experience.

memory cell B or T cell that formed during an immune response; it remains in a resting phase until a secondary immune response.

menstrual cycle Recurring cycle in human females. Includes menstruation, ovulation, repair and priming of uterus for pregnancy.

meristem Region of actively dividing, undifferentiated cells in plants; descendants of meristematic cells give rise to mature plant tissues (e.g., leaves, stems, roots).

mesoderm Primary tissue layer that occurs in most animal embryos; gives rise to internal organs and part of the integument; pivotal in the evolution of large, complex animals.

mesophyll Photosynthetic ground tissue of a leaf; a type of parenchyma.

messenger RNA mRNA. Single-stranded ribonucleotide product of gene transcription; encodes protein-building instructions.

metabolic pathway Sequence of enzyme-mediated reactions by which cells assemble and build or break down organic compounds.

metabolism All the controlled, enzyme-mediated chemical reactions by which cells acquire and use energy to synthesize, store, degrade, and eliminate substances.

metamorphosis Of certain animals (e.g., many insects), drastic transformation of an immature stage to the adult through tissue reorganization and remodeling of parts.

metaphase Of meiosis I, stage when all pairs of homologous chromosomes have become positioned at the spindle equator. Of mitosis or meiosis II, all duplicated chromosomes are positioned at the spindle equator.

methanogen Type of archaebacterium that produces methane gas as a metabolic product.

micelle formation Clustering of bile salts, fatty acids, and monoglycerides into droplets; enhances fat absorption in the small intestine.

microevolution Of a population, any change in allele frequencies resulting from mutation, genetic drift, gene flow, natural selection, or some combination of these.

microfilament Cytoskeletal element; consists of actin subunits. Involved in movement and structural integrity of cells.

microspore Walled, haploid spore that gives rise to a pollen grain in a seed-bearing plant.

microtubule Cytoskeletal element; consists of tubulin subunits. Contributes to cell shape, growth, and motion; constituent of spindles.

microvillus, plural **microvilli** Slender extension from free surface of certain cells; increases surface area (e.g., for absorption).

migration Recurring movement of organisms from one region to another, then back.

mimicry Close resemblance of one species to another; confers a selective advantage upon one or both species by deceiving predators.

mineral An element or inorganic compound formed by natural geologic processes; many are required for normal metabolic function.

mitochondrion, plural **mitochondria** Organelle of ATP formation; site of aerobic respiration's second and third stages.

mitosis Nuclear division mechanism that maintains the parental chromosome number for forthcoming daughter cells. Basis of growth, tissue repair, and often asexual reproduction of eukaryotes.

mixture Two or more elements intermingled in proportions that can and usually do vary.

model Theoretical description of something that has not been directly observed.

molecular clock The time of origin of one lineage or species relative to others may be estimated by comparing the number of neutral mutations; assumes that accumulation of neutral mutations occurs at a fixed rate.

molecule Two or more atoms of the same or different elements joined by chemical bonds.

mollusk Invertebrate having a unique tissue flap (mantle) draped over a soft, fleshy body; most have an external or internal shell (e.g., a gastropod, bivalve, cephalopod).

molt Periodic shedding of worn-out or too-small body structures. Permits some animals to grow in size or renew parts.

monocot Monocotyledon; flowering plant with one embryonic seed leaf (cotyledon), floral parts usually in threes (or multiples of three), and often parallel-veined leaves.

monohybrid cross Intercross between two individuals, each heterozygous for one gene (e.g., *Aa*).

monophyletic group A group descended from a common ancestor in which the derived trait that characterizes the group first evolved.

monosaccharide One of the simple sugars (e.g., glucose) that are unit components of oligosaccharides or polysaccharides.

monotreme Egg-laying mammal.

monsoon Air circulation pattern that moves moisture-laden air arising from warm oceans to continents north or south of them.

morphogen Type of inducer molecule that diffuses through embryonic tissues, activating master genes in sequence; it contributes to mapping out the overall body plan.

morphogenesis Programmed, orderly changes in body size, proportion, and shape of an animal embryo through which all specialized tissues and early organs form.

morphological convergence In response to similar selective pressures, evolutionarily distant lineages evolve in similar ways and end up resembling each other in appearance, function, or both.

morphological divergence In response to differing selective pressures, diverging lineages undergo gradual change from the body form of their common ancestor.

motor neuron Neuron that relays signals from the central nervous system to muscle or gland cells.

motor protein Protein that associates with microtubules or microfilaments and has a role in cell movement.

motor unit A motor neuron and all muscle cells that form junctions with its endings.

multiple allele system Three or more slightly different molecular forms of a gene that occur among the individuals of a population.

muscle fatigue Decline in a muscle's capacity to generate force after prolonged contraction.

muscle fiber Of skeletal muscle, a cylindrical multinucleated fiber that develops through the fusion of many cells during development.

muscle spindle A stretch-detecting sensory organ associated with skeletal muscle.

muscle tension Mechanical force exerted by a contracting muscle; resists opposing forces.

muscle tissue Tissue with arrays of cells able to contract under stimulation, then passively lengthen and return to their resting position.

muscle twitch Single, brief contraction of a muscle in response to a stimulus.

mutation Heritable change in DNA.

mutation rate Occurrence of mutations in a particular gene as a function of time.

mutualism Symbiotic interaction that benefits both partners.

mycorrhiza, plural **mycorrhizae** Mutualistic interaction between a fungus and root.

myofibrils Threadlike, cross-banded structures within a skeletal muscle fiber.

myoglobin A respiratory pigment abundant in cardiac and skeletal muscle cells.

myosin Motor protein that makes up the thick filaments of a sarcomere.

NAD$^+$ Nicotinamide adenine dinucleotide. A nucleotide coenzyme; abbreviated NADH when carrying electrons and H$^+$.

natural killer cell NK cell. Lymphocyte that touch-kills tumor cells and viral-infected cells.

natural selection Microevolutionary process; the outcome of differences in survival and reproduction among individuals that differ in the details of their heritable traits.

negative control In gene expression, regulatory proteins slow or stop transcription or translation.

negative feedback mechanism A homeostatic mechanism by which a condition that changed as a result of some activity triggers a response that reverses the change.

nematocyst Cnidarian capsule that has a dischargeable, tube-shaped thread, sometimes barbed; releases a toxin or sticky substance.

neoplasm Mass of cells (tumor) that have lost control over growth and division.

nephridium plural **nephridia** Unit that controls composition and volume of fluid in some invertebrates (e.g., earthworms).

nephron One of the kidney's urine-forming tubules; filters water and solutes from blood, then selectively reabsorbs portions of both.

nerve Sheathed bundle of the axons of sensory neurons, motor neurons, or both.

nerve cord A longitudinal nerve; most animals have one to three. Chordate nervous systems arise from a dorsal nerve cord.

nerve net Simple nervous system of cnidarians and some other invertebrates; a diffuse mesh of nerve cells in epithelial tissue.

nervous system Organ system with nerve cells interacting in signal-conducting and information-processing pathways. Detects and processes stimuli, and elicits responses from effectors (e.g., muscles and glands).

nervous tissue Tissue of excitable neurons and supporting neuroglia.

net ecosystem production Of ecosystems, total net energy accumulated in producers through their growth and reproduction in a given interval (net primary production).

net population growth rate per individual (r) For population growth equations, a variable combining birth rates and death rates; assumes that both remain constant in specified interval.

neural tube The embryonic and evolutionary forerunner of the brain and spinal cord.

neurotransmitter Signaling molecule secreted by axon endings of a neuron.

neutral mutation Mutation that has little or no effect on phenotype.

neutron Subatomic particle found in an atom's nucleus; has mass but no charge.

neutrophil Most abundant type of white blood cell; engulfs pathogens and has a role in inflammatory responses.

niche Sum of all activities and relationships by which a species obtains and uses resources.

nitrification The chemical conversion of ammonia to nitrate by soil bacteria.

nitrogen cycle Movement of nitrogen from the atmosphere, through the ocean, sediments, soils, and food webs, then back to atmosphere.

nitrogen fixation Conversion of nitrogen gas to forms that plants can take up from soil.

nondisjunction Failure of sister chromatids or homologous chromosomes to separate during meiosis or mitosis. Daughter cells end up with too many or too few chromosomes.

non-ionizing radiation Radiation that carries enough energy to boost electrons to higher energy levels, but not enough to remove them.

nonshivering heat production Hormone-induced increase in metabolic rate in response to prolonged or severe cold exposure.

notochord Of chordates, a rod of stiffened tissue (not cartilage or bone) that is a supporting structure for the body.

nuclear envelope Lipid bilayer membrane enclosing the nucleus of eukaryotes.

nucleic acid Single-stranded or double-stranded molecule composed of nucleotides joined at phosphate groups (e.g., DNA, RNA).

nucleic acid hybridization Any base-pairing between DNA or RNA from different sources.

nucleoid Of bacterial cells, the region in which DNA is physically organized; not separated from the cytoplasm by a membrane.

nucleosome A small stretch of eukaryotic DNA wound around histone proteins.

nucleotide Small organic compound with a five-carbon sugar, a nitrogen-containing base, and a phosphate group.

nucleus Organelle that physically separates DNA from the cytoplasm in a eukaryotic cell.

numerical taxonomy Method of determining the relationship between an unidentified organism and a known group by comparing traits. The greater the number of traits in common, the greater the inferred relatedness.

nutrient Element with a direct or indirect role in metabolism that no other element fulfills.

nutrition Processes of selectively ingesting, digesting, absorbing, and converting food into the body's own organic compounds.

obesity Excess of fat in adipose tissue; caloric intake has exceeded the body's energy output.

ocean A continuous body of saltwater that covers more than 71 percent of the Earth.

olfactory receptor Chemoreceptor for water-soluble or volatile substance.

oocyte Immature egg.

oomycote A nonphotosynthetic stamenopile protist; many are plant pathogens.

operator Part of an operon; a binding site for a regulatory protein.

operon Promoter–operator sequence that controls transcription of more than one bacterial gene.

organ Two or more tissues arrayed in a specific pattern and interacting in some task.

organ system Two or more organs interacting chemically, physically, or both in a task.

organelle Membrane-bound compartment in the eukaryotic cytoplasm; has one or more specialized metabolic functions.

organic compound Molecule containing carbon and hydrogen; may also contain oxygen, nitrogen, and other elements.

osmoreceptor Sensory cell that detects change in solute concentration of surrounding fluid.

osmosis Diffusion of water between two regions separated by a selectively permeable membrane.

osmotic pressure Hydrostatic pressure that counters inward diffusion of water through a selectively permeable membrane inside a cell or enclosed body region.

ovary In flowering plants, enlarged base of one or more carpels. In most animals, a female gonad in which eggs form.

ovulation Release of a secondary oocyte from an ovary, induced by an LH surge.

ovule Tissue mass in which an egg forms in a plant ovary; immature seed.

ovum Mature secondary oocyte; mature egg.

oxidation–reduction reaction Transfer of electrons between reactant molecules.

oxytocin Posterior pituitary hormone; induces lactation and shrinkage of uterus after pregnancy; also affects social behavior of some mammals.

ozone thinning Seasonal thinning of the atmospheric ozone layer; most pronounced above polar regions.

pain Perception of injury to a body region.

pain receptor A nociceptor; a sensory receptor that detects tissue damage.

pancreatic islet Any of the 2 million or so clusters of endocrine cells of the pancreas.

Pangea Paleozoic supercontinent.

parapatric speciation Mode of speciation in which subpopulations of a species that are maintaining contact along a common border evolve into distinct species.

parasitism Interaction in which one organism (the parasite) lives on or in another (the host) and feeds on its tissues.

parasitoid Type of insect larva that grows and develops in a host organism (usually another insect), consumes its soft tissues, and kills it.

parasympathetic nerve An autonomic nerve; its signals cause a slowdown in overall activity and divert energy to basic tasks.

parathyroid gland One of four endocrine glands; its secretions cause a rise in blood calcium levels.

parenchyma Type of simple tissue that makes up the bulk of a plant.

parthenogenesis An unfertilized egg gives rise to an embryo.

partial pressure The contribution of any gas to total atmospheric pressure.

passive transport Diffusion of a solute across a cell membrane, through a transport protein.

pathogen Disease-causing agent that can infect a target species and multiply inside it.

pattern formation During development, sculpting of embryonic cells into specialized animal tissues and organs at expected times, in expected places.

PCR Polymerase chain reaction. A method that rapidly amplifies the number of specific DNA fragments.

peat bog Acidic wetland where peat mosses grow; peat is their compressed remains.

pedigree Chart of genetic connections.

pellicle Of some protists, a flexible body covering of protein-rich material.

peptide hormone Short chain of amino acids that acts as a hormone.

per capita Per individual.

periodic table Tabular arrangement of elements based on their chemical properties.

peripheral vasoconstriction Diameter of arterioles decreases and blood flow to body surfaces is reduced.

peripheral vasodilation Diameter of arterioles increases and blood flow to body surfaces is increased.

permafrost A perpetually frozen layer of soil.

peroxisome Enzyme-filled vesicle that breaks down amino acids and fatty acids to hydrogen peroxide, which is converted to harmless products.

pH scale A measure of the H^+ concentration (acidity) of blood, water, and other solutions. pH 7 is neutral.

pharynx A muscular tube for filter-feeding in invertebrate chordates, and, in some species, gas exchange. In many other animals, part of the digestive tract.

phenotype Observable trait or traits of an individual that arises from gene interactions and gene–environment interactions.

pheromone Hormone-like exocrine gland secretion; diffuses through air and affects a different member of the same species.

phloem A complex tissue that conducts sugars, solutes through a vascular plant.

phospholipid Lipid with a phosphate group. Major constituent of biological membranes.

phosphorus cycle Movement of phosphorus from land, through food webs, to ocean sediments, then back to land.

phosphorylation Enzyme-mediated transfer of a phosphate group between molecules.

photoperiodism Biological response to change in the relative amounts of daylight and darkness.

photoreceptor Light-sensitive sensory cell.

photosynthesis Process by which organisms use sunlight energy to convert carbon dioxide and water to sugars.

photosystem In photosynthetic cells, a cluster of membrane-bound, light-trapping pigments and other molecules.

phototropism Change in the direction of cell movement or growth in response to light.

phycobilin Red to blue photosynthetic accessory pigment.

phylogeny Evolutionary relationships among species, starting with an ancestral form and including branches leading to descendants.

phytochrome A light-sensitive pigment. Its controlled activation and inactivation affect hormones governing many plant activities, including growth, branching, and flowering.

phytoplankton Aquatic community of floating or swimming photoautotrophs.

pigment Any light-absorbing molecule.

pilomotor response Hairs or feathers stand up; creates a layer of still air next to the skin.

pineal gland Light-sensitive endocrine gland; secretes melatonin.

pioneer species Species that can colonize newly formed or newly vacated habitats.

pituitary gland Endocrine gland that interacts with the hypothalamus to control other glands and organs.

placenta Organ that forms from endometrial tissue and extraembryonic membranes. Permits exchange of substances between a pregnant female and her fetus while keeping their bloodstreams separate.

plankton Community of mostly microscopic species that swim or float in lakes or seas.

plant A multicelled photoautotroph with well-developed roots and shoots.

plasma Liquid portion of blood; mainly water in which ions, proteins, sugars, gases, and other substances are dissolved.

plasma membrane Outermost cell membrane; structural and functional boundary between the cytoplasm and fluid surrounding the cell.

plasmid A small, circular molecule of bacterial DNA that carries a few genes and is replicated independently of the chromosome.

plate tectonic theory Idea that great slabs (plates) of the Earth's outer layer float about slowly on the mantle beneath them and have rafted continents to new positions over time.

platelet Cell fragment that circulates in blood; acts in clot formation.

pleiotropy Positive or negative effects that alleles at a single gene locus have on two or more traits.

polar body In vertebrates, one of four cells that forms by meiotic cell division of an oocyte but that does not become the ovum.

pollen grain Sperm-bearing gametophyte of a gymnosperm or angiosperm.

pollination Transfer of pollen to a female part of a flower (stigma).

pollinator Agent that transfers pollen to female floral parts.

polypeptide chain Three or more amino acids linked by peptide bonds.

polyploidy Having three or more of each chromosome type characteristic of a species.

polysaccharide Straight or branched chain of many covalently linked sugar units of the same or different kinds. Most common types are cellulose, starch, and glycogen.

population Group of individuals of the same species in a specified area.

population density Number of individuals per specified area or volume of a habitat.

population distribution Pattern of dispersion of individuals of a population.

population size Number of individuals making up a population.

positive control In gene expression, regulatory proteins enhance transcription or translation.

positive feedback mechanism An event intensifies as a result of its own occurrence.

predation Interaction in which one organism (the predator) eats another (prey), typically killing it.

predator Free-living organism that captures and feeds on other organisms (its prey).

prediction Statement about what you expect to observe in nature.

pressure flow theory Organic compounds flow through phloem in response to pressure and concentration gradients between source regions (e.g., leaves) and sinks (e.g., regions where sugars are being used or stored).

pressure gradient Difference in pressure being exerted in two adjoining regions.

prey Organism that predators can capture and eat.

primary growth Plant growth originating at root tips and shoot tips.

primary immune response Defensive actions by white blood cells elicited by first-time recognition of antigen. Includes antibody- and cell-mediated responses.

primary oocyte An immature egg that is stopped in prophase I of meiosis.

primary producer Type of autotroph that secures energy directly from the environment.

primary productivity Of ecosystems, the rate at which primary producers capture and store energy in their tissues during some interval.

primary succession Sequence of community development from pioneer species to climax stage in a previously barren habitat.

primary wall Of young plant cells, a thin, flexible wall that permits division and changes in shape; consists of cellulose, polysaccharides, glycoproteins.

primate Mammalian lineage; includes prosimians, tarsioids, anthropoids (monkeys, apes, humans).

primer Short nucleotide sequence designed to serve as a site of initiation for DNA synthesis on DNA or RNA.

prion Small infectious protein that causes fatal degenerative diseases of nervous system.

probability The chance that each outcome of an event will occur is proportional to the number of ways in which the outcome can be reached.

probe Short nucleotide sequence, labeled with a tracer, designed to hybridize with part of a specific gene or mRNA.

producer Autotroph (self-feeder); nourishes itself using sources of energy and carbon from the environment. Photoautotrophs and chemoautotrophs are examples.

progesterone Female sex hormone secreted by ovaries and the corpus luteum.

prokaryotic cell Archaean or bacterium; single-celled organism, most often walled; lacks a nucleus and other organelles.

prokaryotic fission Bacterial mode of reproduction. Involves DNA replication, accumulation of new membrane (and usually wall material) at or near the cell midsection, then cytoplasmic division.

prolactin Anterior pituitary hormone that stimulates milk production.

promoter Short stretch of DNA to which RNA polymerase binds and initiates transcription.

prophase Of mitosis, a stage when duplicated chromosomes start to condense, a spindle forms, and the nuclear envelope starts to break up. Duplicated pairs of centrioles move to opposite spindle poles. In prophase I of meiosis, crossing over also occurs.

protein Organic compound consisting of one or more polypeptide chains folded and twisted into a three-dimensional shape.

proteobacteria Most diverse bacterial group.

protist One of the mainly single-celled species of eukaryotes traditionally grouped in the catch-all "kingdom Protista." Currently being classified into groupings that reflect evolutionary relationships.

proto-cell Membrane-bound metabolic machinery; transitional stage that may have preceded the origin of living cells.

proton Positively charged subatomic particle found in an atom's nucleus.

proto-oncogene A gene that, when mutated or overexpressed, helps turn a normal cell into a cancerous one.

protostome Lineage of coelomate, bilateral animals that includes mollusks, annelids, and arthropods. The first indentation to form in protostome embryos becomes the mouth.

proximal tubule Nephron's tubular portion extending from Bowman's capsule.

pseudocoel A body cavity that is not fully lined with tissue derived from mesoderm.

pseudopod Flexible, temporary lobe of membrane-enclosed cytoplasm that amoebas, amoeboid cells, and phagocytic white blood cells use for motility or engulfing food.

puberty Of human development, a post-embryonic stage when gametes start to mature and secondary sexual traits emerge.

pulmonary circuit A blood circulation route that moves blood from the heart's right side, through lungs, then to the heart's left half.

punctuation model of speciation Idea that most morphological changes occur in a brief surge, as populations start to diverge.

Punnett-square method Construction of a simple diagram to predict the probable outcomes of a genetic cross.

pyruvate Three-carbon compound that forms as the end product of glycolysis.

quadrat One of many areas of a given size and shape in which samples are taken or individuals of a population are counted.

radial symmetry Animal body plan having four or more roughly equivalent parts around a central axis, as in a sea anemone.

radioactive decay An atom emits energy as subatomic particles and x-rays as its unstable nucleus disintegrates spontaneously. The process transforms one element into another.

radioisotope Isotope with an unstable nucleus (too many or too few neutrons).

radiometric dating Method of determining the age of a fossil by comparing the relative proportions of parent and daughter radioisotopes in rock samples or fossils.

rain shadow Reduction in rainfall on the leeward side of a high mountain range; results in arid or semiarid conditions.

recombinant DNA A DNA molecule that contains genetic material from more than one organism.

red alga Type of photoautotrophic protist; most are multicelled and aquatic; phycobilins mask their chlorophyll *a*.

red marrow Site of blood cell formation in the spongy tissue of many bones.

reflex Stereotyped, involuntary movement in response to a stimulus.

refractory period Brief interval following an action potential when a small patch of neural membrane is insensitive to stimulation.

regulatory protein Protein that enhances or inhibits protein synthesis.

relaxin Hormone secreted by ovaries and placenta that prepares the cervix and pelvis for giving birth.

releaser Hypothalamic releasing hormone that stimulates secretion by a target gland.

renal corpuscle Bowman's capsule plus the glomerular capillaries it encloses.

reproductive base All individuals of a population that are in the pre-reproductive and reproductive age brackets.

reproductive isolating mechanism Any heritable aspect of body form, function, or behavior that prevents interbreeding between populations of the same species.

reproductive success Production of viable offspring by the individual.

reptile Tetrapod vertebrate that has scaly skin and water-conserving kidneys, and produces amniote eggs (e.g., dinosaur, crocodilian, turtle, snake, lizard, tuatara).

resource partitioning A subdividing of resources in time or space that allows similar species to coexist in a habitat.

respiration Movement of oxygen into an animal's internal environment and carbon dioxide out of it.

respiratory cycle One inhalation and one exhalation.

respiratory membrane The alveolar and capillary endothelia, together with their basement membranes.

respiratory pigment A molecule in body fluids that reversibly binds oxygen (e.g., hemoglobin).

respiratory surface Thin, moist epithelium that functions in gas exchange.

resting membrane potential Of a neuron and other excitable cells, a voltage difference across the plasma membrane that holds steady in the absence of outside stimulation.

restriction enzyme A protein that recognizes and cuts specific sequences of nucleotides in double-stranded DNA.

retina Dense array of photoreceptors at the back of the eye.

reverse transcriptase Enzyme that assembles a single strand of DNA from free nucleotides on an RNA template; found in RNA viruses.

Rh blood typing Method of characterizing red blood cells by a certain membrane surface protein. Rh$^+$ cells have it; Rh$^-$ cells do not.

rhizoid Simple rootlike absorptive structure of some fungi and nonvascular plants.

ribonucleic acid See RNA.

ribosomal RNA rRNA. Structural and functional RNA component of ribosomes.

ribosome Structure upon which polypeptide chains are built. An intact ribosome consists of two subunits of rRNA and proteins.

riparian zone Narrow corridor of vegetation on either side of a stream or river.

RNA Ribonucleic acid. Any of a class of single-stranded nucleic acids with roles in transcription, translation, and catalysis.

RNA polymerase Enzyme that catalyzes the addition of nucleotides to a growing strand of RNA (transcription).

RNA world A presumed period before the origin of life when RNA may have stored protein-building information.

rod cell Vertebrate photoreceptor sensitive to dim light; contributes to the coarse perception of movement across the visual field.

root Plant part, typically belowground; absorbs water and minerals, anchors aboveground parts, and often stores food.

root hair Thin extension of a root epidermal cell; collectively, root hairs greatly increase the surface area for absorbing water and ions.

root nodule Localized swelling on a root that contains mutualistic nitrogen-fixing bacteria.

roundworm Cuticle-covered, bilateral worm with a false coelom and complete digestive system; a nematode.

rubisco RuBP carboxylase. Enzyme that catalyzes attachment of a carbon atom from carbon dioxide to RuBP and starts the C3 photosynthetic pathway.

ruminant Hoofed, herbivorous mammal with multiple stomach chambers.

sac fungus Fungus that forms its sexual spores (ascospores) in sac-shaped cells.

salinization Salt buildup in soil through poor drainage, evaporation, and heavy irrigation.

saliva Glandular secretion that mixes with food and starts starch breakdown in mouth.

salt Compound that releases ions (other than H$^+$ and OH$^-$) in solution.

sampling error An experimental pitfall; arises when the sample or subset of a population, an event, or some other aspect of nature under study is not representative of the whole.

sap Sugary solution that circulates through vascular tissues of plants.

sapwood Functioning secondary xylem of an older woody plant.

sarcomere Basic unit of contraction in skeletal and cardiac muscle. Shortens as a result of ATP-driven interactions between actin and myosin filaments.

scientific theory An explanation of the cause of a range of related phenomena; has been rigorously tested but is still open to revision.

sclerenchyma Simple plant tissue that supports mature plant parts; often protects seeds. Most of its cells have thick, lignin-impregnated walls.

second law of thermodynamics A law of nature stating that the spontaneous direction of energy flow is from organized forms to less organized forms; with each conversion, some energy is randomly dispersed in a form (usually heat) not as useful for doing work.

second messenger Molecule within a cell that mediates a hormonal signal from outside.

secondary oocyte An oocyte that has finished meiosis I just before being released from an ovary at ovulation.

secondary succession Recovery of a community to its climax stage following a habitat disturbance, such as a forest fire.

secondary wall A rigid, permeable wall that forms inside the primary wall of some older plant cells.

seed Mature ovule; an embryo sporophyte and endosperm surrounded by a seed coat.

segmentation Of animal body plans, a series of units that may or may not be similar to one another in appearance. Of tubular organs, an oscillating movement produced by rings of circular muscle in the tube wall.

selective gene expression Controlled activation or suppression of transcription and translation; leads to cell identity.

selective permeability Built-in capacity of a cell membrane to stop some substances from crossing, and to allow others to cross it, at certain times, in certain amounts.

selfish behavior An individual protects or increases its own chance to produce offspring regardless of consequences to its social group.

selfish herd Individuals that cluster together for protection against predators or some other environmental danger.

senescence Processes leading to the natural death of an organism or parts of it (e.g., abscission of leaves from a deciduous tree).

sensation Conscious awareness of a stimulus.

sensory adaptation Decrease in response to a stimulus maintained at constant strength.

sensory neuron Type of neuron that detects a stimulus and relays information about it to an integrating center such as a brain.

sensory receptor Any cell or some part of it that can detect a stimulus.

sex chromosomes Chromosomes that, in certain combinations, determine a new individual's sex.

sexual dimorphism Occurrence of distinctive female and male phenotypes.

sexual reproduction Production of genetically variable offspring by meiosis, gamete formation, and fertilization.

sexual selection Mode of natural selection; favors a trait that gives the individual a competitive edge in attracting or keeping a mate, hence in reproductive success.

sexually-transmitted disease STD. Any one of the diseases spread by sexual intercourse.

shivering response Rhythmic tremors in response to cold; increases heat production.

shoot A stem, leaf, or flower.

sieve tube Conducting tube of phloem.

sister chromatids Two identical DNA molecules (and associated proteins) attached at the centromere until they are separated from each other at mitosis or meiosis; each is then a separate chromosome.

six-kingdom system Classification of all species into the kingdoms Bacteria, Archaea, Protista, Fungi, Plantae, and Animalia.

skeletal muscle tissue Striated contractile tissue; main component of muscles that attach to and move bones.

skin External integument of vertebrates; an outer epidermis and underlying dermis.

sliding-filament model Idea that muscle contraction occurs as a result of ATP-driven interactions between myosin and actin filaments in sarcomeres.

slime mold Predatory protist; amoebalike cells form fruiting bodies during life cycle.

smooth muscle tissue Nonstriated contractile tissue found in soft internal organs.

social behavior Diverse interactions among individuals of a species, which display, send, and respond to forms of communication that have genetic and learned components.

sodium–potassium pump Active transport protein that moves sodium and potassium ions across the cell membrane.

soil Mixture of mineral particles and decomposing organic material, with air and water occupying spaces between the particles.

soil erosion Movement of land under the force of wind, running water, and ice.

solute Any substance dissolved in a solution.

somatic nerve Type of nerve that carries signals from the central nervous system to skeletal muscles, and from sensory receptors into that system.

somites Paired bumps of mesoderm in a vertebrate embryo that give rise to skeletal muscles and bones, and part of the dermis.

species One kind of organism. Of species that reproduce sexually, one or more groups of natural populations in which individuals interbreed and are reproductively isolated from other such groups.

sperm Mature male gamete.

sphincter A ring of smooth muscles that can alternately contract and relax to close off and open a passageway to the body surface.

spinal cord The part of the central nervous system that runs through a canal in the vertebral column.

spirochete Member of a group of spring-shaped bacteria; some are human pathogens.

spleen A lymphoid organ that is a filtering station for blood, a reservoir of red blood cells, and a reservoir of macrophages.

sponge A filter-feeding animal with no body symmetry and no tissues.

spore A reproductive or resting structure of one or a few cells, often walled or coated; protects against harsh conditions, aids in dispersal, or both.

sporophyte A vegetative body that grows by way of mitotic cell divisions from a plant zygote and produces spore-bearing structures.

spring overturn Downward movement of oxygen-rich surface waters and upward movement of nutrient-rich waters from the depths of temperate-zone lakes in spring.

stabilizing selection Mode of natural selection; intermediate phenotypes in the range of variation are favored and extremes are selected against.

stamen A male reproductive part of a flower.

statolith A gravity-sensing mechanism based on clusters of dense particles.

stem cell Undifferentiated animal cell that can divide indefinitely; a portion of daughter cells differentiate into specialized cell types.

steroid hormone Lipid-soluble hormone derived from cholesterol.

sterol Lipid with a rigid backbone of four fused carbon rings.

stimulus A form of energy that can be detected by a sensory receptor.

stoma, plural **stomata** A gap between two guard cells in leaf or stem epidermis; allows the diffusion of water vapor and gases across the epidermis.

stomach Muscular, stretchable sac that mixes and stores ingested food, helps break it up mechanically and chemically, and controls its entry into the small intestine.

stramenopile One of a group of protists having flagella with tinsel-like filaments.

stratification Layering of sedimentary rock; results from deposition of materials over time.

strip logging Logging of forested slopes in a narrow corridor to lessen negative impacts.

strobilus, plural **strobili** A conelike cluster of spore-producing structures (e.g., of cycads).

stromatolite Fossilized mats of shallow-water microbial communities, mainly cyanobacteria.

substrate-level phosphorylation The direct, enzyme-mediated transfer of a phosphate group from a substrate to another molecule.

surface-to-volume ratio Physical relationship in which volume increases with the cube of the diameter, but surface area increases with the square; constrains increases in cell size.

survivorship curve A graph that reflects how many individuals of a cohort survive, on average, at successive ages in their life span.

sympathetic nerve An autonomic nerve; deals mainly with increasing overall body activities at times of excitement or danger.

sympatric speciation In the absence of a physical barrier, a new species arises within the home range of an existing species.

synaptic integration Summation of all excitatory and inhibitory signals arriving at the trigger zone of a neuron or some other excitable cell.

syndrome A set of symptoms that characterize an abnormality or a disorder.

systemic circuit Circulatory route that carries oxygenated blood from the left side of the heart, through all tissues, then carries oxygen-poor blood back to the right half of the heart.

T lymphocyte T cell; a type of white blood cell vital to immune responses (e.g., helper T cells and cytotoxic T cells).

tandem repeat One of many short DNA sequences, occurring one after the other, in a chromosome. Used in DNA fingerprinting.

taproot system A primary root together with its lateral branchings; typical of eudicots.

taste receptor A chemoreceptor for substances dissolved in fluid bathing it.

TCR Receptor on T cell surface; binds to an antigen fragment that has become attached to a self marker on an antigen-presenting cell.

telomere Repetitive DNA cap at chromosome tip; shorter after each nuclear division.

telophase Of meiosis I, a stage when one member of each pair of homologous chromosomes reaches a spindle pole. Of mitosis and of meiosis II, the stage when chromosomes decondense into threadlike structures and daughter nuclei form.

temperature A measure of molecular motion.

temperature zone Globe-spanning latitudinal bands of temperature (e.g., tropical, warm temperate, cool temperate).

tendon Cord or strap of dense connective tissue that attaches muscle to bone.

test, scientific A means to determine the accuracy of a prediction, as by conducting experiments, making observations, or developing models.

testcross Experimental cross to determine whether an individual of unknown genotype that shows dominance for a trait is either homozygous dominant or heterozygous.

testis, plural **testes** A type of gonad (primary male reproductive organ); produces male gametes and sex hormones.

testosterone Male sex hormone produced in testes; functions in sperm formation and development of secondary sexual traits.

tetanus Of a muscle, sustained contraction that results from repeated stimulation of a motor unit. In a disease by the same name, a toxin prevents muscles from being released from contraction.

tetrapod Vertebrate that is a four-legged walker or a descendant of one (e.g., amphibian, reptile, bird, mammal).

thalamus Brain region; a coordinating center for sensory input and a relay station for signals to the cerebrum.

theory of uniformity Theory that Earth's surface changes in slow, uniformly repetitive ways. Helped change Darwin's view of evolution. Has since been replaced by plate tectonics theory.

thermal inversion A layer of dense, cool air trapped beneath a layer of warm air; can keep air pollutants close to the ground.

thermal radiation The surface of a warm body emits heat in the form of radiant energy.

thermoreceptor Sensory cell that detects radiant energy (heat).

thigmotropism Orientation of the direction of growth in response to physical contact with a solid object (e.g., a vine curls around a post).

three-domain system Classification of all species into the domains Bacteria, Archaea, and Eukarya.

threshold Of excitable cells (e.g., a neuron or muscle cell), the minimum amount of change in the resting membrane potential that causes an action potential.

thylakoid membrane In plants, internal portion of a chloroplast's membrane system, often folded into flattened sacs, that forms a single compartment. Pigments and enzymes are embedded in it; site of photosynthesis.

thymus gland Lymphoid organ; its hormones influence T cells, which form in bone marrow but migrate to and differentiate in the thymus.

thyroid gland Endocrine gland; its hormones influence overall growth, development, and metabolic rates of warm-blooded animals.

tight junction Animal cell junction that prevents substances from leaking between adjoining cells.

tissue Of multicelled organisms, a group of cells and intercellular substances that function together in one or more specialized tasks.

tissue culture propagation Inducing a tissue or organism to grow from an isolated cell of a parent tissue, in vitro.

topsoil Uppermost soil layer, the one that is most essential for plant growth.

total fertility rate TFR. Within a population, the average number of children born to a woman during her reproductive years.

tracer Substance with attached radioisotope that researchers can track after delivering it into a cell, a multicelled body, ecosystem, or other system.

trachea A type of air-conducting tube that occurs in respiratory systems. Of land vertebrates, the windpipe that connects the larynx to bronchi.

tracheal system Of insects and some other land-dwelling arthropods, a system of tubes that carry gases from body surfaces to tissues.

tracheid One of two types of water-conducting cells in xylem.

transcription First stage of protein synthesis, in which a strand of RNA is assembled on a DNA template (gene).

transfer RNA tRNA. A class of small RNA molecules that deliver amino acids to a ribosome; each pairs with an mRNA codon during translation.

translation Second stage of protein synthesis. Information encoded in an mRNA transcript guides the synthesis of a new polypeptide chain from amino acids; occurs at ribosomes.

translocation Of cells, a repositioning of a stretch of DNA to a new chromosomal location with no molecular loss. Of vascular plants, distribution of organic compounds through phloem.

transpiration Evaporative water loss from the aboveground parts of a plant.

transposon Transposable element. A stretch of DNA that can jump spontaneously and randomly to a different location in the genome; may cause mutation.

triglyceride A lipid that has three fatty acid tails attached to a glycerol backbone.

trophic level All organisms the same number of transfer steps away from the energy input into an ecosystem.

tubular reabsorption In kidneys, return of water and solutes from a nephron to blood.

tubular secretion In kidneys, excess ions and other substances move from interstitial fluid into the nephron, and are excreted in urine.

tumor Tissue mass with cells dividing at an abnormally high rate. If benign, cells stay in place; if malignant, they metastasize, or move to form tumors in new places in the body.

ultrafiltration Bulk flow of a small amount of protein-free plasma from a blood capillary when the outward-directed effect of blood pressure exceeds the inward-directed osmotic movement of interstitial fluid.

upwelling Upward movement of cold, nutrient-rich water from the ocean depths to the ocean surface.

uracil Nitrogen-containing base of a nucleotide of RNA molecules. Can base-pair with adenine.

urea Waste product formed in the liver from ammonia and CO_2; excreted in urine.

urinary excretion Mechanism by which excess water and solutes are removed from the body through the urinary system.

urinary system Organ system that adjusts the volume and composition of blood, and thereby helps maintain extracellular fluid.

urine Fluid consisting of any excess water, wastes, and solutes; it forms in kidneys by filtration, reabsorption, and secretion.

uterus In pouched and placental female mammals, organ in which embryos develop and are nurtured.

variable A specific aspect of an object or event that may differ over time and among individuals. In an experimental test, a single variable is directly manipulated in an attempt to support or disprove a prediction.

vascular bundle A strand-like array of primary xylem and phloem that threads through a plant's ground tissue system.

vascular cambium A lateral meristem that gives rise to secondary xylem and phloem, which increases stem or root diameter.

vascular cylinder Arrangement of vascular tissues as a central cylinder inside a root.

vasoconstriction Shrinking of blood vessel diameter, especially arterioles.

vasodilation Enlargement of blood vessel diameter, especially arterioles.

vegetative growth A new plant grows from an extension or fragment of its parent.

vein In plants, a vascular bundle inside a leaf. In animals, a vessel that returns blood to the heart and acts as a blood volume reservoir.

venule A small blood vessel that serves as a transitional conducting tube between a small-diameter capillary and a larger diameter vein.

vernalization The induction of flowering by exposure to low temperature.

vertebra, plural **vertebrae** A series of hard bones that function as a skeletal backbone and that protect the spinal cord.

vertebrate Animal having a backbone.

vessel member One cell type in xylem.

vestibular apparatus Organ of equilibrium in the inner ear.

villus, plural **villi** Fingerlike projections from the free surface of an epithelium, as into the lumen of the small intestine.

viroid A bit of RNA that infects plants.

virus A noncellular infectious agent that can be replicated only if its genetic material enters a host cell and subverts metabolic machinery.

viscera All soft organs inside an animal body (e.g., heart, lungs, and stomach).

vision Perception of visual stimuli.

visual accommodation Adjustments in a lens position or shape that focus light on a retina.

vitamin Any of more than a dozen organic substances that an organism requires in small amounts for metabolism but generally cannot synthesize for itself.

warning coloration Pattern or coloration that makes a toxic organism (or its mimics) easy to detect and avoid.

watershed Region from which water drains into a single stream or river.

water–vascular system Of sea stars and sea urchins, a system of many tube feet that are deployed in synchrony for smooth movement.

wavelength A wavelike form of energy in motion. The horizontal distance between the crests of every two successive waves.

wax A type of lipid with long-chain fatty acids attached to long-chain alcohols or carbon rings.

white blood cell Leukocyte. A type of blood cell that functions in basic housekeeping, nonspecific defenses, and adaptive immunity (e.g., eosinophil, neutrophil, macrophage, or lymphocyte).

X chromosome inactivation The programmed condensation of one of the X chromosomes in somatic cells of a mammalian female.

xanthophyll Yellow-orange carotenoid. An accessory pigment.

xenotransplantation Transfer of an organ from one species to another.

x-ray diffraction image Pattern formed when x-rays that have been directed at a molecule are scattered; the resulting pattern of streaks and dots is used to calculate positions of atoms in the molecule.

xylem Of vascular plants, a complex tissue that conducts water and solutes through pipelines of interconnected walls of cells, which are dead at maturity.

yellow marrow A fatty tissue in the cavities of most mature bones.

Y-linked gene Gene on a Y chromosome.

yolk Protein-rich and lipid-rich substance that nourishes embryos in animal eggs.

yolk sac Extraembryonic membrane. In most shelled eggs, it holds nutritive yolk; in humans, part becomes a site of blood cell formation and some cells give rise to forerunners of gametes.

zero population growth No overall increase or decrease in population size during a specified interval.

zygomycete Fungus that forms a thick-walled sexual spore (a diploid zygote) in a thin cover.

zygote First cell of a new individual, formed by fusion of a sperm nucleus with an egg nucleus at fertilization; a fertilized egg.

Art Credits and Acknowledgments

This page constitutes an extension of the copyright page. We have made every effort to trace the ownership of all copyrighted material and to secure permission from copyright holders. In the event of any question arising as to the use of any material, we will be pleased to make the necessary corrections in future printings. Thanks are due to the following authors, publishers, agents, and for permission to use the material indicated.

Page i, iii, Frans Lanting/Minden Pictures

TABLE OF CONTENTS **Page iv** bottom left, Art by Raychel Ciemma; **Page v** top, from left, Lisa Starr; Larry West/FPG/Getty Images; © Professors P. Motta and T Naguro/SPL/Photo Researchers, Inc. **Page vi** bottom left, © Jennifer W. Shuler/Science Source/Photo Researchers, Inc. **Page vii** top, from left, © George Lepp/CORBIS; (both) Courtesy of Carl Zeiss MicroImaging, Thornwood, NY; © Mc Leod Murdo/Corbis Sygma; Model, courtesy of Thomas A. Setitz from *Science*; Courtesy of Joseph DeRisa from *Science*, 1997 Oct. 24; 278 (5338) 680–686. **Page viii** left, (above) © Alan Solem; (below) Courtesy of Professor Martin F. Yanofsky, UCSD; **Page ix** top, from left, © P. Hawtin, University of Southampton/SPL/Photo Researchers, Inc.; © Science Photo Library/Photo Researchers, Inc.; © John Clegg/Ardea, London; © Robert C. Simpson/Nature Stock; Gerry Ellis/The Wildlife Collection. **Page x** Top © R. J. Erwin/Photo Researchers, Inc. **Page xi** Top, from left, © Cory Gray; © Illustration by Karen Carr; © Bruce Iverson; © Jim Christensen, Fine Art Digital Photographic Images. **Page xii** bottom left, © Science Photo Library/Photo Researchers, Inc. **Page xiii** Top, from left, © AP/Wide World Photos; © Kevin Fleming/CORBIS; © Michael Neveux; © NSIBC/SPL/Photo Researchers, Inc. **Page xiv** Top, © NIBSC/SPL/Photo Researchers, Inc. **Page xv** top, from left, © Francois Gohier/Photo Researchers, Inc.; © Archivo Iconografico, S.A./CORBIS; © Dow W. Fawcett/Photo Researchers, Inc.; © Amos Nachoum/CORBIS **Page xvi** bottom left, © C. James Webb/Phototake USA. **Page xvii** top, from left, © Pr. Alexande Meinesz, University of Nice-Sophia Antipolis; © Eric and David Hosking/CORBIS; © James Marshall/CORBIS. © Hank Fotos Photography

INTRODUCTION NASA Space Flight Center

CHAPTER 1 **Page 2** Left, © Mark M. Lawrence/CORBIS. **the big picture** (page 2) From left, Lisa Starr with PDB ID:1BNA; H.R. Drew, R.M. Wing, T. Takano, C. Broka, S. Tanaka, K. Itakura, R.E. Dickerson; Structure of a B-DNA Dodecamer. Conformation and Dynamics, PNAS; right, © Peter Scoones; (page 3) From left, © Nick Brent; right, © Raymond Gehman/CORBIS. **Page 3** Top, © Peter Turnley/CORBIS. **1.1** (a) Lisa Starr, rendered with Atom In A Box, © Dauger Research, Inc. 1.1 (b, above left) Lisa Starr with PDB file courtesy of Dr. Christina A. Bailey, Department of Chemistry & Biochemistry, California Polytechnec State University, San Luis Obispo, CA (b, above center) Lisa Starr with PDB ID: 1BBB; Silva, M. M., Rogers, P. H., Arnone, A; A third quaternary structure of human hemoglobin A at 1.7-A resolution; J Biol Chem 267 pp. 17248 (1992); (b, above right) Lisa Starr with PDB file from Klotho Biochemical Compounds Declarative Database; (b, below) Lisa Starr; (c) Lisa Starr; (d) ©Science Photo Library/Photo Researchers; (e) © Bill Varie/CORBIS; (f) © Jeffrey L. Rotman/CORBIS; (g) © Jeffrey L. Rotman/CORBIS; (h) © Jeffrey L. Rotman/CORBIS; (i) © Peter Scoones; (j) NASA; (k) NASA. **1.2** Lisa Starr. **1.3** (a-e) © Jack de Coningh. **1.4** Gary Head and Lisa Starr **1.5** © Y. Arthus-Bertrand/Peter Arnold, Inc. **1.7** (page 8) clockwise from above, © Lewis Trusty/Animals Animals; © Emiliania Huxleyi photograph, Vita Pariente, scanning electron micrograph taken on a Jeol T330A instrument at Texas A&M University Electron Microscopy center; © Carolina Biological Supply Company; © R. Robinson/Visuals Unlimited, Inc.; (e) © Oliver Meckes/Photo Researchers, Inc.; Courtesy of James Evarts; (page 9) clockwise from above left, © John Lotter Gurling/Tom Stack & Associates; (h) © Edward S. Ross; (i) © Robert C. Simpson/Nature Stock; (j) © Edward S. Ross; (k) © Joe McDonald/CORBIS; (l) © CNRI/SPL/Photo Researchers, Inc.; (m) © P. Hawtin, University of Southampton/SPL/Photo Researchers, Inc. **1.8** Top, All Courtesy of Derrell Fowler, Tecumseh, Oklahoma; bottom, © Nick Brent, enhanced by Lisa Starr. **1.9** Lisa Starr. **Page 11** Left, © Raymond Gehman/CORBIS; center, © LWA-Stephen Welstead/CORBIS; right, © Lester Lefkowitz/CORBIS. **Page 12** Right, © Royalty-Free/CORBIS. **1.10** (a) © Chris D. Jiggins; (b) © www.thais.it; top background, © Wolfgang Kaehler/CORBIS; bottom right, © Martin Reid. Art, Lisa Starr. **Page 15** © Digital Vision/PictureQuest. **Page 16** (a–d) © Gary Head.

Page 17 Unit I © Wim van Egmond/Micropolitan Museum.

CHAPTER 2 **Page 18** Top, (a) © David Arky/CORBIS. **the big picture** (page 18) Lisa Starr; (page 19) From left, Art, Lisa Starr with PDB ID:1BNA; H.R. Drew, R.M. Wing, T. Takano, C. Broka, S. Tanaka, K. Itakura, R. E. Dickerson; Structure of a B-DNA Dodecamer. Conformation and Dynamics; PNAS; center, © Steve Lissau/Rainbow; right, © FoodPix. **Page 19** Top, © Dinodia. **2.2** (a, b) Lisa Starr; (c) Lisa Starr, rendered with Atom In A Box, © Dauger Research, Inc. **2.3** Art, Lisa Starr. **2.4** (a) © John Greim/Medichrome; (b, c) Art by Raychel Ciemma; (d) © Harry T. Chugani, M.D., UCLA School of Medicine **Page 22** © Michael S. Yamashita/CORBIS. **2.5** Lisa Starr, rendered with Atom In A Box, © Dauger Research, Inc. **2.6** Lisa Starr. **2.7** Gary Head and Lisa Starr. **2.8** Art, (a, b) Lisa Starr; photographs, (a) above, Gary Head; below, © Bruce Iverson; (c) Lisa Starr with PDB ID:IBNA; H.R. Drew, R.M. Wing, T. Takano, C. Broka, S. Tanaka, K. Itakura, R. E. Dickerson; Structure of a B-DNA Dodecamer. Conformation and Dynamics, PNAS. **2.9** (a,b,c, left) Lisa Starr with PDB file from NYU Scientific Visualization Lab; (b, right) © Steve Lissau/Rainbow; (c, right) © Kennan Ward/CORBIS. **2.10** Lisa Starr. **2.11** (a) © Lester Lefkowitz/CORBIS; (b) Lisa Starr. **2.12** Lisa Starr. **2.13** © Michael Grecco/Picture Group **Page 31** © National Gallery Collection; By kind permission of the Trustees of the National Gallery, London/CORBIS

CHAPTER 3 **3.1** Left, © 2002 Charlie Waite/Stone/Getty Images; center, John Collier. Great Britain, 1850-1934, *Priestess of Delphi,* 1891, London, oil on canvas, 160.0 x 80.0cm. Gift of the Rt. Honourable, the Earl of Kintore,1893; right, Lisa Starr, with PDB files from NYU Scientific Visualization Lab. **the big picture** (page 32) From left © Wayne Bennett/CORBIS; right, Lisa Starr; (page 33) From left, Lisa Starr with PDB file courtesy of Dr. Christina A. Bailey, Department of Chemistry & Biochemistry, California Polytechnic State University; San Luis Obispo, CA; center, Lisa Starr with PDB ID: 1BBB; Silva, M. M., Rogers, P. H., Arnone, A.; A third quaternary structure of human hemoglobin A at 1.7-A resolution; J Biol Chem 267, pp. 17248; right, Lisa Starr with PDB ID: 1BNA; H. R. Drew, R. M. Wing, T. Takano, C. Broka, S. Tanaka, K. Itakura, R. E. Dickerson; Structure of a B-DNA Dodecamer. Conformation and Dynamics, PNAS. **Page 33** Top right, Lisa Starr with PDB file from NYU Scientific Visualization Lab **3.2** (a) Lisa Starr with PDB file from NYU Scientific Visualization Lab (**b**) Lisa Starr with PDB file from Klotho Biochemical Compounds Declarative Database **3.3** Gary Head **3.4** Left © Eric and David Hosking/CORBIS; right, © Wayne Bennett/CORBIS; below, Lisa Starr. **3.5** Lisa Starr. **3.6** Lisa Starr with PDB file from NYU Scientific Visualization Lab. **3.7** (a) © Dr. W. Michaelis/Universitat Hamburg; (b) both, Courtesy of K.O. Stetter & R. Rachel, University of Regensburg © Boetius et all. 2000, Nature 407, 623-626; (b, right) Seth Gold. **3.8** Ian R. MacDonald **3.9** © John Sibbick. **3.10** Lisa Starr **3.11** Lisa Starr **3.12** Art, Lisa Starr; photograph, © Steve Chenn/CORBIS **3.13** Art, Lisa Starr; photograph, © David Scharf/Peter Arnold, Inc. **3.14** (a) Lisa Starr with PDB file courtesy of Dr. Christina A. Bailey, Department of Chemistry & Biochemistry, California Polytechnic State University, San Luis Obispo, CA; (b-d) Art, Precison Graphics. **3.15** (a, b) Art, Precision Graphics; photograph, © Kevin Schafer/CORBIS **3.16** (a) Lisa Starr with PDB file courtesy of Dr. Christina A. Bailey, Department of Chemistry & Art, Lisa Starr; (b) Precision Graphics (c) Lisa Starr **3.17** (a) © Scott Camazine/Photo Researchers, Inc. (b) Lisa Starr (c) Precision Graphics. **3.18** (a) Gary Head; (b-e) Lisa Starr and Chris Keeney with PDB files from NYU Scientific Visualization Lab. **3.19** (a) Lisa Starr; (b, left) Lisa Starr; (b, right) Lisa Starr After: Introduction to Protein Structure 2nd ed., Branden & Tooze, Garland Publishing, Inc.; (c, left) Lisa Starr with PDB ID: 1BBB; Silva, M. M., Rogers, P. H., Arnone, A.; A third quaternary structure of human hemoglobin A at 1.7-A resolution; J Biol Chem 267 pp. 17248 (1992); (c, right) Lisa Starr After: Introduction to Protein Structure 2nd ed., Branden & Tooze, Garland Publishing, Inc. **3.20** (a, b) Lisa Starr with PDB ID: 1BBB; Silva, M. M., Rogers, P. H., Arnone, A.; A third quaternary structure of human hemoglobin A at 1.7-Å resolution; J Biol Chem 267 pp. 17248 (1992). **3.21** (a, b) Gary Head and Lisa Starr with PDB files from New York University Scientific Visualization; (c) Dr. Gopal Murti/SPL/Photo Researchers, Inc. (d) photograph, Courtesy of Melba Moore. **3.22** Gary Head. **3.23** (a) Gary Head; (b) Lisa Starr **3.24** Lisa Starr with PDB ID:1BNA; H.R. Drew, R.M. Wing, T. Takano, C. Broka, S. Tanaka, K. Itakura, R.E. Dickerson; Structure of a B-DNA Dodecamer. Conformation and Dynamics; PNAS V. 78 2179, 1981 Lisa Starr. **Page 49**, left, Art by Lisa Starr with PDB ID: 1AKJ; Gao, G. F., Tormo, J., Gerth, U. C., Wyer, J. R., McMichael, A. J., Stuart, D. I., Bell, J. I., Jones, E. Y., Jakobsen, B. K.; Crystal structure of the complex between human CD8alpha(alpha) and HLA-A2; Nature 387 pp. 630 (1997) **3.25** Art, Lisa Starr; photograph, © Kevin Fleming/CORBIS

CHAPTER 4 **4.1** (a-c) © Tony Brian, David Parker/SPL/Photo Researchers, Inc. **the big picture** (page 50) From left, Art by Raychel Ciemma; right, Lisa Starr; (page 51) Left and right, Art, Lisa Starr. **Page 51** Top, © Tony Brian, David Parker/SPL/Photo Researchers, Inc. **4.2** Lisa Starr. **4.3** Art assembly, Gary Head; Art, Lisa Starr. Photographs: (hummingbird) © Robert A. Tyrrell; (human), © Pete Saloutos/CORBIS; (redwood), © Sally A. Morgan, Ecoscene/CORBIS **4.5** Left, © Armed Forces Institute of Pathology; right, © National Library of Medicine. **4.6** Bottom left, © Leica Microsystems, Inc., Deerfield, IL; right, Gary Head **4.7** Left, Gary Head; right, © Geoff Tompkinson/Science Photo Library/Photo Researchers, Inc. **4.8** (a) © Jeremy Pickett-Heaps, School of Botany, University of Melbourne; (b) © Jeremy Pickett-Heaps, School of Botany, University of Melbourne; (c) © Jeremy Pickett-Heaps, School of Botany, University of Melbourne; (d) © Jeremy Pickett-Heaps, School of Botany, University of Melbourne. **4.9** (a) Precision Graphics (b) Lisa Starr (c) Raychel Ciemma. **4.10** (page 56) Left, Lisa Starr with integrin: PDB ID:1JV2; Xiong, J.-P., Stehle, T., Diefenbach, B., Zhang, R., Dunker, R., Scott, D. L., Joachimiak, A., Goodman, S. L., Arnaout, M. A.: Crystal Structure of the Extracellular Segment of Integrin $\alpha V\beta 3$ Science 294 pp. 339 (2001); (page 57), Lisa Starr, Chris Keeney, and Leif Buckley with Human growth hormone: PDB ID:1A22; Clackson, T., Ultsch, M. H., Wells, J. A., de Vos, A. M.: Structural and functional analysis of the 1:1 growth hormone:receptor complex reveals the molecular basis for receptor affinity. J Mol Biol 277 pp. 1111 (1998); HLA: PDB ID: 1AKJ; Gao, G. F., Tormo, J., Gerth, U. C., Wyer, J. R., McMichael, A. J., Stuart, D. I., Bell, J. I., Jones, E. Y., Jakobsen, B. K.; Crystal structure of the complex between human CD8alpha and HLA-A2; Nature 387 pp. 630 (1997); glut1: PDB ID:1JA5; Zuniga, F. A., Shi, G., Haller, J. F., Rubashkin, A., Flynn, D. R., Iserovich, P., Fischbarg, J.: A Three-Dimensional Model of the Human Facilitative Glucose Transporter Glut1 J. Biol. Chem. 276 pp. 44970 (2001); calcium pump: PDB ID:1EUL; Toyoshima, C., Nakasako, M., Nomura, H., Ogawa, H.: Crystal Structure of the Calcium Pump of Sarcoplasmic Reticulum at 2.6 Angstrom Resolution. Nature 405 pp. 647 (2000); ATPase: PDB ID:18HE; Menz, R. I., Walker, J.E., Leslie, A.G.W.: Structure of Bovine Mitochondrial F1-ATPase with Nucleotide Bound to All Three Catalytic Sites: Implications for the Mechanism of Rotary Catalysis. Cell (Cambridge, Mass.)106 pp. 331 (2001); **4.11** (a) © K.G. Murti/Visuals Unlimited; (b) © R. Calentine/Visuals Unlimited; (c) © Gary Gaard and Arthur Kelman; (d) Lisa Starr. **4.12** top, (a) © Russell Kightley/Science Photo Library/Photo Researchers, Inc.; (b) © University of California Museum of Paleontology; (c) © University of California Museum of Paleontology. **4.13** © M.C. Ledbetter, Brookhaven National Laboratory. **4.14** © Micrograph, Gl L. Decker **4.15** Top left, Lisa Starr; top right, © Stephen L. Wolfe; (a) © Stephen L. Wolfe; (b) Lisa Starr. **4.16** Top left, Lisa Starr; (a) © Stephen L. Wolfe; (b) Stephen L. Wolfe; (c) right, Art, computer enhanced by Lisa Starr; (d) right, Art, computer enhanced by Lisa Starr (e) Gary Grimes, computer enhanced by Lisa Starr. **4.17** Art, Lisa Starr and Raychel Ciemma; photograph (right), © Keith R. Porter. **4.18** Art, Lisa Starr; photograph, © Dr. Jeremy Burgess/SPL/Photo Researchers, Inc. **4.19** Lisa Starr. **4.20** Lisa Starr. **4.21a-c** Lisa Starr; photograph, courtesy Mary Osborn, Max Planck Institute for Biophysical Chemistry, Goettingen, FRG. **4.22** Lisa Starr. **4.23** (a) Precision Graphics after Stephen L. Wolfe, Molecular and Cellular Biology, Wadsworth, 1993. (b) © CNRI/SPL/Photo Researchers, Inc. **4.24** (a) Raychel Ciemma (b) Lisa Starr; (c-e) Raychel Ciemma **4.25** (a) © George S. Ellmore (b) © Science Photo Library/Photo Researchers, Inc.; right, © Bone Clones, www.boneclones.com. **4.26** Ronald Hoham, Dept. of Biology, Colgate University. **4.26** Lisa Starr and Leif Buckley. **4.27** (a,b) From "Tissue & Cell," Vol. 27, pp.421-427, Courtesy of Bjorn Afzelius, Stockholm University.

CHAPTER 5 **5.1** Left, © Chris Keeney; right, Lisa Starr with PDB ID: 1DGF; Putnam, C. D., Arvai, A. S., Bourne, Y., Tainer, J. A.: Active and Inhibited Human Catalase Structures: Ligand and Nadph Binding and Catalytic Mechanism J.Mol.Biol. 296 pp. 295 (2000). **the big picture** (page 72) From left, © William Dow/CORBIS; Lisa Starr; (page 73) From left, © Scott McKiernan/ZUMA Press; Lisa Starr. **Page 73** © Paul Edmondson/CORBIS. **5.2** Top, © Craig Aurness/CORBIS; bottom, © William Dow/CORBIS. **5.3** Lisa Starr. **5.4** Lisa Starr with PDB file from Klotho Biochemical Compounds Declarative Database. **5.5** Lisa Starr. **5.6** Lisa Starr, from B. Alberts, et al., Molecular Biology of the Cell, 1983, Garland Publishing. **5.7** Lisa Starr. **5.8** Lisa Starr. **5.9** Lisa Starr. **5.10** Lisa Starr with PDB ID: 1DGF; Putnam, C. D., Arvai, A. S., Bourne, Y., Tainer, J. A.: Active and Inhibited Human Catalase Structures: Lingand Nadph Binding and Catalytic Mechanism J Mol Biol. 296, p. 295 (2000). **5.11** Lisa Starr. **5.12** Lisa Starr. **5.13** (a) Gary Head; (b) © Scott McKiernan/ZUMA Press. **5.14** (a) Gary Head; (b) © Foodpix/Bill Boch; (c) © Woods Hole Oceanographic Institution. **5.15** Lisa Starr. **5.16** Top, © Andrew Lambert Photography/Science Photo Library/Photo Researchers; Art, Raychel Ciemma. **5.17** Lisa Starr. **5.18** Lisa Starr and Chris Keeney with PDB files from NYU Scientific Visualization Lab. **5.19** Lisa Starr, After: David H. MacLennan, William J. Rice and N. Michael Green, " The Mechanism of Ca2+ Transport by Sarco (Endo)plasmic Reticulum Ca2+-ATPases."JBC Volume 272, Number 46, Issue of Nov. 14, 1997 pp. 28815-28818. **Page 86** © Hubert Stadler/CORBIS. **5.20** Precision Graphics. **5.21** Art, top, Raychel Ciemma; bottom (all), © M. Sheetz, R. Painter, and S. Singer, J of Cell Biol., 70:193 (1976) by permission, The Rockefeller University Press. **5.22** Lisa Starr. **5.23** Both, © R.G.W. Anderson, M.S. Brown and J.L. Goldstein. Cell 10:351 (1977). **5.24** Chris Keeney. **5.25** (a) © Juergen berger/Max Planck Inst./SPL/Photo Researchers, Inc.; (b) Lisa Starr. **Page 90** Lisa Starr with PDB ID: 1CBJ; Hough, M.A. Hasnain, S.S. Crystallographic structures of bovine copper-zinc superoxide dismutase reveal asymmetry in two subunits: functionally important three and five coordinate copper sites captured in the same crystal. J. Mol. Biol. v287 pp. 579, 1999. **5.26** © Frieder Sauer/Bruce Coleman. **5.27** © Prof. Marcel Bessis/SPL/Photo Researchers, Inc.

CHAPTER 6 **6.1** Both, NASA. **the big picture** (page 92) From left, © 2002 PhotoDisc; Lisa Starr. **Page 93** © Wendy A. Kozlowski. **6.2** Left, © 2002 PhotoDisc; right, Precision Graphics. **6.3** Lisa Starr with PDB files from NYU Scientific Visualization Lab. **6.4** (a,b) Lisa Starr after Stephen L. Wolfe, *Molecular and Ceullar Biology*, Wadsworth. **6.5** © Larry West/FPG/Getty Images. **6.6** Art, Raychel Ciemma; micrograph, Carolina Biological Supply Company. **6.7** Left, © Craig Tuttle/CORBIS; (a-c) Art, Lisa Starr with Preface, Inc.; (d) Lisa Starr with Light Harvesting Complex PDB ID: 1RWT; Liu, Z., Yan, H., Wang, K., Kuang, T., Zhang, J., Gui, L., An, X., Chang, W.: Crystal Structure of Spinach Major Light-Harvesting Complex at 2.72 A Resolution Nature 428 pp. 287 (2004). **6.8** Lisa Starr with Preface, Inc. **Page 97** © Darron Luesse, Department of Biology, Indiana University. **6.9** (a, top) Harindar Keer, Thorsten Ritz Laboratory at UC Irvine, Dept. of Physics and Astronomy, using VMD proprietary software; (a, bottom) Lisa Starr; (b-d) Lisa Starr with Light Harvesting Complex PDB ID 1RWT; Liu, Z., Yan, H., Wang, K., Kuang, T., Zhang, J., Gui, L., An, X., Chang, W.: Crystal Structure of Spinach Major Light-Harvesting Complex at 2.72 A Resolution Nature 428 pp. 287 (2004). **Page 100** Top right, Lisa Starr with Light Harvesting Complex PDB ID: 1RWT; Liu, Z., Yan, H., Wang, K., Kuang, T., Zhang, J., Gui, L., An, X., Chang, W.: Crystal Structure of Spinach Major Light-Harvesting Complex at 2.72 A Resolution Nature 428 pp. 287 (2004). **6.10** Lisa Starr. **6.11** Chris Keeney. **6.12** Top left, Courtesy of John S. Russell, Pioneer High School; center left, © Foodpix/Bill Boch; bottom left, © Chris Hellier/CORBIS; top center, micrograph, Bruce Iverson, computer-enhanced by Lisa Starr; center center, micrograph, Ken Wagner/Visuals Unlimited, computer-enhanced by Lisa Starr; bottom center, micrograph, James D. Mauseth, University of Texas; Art, (all) Gary Head. **Page 104** (top left) Lisa Starr. **6.13** Gary Head. **6.14** © E.R. Degginger. **6.15** (a) © Herve Chaumeton/Agence Nature; (b) © Douglas Faulkner/Sally Faulkner Collection.

CHAPTER 7 **7.1** © Louise Chalcraft-Frank and FARA. **the big picture** (page 106), right © Professors P. Motta and T Naguro/SPL/Photo Researchers, Inc.; art, Lisa Starr; (page 107) From left, © Randy Faris/CORBIS; © Gary Head; **Page 107** Top, © Professors P. Motta and T Naguro/SPL/Photo Researchers, Inc. **7.2** Raychel Ciemma and Gary Head. **7.3** (page 108) Top left, © Jim Cummins/CORBIS; top right, © John Lotter Gurling/Tom Stack & Associates; bottom, © Chase Swift/CORBIS; (page 109) Art, Lisa Starr with Gary Head. **7.4** (page 110), Lisa Starr; (page 111) (a-f) Lisa Starr and Gary Head, after Ralph Taggart. **7.5** from left, Raychel Ciemma; Lisa Starr; © Professors P. Motta and T. Naguro/SPL/Photo Researchers, Inc. **7.6** Art, Lisa Starr. **7.7** Gary Head. **7.8** Top, Raychel Ciemma, (below) Lisa Starr. **7.9** Lisa Starr with Preface, Inc. **7.10** (a) © Adrian Warren/Ardea, London; (b) © Foodpix/Ben Fink; (c) ©Foodpix/Ben Fink; (d) Lisa Starr with Gary Head. **7.11** Lisa Starr. **7.12** Left, © Randy Faris/CORBIS; right, Gladden Willis, MD/Visuals Unlimited. **Page 118** © Lois Ellen Frank/CORBIS. **7.13** © Gary Head; art, Lisa Starr. **Page 120** © R. Llewellyn/SuperStock, Inc. **Page 121** Lisa Starr with Gary Head.

Page 123 Unit II © Francis Leroy, Biocosmos/Science Photo Library/Photo Researchers, Inc.

CHAPTER 8 **8.1** Left, micrograph, Dr. Pascal Madaule, France; inset, Courtesy of the family of Henrietta Lacks. **the big picture** (page 124) from left, © L. Willatt, East Anglian Regional Genetics Service/SPL/Photo Researchers, Inc.; © Jennifer W. Shuler/Science Source/Photo Researchers, Inc.; (page 125) from left, Gary Head; © Science Photo Library/Photo Researchers, Inc. **Page 125** Micrograph, Dr. Pascal Madaule, France. **8.2** (a,b) Gary Head; bottom © Divital Vision/Getty Images. **8.3** (a) From Allen TD, Jack EM, Harrison CJ (1988). The three dimensional structure of human metaphase chromosomes determined by scanning electron microscopy. In Adolph KW (1988) Chromosomes and Chromatin Volume II, CRC Press. Boca Raton, FL. Chapter 10, Fig.5, p.58; (b) Raychel Ciemma and Lisa Starr; (c) © B. Hamkalo; (d) © O. L. Miller, Jr., Steve L. McKnight. **8.4** Raychel Ciemma and Gary Head. **8.5** Left © L. Willatt, East Anglian Regional Genetics Service/SPL/Photo Researchers, Inc.; (a-c) Lisa Starr. **Page 129** Bottom right, Raychel Ciemma. **8.6** (pages 130-131) Photographs, © Jennifer W. Shuler/Science Source/Photo Researchers, Inc.; Art, Raychel Ciemma. **8.7** (a) Art, Raychel Ciemma; Micrograph, D. M. Phillips/Visuals Unlimited; (b) Art, Lisa Starr; Micrograph, R. Calentine/Visuals Unlimited. **8.8** © Jennifer W. Shuler/Science Source/Photo Researchers, Inc. **8.9** Bottom, © Lennart Nilsson from Behold Man, 1974 by Albert Bonniers Forlog and Little, Brown & Company, Boston. **Page 133** Top, © Lennart Nilsson from *A Child Is Born* 1966, 1977 Dell Publishing Company, Inc. **8.10** (a, b) © Phillip B. Carpenter, Department of Biochemistry and Molecular Biology. **8.11** © Science Photo Library/Photo Researchers, Inc. **8.12** Betsy Palay. **8.13** Left, © Ken Greer/Visuals Unlimited; center, © Biophoto Associates/Science Source/Photo Researchers, Inc.; right, © James Stevenson/SPL/Photo Researchers, Inc. **Page 136** Raychel Ciemma and Gary Head. **8.14** From Allen TD, Jack EM, Harrison CJ (1988) *The three dimensional structure of human metaphase chromosomes determined by scanning electron microscopy*. In Adolph KW (1988) *Chromosomes and Chromatin Volume II*, CRC Press. Boca Raton FL. Chapter 10, Fig. 5, p. 58.

CHAPTER 9 **9.1** (a) © Andrew Syred/Photo Researchers, Inc.; (b) © George D. Lepp/CORBIS; (c) © Dan Kline/Visuals Unlimited. **the big picture** (page 138) From left, Courtesy of Carl Zeiss MicroImaging, Thornwood, NY; Lisa Starr; (page 139) From left, Lisa Starr; © Francis Leroy, Biocosmos/Science Photo Library/Photo Researchers, Inc. **Page 139** © Tomohiro Kono/Tokyo University of Agriculture, enhanced by Lisa Starr. **9.2** Image courtesy of Carl Zeiss MicroImaging, Thornwood, NY. **9.3** Raychel Ciemma. **9.4** © L. Willatt, East Anglian Regional Genetics Service/SPL/Photo Researchers, Inc. **Page 141** Art, Raychel Ciemma. **9.5** (pages 142-143) Photography, Courtesy John Innes Foundation Trustees, computer enhanced by Gary Head; Art, Raychel Ciemma. **9.6** (a,b) Raychel Ciemma; (c–f) Lisa Starr. **9.7** Raychel Ciemma. **9.8** Seth Gold. **9.9** Lisa Starr. **9.10** Art, Lisa Starr; right, © Francis Leroy, Biocosmos/Science Photo Library/Photo Researchers, Inc. **9.11** Lisa Starr. **9.12** © Ron Neumeyer, www.microimaging.ca. **9.13** (a,b) © Lisa O'Connor/ZUMA/Corbis.

CHAPTER 10 **10.1** Art, Lisa Starr; left, © Children's Hospital & Medical Center/CORBIS; right © Simon Fraser/RVI, New Castle-Upon-Tyne/SPL/Photo Researchers, Inc. **the big picture** (page 150) From left, © George Lepp/CORBIS; Raychel Ciemma and Precision Graphics; (page 151) From left, © Ted Somes; D. & V. Hennings. **Page 151** © Science Photo Library/Photo Researchers, Inc. **10.2** © The Moravian Museum, Brno. **10.3** © Jean M. Labat/Ardea, London; Art, Jennifer Wardrip. **10.4** Lisa Starr. **10.5** Precison Graphics. **10.6** Raychel Ciemma and Precison Graphics. **10.7** Raychel Ciemma and Precison Graphics. **10.8** Raychel Ciemma. **10.9** Raychel Ciemma and Precison Graphics. **10.10** © David Scharf/Peter Arnold, Inc.; Art, Precision Graphics. **10.11** Top, William F. Ferguson; bottom, © Francesc Muntada/CORBIS; Art, Raychel Ciemma. **10.12** All, Ted Somes. **10.13** © Bettman/CORBIS. **10.14** From top, © Frank Cezus/FPG; © Frank Cezus/FPG; © Ted Beaudin/FPG; © Michael Prince/CORBIS. **10.15** (a,b) Gary Head; (c) Courtesy of Ray Carson, University of Florida News and Public Affairs. **10.16** D. & V. Hennings. **10.17** © Pamela Harper/Harper Horticultural Slide Library; Art, Lisa Starr from Prof. Otto Wilhelm Thome, Flora von Deutschland Osterreich und der Schweiz. 1885, Gera, Germany. **Page 163** © Gideon Mendel/CORBIS. **10.18** Left, © Tom and Pat Leeson/Photo Researchers, Inc.; right, © Rick Guidotti, Positive Exposure. **10.19** © Leslie Faltheisek. Clacritter Manx.

CHAPTER 11 **11.1** © Reuters/CORBIS. **the big picture** (page 166) From left. © 2001 PhotoDisc, Inc.; © 2001 EyeWire, Inc.; © Stapleton Collection/CORBIS; (page 167) From left, Raychel Ciemma; © Saturn Stills/SPL/Photo Researchers, Inc. **Page 167** © Daniel Weinberger, M.D., E. Fuller Torrey, M.D., Karen Berman, M.D., NIMH Clinical Brain Disorders Branch, Division of Intramural Research Programs, NIMH 1990. From: When Someone Has Schizophrenia, A brief overview of the symptoms, treatments, and research findings. 2001. **Page 168** © Jose Luis Pelaez, Inc./CORBIS. **11.2** Raychel Ciemma and Preface, Inc. **11.3** (a) Precision Graphics and Gary Head; (b) Robert Demarest with permission from M. Cummings, Human Heredity: Principles and Issues, 3rd Edition, p. 126. © 1994 by Brooks/Cole. All rights reserved; (c) Robert Demarest after Patten, Carlson & others; bottom right (girl), © 2001 PhotoDisc, Inc.; (boy), © 2001 EyeWire, Inc. **11.4** Art, Gary Head and Raychel Ciemma; (b) © Charles D. Winters/Photo Researchers, Inc.; (f) © Omikron/Photo Researchers, Inc. **11.5** Raychel Ciemma. **11.6** © Stapleton Collection/CORBIS. **11.7** Art, Precision Graphics; right, © Dr. Victor A. McKusick. **11.8** © Steve Uzzell. **11.9** Top left, © Frank Trapper/Corbis Sygma; (a,b) Lisa Starr. **11.11** Lisa Starr; **11.13** Art, After V. A. McKusick, Human Genetics, 2nd Ed., © 1969. Reprinted by permission of the author; right, © Bettman/CORBIS. **11.14** © Eddie Adams/AP Wide World Photos. **Page 176** Precision Graphics. **Page 177** Precison Graphics. **11.15** (a,b) Courtesy G. H. Valentine. **11.16** From "Multicolor Spectral Karyotyping of Human Chromosomes," by E. Schrock, T. Ried, et al, Science, 26 July 1996, 273:495. Used by permission of E. Schrock, T. Reid and the American Association for the Advancement of Science. **11.17** (a) Raychel Ciemma; (b) © CNRI/Photo Researchers, Inc. **11.18** Preface, Inc. **11.19** © UNC Medical Illustration and Photography. **11.20** © Saturn Stills/SPL/Photo Researchers, Inc. **11.21** From Lennart Nilsson, *A Child is Born*, (c) 1966, 1977 Dell Publishing Company, Inc.; Art, Lisa Starr. **11.22** © Matthew Alan/CORBIS; inset © Fran Heyl Associates/Jacques Cohen, computer-enhanced by © Pix Elation. **11.23** (a) © Carolina Biological/Visuals Unlimited; (b) © Terry Gleason/Visuals Unlimited; (c) Raychel Ciemma and Preface, Inc. **Page 183** Bottom left, Precison Graphics.

CHAPTER 12 **12.1** (a) © C. Barrington Brown, 1968 J. D. Watson; (b) © Mc Leod Murdo/CORBIS Sygma. **the big picture** (page 184) From left, Lisa Starr; Lisa Starr with PDB ID: 1BBB; Silva, M. M., Rogers, P. H., Arnone, A.: A third quaternary structure of human hemoglobin A at 1.7-A resolution. J Biol Chem 267 pp. 17248 (1992); (page 185) From left, Art, Precision Graphics; © James King-Holmes/SPL/Photo Researchers, Inc. **Page 185** © PA News Photo Library. **12.2** Raychel Ciemma; **12.3** Art, Lisa Starr; bottom, © Eye of Science/Photo Researchers, Inc. **12.4** Gary Head **12.5** © SPL/Photo Researchers, Inc. **12.6** Lisa Starr with PDB ID: 1BBB; Silva, M. M., Rogers, P. H., Arnone, A.: A third quaternary structure of human hemoglobin A at 1.7-A resolution. J Biol Chem 267 pp. 17248 (1992). **Page 189** Bottom left, Preface Inc. **12.7** © 1956-2004 The Novartis Foundation (www.novartis-found.org.uk), formerly the Ciba Foundation, reproduced with permission. **12.8** Precision Graphics. **12.9** Precision Graphics. **12.10** Top, (1-3), © James King-Holmes/SPL/Photo Researchers, Inc.; (4) © PA News Photo Library; bottom, from left, © Reuters/Landov; © P.A. NEWS/CORBIS KIPA; © Photo courtesy of the College of Veterinary Medicine, Texas A & M University; © Photo courtesy of the College of Veterinary Medicine, Texas A & M University.

CHAPTER 13 **13.1** © Vaughan Fleming/SPL/Photo Researchers, Inc. **the big picture** (page 194), From left (top left) Lisa Starr with PDB ID: 1BBB; Silva, M. M., Rogers, P.H., Arnone, A.: A third quaternary structure of human hemoglobin A at 1.7- Å resolution, J Mol Biol Chem 267 pp. 17248 (1992); Lisa Starr with, Theoretical model; PDB ID: 1K7N; C.Q.LIU, S.X.LIU, SQ.LIU, M.W.JIA, JHE, The Research of MRNA's Conformation and Interaction Between MRNA and TRNA in Translation (To be Published); right/left, © Model by Dr. David B. Goodin, The Scripps Research Institute; right, Model, courtesy of Thomas A. Setitz from Science; (page 195) From left, Lisa Starr; right/left © Nik Kleinberg; right © Steve Terrill/CORBIS. **Page 195** Lisa Starr with PDB ID: 2AAI; Rutenber, E., Katzin, B.J., Ernst, S., Collins, E.J., Mlsna, D., Ready, M.P., Robertus, J.D.: Crystallographic Refinement of ricin to 2.5 A. Proteins 10pp. 240 (1991). **13.2** (a,b) Precison Graphics; (c) Lisa Starr. **13.3** (a-d) Art, Lisa Starr. **13.4** Gary Head. **13.5** Lisa Starr. **13.6** Precison Graphics and Gary Head. **13.7** Top, Model by Dr. David B. Goodin, The Scripps Research Institute; bottom, Lisa Starr. **13.8** (a) Model, courtesy of Thomas A. Steitz from Science; (b) Lisa Starr. **13.9** (a-k) Lisa Starr. **13.10** Lisa Starr. **13.11** background © Steve Terrill/CORBIS; left inset © Nik Kleinberg; middle inset, © Wayne Armstrong. **13.12** © John W. Gofman and Arthur R. Tamplin. From Poisoned Power: The Case Against Nuclear Power Plants Before and After Three Mile Island, Rodale Press, PA, 1979. **13.13** Lisa Starr. **13.14** © Dr. M.A. Ansary/Science Photo Library/Photo Researchers, Inc.

CHAPTER 14 **14.1** (a) From the archives of www.breastpath.com, courtesy of J.B. Askew, Jr., M.D., P.A. Reprinted with permission, © 2004 Breastpath.com; (b) Courtesy of Robin Shoulla and Young Survival Coalition. **the big picture** (page 206) From left, Raychel Ciemma; Lisa Starr; (page 207) From left, From the collection of Jamos Werner and John T. Lis; Courtesy of Edward B. Lewis, California Institute of Technology. **Page 207** Lisa Starr with PDB ID:1N5O; Williams, R. S., Glover, J. N. M.: "Structural Consequences of a Cancer-Causing Brca1-Brct Missense Mutation" J. Biol. Chem. 278 pp. 2630 (2003). **14.2** Raychel Ciemma and Gary Head. **14.3** (left) Lisa Starr with PDB ID: 1CJG; Spronk, C. A. E. M., Bonvin, A. M. J. J., Radha, P. K., Melacini, G., Boelens, R., Kaptein, R.: The Solution Structure of Lac Repressor Headpiece 62 Complexed to a Symmetrical Lac Operator. Structure (London) 7 pp. 1483 (1999). Also PDB ID: 1LBI; Lewis, M., Chang, G., Horton, N. C., Kercher, M. A., Pace, H. C., Schumacher, M. A., Brennan, R. G., Lu, P.: Crystal structure of the lactose operon repressor and its complexes with DNA and inducer. Science 271 pp. 1247 (1996); lactose pdb files from the Hetero-Compound Information Centre - Uppsala (HIC-Up). **Page 209** © Lois Ellen Frank/CORBIS. **14.4** Chris Keeney. **14.5** From the collection of Jamos Werner and John T. Lis. **14.6** (a) © Visuals Unlimited; (b) UCSF Computer Graphics Laboratory, National Institutes, NCRR Grant 01081. **14.7** (a) © Dr. Karen Dyer Montgomery; (b) Raychel Ciemma. **14.8** © Jack Carey. **14.9** Top © Lisa Starr; (a-d) © Carolina Biological/Visuals Unlimited. **14.10** Left, © Walter J. Ghering/University of Basel, Switzerland; right, Courtesy of Edward B. Lewis, California Institute of Technology. **14.11** (a) © Palay/Beaubois after Robert F. Weaver and Philip W. Hedrick, Genetics. © 1989 W.C. Brown Publishers; (b,c) © Jim Langeland, Jim Williams, Julie Gates, Kathy Vorwerk, Steve Paddock and Sean Carroll, HHMI, University of Wisconsin-Madison. **14.12** © Jim Langeland, Jim Williams, Julie Gates, Kathy Vorwerk, Steve Paddock and Sean Carroll, HHMI, University of Wisconsin-Madison. **14.13** © Lawrence Berkeley National Laboratory.

CHAPTER 15 **15.1** Left, © AP/Wide World Photos; center © Charles O'Rear/CORBIS; right © ScienceUV/Visuals Unlimited. **the big picture** (page 218) From left, © Jim Bourg/Reuters/Corbis; right © Professor Stanley Cohen/SPL/Photo Researchers, Inc; (page 219) From left, © Lowell Georgis/CORBIS; right © Jeans for Gene Appeal. **Page 219** © IRRI Photo Bank Institute (IRRI). **15.2** Left, Lisa Starr; right © Volker Steger/SPL/Photo Researchers, Inc. **15.3** © Jim Bourg/Reuters/Corbis. **Page 222** © Professor Stanley Cohen/SPL/Photo Researchers, Inc. **15.4** (a) Art, Lisa Starr; (b) Lisa Starr. **15.5** Chris Keeney with permission of © QIAGEN, Inc. **15.6** Lisa Starr. **15.7** Lisa Starr. **15.8** Lisa Starr. **15.9** Lisa Starr. **15.10** Left © David Parker/SPL/Photo Researchers, Inc.; right © Cellmark Diagnostics, Abingdon, UK. **15.11** Top left, © TEK IMAGE/Photo Researchers, Inc.; art, Lisa Starr. **15.12** (a) Courtesy Calgene LLC; (b) © Dr. Vincent Chaing, School of Forestry and Wood Projects, Michigan Technology University. **15.13** (a–c) Lisa Starr; (e) © Keith V. Wood; (d) © Lowell Georgis/CORBIS. **15.14** (a) Transgenic goat produced using nuclear transfer at GTC Biotherapeutics. Photo used with permission; (b) © Work of Atsushi Miyawaki, Qing Xiong, Varda Lev-Ram, Paul Steinbach, and Roger Y. Tsien at the University of California, San Diego; (c) © Adi Nes, Dvir Gallery Ltd. **15.15** (a) © Jeans for Gene Appeal; (b) Courtesy Dr. Paola Leone, Cell & Gene Therapy Center/University of Medicine 7 Dentistry of New Jersey. **15.16** © Matt Gentry/Roanoke Times. **15.17** Courtesy of Joseph DeRisa. From Science, 1997 Oct. 24; 278 (5338) 680–686. **15.18** (a) © Mike Stewart/Corbis Sygma; (b) © Simon Kwong/REUTERS/Landov.

Page 235 Unit III © Wolfgang Kaehler/CORBIS.

CHAPTER 16 **16.1** Left, © Bettmann/CORBIS; right, © St Bartholomew's Hospital/Science Photo Library/Photo Researchers, Inc. **the big picture** (page 236) From left, © Christopher Ralling; right, © David Parker/SPL/Photo Researchers, Inc.; (page 237) Left/left, © Peter Bowater/Photo Researchers, Inc.; left/right, © Owen Franken/CORBIS; right, Gary Head. **Page 237** Top, © Bettmann/CORBIS. **16.2** (a) © Wolfgang Kaehler/CORBIS; (b) © Earl & Nazima Kowall/CORBIS; (c) © Wolfgang Kaehler/CORBIS; (d) © Edward S. Ross; (e) © Edward S. Ross. **16.3** (left) Art, Gary Head; (right) © Bruce J. Mohn; (inset) © Phillip Gingerich, Director, University of Michigan. Museum of Paleontology. **16.4** (a) © Jonathan Blair/CORBIS; (b) © Biophoto Associates/Photo Researchers, Inc.; (c) © John Shaw/Photo Researchers, Inc. **Page 16.5** (a) Courtesy George P. Darwin, Darwin Museum, Down House; (b) © Christopher Ralling; (c) © Heather Angel; (c,d) Art, Precision Graphics (e) © Dieter & Mary Plage/Survival Anglia. **16.6** (a) © Joe McDonald/CORBIS; (b) © Karen Carr Studio/www.karencarr.com. **16.7** (a) Heather Angel; (b) © Kevin Schafer/CORBIS; (c) © Dr. P. Evans/Bruce Coleman, Ltd.; (d) © Alan Root/Bruce Coleman Ltd.; **16.8** © Down House and The Royal College of Surgeons of England; **16.9** (a) © Gary Head; (b) © John W. Merck, Jr., University of Maryland. **16.10** Left, © Thomas Mangelsen; right, © Theo Allofs/CORBIS. **16.11** Left, © Francois Photo Researchers, Inc. **16.12** Left, © Peter Bowater/Photo Researchers, Inc.; top center, © Owen Franken/CORBIS; top right © Sam Kleinman/CORBIS; center, © Jim Cornfield/CORBIS; center right, © Christopher Briscoe/Photo Researchers, Inc.; bottom, © Alan Solem. **16.13** Gary Head. **Page 248** © Terry Whittaker, Frank Lane Picture Agency/CORBIS. **16.14** Gary Head. **16.15** all, Courtesy of Hopi Hoekstra, University of California, San Diego. **16.16** Gary Head. **16.17** Precision Graphics, using NIH data. **16.18** © Peter Chadwick/Science Photo Library/Photo Researchers. **16.19** Left, © Thomas Bates Smith; right, © Thomas Bates Smith. **16.20** © Bruce Beehler, enhanced by Chris Keeney. **16.21** (a, b) Precision Graphics after Ayala and others; bottom, © Michael Freeman/CORBIS. **Page 254** © Steve Bronstein/The Image Bank/Getty Images. **16.22** Precision Graphics, after computer models developed by Jerry Coyne. **16.23** © Frans Lanting/Minden Pictures (computer-modified by Lisa Starr); Art, Raychel Ciemma. **16.24** Left, © David Neal Parks; right, © W. Carter Johnson. **16.25** John Kalusmeyer, University of Michigan Exhibit of Natural History.

CHAPTER 17 **17.1** (a) NASA Galileo Imaging Team; (b) top, Art by Don Davis; (b) bottom NASA Galileo Imaging Team. **the big picture** (page 258) from left, Raychel Ciemma; right (both) © Jack Jeffrey Photography; (page 259), from left © Carnegie Museum of Natural History; right, Gary Head. **Page 259,** Top, © David A. Kring, NASA/Univ. Arizona Space Imagery Center. **17.2** left © H. P. Banks; right, © Jonathan Blair. **17.3** © Jonathan Blair/CORBIS. **17.4** (a) Gary Head; (b) © 2001 PhotoDisc, Inc; (c,d) Lisa Starr. **Page 263, 17.6** © CORBIS. **17.7** (a) Leif Buckley; (b) Leif Buckley and Lisa Starr. **17.8** (a-d) Lisa Starr, after A. M. Ziegler, C. R. Scotese, and S. F. Barrett, "Mesozoic and Cenozoic Paleogeographic Maps," and J. Krohn and J. Sundermann (Eds.), Tidal Frictions and the Earth's Rotation II, Springer-Verlag, 1983; (e) © Martin Land/Photo Researchers, Inc.; (f) © John Sibbick. **17.9** Raychel Ciemma. **17.10** (a) J. Scott Altenbach, University of New Mexico, computer enhanced by Lisa Starr; (b) © Frans Lanting/Minden Pictures; computer enhanced by Lisa Starr; (c) © Stephen Dalton/Photo Researchers, Inc.; art, Lisa Starr and Raychel Ciemma, art reference, Natural History Collection, Royal BC Museum; **17.11** (a) Courtesy of Professor Richard Amasino, University of Wisconsin-Madison; (b) Courtesy of Professor Richard Amasino, University of Wisconsin-Madison; (c) Courtesy of Professor Martin F. Yanofsky; (d) © Jose Luis Riechmann; **17.12** Raychel Ciemma; **17.13** (a) top, © Courtesy of Prof. Richard Amasino, University of Wisconsin-Madison; (a) bottom, © Jennifer Grenier, Grace Boekhoff-Falk and Sean Carroll, HMI, University of Wisconsin-Madison; (b) top, © Herve Chaumeton/Agence Nature; (b) bottom, © Jennifer Grenier, Grace Boekhoff-Falk and Sean Carroll, HMI, University of Wisconsin-Madison; (c) top, © Peter Skinner/Photo Researchers, Inc.; (c) bottom, Courtesy of Dr. Giovanni Levi; (d) © Dr. Chip Clark. **Page 270** © TEK IMAGE/Photo Researchers, Inc.; **17.14** Precision Graphics. **17.15** left © Kjell B. Sandved/Visuals Unlimited; center, © Jeffrey Sylvester/FPG/Getty Images; right, © Thomas D. Mangelsen/Images of Nature. **17.16** (a, b) Art, Jennifer Wardrip. **17.17** (a) © John Alcock, Arizona State University; (b) © Tui Roy/Minden Pictures; **17.17** (c) © Alvin E. Staffan/Photo Researchers, Inc. **17.18** Top left, © Digital Vision/PictureQuest; top, © Joe McDonald/CORBIS. **17.19** (a) © Graham Neden/CORBIS; (b) © Kevin Schafer/CORBIS; center, © Ron Blakey, Northern Arizona University (c) © Rick Rosen/Corbis SABA. **17.20** (a-c) Preface, Inc. (d) all, © Jack Jeffrey Photography. **17.21** Top, © Steve Gartlan; bottom left and right © Below Water Photography/www.belowwater.com. **17.22** left © Lance Nelson/CORBIS; center, © Eric Crichton/CORBIS; right, © Maximilian Stock Ltd./Foodpix. **17.23** Lisa Starr after W. Jensen and F. B. Salisbury, Botany: An Ecological Approach, Wadsworth, 1972. **17.24** (a) Courtesy of Dr. Robert Mesibov; (b) Courtesy of Dr. Robert Mesibov; **17.24** (c) Lisa Starr. **17.25** Courtesy of Daniel C. Kelley, Anthony J. Arnold, and William C. Parker, Florida State University Department of Geological Science. **Page 278** (bottom left) Gary Head. **17.26** Left, Lisa Starr; right, © Carnegie Museum of Natural History. **17.27** from left © Science Photo Library/Photo Researchers, Inc.; © Galen Rowell/CORBIS; © Kevin Schafer/CORBIS; Courtesy of Department of Entomology, University of Nebraska-Lincoln; Bruce Coleman, Ltd. **17.28** Gary Head. **17.29** Gary Head. **17.30** from left, © Phillip Colla Photography; © Randy Wells/CORBIS © Cousteau Society/Getty Images; © Robert Dowling/CORBIS; Art, Gary Head. **17.31** Lisa Starr. **17.32** Lisa Starr. **17.33** © Gulf News, Dubai, UAE

CHAPTER 18 **18.1** Inset, Courtesy of Agriculture Canada; © Raymond Gehman/CORBIS. **the big picture** (page 286) From left, © Jeff Hester and Paul Scowen, Arizona State University, and NASA; ©Sidney W. Fox; (page 287) From left, © Chase Studios/Photo Researchers, Inc.; Raychel Ciemma. **Page 287** © Philippa Uwins/The University of Queensland. **18.2** © Jeff Hester and Paul Scowen, Arizona State University, and NASA. **18.3** © Chesley Bonestell; inset art, Raychel Ciemma. **18.4** (a) © Tim Thompson/CORBIS; (b) © Dr. Ken MacDonald/SPL/Photo Researchers, Inc.; (c) © Micheal J. Russell, Scottish Universities Environmental Research Centre. **18.5** (a) © Sidney W. Fox; (b) From Hanczyc, Fujikawa, and Szostak, Experimental Models of Primitive Cellular Compartments: Encapsulation, Growth, and Division;www.sciencemag.org Science 24 October 2003; 302;529, Figure 2, page 619. Reprinted with permission of the authors and AAAS; (c) Preface, Inc. **18.6** (a) © Stanley M. Awramik; (b,c) Bruce Runnegar, NASA Astrobiology Institute; (d) © N.J. Butterfield, University of Cambridge. **18.7** (a) © Chase Studios/Photo Researchers, Inc.; (b) © John Reader/SPL/Photo Researchers, Inc.; (c) © Sinclair Stammers/SPL/Photo Researchers, Inc. **18.8** Raychel Ciemma. **18.9** Left, © Robert Trench, Professor Emeritus, University of British Columbia; (b) right, Courtesy of Isao Inouye, Institute of Biological Sciences, University of Tsukuba. **18.10** Raychel Ciemma and Precision Graphics.

Page 299 Unit IV © Layne Kennedy/CORBIS.

CHAPTER 19 **19.1** © The Bridgeman Art Library/Getty Images. **the big picture** (page 300) From left, Lisa Starr; (page 301) From left, © NIBSC/SPL/Photo Researchers, Inc.; © Camr, Barry Dowsett/Science Photo Library/Photo Researchers, Inc. **Page 301** © Carl Cook. **19.2** (a,b) Lisa Starr. **19.3** (a) © P. Hawtin, University of Southampton/SPL/Photo Researchers, Inc.; (b) © Dr. Dennis Kunkel/Visuals Unlimited. **19.4** Raychel Ciemma. **19.5** Lisa Starr. **19.6** (a) © Dr. Jeremy Burgess/SPL/Photo Researchers, Inc.; (b) © P. W. Johnson and J. MeN. Sieburth, Univ. Rhode Island/BPS. **19.7** © Dr. Terry J. Beveridge, Department of Microbiology, University of Guelph, Ontario, Canada. **19.8** © Dr. Manfred Schloesser, Max Planck Institute for Marine Microbiology. **19.9** (a) © Stem Jems/Photo Researchers, Inc.; (b) © California Department of Health Services; (c) © Bernard Cohen, M.D., Dermatlas; http://www.darmatalas.org. **19.10** Lisa Starr. **19.11** (a) © Courtesy Jack Jones, Archives of Microbiology, Vol. 136, 1983, pp. 254-261. Reprinted by permission of Springer-Verlag. (b) © Dr. John Brackenbury/Science Photo Library/Photo Researchers, Inc. 19.12 (a) © Martin Miller/Visuals Unlimited; (b) © Alan L. Detrick, Science Source/Photo Researchers, Inc.; (c) © Dr. Harald Huber, Dr. Michael Hohn, Prof. Dr. K.O. Stetter, University of Regensburg, Germany. **19.13** (a-d)

Art, Leif Buckley and Lisa Starr; (e) © CAMR/A. B. Dowsett/SPL/Photo Researchers, Inc.; (f) © Dr. Linda Stannard, Uct/Spl/Photo Researchers, Inc. **19.14** Art, Palay/Beaubois and Precision Graphics; top left, © Science Photo Library/Photo Researchers, Inc. **Page 310** Top, © Sercomi/Photo Researchers, Inc.; bottom, © Camr, Barry Dowsett/Science Photo Library/Photo Researchers, Inc. **19.15** (a) © Lily Echeverria/Miami Herald; (b) © APHIS photo by Dr. Al Jenny; (c) Art, Lisa Starr with PDB ID: 1QLX; Zahn, R., Liu, A., Luhrs, T., Riek, R., Von Schroetter, C., Garcia, F. L., Billeter, M., Calzolai, L., Wider, G., Wuthrich, K.: NMR Solution Structure of the Human Prion Protein Proc. Nat. Acad. Sci. USA 97 pp. 145 (2000). **Page 312** Leif Buckley and Lisa Starr. **19.16** Chris Keeney with permission of © FSIS/USDA/FDA. **19.17** © AP/Wide World Photos

CHAPTER 20 **20.1** Left, © Ric Ergenbright/CORBIS; right © Adam Woolfitt/CORBIS. **the big picture** (page 314) From left, Lisa Starr with Gary Head; © Astrid Hanns-Frieder michler/SPL/Photo Researchers, Inc; (page 315) From left, © Lewis Trusty/Animals Animals; right, © Robert C. Simpson/Nature Stock. **Page 315** © Wim Van Egmond. **20.2** Lisa Starr with Gary Head. **20.3** (a) © Dr. Stan Erlandsen, University of Minnesota; (b) © Oliver Meckes/Photo Researchers, Inc.; **20.4** Top, © Dr. David Phillips/Visuals Unlimited. Art, Raychel Ciemma. **20.5** © Astrid Hanns-Friedermichler/SPL/Photo Researchers, Inc.; **20.6** (a) Courtesy of Allen W. H. Bé and David A. Caron; (b) © John Clegg/Ardea, London. **20.7** (a) © Andrew Syred/SPL/Photo Researchers, Inc.; (b) Courtesy James Evarts. **20.8** Left, (mosquito) © Sinclair Stammers/Photo Researchers, Inc.; top right, © London School of Hygiene & Tropical Medicine/Photo Researchers, Inc.; bottom right, © Moredum Animal Health, Ltd./Photo Researchers, Inc. Art, Leonard Morgan. **20.9** (a) © Wim van Egmond/Micropolitan Museum; (b) © Frank Borges Llosa/www.frankley.com. **20.10** (a) © Dr. David Phillips/Visuals Unlimited; (b) © Lexey Swall/Staff from article, "Deep Trouble: Bad Blooms" October 3, 2003 by Eric Staats. **20.11** © Susan Frankel, USDA-FS; inset © Dr. Pavel Svihra. **20.12** (a) © Dee Breger, Drexel University; (b) © Emiliania huxleyi. Photograph by Vita Pariente. Scanning electron micrograph taken on a Jeol T330A instrument at the Texas A & M University Electron Microscopy Center. **20.13** (a) © Jeffrey Levinton, State University of New York, Stony Brook; (b) © Lewis Trusty/Animals Animals; (c) T. Garrison, Oceanography: An Invitation to Marine Science, Brooks/Cole, 1993. **20.14** Art, Raychel Ciemma; bottom, © PhotoDisc/Getty Images. **20.15** © Wim van Egmond. **20.16** (a) © Lawson Wood/CORBIS; (a) art, Art, Raychel Ciemma; (b) © D. S. Littler; (c) Courtesy of Professor Astrid Saugestad; (d) Courtesy Microbial Culture Collection, National Institute for Environmental Studies, Japan; (e) © Wim van Egmond. **20.17** Raychel Ciemma. **20.18** (a) © Edwards S. Ross; (b) © Courtesy of www.hiddenforest.co.nz. **20.19** (a) Leonard Morgan; (b) © M. Claviez, G. Gerish, and R. Guggenheim; (c-e) © Carolina Biological Supply Company; (f) Courtesy Robert R. Kay from R. R. Kay, et al., Development, 1989 Supplement, pp. 81-90, (c) The Company of Biologists Ltd., 1989. **20.20** (a-e) © Robert C. Simpson/Nature Stock. **20.21** Left, Micrograph Garry T. Cole, University of Texas, Austin/BPS; Art, Raychel Ciemma after T. Rost, et al., Botany, Wiley, 1979. **20.22** © Jane Burton/Bruce Coleman, Ltd. **20.23** Art, Raychel Ciemma; (a,b) Micrograph Ed Reschke; top, Micrograph J. D. Cunningham/Visuals Unlimited. **20.24** (a) © Michael W. Clayton/University of Wisconsin-Madison, Department of Biology; (b) © North Carolina State University, Department of Plant Pathology; (c) © Michael Wood/mykob.com. **20.25** (a) © Dr. P. Marazzi/SPL/Photo Researchers, Inc.; (b) © Harry Regin. **20.26** (a) © Mark E. Gibson/Visuals Unlimited; (b) © Edward S. Ross; (c) © 1977 Sherry K. Pittam; (d) © Mark Mattock/Planet Earth Pictures; (e) After Raven, Evert, and Eichhorn, Biology of Plants, 4th Ed., Worth Publishers, Nwe York, 1986. **20.27** (a) © 1990 Gary Braasch; (b) © F. B. Reeves. **20.28** Left © W. P. Armstrong; right, Courtesy Brian Duval.

CHAPTER 21 **21.1** © T. Kerasote/Photo Researchers, Inc. **the big picture** (page 334) From left, Lisa Starr; Raychel Ciemma; (page 335) From Left, Raychel Ciemma; © Sanford/Agliolo/CORBIS. **Page 335** © Jean Miele/CORBIS. **Page 336** Top, © Reprinted with permission from Elsevier; bottom © Patricia G. Gensel. **21.2** Raychel Ciemma after E. O. Dodson and P. Dodson, Evolution: Process and Product, Third Ed., p. 401, PWS. **21.3** Gary Head. **21.4** Top center, © Jane Burton/Bruce Coleman Ltd.; Art, Raychel Ciemma. **21.5** (a) © Craig Wood/Visuals Unlimited; (b) © Fred Bavendam/Peter Arnold, Inc.; (c) © John D. Cunningham/Visuals Unlimited. **21.6** (a) © University of Wisconsin-Madison, Department of Biology, Anthoceros CD; (b) © National Park Services, Paul Stehr-Green; (c) © National Park Services, Martin Hutten. **21.7** © Jeri Hochman and Martin Hochman, Illustration by Zdenek Burian. **21.8** (a) © Winfried Wisniewski, Frank Lane Picture Agency/CORBIS; (b) © Colin Bates; (c) © W. H. Hodge; (d) © Craig Lovell/CORBIS. **21.9** © A. & E. Bomford/Ardea, London; art, Raychel Ciemma. **21.10** Top inset, © Brian Parker/Tom Stack & Associates; bottom, © Field Museum of Natural History, Chicago (Neg. #7500C); top left, art, Raychel Ciemma. **Page 343** Top right, George J. Wilder/Visuals Unlimited, computer enhanced by Lachina Publishing Services, Inc. **21.11** (a) © Ralph Pleasant/FPG/Getty Images; (b) © Earl Roberge/Photo Researchers, Inc.; (c) © George Loun/Visuals Unlimited; (d) Courtesy of Water Research Commission, South Africa. **21.12** (a) © Jeff Gnass Photography; (b) © Robert & Linda Mitchell Photography; (c) © Kingsley R. Stern; (d) © E. Webber/Visuals Unlimited; (e) © Michael P. Gadomski/Photo Researchers, Inc.; (f) © Sinclair Stammers/Photo Researchers, Inc.; (g) © Dr. Daniel L. Nickrent; (h) © William Ferguson. **21.13** Left, © Robert Potts, California Academy of Sciences; (a) © Robert & Linda Mitchell Photography; (b) © R. J. Erwin/Photo Researchers, Inc.; art, Raychel Ciemma. **21.14** (a) Raychel Ciemma; (b) © K. Simons and David Dilcher for color reconstruction image. **21.15** Top left (inset), © Ed Reschke; top right (inset), © Lee Casebere; bottom left (inset), © Robert & Linda Mitchell Photography; bottom right (inset), © Runk & Schoenberger/Grant Heilman, Inc.; right © Karen Carr Studio/www.karencarr.com; left art, Gary Head. **21.16** Raychel Ciemma. **21.17** Preface, Inc. **21.18** (a) © Michelle Garrett/CORBIS; (b) © Sanford/Agliolo/CORBIS; (c) © Gregory G. Dimijian/Photo Researchers, Inc.; (d) © Darrell Gulin/CORBIS; (e) © Peter F. Zika/Visuals Unlimited; (f) © DLN/Permission by Dr. Daniel L. Nickrent. **21.19** Gerry Ellis/The Wildlife Collection. **21.20** Left, © 1989 Clinton Webb; center, © 1991 Clinton Webb; right © Gary Head.

CHAPTER 22 **22.1** © K.S. Matz. **the big picture** (page 352) From left, Leonard Morgan; right/left © David Sailors/CORBIS; right/right © Brandon D. Cole/CORBIS; (page 353) From Left, left/left © Science Photo Library/Photo Researchers, Inc.; left/right © Alex Kirstitch; right © Herve Chaumeton/Agence Nature. **Page 353** © Callum Roberts, University of York. **22.2** Leonard Morgan. **22.3** Raychel Ciemma. **22.4** (a) © Robert Brons/livingreefimages.com; (b) © Neville Pledge/South Australian Museum; (c) © Neville Pledge/South Australian Museum; (d) © Dr. Chip Clark. **22.5** Gary Head. **22.6** (a) © Bruce Hall; (b) © David Sailors/CORBIS; (b) art, Raychel Ciemma. **Page 358**, Top left, Gary Head. **22.7** Raychel Ciemma after Euguen Kozloff. **22.8** (a, b) Raychel Ciemma; (c) Courtesy of Dr. William H. Hamner; (d) © Brandon D. Cole/CORBIS; (e) © Jeffrey L. Rotman/CORBIS; (f) © A.N.T./Photo Researchers, Inc. **22.9** Top & bottom left, © Wim van Egmond/Micropolitan Museum; art, Precision Graphics after T. Storer, et al., General Zoology, Sixth Edition. **22.10** All art, Raychel Ciemma. **22.11** Top right, © Andrew Syred/SPL/Photo Researchers, Inc.; art, Raychel Ciemma and Lisa Starr. **22.12** © James Marshall/CORBIS; art, Raychel Ciemma and Lisa Starr. **22.13** (a) © Cabisco/Visuals Unlimited. (b) © Science Photo Library/Photo Researchers, Inc.; (c) © Jon Kenfield/Bruce Coleman Ltd.; (d) Precision Graphics, adapted from Rasmussen, "Ophelia," Vol. 11, in Eugene Kozloff, Invertebrates, 1990. **22.14** Raychel Ciemma. **22.15** Both, © J. A. L. Cooke/Oxford Scientific Films. **22.16** (a) Palay/Beaubois; (b) © B. Borrell Casals/Frank Lane Picture Agency/CORBIS; (c) © Joe McDonald/CORBIS; (d) © Jeff Foott/Tom Stack & Associates; (e) © Frank Park/ANT Photo Library; (f) © Alex Kirstitch. **22.17** (a) Illustrations by Zdenek Burian, © Jeri Hochman and Martin Hochman; (b) Raychel Ciemma; (c) © Alex Kirstitch; (d) © Bob Cranston. **22.18** Lisa Starr. **22.19** (a) © Sinclair Stammers/SPL/Photo Researchers, Inc.; (b) © L. Jensen/Visuals Unlimited; (c) © Dianora Niccolini. **22.20** © Jane Burton/Bruce Coleman, Ltd. **22.21** Precision Graphics. **22.22** (a) © Jeff Hunter/The Image Bank/Getty Images; (b) © Peter Parks/Imagequest-marine.com; (c) © Science Photo Library/Photo Researchers, Inc. **22.23** (a) © Angelo Giampiccolo/FPG/Getty Images; (b) © Frans Lemmens/The Image bank/Getty Images. **22.24** (a) © CORBIS; (b) ©John H. Gerard; (c) © D. Suzio/Photo Researchers, Inc.; (d) © Andrew Syred/Photo Researchers, Inc. **22.25** Precision Graphics. **22.26** Raychel Ciemma. **22.27** (a) © David Maitland/Seaphot Limited/Planet Earth Pictures; (b-g) Edward S. Ross; (h) © Mark Moffett/Minden Pictures; (i) Courtesy of Karen Swain, North Carolina Museum of Natural Sciences; (j) © Chris Anderson/Darklight Imagery; (k) © Joseph L. Spencer. **22.28** Top left © Herve Chaumeton/Agence Nature; (a) © Herve Chaumeton/Agence Nature; (b) © Fred Bavendam/Minden Pictures; (c) © George Perina, www.seapix.com; (d) © Jan Haaga, Kodiak Lab, AFSC/NMFS. **22.29** L. Calver. **22.30** © Walter Deas/Seaphot Limited/Planet Earth Pictures. **22.31** © J. Solliday/BPS. **22.32** © Wim van Egmond/Micropolitan Museum.

CHAPTER 23 **23.1** Art, Raychel Ciemma; right © James Reece, Nature Focus, Australian Museum. **the big picture** (page 376) From left, © John and Bridgette Sibbick; Photo by Lisa Starr; courtesy of John McNamara, www.paleo-direct.com. (page 377) From left © Bill M. Campbell, MD; © Illustration by Karen Carr; © Douglas Mazonowicz/Gallery of Prehistoric Art. **Page 377** © P. Morris/Ardea London. **23.2** Art, Raychel Ciemma. **23.3** (a,b) *Redrawn from Living Invertebrates*, V. & J. Pearse and M. & R. Buchsbaum, The Boxwood Press, 1987. Used by permission; (c) © 2002 Gary Bell/Taxi/Getty Images. **23.4** Left, Seth Gold and Lisa Starr; center, © Brandon D. Cole/CORBIS; right, © Brandon D. Cole/CORBIS. **23.5** (a) © John and Bridgette Sibbick; (b, c) © Jenna Hellack, Department of Biology, Univerisy of Central Oklahoma. **23.6** (a-c) Raychel Ciemma, adapted from A. S. Romer and T. S. Parsons, *The Vertebrate Body, Sixth Edition*, Saunders, 1986; right, Photo by Lisa Starr; courtesy of John McNamara, www.paleodirect.com. **23.7** Gary Head. **23.8** (a) © Jonathan Bird/Oceanic Research Group, Inc.; (b) © Gido Braase/Deep Blue Productions; (c) © Ivor Fulcher/CORBIS; (d) © Roger Archibald; (e) Lisa Starr and Raychel Ciemma. **23.9** (a) © Norbert Wu/Peter Arnold, Inc.; (b) © Wernher Krutein/photovault.com; (c) © Alfred Kamajian; (d, e) Art, Laszlo Meszoly and D. & V. Hennings. **23.10** Left art, Leonard Morgan, adapted from A. S. Romer and T. S. Parsons, *The Vertebrate Body, Sixth Edition*, Saunders College Publishing, 1986; (a) © Bill M. Campbell, MD; (b) © Stephen Dalton/Photo Researchers, Inc.; (c) © John Serraro/Visuals Unlimited. **23.11** © Juan M. Renjifo/Animals Animals. **23.12** (a) © Pieter Johnson; (b) © Stanley Sessions/Hartwick College. **23.13** (a) © 1989 D. Braginetz; (b) © Z. Leszczynski/Animals Animals. **23.14** (a) © Illustration by Karen Carr; (b) © Karen Carr Studio/www.karencarr.com; bottom intext, © Julian Baum/SPL/Photo Researchers, Inc. **Page 388** © S. Blair Hedges, Pennsylvania State University. **23.15** Raychel Ciemma. **23.16** (a) © Kevin Schafer/CORBIS; (b) Raychel Ciemma; (c) © Joe McDonald/CORBIS; (d) © David A. Northcott/CORBIS; (e) © Pete & Judy Morrin/ARDEA LONDON; (f) © Stephen Dalton/Photo Researchers, Inc.; (f) art, Raychel Ciemma; (g) © Kevin Schafer/Tom Stack & Associates. **23.17** (a) Lisa Starr; (b) Raychel Ciemma. **23.18** (a) © Gerard Lacz/ANT Photolibrary; (b,c) Courtesy of Dr. M. Guinan, University of California-Davis, Anatomy, Physiology and Cell Biology, School of Veterinariy Medicine; (d) © Kevin Schafer/CORBIS; **23.19** (a) © Sandy Roessler/FPG/Getty Images; (b) Art, Raychel Ciemma after M. Weiss and A. Mann, Human Biology and Behavior, 5th Edition, HarperCollins, 1990; (c) © Jean Phillipe Varin/Jacana/Photo Researchers, Inc. (d) © Corbis Images/PictureQuest; (e) © Merlin D. Tuttle/Bat Conservation International; (f) © Marine Themes Stock Photo Library; (g) © Mike Johnson. All rights reserved, www.earthwindow.com. **23.20** (a–d) Lisa Starr; (e) © D. & V. Blagden/ANT Photo Library; (f) © Nigel J. Dennis; Gallo Images/CORBIS; (g) © Tom Ulrich/Visuals Unlimited. **23.21** (a) © Larry Burrows/Aspect Photolibrary; (c) © Dallas Zoo, Robert Cabello; (d) bottom left, © Bone Clones®, www.boneclones.com; (d) bottom right, © Gary Head; top right, © Allen Gathman, Biology Department, Southeast Missouri State University. **Page 395** Top left, D. & V. Hennings. **23.22** © Gerry Ellis/The Wildlife Collection; inset © Utah's Hogle Zoo. **23.23** (a) From left, © MPFT/Corbis Sygma; (a) National Museum of Ethiopia, Addis Ababa. © 1985 David L. Brill; (a) Original housed in National Museum of Ethiopia, Addis Ababa. © 1999 David L. Brill; (a) National Museum of Tansania, Dar es Salaam, © 1985 David L. Brill; (a) Transvaal Museum, Pretoria. © 1985 David L. Brill; (a) National Museum of Kenya, Nairobi. © 1985 David L. Brill; (b) © Dr. Donald Johanson, Institute of Human Origins; (c) © Louise M. Robbins; (d) © Kenneth Garrett/National Geographic Image Collection. **23.24** © Jean Paul Tibbles. **23.25** Top, © Elizabeth Delaney/Visuals Unlimited; bottom (all), © John Reader. **23.26** Left, American Museum of Natural History. © 1996 David L. Brill; right, MUSEE DE L'HOMME, Paris. © 1985 David L. Brill. **23.27** Left, Housed in National Museum of Ethiopia, Addis Ababa. © 2001 David L. Brill; right art, Lisa Starr. **23.28** Left, © Douglas Mazonowicz/Gallery of Prehistoric; right, Lisa Starr. **23.29** © California Academy of Sciences. **23.30** © Tom McHugh/Photo Researchers, Inc.

CHAPTER 24 **24.1** Left, © Vvg/Science Photo Library/Photo Researchers, Inc.; right © Michael Davidson/Mortimer Abramowitz Gallery of Photomicrography/www.olympusmicro.com. **the big picture** (page 402) From left, left/left, © Bruce Iverson; left/right © Dr. Robert

Wagner/University of Delaware, www.udel.edu/Biology/Wags; right/left © Pat Johnson Studios Photography; right/right © Darrell Gulin/Getty Images; (page 403) From left, Gary Head; Slim Films. **Page 403** © Star Tribune/Minneapolis-St. Paul. **24.2** Left, Raychel Ciemma; top, Courtesy of Charles Lewallen; center & bottom, © Bruce Iverson. **24.3** left © 2000 PhotoDisc, Inc, with art by Lisa Starr; top right © Cnri/Spl/Photo Researchers, Inc.; bottom right © Dr. Robert Wagner/University of Delaware, www.udel.edu/Biology/Wags. **24.4** Left © Pat Johnson Studios Photography; right, © Darrell Gulin/The Image Bank/Getty Images. **24.5** (a) © Cory Gray; (b) © PhotoDisc/Getty Images; (c) © Heather Angel; (d) © Biophoto Associates/Photo Researchers, Inc. **24.6** Gary Head. **24.7** © Galen Rowell/Peter Arnold, Inc. **24.8** Gary Head. **24.9** Left art, Gary Head; right, © Niall Benvie/CORBIS. **24.10** Left © Kennan Ward/CORBIS; right © G. J. McKenzie (MGS). **24.11** © Frank B. Salisbury. **24.12** Slim Films. **24.13** (a,b) Courtesy of Dr. Kathleen K. Sulik, Bowles Center for Alcohol Studies, the University of North Carolina at Chapel Hill; (c) © John DaSiai, MD/Custom Medical Stock. **24.14** (a) Courtesy of Dr. Consuelo M. De Moraes; (b-d) © Andrei Sourakov and Consuelo M. De Moraes.

Page 415 Unit V © Jim Christensen, Fine Art Digital Photographic Images.

CHAPTER 25 **25.1** Left, © Michael Westmoreland/CORBIS; right, © Reuters/CORBIS. **the big picture** (page 416) From left, left/left, © Ernest Manewal/Index Stock Imagery. left/right © Darrell Gulin/CORBIS; right, © Andrew Syred/Photo Researchers, Inc.; (page 417) From left, © Mike Clayton/University of Wisconsin Botany Department, Lisa Starr. **Page 417** © Allstock/Stone/Getty Images. **25.2** Raychel Ciemma. **25.3** Raychel Ciemma. **25.4** (a) From top, © Bruce Iverson; (a) © Ernest Manewal/Index Stock Imagery; (a) © Simon Fraser/Photo Researchers, Inc.; (a) © Andrew Syred/Photo Researchers, Inc.; Art, Gary Head; (b) from top, © Mike Clayton/University of Wisconsin Department of Botany; (b) © Darrell Gulin/CORBIS; (b) © Gary Head; (b) © Andrew Syred/Photo Researchers, Inc.; (b) art, Gary Head. **25.5** Art, Precision Graphics. **25.6** Left, © Donald L. Rubbelke/Lakeland Community College; right © Andrew Syred/Photo Researchers, Inc. **25.7** (a) © Dr. Dale M. Benham, Nebraska Wesleyan University; (b) © D. E. Akin and I. L. Risgby, Richard B. Russel Agricultural Research Center, Agricultural Research Service, U.S. Dept. Agriculture, Athens, GA; (c) © Kingsley R. Stern. **25.8** (a-c) Lisa Starr; bottom © Andrew Syred/Photo Researchers, Inc. **25.9** © George S. Ellmore. **25.10** (a) top © Gary Head; (a) bottom, © Dale M. Benham, Ph.D., Nebraska Wesleyan University; (b–d) Raychel Ciemma. **25.11** All art, D. & V. Hennings; (a) center, © Mike Clayton/University of Wisconsin Botany Department; right, © James W. Perry; (b) center, © Carolina Biological Supply Company; right © James W. Perry. **25.12** All art, D. & V. Hennings. **Page 424** © 2001 PhotoDisc, Inc./Getty. **25.13** © David Cavagnaro/Peter Arnold, Inc. **25.14** (a) © N. Cattlin/Photo Researchers, Inc.; (b) Raychel Ciemma; (c) © C. E. Jeffree, et al., Planta, 172(1): 20-37, 1987. Reprinted by permission of C. E. Jeffree and Springer-Verlag; (d) © Jeremy Burgess/SPL/Photo Researchers, Inc. **25.15** (a) © Simon Fraser/Photo Researchers, Inc.; (b) © Gary Head. **25.16** (a) Left, © John Limbaugh/Ripon Microslides, Inc.; (a) art, After Salisbury and Ross, Plant Physiology, Fourth Edition, Wadsworth; (b) top, © Mike Clayton/University of Wisconsin Department of Botany; (b) bottom, © Mike Clayton/University of Wisconsin Department of Botany. **25.17** © Carolina Biological Supply Company; **25.18** Left, © Omikron/Photo Researchers, Inc.; center, © Omikron/Photo Researchers, Inc.; right, © Omikron/Photo Researchers, Inc. **25.19** (a,b) Raychel Ciemma; **25.20** Raychel Ciemma **25.21** (a,c) Lisa Starr; (b) © H. A. Core, W. A. Cote, and A. C. Day, Wood Structure and Identification, 2nd Ed., Syracuse University Press, 1979. **Page 430** Bottom right, D. & V. Hennings. **25.22** (a,b) © Edward S. Ross. **Page 431** Top left, Lisa Starr. **25.23** (a) © Jon Pilcher; (b) © George Bernard/SPL/Photo Researchers, Inc.; (c) © Peter Ryan SPL/Photo Researchers, Inc.

CHAPTER 26 **26.1** Left, © OPSEC Control Number #4 077-A-4; right, © Billy Wrobel, 2004. **the big picture** (page 432) From left, © William Ferguson; © Andrew Syred/Photo Researchers, Inc.; (page 433) From left, left/left, © Jeremy Burgess/SPL/Photo Researchers, Inc.; left/right © Jeremy Burgess/SPL/Photo Researchers, Inc.; right © J.C. Revy/Science Photo Library/Photo Researchers, Inc. **Page 433** © Keith Weller/USDA-ARS. **26.2** (a) © William Ferguson; (b) © Robert Frerch/Stone/Getty Images; (c) Courtesy of NOAA. **26.3** © Andrew Syred/Photo Researchers, Inc.; **26.4** © Prof. DJ Read, University of Sheffield; **26.5** (a) © Adrian P. Davies/Bruce Coleman; (a) art, Jennifer Wardrip (b) © NifTAL Project, Univ. of Hawaii, Maui. **26.6** (a, c) Leonard Morgan; (b) © Mike Clayton/University of Wisconsin Department of Botany; (b, c-right) Lisa Starr; **26.7** Left, © Alison W. Roberts, University of Rhode Island; center, © H. A. Core, W. A. Cote and A. C. Day, *Wood Structure and Identification,* 2nd Ed., Syracuse University Press, 1979; right, © H. A. Core, W. A. Cote and A. C. Day, *Wood Structure and Identification*, 2nd Ed., Syracuse University Press, 1979; art, Lisa Starr. **26.8** Left, © The Ohio Historical Society, Natural History Collections; Raychel Ciemma. **26.9** (a,b) © Claude Nuridsany & Marie Perennou/Science Photo Library/Photo Researchers, Inc.; **26.10** © micrograph by Ken Wagner/Visuals Unlimited, computer-enhanced by Lisa Starr. **26.13** (a) © Don Hopey/Pittsburgh Post-Gazette, 2002, all rights reserved. Reprinted with permission; (b) © Jeremy Burgess/SPL/Photo Researchers, Inc.; (c) © Jeremy Burgess/SPL/Photo Researchers, Inc. **26.14** (a) © James D. Mauseth, MCDB; (b) © J.C. Revy/Science Photo Library/Photo Researchers, Inc.; (c) © Martin Zimmerman, Science, 1961, 133:73-79, © AAAS. **26.15** Left, Gary Head; right, Palay/Beaubois; bottom right, Precision Graphics. **26.16** (a) © NOAA; (b) USDA/Forestry Service; (c) © David W. Stahle, Department of Geosciences, University of Arkansas.

CHAPTER 27 **27.1** Left, Courtesy of Caroline Ford, School of Plant Sciences, University of Reading, UK; right © James L. Amos/CORBIS. **the big picture** (page 446) From left, Raychel Ciemma; © Herve Chaumeton/Agence Nature; (page 447) From left, © Cathlyn Melloan/Stone/Getty Images; © Roger Wilmshurst; Frank Lane Picture Agency/CORBIS. **Page 447** © Dr. John Hilty. **27.2** Art, Raychel Ciemma and Precision Graphics; (b) left © John McAnulty/CORBIS; (b) right, © Robert Essel NYC/CORBIS. **27.3** (a) © David M. Phillips/Visuals Unlimited; (b) © Dr. Jeremy Burgess/SPL/Photo Researchers, Inc.; (c) © David Scharf/Peter Arnold, Inc. **27.4** Left. © John Alcock, Arizona State University; center, (bat) © Merlin D. Tuttle, Bat Conservation International; Top & bottom right, © Thomas Eisner, Cornell University. **27.5** Raychel Ciemma. **27.6** Left/left, © Michael Clayton, University of Wisconsin; bottom left, Raychel Ciemma; center/left, © Michael Clayton, University of Wisconsin; center, © Dr. Charles Good, Ohio State University, Lima; center/right, © Michael Clayton, University of Wisconsin; right/right, © Michael Clayton, University of Wisconsin. **27.7** (a) © R. Carr; (b) © Gregory K. Scott/Photo Researchers, Inc.; (c) © Robert H. Mohlenbrock USDA-NRCS PLANTS Database/USDA SCS. 1989. "Midwest wetland flora; field office illustrated guide to plant species." Midwest national Technical Center, Lincoln, NE; (d) From left, © Dr. Dan Legard, University of Florida GCREC, 2000; (d) © Andrew Syred/SPL/Photo Researchers, Inc.; (d) © Richard H. Gross. **27.8** © Darrell Gulin/CORBIS; **27.9** (a-e) © Professor Dr. Hans Hanks-Ulrich Koop. **27.10** © Mike Clayton/University of Wisconsin Department of Botany. **27.11** Art, Raychel Ciemma; top right, © Barry L. Runk/Grant Heilman, Inc.; center, © James D. Mauseth, University of Texas; bottom right, © Herve Chaumeton/Agence Nature. **27.12** © Sylvan H. Wittwer/Visuals Unlimited; **27.13** Top left, © Adam Hart-Davis/Photo Researchers, Inc.; (a–e) Art, Gary Head; (f) both, © Eric B. Brennan. **27.14** (a,b) Lisa Starr; (c) © Cathlyn Melloan/Stone/Getty Images. **Page 460** Bottom left, Gary Head. **27.15** (a) © Michael Clayton, University of Wisconsin; (b,c) © Muday, GK and P. Haworth (1994) "Tomato root growth, gravitropism, and lateral development: Correlations with auxin transport." "Plant Physiology and Biochemistry 32, 193-203" with permission from Elsevier Science. **27.16**: (a,b) Micrographs courtesy of Randy Moore from "How Roots Respond to Gravity" M. L. Evans, R. Moore, and K. Hasenstein, Scientific American, December 1986. **27.17** © Gary Head. **27.18** (a–d) Art, Gary Head; (e) © Ray Evert, University of Wisconsin. **27.20** (a) Top, © Juergen Berger, Max Planck Institute for Developmental Biology? Tuebingen, Germany; (a, below and b-all) © Jose Luis Riechmann; (c) art, Lisa Starr. **27.21** Left, © Roger Wilmshurst; Frank Lane Picture Agency/CORBIS; right, © Dr. Jeremy Burgess/Photo Researchers, Inc. **27.22** Left, © Eric Welzel/Fox Hill Nursery, Freeport, Maine; art, Lisa Starr. **27.23** © Grant Heilman Photography, Inc.

Page 467 Unit VI © Kevin Schafer.

CHAPTER 28 **28.1** Left, © Ohlinger Jerry/CORBIS Sygma; right, © Sachs Ron/CORBIS Sygma. **the big picture** (page 468) From left, © Ray Simmons/Photo Researchers, Inc.; © Ed Reschke; ©Ed Reschke; © Triarch/Visuals Unlimited; (page 469) From left, © Mauro Fermariello/Photo Researchers, Inc.; Robert Demarest. **Page 469** © Science Photo Library/Photo Researchers, Inc. **28.2** (a) © Manfred Kage/Bruce Coleman, Ltd.; (b) Top right, © Focus on Sports; (c) left © Ray Simmons/Photo Researchers, Inc.; (c) center, © Ed Reschke/Peter Arnold, Inc.; (c) right © Don W. Fawcett; all art, Lisa Starr. **28.3** Top, © Gregory Dimijian/Photo Researchers, Inc.; bottom, Raychel Ciemma, adapted from C. P. Hickman, Jr., L. S. Roberts, and A. Larson, *Integrated Principles of Zoology*, Ninth Edition, Wm. C. Brown, 1995. **28.4** Leif Buckley. **28.5** (a) top, © John Cunningham/Visuals Unlimited; (b,c) top © Ed Reschke; (d) top, © Science Photo Library/Photo Researchers, Inc.; (e) top, © Michael Abbey/Photo Researchers, Inc.; (f) top, © University of Cincinnati, Raymond Walters College, Biology (a-f) bottom, Lisa Starr and Leif Buckley. **28.6** © Roger K. Burnard; Art, left, Joel Ito; right, L. Calver. **28.7** © Science Photo Library/Photo Researchers, Inc. **28.8** Top, © Tony Mcconnell/Science Photo Library/Photo Researchers, Inc.; (a,b) © Ed Reschke; (c) © Biophoto Associates/Photo Researchers, Inc. **28.9** Left, © Kim Taylor/Bruce Coleman, Ltd.; right, © Triarch/Visuals Unlimited. **28.10** (a) © Mauro Fermariello/Photo Researchers, Inc.; (b) Courtesy Nature Biotechnology. **28.11** (a-c) Art, Palay/Beaubois; (d) Art, Seth Gold and Lisa Starr. **28.12** (a) Robert Demarest; (b) © John D. Cunningham/Visuals Unlimited. **28.13** Robert Demarest. **28.14** (a) Lisa Starr; (b) © Frank Trapper/CORBIS Sygma; (c) © AFP/CORBIS. **Page 479** Bottom right, © Pascal Goetgheluck/Science Photo Library/Photo Researchers, Inc. **Page 480** © Dr. Preston Maxim and Dr. Stephen Bretz, Department of Emergency Services, San Francisco General Hospital. **28.15** © Sean Sprague/Stock, Boston. **28.16** © David Macdonald.

CHAPTER 29 **29.1** (a) © CORBIS; (b) © PA Photos. **the big picture** (page 482) Left and right, Lisa Starr; (page 483) From left, Lisa Starr; Kevin Somerville and Precision Graphics; © C. Yokochi and J. Rohen, *Photographic Anatomy of the Human Body,* 2nd Ed., Igaku-Shoin, Ltd., 1979. **Page 483** © Manni Mason's Pictures. **29.2** (a) Robert Demarest; (b) Lisa Starr. **29.3** Kevin Somerville. **29.4** Lisa Starr. **29.5** Lisa Starr. **29.6** (a,b,d,e) Art, Precision Graphics; (c) © Jeff Greenberg/Index Stock Imagery. **29.7** (a, c) Lisa Starr; (b) © Dr. Constantino Sotelo from International *Cell Biology*, p. 83, 1977. Used by permission of the Rockefeller University Press. **29.8** Left, Micrograph by Don Fawcett, Bloom and Fawcett, 11th edition, after J. Desaki and Y. Uehara/Photo Researchers, Inc.; right, Kevin Somerville. **29.9** Gary Head. **29.10** (a, b) Robert Demarest. **29.11** Robert Demarest. **29.12** (a–c) Raychel Ciemma and Lisa Starr. **29.13** Kevin Somerville and Precision Graphics. **29.14** Robert Demarest and Precision Graphics. **29.15** Left art, Robert Demarest; right, © Manfred Kage/Peter Arnold, Inc. **29.16** Kevin Somerville. **29.17** Kevin Somerville. **29.18** (a) art, Raychel Ciemma and Lisa Starr; (a) © Colin Chumbley/Science Source/Photo Researchers, Inc.; (b) © C. Yokochi and J. Rohen, *Photographic Anatomy of the Human Body*, 2nd Ed., Igaku-Shoin, Ltd., 1979. **29.19** (a) Palay/Beaubois after Penfield and Rasmussen, *The Cerebral Cortex of Man*, © 1950 Macmillan Library Reference. Renewed 1978 by Theodore Rasmussen. Reprinted by permission of The Gale Group.; (b) © Colin Chumbley/Science Source/Photo Researchers, Inc. **29.20** (a) Raychel Ciemma; (b) © Marcus Raichle, Washington Univ. School of Medicine. **29.21** Lisa Starr. **29.23** (a,b) © E. D. London, et al., *Archives of General Psychiatry*, 47:567-574, 1990. **29.24** © Ed Kashi/CORBIS. **29.25** Art, Robert Demarest; © Herve Chaumeton/Agence Nature. **29.26** © Kathy Plonka, *The Spokesman-Review*.

CHAPTER 30 **30.1** © AP/Wide World Photos. **the big picture** (page 504) From left, © David Turnley/CORBIS; Art, Palay/Beaubois after Penfield and Rasmussen, *The Cerebral Cortex of Man*, © 1950 Macmillan Library Reference. Renewed 1978 by Theodore Rasmussen. Reprinted by permission of The Gale Group; © Colin Chumbley/Science Source/Photo Researchers, Inc; (page 505) From left, Robert Demarest; © Lennart Nilsson © Boehringer Ingelheim International GmbH. **Page 505** © Phillip Colla, Ocean-Light.com. All Rights Reserved Worldwide. **30.2** (a) From Hensel and Bowman, *Journal of Physiology*, 23:564-568, 1960; (b) © David Turnley/CORBIS. **30.3** Art, Palay/Beaubois after Penfield and Rasmussen, *The Cerebral Cortex of Man*, © 1950 Macmillan Library Reference. Renewed 1978 by Theodore Rasmussen. Reprinted by permission of The Gale Group; right, © Colin Chumbley/Science Source/Photo Researchers, Inc. **30.4** Raychel Ciemma. **30.5** Precision Graphics. **30.6** Robert Demarest. **30.7** Top, Kevin Somervill; Lisa Starr. **Page 509** © AFP Photo/Timothy A. Clary/CORBIS. **30.8** Gary Head. **30.9** (a,b,e) Art, Robert Demarest; (a) right, © Fabian/CORBIS Sygma; (c) Precision Graphics; (d) © Medtronic Xomed; (e) top, © Dr. Thomas R. Van De Water, University of Miami Ear Institute. **30.10** Both, © Robert E. Preston, courtesy Joseph E. Hawkins, Kresge Hearing Research Institute, University of Michigan Medical School; **30.11** (a) top, © E. R. Degginger; (a) art, Raychel Ciemma after M. Gardiner, The Biology of Vertebrates, McGraw-Hill, 1972; (b, c) Raychel Ciemma.

30.12 Robert Demarest. **30.13** (a) © Richard Megna/ Fundemental Photographs, NYC; (b,c) Kevin Somerville, enhanced by Lisa Starr. **30.14** Top, © Lennart Nilsson © Boehringer Ingelheim International GmbH; art, Micrograph, Lennart Nilsson © Boehringer Ingelheim International. **30.15** www.2.gasou.edu/psychology/ courses/muchinsky and www.occipita.cfa.cmu.edu. **30.16** Kevin Somerville. **30.17** Courtesy of Dr. Bryan Jones, University of Utah School of Medicine. **30.18** © Eric A. Newman, enhanced by Lisa Starr. **30.19** © Chase Swift. **30.20** © F. Spoor using Voxel-man.

CHAPTER 31 **31.1** Left, Courtesy of Michael Lannoo; right; © David Aubrey/CORBIS. **the big picture** (page 518) From left, Lisa Starr with PDB ID: 1MSO; Smith, G. D., Pangborn, W. A., Blessing, R. H.: *The Structure of T6 Human Insulin at 1.0 A Resolution Acta Crystallogr., Sect.D 59 pp. 474 (2003)*; (page 519) From left, Courtesy of Dr. Erica Eugster; © James King-Holmes/Photo Researchers, Inc. **Page 519** Courtesy of Wandering Eye Production. Used by permission. **Page 520** Top left, Lisa Starr with PDB ID: 1MSO; Smith, G. D., Pangborn, W. A., Blessing, R. H.: *The Structure of T6 Human Insulin at 1.0 A Resolution Acta Crystallogr., Sect.D* 59 pp. 474 (2003). **31.2** Kevin Somerville. **31.3** Lisa Starr **31.4** Robert Demarest. **31.5** Art, Robert Demarest; top right, Courtesy of Dr. Erica Eugster; bottom right, © Lisa Starr. **31.6** Leonard Morgan. **31.7** (a) © Gary Head; (a) Art, Raychel Ciemma; (b) © Bettmann/CORBIS. **31.8** © Biophoto Associates/SPL/Photo Researchers, Inc. **31.9** Leonard Morgan. **31.10** (a) © The Stover Group/D. J. Fort; (b) © Joeseph Kiesecker, Penn State University. **31.11** (a,b) © James King-Holmes/Photo Researchers, Inc. **31.12** Top, © Frans Lanting/Bruce Coleman, Ltd.; art, From R. C. Brusca and G. J. Brusca, *Invertebrates*, © 1990 Sinauer Associates. Used by permission. **31.13** © Dr. Carlos J. Bourdony. Page 534 Robert Demarest **31.14** Courtesy of G. Baumann, MD, Northwestern University. **31.15** © Kevin Fleming/CORBIS.

CHAPTER 32 **32.1** © Michael Neveux. **the big picture** (page 536) Feom left, D. & V. Hennings; Joel Ito; (page 537) From left, Robert Demarest; Robert Demarest. **Page 537** © Steve Cole/PhotoDisc Green/Getty Images. **32.2** © Linda Pitkin/Planet Earth Pictures. **32.3** Bottom left, © Stephen Dalton/Photo Researchers, Inc.; art, Precision Graphics. **32.4** Bottom left, © Yokochi and J. Rohen, *Photographic Anatomy of the Human Body*, 2nd Ed., Igaku-Shoin, Ltd., 1979; top art, Raychel Ciemma; bottom art, D. & V. Hennings. **32.5** (a,b) Joel Ito; top right © Ed Reschke. **32.6** K. Kasnot. **32.7** (a,b) © Professor P. Motta/Department of Anatomy/ La Sapienza, Rome/SPL/Photo Researchers, Inc. **32.8** Robert Demarest. **32.9** © N.H.P.A./ANT Photolibrary. **32.10** (a,b) Raychel Ciemma. **32.11** (a) bottom, © Dance Theatre of Harlem, by Frank Capri; (b,c) © Don Fawcett/ Visuals Unlimited, from D. W. Fawcett, The Cell, Philadelphia; W. B. Saunders Co., 1966; (a) Art, Robert Demarest; compilation by Gary Head. **32.12** Nadine Sokol and Gary Head. **32.14** Gary Head. **32.15** Kevin Somerville and Gary Head. **Page 547** © Sarto-Lund/Stone/Getty Images. **32.16** Painting by Sir Charles Bell, 1809, courtesy of Royal College of Surgeons, Edinburgh. **32.17** (a) © Paul Sponseller, MD/Johns Hopkins Medical Center; (b) Courtesy of the family of Tiffany Manning.

CHAPTER 33 **33.1** © Mark Thomas/Science Photo Library. **the big picture** (page 550) From left, Precision Graphics; right © National Cancer Institute/Photo Researchers, Inc.; (page 551) From left, © Sheila Terry/ SPL/Photo Researchers, Inc.; Lisa Starr. **Page 551** Top right, © Faye Norman/Science Photo Library; bottom left, From A. D. Waller *Physiology: The Servant of Medicine*, Hitchcock Lectures, University of London Press, 1910. **33.2** Top left, © Darlyne A Murawski/Getty Images; bottom left, © Getty Images; (a,c) art, Raychel Ciemma; (b,d) Precision Graphics. **33.3** (a-c) Precision Graphics; (d) After M. Labarbera and S. Vogel, American Scientist, 1982, 70:54-60. 33.4; Top, © National Cancer Institute/Photo Researchers, Inc.; **33.4** Art, Lisa Starr. **33.5** Left, © 2001 EyeWire; Art, Lisa Starr with art references from *Bloodline Image Atlas*, University of Nebraska-Omaha/Sherri Wicks, Human Physiology and Anatomy, University of Wisconsin Biology Web Education System, and others. **33.6** (a) © Lester V. Bergman & Associates, Inc.; (b) © Lester V. Bergman & Associates, Inc.; (c) Gary Head after A. Ayala and J. Kiger, Modern Genetics, © 1980 Benjamin-Cummings. **33.7** Nadine Sokol after G.J. Tortora and N. Anagnostakos, *Principles of Anatomy and Physiology*, 6th Edition. © 1990 by Biological Sciences Textbooks, Inc., A & P Textbooks, Inc., and Ellia-Sparta, Inc. Reprinted by permission of John Wiley & Sons, Inc. **33.8** Kevin Somerville. **33.9** Precision Graphics. **33.10** Gary Head. **33.11** (a) © C. Yokochi and J. Rohen, *Photographic Anatomy of the Human Body, 2nd Ed.*, Igaku-Shoin, Ltd., 1979; (b,c) Raychel Ciemma. **33.12** Precision Graphics. **33.13** (a) left © Don W. Fawcett; (a) Art, Lisa Starr; (b) Raychel Ciemma. **33.14** Robert Demarest. **33.15** Precision Graphics. **33.16** Art, Precision Graphics; right, © Jose Pelaez, Inc./CORBIS. **33.17** Left, © Sheila Terry/SPL/Photo Researchers, Inc.; inset, Courtesy of Oregon Scientific, Inc. **33.18** Left, © Biophoto Associates/ Photo Researchers, Inc.; right, Lisa Starr. **33.19** (a) Left art, Lisa Starr, using © 2001 PhotoDisc, Inc.; Dr. John D. Cunningham/Visuals Limited; (b,c) Kevin Somerville. **33.20** Photograph, Professor P. Motta/Department of Anatomy/University La Sapienca, Rome/SPL/Photo Researchers, Inc. **33.21** (a) © Ed Reschke; (b) © Biophoto Associates/Photo Researchers, Inc. **33.22** © Lester V. Bergman/CORBIS. **33.23** Precision Graphics. **33.24** (a,b) Raychel Ciemma; (c) Lisa Starr. **Page 570** Below right, Raychel Ciemma and Robert Demarest. **33.25** © Lennart Nilsson from Behold Man, (c) 1974 by Albert Bonniers Forlag and Little, Brown and Company, Boston.

CHAPTER 34 **34.1** © Lowell Tindell. **the big picture** (page 572) From left, © Biology Media/Photo Researchers, Inc.; © Mark L Stephenson/CORBIS; (page 573) Both, Lisa Starr. **Page 573** © NIBSC/Photo Researchers, Inc. **34.2** Art, Lisa Starr, with art references from *Bloodline Image Atlas*, University of Nebraska-Omaha/Sherri Wicks, Human Physiology and Anatomy, University of Wisconsin Biology Web Education System, and others.; bottom right, © Biology Media/Photo Researchers, Inc. **Page 575** © Mark L Stephenson/CORBIS. **34.3** Art, Raychel Ciemma; bottom right © NSIBC/SPL/Photo Researchers, Inc. **34.4** Art, Lisa Starr; 34.4: right © Robert R. Dourmashkin, courtesy of Clinical Research Centre, Harrow, England. **34.5** © David Scharf/Peter Arnold, Inc.; Art, Lisa Starr. **34.6** Art, Lisa Starr; top center, © Ken Cavanagh/Photo Researchers, Inc. **34.7** Precision Graphics. **34.8** Lisa Starr. **34.9** Preface, Inc. **34.10** Raychel Ciemma. **34.11** Top, Lisa Starr, from Harris, L. J.; Larson, S. B.; Hasel, K. W.; McPherson, A.; *Biochemistry 36*, p. 1581 (1997). Structure of rendered with RIBBONS. (a–c) Lisa Starr. **Page 582** Lisa Starr. **34.12** Lisa Starr. **34.13** Lisa Starr. **34.14** © Dr. A. Liepins/SPL/Photo Researchers, Inc. **34.15** © Lowell Georgia/Science Source/Photo Researchers, Inc. **34.16** Top, © David Scharf/Peter Arnold, Inc.; bottom, © Mednet/Phototake, Inc. **34.17** © Greg Ruffing. **34.18** © Zeva Oelbaum/Peter Arnold, Inc. **34.19** Top left, © NIBSC/Photo Researchers, Inc.; art, Raychel Ciemma after Stephen Wolfe, *Molecular Biology of the Cell*, Wadsworth, 1993. **34.20** Photo courtesy of MU Extension and Agricultural Information.

CHAPTER 35 **35.1** © Ariel Skelley/CORBIS. **the big picture** (page 592) From left, © John Lund/Getty Images; right, © Peter Parks/Oxford Scientific Films; (page 593) From left, Kevin Somerville; © CNRI/SPL/Photo Researchers, Inc. **Page 593** © James Stevenson/Photo Researchers, Inc. **35.2** Gary Head and Precision Graphics. **35.3** Precision Graphics. **35.4** (a) © David Nardini/Getty Images; (b) © John Lund/Getty Images; (c) © Joe McBride/Getty Images. **35.5** Lisa Starr with PDB ID 1A6M:Vojtechovsky, J., Berendzen, J., Chu, K., Schlichting, I., Sweet, R. M.: Implications for the Mechanism of Ligand Discrimination and Identification of Substates Derived from Crystal Structures of Myoglobin-Ligand Complexes at Atomic Resolution To be Published. **35.6** (a) © Peter Parks/Oxford Scientific Films; (b) © Herve Chaumeton/ Agence Nature; art, Precision Graphics. **35.7** Top, © Joe Warfel/Eight-Eye Photography; center, © D. E. Hill; art, Redrawn from *Living Invertebrates*, V & J. Pearse/M. & R. Buchsbaum, The Boxwood Press, 1987. **35.8** © Ed Reschke; art, Precision Graphics. **Page 597** © C. C. Lockwood. **35.9** Raychel Ciemma and Precision Graphics. **35.10** Raychel Ciemma. **35.11** Lisa Starr. **35.12** Top left, © H. R. Duncker, Justus-Liebig University, Giessen, Germany; art, Raychel Ciemma. **35.13** Kevin Somerville. **35.14** Left art, modified from A. Spence and E. Mason, *Human Anatomy and Physiology*, Fourth Edition, 1992, West Publishing Company; Courtesy of Kay Elemetrics Corporation. **35.15** (a) © 2000 PhotoDisc, Inc.; (b) © SIU/Visuals Unlimited; (c) © SIU/ Visuals Unlimited; (a,b,c) art, Lisa Starr. **35.16** Art, Precision Graphics; right, © Francois Gohier/Photo Researchers, Inc. **35.17** (a) © R. Kessel/Visuals Unlimited; (b, c) Art, Lisa Starr. **35.18** Leonard Morgan. **35.19** (a) © Lennart Nilsson from Behold Man, © 1974 by Albert Bonniers Forlag and Little, Brown and Company, Boston; (b) © CNRI/SPL/ Photo Researchers, Inc. **35.20** (a) © O. Auerbach/Visuals Unlimited; (b) © O. Auerbach/Visuals Unlimited. **35.21** Courtesy of Dr. Joe Losos. **35.22** Leif Buckley.

CHAPTER 36 **36.1** Courtesy of Kevin Wickenheiser, University of Michigan. **the big picture** (page 610) From left, © W. Perry Conway/CORBIS; Kevin Somerville; (page 611) From left, © Elizabeth Hathon/CORBIS; © Gary Head. **Page 611** © Gusto/Photo Researchers, Inc. **36.2** Gary Head and Precision Graphics. **36.3** Raychel Ciemma. **36.4** (a) © W. Perry Conway/CORBIS; (a,b) Art, adapted by Lisa Starr from A. Romer and T. Parsons, *The Vertebrate Body, Sixth Edition*, Saunders Publishing Company, 1986. **36.5** Kevin Somerville. **36.6** Nadine Sokol. **36.7** After A. Vander, et al., Human Physiology: Mechanisms of Body Function, Fifth Edition, McGraw-Hill, 1990. Used by permission. **36.8** (a) © Microslide courtesy Mark Nielsen, University of Utah; (b) After A. Vander, et al., *Human Physiology: Mechanisms of Body Function, Fifth Edition*, McGraw-Hill, 1990. Used by permission. **36.9** Art, Lisa Starr after Sherwood and others; top center, © Microslide courtesy Mark Nielsen, University of Utah; center right, © D. W. Fawcett/Photo Researchers, Inc. **36.10** Raychel Ciemma and Lisa Starr. **36.11** Left, © Ralph Pleasant/FPG/Getty Images, right, Precision Graphics. **36.12** Kevin Somerville and Precision Graphics. **36.13** Top, (pyramid) © 2001 PhotoDisc, Inc.; bottom, © Elizabeth Hathon/CORBIS. **Page 623** © Gary Head. **36.14** © Gary Head. **36.15** © Dr. Douglas Coleman, The Jackson Laboratory; art, Precision Graphics and Gary Head. **36.16** © Reuters NewsMedia/CORBIS. **36.17** © Gunter Ziesler/ Bruce Coleman, Inc.

CHAPTER 37 **37.1** © Archivo Iconografico, S.A./CORBIS. **the big picture** (page 630) From left, Robert Demarest; From T. Garrison, *Oceanography: An Invitation to Marine Science*, Brooks/Cole, 1993. All rights reserved; (page 631) From left, Robert Demarest; © Dan Guravich/CORBIS. **Page 631** @ Lawrence Lawry/Science Photo Library/Photo Researchers, Inc. **37.2** Gary Head and Precision Graphics. **37.3** (a,b) From T. Garrison, *Oceanography: An Invitation to Marine Science*, Brooks/Cole, 1993. All rights reserved. **37.4** Top, © David Noble/FPG/Getty Images; center, © Claude Steelman/Tom Stack & Associates; bottom, © Gary Head. **37.5** Robert Demarest. **37.6** Robert Demarest. **37.7** Top, Robert Demarest; bottom, Precision Graphics. **37.8** © Evan Cerasoli; top art, Kevin Somerville; bottom art, Robert Demarest. **37.9** © Air Force News/Photo by Tech. Sgt. Timothy Hoffman. **37.10** (a) © Bob McKeever/Tom Stack & Associates; (b) © S. J. Krasemann/Photo Researchers, Inc. **37.11** © David Parker/SPL/Photo Researchers, Inc. **37.12** Top, © Dan Guravich/CORBIS; bottom, © CORBIS-Bettmann. **37.13** Art, Precision Graphics; © Gary Head. **Page 643** Bottom left, Robert Demarest.

CHAPTER 38 **38.1** (a) © Lennart Nilsson from *A Child is Born*, © 1966, 1977 Dell Publishing Company, Inc.; (b) © 1999 Dana Fineman/CORBIS Sygma. **the big picture** (page 644) From left, © Ron Austing; Frank Lane Picture Agency/CORBIS; © Carolina Biological Supply Company; (page 645) From left, Raychel Ciemma; © Lennart Nilsson, *A Child is Born*, © 1966, 1977 Dell Publishing Company, Inc. **Page 645** © Dow W. Fawcett/Photo Researchers, Inc. **38.2** © Fred SaintOurs/University of Massachusetts-Boston; art, Lisa Starr. **38.3** (a) © Marc Moritsch; (b) © Photo Researchers, Inc. **38.4** (a) © Frieder Sauer/Bruce Coleman, Ltd; (b) © Matjaz Kuntner; (c) © Ron Austing; Frank Lane Picture Agency/CORBIS; (d) © Doug Perrine/seapics.com; (e) © Carolina Biological Supply Company; (f) © Fred McKinney/FPG/Getty Images; (g) © Gary Head. **38.5** Art, Palay/Beaubois and Precision Graphics. **38.6** (a) Art, Raychel Ciemma; (b–j) © Carolina Biological Supply Company; (b–j) art, L. Calver. **38.7** Art, Robert Demarest. **38.8** (a, b) Art, Precision Graphics; (c) © Gary Head. **38.9** (a–d) © Dr. Maria Leptin, Institute of Genetics, University of Koln, Germany. **38.10** (a) Lisa Starr; (b) Raychel Ciemma after B. Burnside, *Developmental Biology*, 1971, 26:416-441. Used by permission of Academic Press. **38.11** Art, Precision Graphics; (Photographic series) © Carolina Biological Supply Company; far right © Peter Parks/Oxford Scientific Films/Animals, Animals. **38.12** (a,b) Art, Lisa Starr; (c) © Professor Jonathon Slack. **38.13** Left, © Peter Parks/Oxford Scientific Films/Animals, Animals; (a,b) Art, Raychel Ciemma after S. Gilbert, Developmental Biology, Fourth Edition. **38.14** Art, Raychel Ciemma with Lisa Starr; right, © Laura Dwight/ CORBIS. **38.15** Raychel Ciemma with Lisa Starr. **38.16** (a,b,c) Art, Raychel Ciemma; (b) © Ed Reschke. **38.19** Raychel Ciemma. 662: 38.20 Left art, Raychel Ciemma; top right art, Robert Demarest; bottom right, Photograph Lennart Nilsson from *A Child is Born*, © 1966, 1977 Dell Publishing Company, Inc. **38.21** Raychel Ciemma with Precision Graphics. **38.22** K. Sommerville, Robert Demarest, and Preface, Inc. **38.23** Raychel Ciemma; **38.24** Preface, Inc. **38.25** © Lester Lefkowitz/CORBIS. **38.26** (a) © Dr. E. Walker/Photo Researchers, Inc.; (b) © Western Ophthalmic Hospital/Photo Researchers, Inc.; (c) © Kenneth Greer/Visuals Unlimited; (d) © CNRI/Photo Researchers, Inc. **38.27** © Todd Warshaw/Getty Images. **38.28** Raychel Ciemma. **38.29** Raychel Ciemma. **38.30** Raychel Ciemma. **38.31** (a-d) Art, Raychel Ciemma; (a–d)